The CONCIERGE

ABBY CORSON

The CONCIERGE

ABBY CORSON

Black&White

Black&White

First published in the UK in 2024 by Black & White Publishing
An imprint of Black & White Publishing Group
A Bonnier Books UK company
4th Floor, Victoria House, Bloomsbury Square, London, WC1B 4DA
Owned by Bonnier Books, Sveavägen 56, Stockholm, Sweden

Paperback ISBN: 978-1-7853-0680-8
eBook ISBN: 978-1-7853-0681-5
Audio ISBN: 978-1-7853-0679-2

A CIP catalogue record for this book is available from the British Library.
Typeset by IDSUK (Data Connection) Ltd
Printed and bound in Great Britain by Clays Ltd, Elcograf S.p.A

1 3 5 7 9 10 8 6 4 2

Black & White Publishing is an imprint of Bonnier Books UK
www.bonnierbooks.co.uk

For Philip

Tap one. Tap two. Tap three.

Sorry about that. I have to tap my head three times when I have a bad or intrusive thought. That time I was thinking about how much worse everything would have been if my father was still alive.

You can delete that bit from the transcript, Helen. Actually, leave it in. I guess it adds to the authenticity of the tale.

I suppose it would be fitting to explain that I am talking into a dictaphone and the lovely Helen will be typing out my story for you to read. She will have a certain amount of creative control—sorting out moments when I get a bit tongue-tied or slightly muddled—but I have told her to leave in as much as possible, so as not to miss any of the important bits. This is my account of the Cavengreen Hotel murder, best we get that bit in early on.

Tap one. Tap two. Tap three.

That was me remembering the moment I found the body.

Note to Helen: remind me to remind you to ask me if I still want all my head taps to be left in before publishing. I know we spoke before about how my OCD is important to the story, but let's have another chat about it when you're writing this up.

You are probably wondering why I can't write my own book and need the assistance of Helen. I am a seventy-three-year-old man, you see. And before you say it, I know a lot of seventy-year-olds who can use computers too; I just don't happen to be one of them. Prefer the classic pen and paper. When Helen and I first spoke about writing my story, she took one look at my handwriting and suggested I use the dictaphone. Apparently it is easier to decipher my Yorkshire accent than my scribbles. I am not offended, though. Aside from the odd lines and circles on maps to highlight local walks and pubs for the hotel guests, it isn't often I use a pen and paper for anything other than my own reminders. To buy milk and the like.

And about the head tapping, that's something I've always done. A way of coping after my dad started whacking me when I was eight. I don't normally recite the taps out loud. But I will do that for Helen, so she can decide if she wants to put them in the book or not. It is always three taps. Everything is done in threes. Flicking light switches on and off three times before leaving a room. Three tight squeezes of the steering wheel before setting off in the car. Three taps on a glass before a first sip. Three twists of the knob to find the right temperature. (That only works on my sinks at home, not the fancy new automatic ones in the hotel.) And when I found the body, I remember blinking three times before running for help. The pause while I did it was one of the things that made them suspect it was me. Supposedly, it was long enough to kill someone. We will get to that bit later.

Right, so, this might embarrass her a bit, but I want to start by thanking Helen for turning my ramblings into a book. She's a good 'un, is Helen. I've known her for donkey's years. She and my younger sister went to school together. Helen organised the funeral when she died. Everything down to the purple tulips and little photograph of my dearest Josie on the order of service.

This book was Helen's idea. She relocated down to London years back to work in some swish publishing house, and we lost touch for a while. But, just like everyone else, she moved back up north for the fresh country air once she retired, and we've rekindled our friendship. She says she'll do anything for a good book. I suppose that's why she's offered to give me a helping hand. Misses the work. And it's just as well; I wouldn't get very far doing this by myself.

Helen has given me a list of what to talk about and in what order, since she knows how a book should go. It starts with a bit of this and that about my background, then my job at the hotel, and then I move on to the murder and how I ended up here. You're probably wondering where 'here' is. For a bit of fun, I'm not going to tell you just yet. I could be in a prison cell, or my little cottage in the Dales, or some beach on the Costa del Sol. (I'll give you a hint: I'm not in Spain.)

Last thing for this chapter. My name is Hector. Hector Harrow.

CHAPTER

2

Helen popped her head round the door just now to tell me I don't need to introduce the chapter by giving an overview of what will be contained within it. I suppose I have just let the cat out of the bag about my location. Helen doesn't mosey in and out of prison cells willy-nilly. So, I confess—I am at home. In my lounge room to be exact. In a big, reddish brown Chesterfield armchair holding a cup of English breakfast, no milk, and looking out at my little garden, complete with a stone wall at the end and a few pairs of socks and undies on a washing line. Must remember to fetch those in before the rain comes.

Hopefully that admission didn't spoil anything for you. There are plenty more surprises along the way, don't you worry about that.

❦

I have never been one to talk about myself. I've always assumed no one cared what I had to say. Occasionally some guests—usually Americans—would be curious about what life was like growing up in the Yorkshire Dales, but I would answer in as few words as possible, and it was never the truth. What was I going to say? 'Well, my father used to beat the living daylights out of me for no reason, but my mother made a fantastic apple pie, and the country views were a delight.' That would just make them uncomfortable. And I'm sure management would have had something to say about my bothering the guests. Not that I ever would have. Always the professional, that's me. Except that one time they interrogated me for over four hours. Wouldn't even let me have a glass of water. And I was parched after the shock of seeing all that blood.

Tap one. Tap two. Tap three.

That was the first time in my life I ever lost my temper. It felt like I was possessed by my father. I will talk a bit about him now.

My father—Rodney was his name. He'd be down there in hell. There is no doubt about that. He was an alcoholic from the day I was born to the day he dropped dead. There is always an alcoholic parent in troubled tales like this.

Helen made me laugh when we first talked about this part of the book. She said that I make the perfect protagonist because of—she used a good word that I have forgotten now.

Helen, make a note to type that word here please.

The juxtaposition *[editor's note]* of my awful upbringing with the quite nice life I went on to lead, working in one of England's finest countryside hotels.

School was always a bit of an escape for me. Not that I was any good at it. Just the local comprehensive—I wasn't clever enough for grammar school, let alone university. And anyway, I knew I'd be having to get a job straight off. It's a funny story, how I got my start at Cavengreen Hotel. I was only sixteen. My father needed a refill of some tablets that would hopefully *not* prolong the life of his liver, so I cycled to the local pharmacy to pick them up. On the way, I saw a man with a posh car pulled over on the side of the road. He had a wispy grey moustache and an olive-green three-piece suit. Back then, I had never seen someone look so smart—not in real life, that is. The man looked stressed, and as I got closer I saw his tyre was as flat as a squashed cigarette butt.

'Young lad!' he called out to me. 'Come here!'

I braked to a stop and rested my bike against the wobbly stone wall that ran alongside the road. It was a sunny day and I remember shuffling from foot to foot to try and find the exact position in which the man's head would block the sun from my eyes.

'I'll give you two pounds if you help me change this tyre,' the man offered. 'Three if you do it in under ten minutes.'

I had seen my dad change the odd tyre, and two, possibly three pounds was a lot of money back then, so I got stuck into it.

The man didn't say anything as I worked, but I noticed him tapping his foot impatiently and he checked his pocket watch several times. When I was done, I stood up, dusted some of the black off my hands and asked the man how long it had taken me.

'Ten minutes, three seconds,' he announced. 'Here's your two pounds.'

He handed me two notes.

I mustn't have looked best pleased because he asked if there was something wrong. I knew better than to offend a toff, so I thanked him for the opportunity and said I hoped I could use the experience to find a job.

He smiled at me. It was a crooked smile, but it was kind. He invited me to come to a place called Cavengreen Hotel at six the next morning to do some odd jobs for him. Shoeshining, polishing floors, cleaning bird poo off the walls and the like, he said. And that is how it all started. I was the happiest birdshit cleaner the world ever did see.

Bloomin' Paula McDavidson from the *Yorkshire Sun* newspaper has been knocking again. She never listens. That's another reason I want to do this book sharpish: so none of the others that were there at the hotel can tell my story first. There are three main characters in this: one is me, one is dead, and the other is the murderer. Fat chance either of the others are going to try and publish a book, so it is down to me to get the truth out there before the twins or American Dave flood the world with a pack of lies. I told Paula that she will find out all she needs to know in due course. That won't stop her, though. She'll be hammering on the door again in a couple of days, mark my words.

Helen gave me some feedback on what I recorded yesterday. She told me she liked it, so that has given me a little confidence boost. She said that, despite my thick accent, I speak very clearly, which is probably thanks to my many years at Cavengreen. When I started out as a young lad, I'd say things like 'eh up' for 'hello', and ''ow do?' for 'how are you?', but the out-of-town guests hadn't the foggiest what I was on about. Helen's only criticism was that I probably didn't need to list what was on my washing line, but she said she would trim that bit down when she writes this up. Today, Helen wants me to chat a bit about the hotel. Setting the scene is what she called it.

The man that I mentioned, the one I changed the tyre for, his name was Mr Thomas. He was the hotel manager at the time. It wasn't until his funeral twenty years after I met him that I found out his first name was Basil. He was the nicest man I have ever known. He gave a young lad a chance when he didn't have to, and I will always remember him fondly. Every day at 6 am, seven days a week, I would cycle the thirty minutes to the hotel. Wind, rain, shine, the storm of '72, I never missed a day. One time I turned up with chickenpox because I didn't want to let the team down. They sent me home right away, but Mr Thomas still gave me my wages, even when I was off sick. I learnt everything I know about hard work from that man.

As you will probably have gathered from the title of this book, I eventually climbed the ladder up to hotel concierge, but along the way I worked as a porter, then valet. I did a few months in the kitchen, but that wasn't for me, so they moved me to the butler position, and after that I became the concierge. It was my job to make sure that the guests' every want and need was taken care of. Whether it was a taxi at 3 am for a lady they'd met at the hotel bar to travel home in, a plate of French fries with all the crunchy bits removed, or a marriage proposal staged on the lawn, I handled it all. Helen has suggested I talk about the strangest request I ever had. That would probably be the time I set up a screening of the Disney movie *One Hundred and One Dalmatians* in one of the suites, complete with treats and cosy bedding on the floor. The audience was the guest's two beloved poodles. There were plenty of other strange requests over the years, most of which involve very famous people from Hollywood, but I would never breach confidentiality.

You are probably getting the picture by now that Cavengreen was and is not your average hotel. No, no. The hotel proudly displays five stars on the front of the archway that sits at the end of a four-hundred-yard-long gravel driveway. Chauffeurs escort their guests around a large turning circle with a fountain in the middle that lights up at night and has speakers built into the sides that play Vivaldi and the like. Three full-time horticulturists look after the gardens, which include a hedge maze, a rose garden, and a small pond dotted with lily pads. I never get sick of walking through them. Loads of people bring along those fancy cameras with the big lenses or look at everything through their phones, but I prefer to enjoy the smells and colours without distraction.

If you were to see it from above, the hotel is shaped like a T. The top of the T is the part that guests see when they first arrive. The whole building is made from limestone and the entire front is lined with columns. Couples like to take their wedding photographs there. The climbing ivy makes for quite the backdrop.

The west wing houses the hotel's Michelin-starred restaurant, Lavender Plates. As you would imagine, all the chinaware is lavender-coloured with golden rims. The custom-designed wallpaper is hand-painted with watercolour sketches of lavender over the top of a white silk background. The ceilings in Lavender Plates are double the height of anywhere else in the hotel and a huge sparkly chandelier was imported from the United Arab Emirates to add some glitz to the place. Towering floor-to-ceiling glass double doors lead out onto a terrace overlooking the hotel's driveway. In summer, we would open the doors and allow a light breeze to flow through. The guests loved it.

All the seats are upholstered with cream velvet and the white marble tables have ornate gold legs. The waiters and waitresses set the tables in a very particular way; every spoon, fork and knife has its place and must be a certain distance from the plates and glassware. You would be hard pressed to find fault with Lavender Plates. It is very smart. Serves a seasonal tasting menu of seven tiny dishes. I much prefer one big meal, but the few times I have eaten there it has been very good indeed. The kitchen is completely open so everyone in the restaurant can see what is going on. From memory, the last time I dined there I had some type of fish with a burnt honey glaze and a white chocolate dessert with roasted cherries. If you like that sort of thing, fancy stuff, you'd like Lavender Plates. It was all a bit wasted on me. I am a pie-and-mash kind of man. But no one would deny it is good food. And at two hundred quid a pop, you would expect so. I dined for free, of course. Staff were always recruited to taste the new dishes.

Then there is Hugo's cocktail bar, modelled on a moody whisky lounge in Tokyo. The hotel brought in a light-up onyx countertop from Japan, as well as golden light fixtures and a particular type of tumbler that keeps the ice separate from the alcohol, so as not to water down the flavour. It is all in the details at Cavengreen, that is what I am trying to get across.

In the east wing of the hotel there are some offices for the manager, reservations and marketing. There is also a library, where we would hold wine tastings and serve pre-dinner canapés every evening. There is a fireplace and lots of old books that are dusted every fortnight. Think squeaky leather sofas, a royal blue carpet, lots of dark wood, and you are probably on the right track. Some of the books in there would be worth a bob or two. I reckon there are some valuable originals. I am partial to a good murder mystery myself and would often borrow a novel for a weekend of reading at home.

Between the east and west wings was my domain: the lobby. The first point of contact for guests visiting the hotel. This was the place where first and last impressions were formed, so everyone was always on their best behaviour. The lovely ladies on reception (plus Kyle on Saturdays and Sundays) were always smiling and ever so kind to me. They used to say I was 'cute' and that they wished I was their grandpa. A little patronising, but nice nonetheless. At the time of the murder, there was Monique, Chloe and Shamila working on the front desk. Fiona was their boss, and she'd been managing the reception team for the past fifteen years. She's still there, in fact. She's a very dear friend of mine. Lost her husband to cancer two years ago. Lovely fella. It is a shame, really.

My desk was on the other side of the staircase to reception. I had a telephone, lots of maps and information booklets about the local area, a directory of contacts that I used to source whatever the guests needed, and a little fridge with bottled water and a few soft drinks should anyone want a refreshment. I used to burn candles all around the lobby, so subtle notes of vanilla, pepper and grapefruit filled the air. Many years ago, we worked with a perfumery to bottle the perfect Cavengreen scent. Candles and diffusers were available for the guests to purchase, should they so choose.

Now, to the bottom part of the T, the trunk. That is the south wing. This is where you'll find all the rooms—two floors of them, to be precise. In the last refurbishment, they painted all the walls white and rolled out a soft pale-pink carpet. Each suite has the black outline of a flower painted onto a white door. There are all sorts: tulips, roses, poppies, lilies and so on. Every room at Cavengreen Hotel is a suite. That means they've all got a separate sitting area and powder room, as well as either a balcony or terrace and a large master bathroom with a roll-top bath. We got lots of requests for romantic baths, and I always made sure I had plenty of rose petals, bath bombs, candles and massage oils in stock so I could put together a little pack for those guests who requested it.

On the top level of the south wing there are a few luxury suites, as we called them. These have their own bar stocked with alcohol and snacks—all free to the guests. Except it is actually included in the room price. I probably shouldn't have said that, but surely it is assumed. I suppose my loose lips don't matter so much now. All the luxury suites have a jacuzzi spa on the balcony and a fireplace that separates the lounge from the bedroom. The rooms are classic with traditional details like sconces, cornices, and ceiling roses, but they have also been fitted with all the mod cons that people don't seem to be able to live without nowadays. I would rather sit in silence than watch that drivel on television. But that is just me. Wi-Fi is available too, of course. It is near impossible to get phone signal out here so the Wi-Fi is the only way to stay connected.

There is even a special bridal suite which is spread over two levels. As well as the above, it has a dressing room with hair and make-up stations. Each suite is attended to by the hotel's twenty-four-hour butler service; there are twelve of them on staff. Plus there are chefs, maids, security guards, wedding planners, maintenance men, waitstaff and so many more people. You will be introduced to some of them as I tell this story.

That bloomin' busybody Paula McDavidson is opening my gate again. What the devil could she possibly want? I tell you what, I am going to take the dictaphone to the door with me, then Helen can transcribe exactly what her raspy, chain-smoking gob says.

Helen, you might have to change Paula's name and the name of the newspaper.

Hector: Paula, I've already told you I'm not going to give you any information.

Paula: I need a comment from you for my story.

Hector: No comment. I told you that this morning. I'm closing the door now.

Paula: Wait—this is for a different article. The twins have decided to tell their story.

Hector: Those twins know nothing. They were hiding in their room, drinking champagne the whole time the hotel was on lockdown.

Paula: And why is that?

Hector: Because they knew I'd be after them once I found out what they said I'd done.

Paula: And what exactly did you do, Hector?

Hector: None of your damn business! Goodbye!

That woman could make enemies in the depths of hell. Calls herself a journalist. She is just a nosy so-and-so on a salary. Gets everyone to write her stories for her and then scribbles her name on the top line. And I have gone and walked right into her trap, like the classic fool that I am. The twins will twist my words in their own way to make it sound like I am some nutter who got away with murder. They knew it wasn't me, but that didn't stop them lying to the police, did it?

Tap one. Tap two. Tap three.

I am just going to pause a moment to take some deep breaths. And now my brew has gone cold! This could not get much worse.

Right, Helen, I think I'm going to have to call it a day. Paula has rattled me. A good night's sleep is what I need. Tomorrow I will pick up from where I left off and we'll talk about the guests that checked in that week. The murder week . . .

CHAPTER

4

It was an odd kind of week, the murder week. Mr Potts called an all-in staff meeting for eight o'clock Monday morning. Mr Potts was the hotel's manager at the time. I have seen plenty of managers come and go through the years, some good, some not so good. Mr Potts would sit somewhere in the middle, I would say. He is a tall, lanky fellow, probably in his late forties, early fifties. If he is reading this, I hope that doesn't offend him. But then again, it doesn't matter so much now if it does. Let us say mid-forties, just to be polite. Whatever his age, he has done well not to get any grey hairs yet. I went grey in my mid-thirties. My hairline has stayed pretty set in place, luckily. But Mr Potts has a great head of raven-black hair. He obviously gets his eyebrows done and probably has his nails manicured too. Nothing wrong with that.

Mr Potts has an interesting temperament. Some days he would be on the warpath, and you would want to steer clear. Other days, he would stop and share a joke with the staff, but he would always catch himself after a minute or so and return to his staunch, very formal demeanour. Sometimes people in positions of power are just like that. Think they have to be stand-offish to command respect.

All the staff gathered in the library, which was closed to guests until 4 pm. Some of the young ones slumped on the leather sofas, a couple fiddled with the lid of the globe bar that hid a few bottles of nice Scotch. I would never let myself fully relax at work. That is not professional, in my opinion. There was always an at-work Hector and an at-home Hector. At-work Hector stood up straight, shoulders back, and maintained a soft, approachable smile. At-home Hector likes to eat fish and chips on the settee while doing newspaper puzzles. I am just saying, different environment, different Hector. Anyhow, Mr Potts stood by the unlit fireplace with the head of marketing, Sandra, on one side, and the head of finance, Rosanne, on the other. Serious faces all round.

'The Cavengreen family have made the decision to sell the hotel,' Mr Potts said, after he had shushed the room several times. He was very matter-of-fact about it. Naturally, people shared worried glances. In the whole time I had worked at the hotel, it had never changed hands. I still haven't ever met the Cavengreens. They never interfered, but as far as I know they were nice people who wanted to employ locals and keep them employed. None of this 'redundancies every few months' malarky like you get at the big chains. A change of owners would almost certainly mean a staff shake-up. And the likes of me, being seventy-three and not as shiny as the young 'uns, I was sure I would be first to get the boot.

There was not much more left to be said. Little groups of employees gossiped in the hallways after the meeting, exchanging baseless opinions on what they thought might happen. It is always dangerous to speculate, so I just got back to work behind my desk. That is not to say it wasn't on my mind.

After lunch, Fiona came over and let me know that she had overheard Mr Potts telling Rosanne that the new owners—Americans by the sound of it—were planning on replacing the concierge service with some fancy iPad system that would be available in each suite. I would be out of a job. What's more, the new owners were due to arrive at the hotel that evening, to survey their purchase.

To them, we were just another drop in their property portfolio. To us, the people working at the hotel, this was our livelihood. The police would call this 'motive' when they tried to pin the murder on me. And believe you me when I say it was hard to wriggle my way out of that narrative.

Back to the guests. The hotel was at seventy-five per cent capacity that week, due to be one hundred per cent by the weekend. But by the time the weekend came, the hotel was on lockdown and no guests were allowed to check in—or check out, for that matter. Seventy-five per cent capacity was par for the course, given it was mid spring and we were coming off the back of a busy and unusually humid Easter. Check-in days are Mondays, Wednesdays and Fridays, and guests are required to pay and stay for a minimum of two nights. If they want to stay longer, they can, but they must stay an even number of nights so as not to mess up the system. But at over one thousand quid a night, most people only stay for two.

The murder happened on a Thursday, so if you're following, you'll have realised that we might have had some leftover guests from the Monday check-in (and we did have a few), but mostly they would have been Wednesday arrivals. I am not going to reel off the names of everyone present in the hotel, but I will describe the main players, those who are essential to the story. And that includes the victim, of course.

Monday evening, as rumoured, the Americans arrived: four of them. They were already complaining loudly about the wet weather when they filed through the door at quarter past seven. They thought May would have been a little sunnier for them. Mr Potts had gathered a sample of his favourite employees, the ones who presented the best, myself included, to greet them in a line at the entrance like they were the royal family. Fiona handed out champagne but two of them didn't drink alcohol. It was a rocky start.

You might remember me mentioning American Dave earlier; he was one of this lot. From the moment I met him, I knew he was a loud-mouthed good-for-nothing, with his obnoxiously sized cowboy hat and blue Ralph Lauren jumper draped over his shoulders. Who wears a cowboy hat in the Yorkshire Dales? One big gust of wind and it would be up and over the hills. Some of the girls on reception swooned when they first saw him. The word 'hunk' was thrown around. Apparently they liked his suntan and sandy blond hair. 'Dreamy,' they said. I know he is already in talks to release his own book about the goings-on at Cavengreen, but hopefully mine will hit the shelves first. His will be full of exaggerations and blurred memories from his late-night whisky-drinking. Not to mention, I have my reputation to protect; I doubt he'd have many nice things to say about me.

Tanya—another of the Americans—was American Dave's shadow. She wore a wedding ring but was inappropriately touchy-feely with American Dave whenever the two Yanky paper pushers weren't around. You see these things as a concierge.

Riley and Jackson were the names of the other two, I think. Very American names. Not my cup of tea. Don't expect them to feature much in this story. God knows where they were during all this. Those two lingered in the background, clearly there for show rather than their opinions. One was in charge of social media or some nonsense, and the other was an accountant. I forget which one was which.

The group took up four of the rooms, a suite each. The only other Monday check-ins who were still at the hotel on the murder day were Sue and Martin Bainbridge, and Olive—Sue's daughter, Martin's stepdaughter. Olive was due to have her wedding at the hotel Wednesday afternoon. The bride-to-be spent the first two days of her stay bossing the staff around and making her wedding planner cry. That is it for Monday check-ins.

Olive's husband-to-be, Patrick, checked in on Wednesday morning. He looked bleary-eyed, as his mates Ray and Jamil had organised a stag-do at a pub not too far from Cavengreen. Ray and Jamil shared a suite, and that was where Patrick stayed before joining his new wife in the bridal suite after the wedding celebrations. Aside from being hungover on his wedding day, Patrick seemed like a decent man. He was mostly polite and softly spoken.

His groomsmen, on the other hand, were abrasive and out of place. Public school education, that much was obvious, but still too young to appreciate the elegance of Cavengreen. Money, yes, it was clear that they had plenty, but they would have been more at home on a booze cruise around Ibiza. Nevertheless, I treat all guests equally. That is what a good concierge must do. And really, who am I to look down on anyone? I am just a concierge, at the end of the day.

The twins, Ruby and Oksana, also checked in on the Wednesday. They were the kind of girls who were born with a silver spoon and no manners. Used to getting whatever they wanted and unable to show appreciation. They arrived with a Mercedes-Benz boot full of suitcases that they demanded be taken up to their suite *immediately*.

A nervous-looking make-up artist and hair stylist carrying bags of kit trailed behind them as the twins were shown their room, which apparently was not up to their expected standard. That is what the porter, Joe, told me. He said they had yelled this at him.

Ruby and Oksana were Olive's bridesmaids. They were identical, but after a few glances it was easy to tell them apart. Ruby was the louder and ruder of the two; Oksana was the sheep. Oksana had a slightly rounded face, while Ruby's was pointed. They were both nasty. Blessed with good looks but horrid personalities, they made quite the impact when they entered a room. If I had to hazard a guess, I'd say they were of either Serbian or Croatian descent. Both girls had long, straight, light brown hair, blue eyes and puffy lips that did not look natural. At one point during their stay, I heard them giggling about how they were sure they would upstage the bride. On her wedding day of all days!

They would strut through the lobby and fling their handbags on my desk before making their demands. As if I'd have any interest in your bloomin' handbag—it could be from the charity shop for all I care. Fiona let me know that the bags were Chanel. Very expensive, so I hear. Well, I saw a lot of expensive bags during my time as the concierge. On the first day, the twins demanded a specific type of tonic water that, after an hour of telephone calls, I finally tracked down at a boutique gin shop in Manchester. Do you know how long that drive is? I had to send one of the porters. Anyway, they got the tonic water, but of course there were hissy fits all round when it didn't arrive on time. They also wanted silk pillowcases, a dehumidifier for their room, and cornflakes with skim milk and raspberries. These were easier to attain.

I will continue to reveal the horrors of the twins as this story goes on, but next I want to introduce a gentleman from Scotland named Alec Maclean who arrived at around 11.30 am on Wednesday. He asked me if I could arrange to have the bangers and mash from the local pub delivered, which I was happy to do for him. Nigel at the Ferret Inn is a long-time acquaintance of mine, so he delivered the meal himself, piping hot.

Alec told me he had come to the hotel to work on his novel as he was suffering from writer's block and needed a change of scenery. Writer's block is something I have yet to encounter, perhaps because I am telling a true story. Maybe I will get talker's block at some point. If that happens, I am sure Helen will have some tips for me after her decades in the book business. Alec had a deep, booming voice, and a messy, wiry beard that he seemed to have neglected due to his writing ailment. He carried a pen everywhere he went, and he chewed on it when he had nothing else to do with his hands. I believe his book will be published posthumously. Read into that what you will.

Lastly, a gentleman named Bruno Tatterson checked in. It was odd because he didn't have a suitcase, claiming that he only intended to go from his room to the spa and back, for which he would wear the robe provided, and then to dinner in the clothes he arrived in. The hotel supplied all the additional amenities a man could need. He rolled his eyes when I reminded him that a wedding would be taking place in the gardens the next day and suggested he avoid that area between four and six. Whenever there was a wedding, I would always inform guests who weren't attending in advance and offer them a complimentary spa treatment or cocktails at Hugo's as a way of keeping them occupied in an area of the hotel where they could avoid any disruptions. No one wants to be around a wedding they are not invited to. But weddings are the hotel's bread and butter, so the show had to go on.

Bruno happily accepted a complimentary massage. He briefly mentioned that he was recovering from a recent heartbreak, so he was enjoying a bit of R & R in the countryside. Naturally, I didn't pry, but I was prepared to listen should he wish to discuss his personal life further. In my many years as a concierge, I would often play the part of a therapist, among other things.

That is a bit of an overview of everyone you need to know about, guest wise. Two of the people I mentioned in this chapter will die at the hotel, though only one will be murdered.

It is no wonder you encouraged me to write this book, Helen. It is quite the story.

CHAPTER

5

Helen was over yesterday, helping me consolidate my thoughts. I think I jinxed myself the other day by saying I'd not yet encountered writer's—or talker's—block.

Whenever Helen comes over, she always does the same three things before she sits down for a brew.

I hope you don't mind me sharing this, Helen.

First, she opens all the windows to let in some fresh air. She says it is stuffy in here, but that is not something I notice. Next, she washes her hands and dries them on the tea towel that hangs on the oven handle. I have to use all my strength not to refold it into a perfect three-fold after she has unravelled it. This normally involves me leaving the kitchen and going into the lounge. Helen follows and, third, starts fussing over me, making sure I am comfortable and well fed.

Sorry, Helen. I am not saying I don't appreciate your kindness; you are a very good friend. But, as you know, I have kept myself alive these last seventy-three years, so there is no need to fuss too much.

She says she worries because I live alone, although I believe she does too, not that she shares much.

Helen, I feel like you know everything under the bloomin' sun there is to know about me, but I don't even know if you're currently romantically involved with anyone. Before she died, Josie mentioned that you were hoping for a proposal from some mystery man whose name you didn't share. I don't know what happened with that, but I don't recall spotting a ring. What a terrible friend I am—although, in my defence, you've always been very private. But things are too *me, me, me* right now, and we've still got lots to catch up on about your time away in London. Over a hot brew, next time I see you.

As I was saying, living alone is not something that has ever really bothered me. It would have been nice to have a wife and kids, but it just didn't happen like that for me. I had my heart broken three times, and after that I decided to stop looking for love. So, I live alone. And that suits me and my little habits quite well. Everything is just as I like it, except for the occasional tea towel out of place. But I fix that as soon as Helen leaves.

Sorry again, Helen.

This cottage is the same one I have lived in my whole life. My father left it to me and my sister in his will. It was the least he could do. And my sister left me her half when she passed away, bless her. It has been paid off for a while now, but it guzzles gas and electricity like a sports car, so that's where a lot of my pension goes each month. The limestone wall out the front has had to be fixed a few times. I used to do it myself, but I can't be doing things like that until I get my hip done. I can barely lift the shopping, let alone slabs of stone. The wall props up a slightly wonky wrought-iron gate and then a small path leads to my white front door. It's not much, but it's a nice home for one.

Three bedrooms, though all very small. One lavatory upstairs and one downstairs. I repainted the entire house cream once Dad dropped dead. Redid the carpets too. I didn't want even the tiniest skin cell from him remaining. I sold most of the furniture at a car boot, but I kept all my mum's cake trays and the like. My father never bothered with the kitchen, so I didn't have to do much in there. Just a few appliance upgrades. I keep the door to their old bedroom closed and never go in. That means my room is not the biggest, but it will do, considering it is only me. It is just about big enough for a double bed, and that is big enough for someone who lives alone.

Yesterday, Helen got me to sit in front of a mirror and describe myself. She said that you readers would like to have a clear picture of me, which is fair enough since we are going to be spending a fair amount of time together. Helen will insert a transcript of that audio here.

You know, Helen, I can't say I have ever sat in front of a mirror and studied myself like this before. Right: from top to bottom, you say? Well, I have a shortish mop of grey hair on my head. Or should I say silver? Does that make me sound more dashing? Let's go with silver. My eyebrows are grey—or silver—too. I have to comb them with a little brush in the mornings as they're normally this way, that way and every which way when I wake up. I have blue-grey eyes and pale skin. Even if I go on holiday I'll always burn and never tan. Not that I sit in the sun much.

I've never been a big drinker, so I don't have any of them spider veins that you see on those down the pub. My father had them all over his big, bulbous nose. He never made it to my age, but even by the time he died he looked older than I do now. Not to toot my own horn, but my skin is pretty smooth, all things considered. A few new wrinkles popped up on the forehead after all this murder malarky, though.

I wouldn't say I'm tall, but I'm not short. Five foot ten and a half. Don't forget the half. And I am slim but not skinny. You might say I've got a slight frame. I walk with a bit of a hobble now that the old hip has carked it. I've been on the waitlist for a replacement since last year.

Clothes. When I'm at home, I normally like to wear comfortable trousers and a shirt. I have different shirts for different occasions. Once I find something I like, I normally buy it in a few colours. And when I was working at Cavengreen, my uniform was a smart navy suit with the hotel's logo on the breast pocket, a crisp white shirt, a blue tie that I attached my gold name pin to, and my always-shined black shoes. The top hat wasn't mandatory, but I thought it was a nice touch. I kept the name pin when I left. It is on the mantelpiece as a reminder to always stay true to who I am, no matter the circumstance.

I must say, now that I have done it, I am glad Helen suggested that mirror exercise. Otherwise, I would be struggling to find many more adjectives for myself other than old and grey.

Helen also told me to run through a regular day with you, but I am not sure how helpful that would be in pushing this story along, considering a regular day now looks very different to a regular day back then. Instead, I will recap the day before the murder. That way you will get an idea of what a normal day looked like at Cavengreen, but with some bits relevant to this book in there too.

That morning, like every morning, I woke at 5 am and took three deep breaths before getting out of bed on the left side. The tap in my shower has always been a bit dodgy, but it is close to three twists to find the perfect temperature. Three small pumps of body wash and then three laps around my mouth with my toothbrush. Three, or possibly six, squares of lavatory roll for my business and then I got dressed and headed out to the car. I upgraded from a bicycle to a car about ten years ago, when the hip first started playing silly buggers. Before I set off, I tapped the steering wheel three times.

At Cavengreen, I parked in the same spot as I did every other day. The hotel made a RESERVED plaque for me because I would get flustered if a new staff member or one of the young folk would park where I normally did. I was there by ten to six, which left just enough time to make sure that everything on my desk was neatly back in place after the night cleaners had been. That meant my pen and paper were perfectly aligned, the labels on the water bottles in the fridge were all facing forward, and my maps and guides were stacked in three perfect rows. Fiona always picked up coffees for me and herself on her way in, and mine was in my hand by 6 am. That morning, she'd written a little message on the side of the paper cup: 'have a good day'. Then the workday began with a briefing from Fiona on all the important goings on.

Once the clock ticked over to 9 am, I started telephoning anyone who had recently made a booking. It was part of our personal concierge service to make them feel special from the moment they booked to the moment they arrived back home. I asked them things like their dietary requirements, if they were staying at the hotel for a particular occasion, what kind of pillow they liked, if they would like me to book the hotel restaurant for them one evening, and if they had any special requests. It was normally just a five- or ten-minute conversation, and I would get one of the girls on reception to pop the notes on their file so that we had everything ready for them when they checked in. We would always try to greet our guests with a personal touch, like,

'Happy fourth anniversary,' or, 'Welcome to the Yorkshire Dales,' if they had never been here before. Just to make them feel a bit special.

On this particular day, the day before the murder, the bride, Olive, came down for breakfast just after 9 am. Her hair was all bunched up in those rollers that make women look like Medusa. She seemed stressed. Her mother was scuttling after her, also in a bit of a frenzy. On their way through the lobby, I heard the bride asking her mother to just give her some space. The bride was only at breakfast for fifteen minutes before returning to her suite in tears. The twins, Ruby and Oksana, trailed along, telling her everything would be okay, but smirking behind her back. Like I said, it was not my business to pry, but those were the sort of things I noticed. To the guests, it was almost like I was a piece of furniture rather than a human with eyes and ears. You would be surprised how openly they displayed their emotions in front of me. Sometimes I felt like one of those oil paintings whose eyes seem to follow you wherever you go.

Check-in at the hotel was from eleven. The groom and his two groomsmen arrived first. They had a lot of suit bags, so I helped the porters take everything up to their suite, making sure to check the coast was clear to avoid a premature run-in with an emotional bride. Luckily, Fiona had carefully planned this arrival and the boys' room was downstairs, while the entrance to the bridal suite was at the far end of the top-floor corridor. There was whisky and ice already waiting for the trio, something they had requested during our pre-arrival telephone call. They also wanted burgers, presumedly to cure their hangovers. I quietly offered to send up some rehydration sachets and painkillers. We needed that groom looking and feeling his best by the afternoon. In my day, I have seen many an angry bride lose their cool over a too-drunk or too-hungover husband at the altar. The groom accepted my offer and, as far as I know, it worked.

By the time I returned to my desk, Alec Maclean, the Scottish writer, was checking in and, as you know, I arranged for his bangers and mash to be delivered. About half an hour after that, Bruno Tatterson arrived, bagless. I noticed Fiona giggling shyly and fluttering her eyelashes as he checked in, which she does when a guest is a bit of a looker, which I suppose he was, but in a more mature, rugged way than American Dave. About ten years younger than me, I'd say. Bruno looked familiar—perhaps from the telly or maybe movies. The hotel is often frequented by celebrities and royalty. Half of them I don't have the foggiest idea who they are, but Bruno rang some sort of bell for me. The most famous person we've had at the hotel is *[name removed for legal reasons]*. I mean, the whole world knows who he is, even an old fart like me. He arrived at the hotel with one younger lady on the Monday, pretended to check out with her on the Wednesday, and then arrived back at the hotel an hour later with another young lady. It was funny watching him pretend to ooh and aah at things he had already seen earlier that day. But the staff were under strict instructions to play along. Discretion is factored into the price tag at a place like Cavengreen.

Mr Potts would circle the hotel like a hawk from about 11.30 am. He checked every surface for dust and then twisted the vases this way and that until he found the angle that best showcased the flowers. This was quite grating for me, as I normally gave the vase on my desk three swift twists to set its position. I would find myself twitching a little when Mr Potts came over and twisted it two or four times. When he had finished his loop of the lobby, I would normally give the vase three more turns, just to resettle my angsty hands.

If anything was not as it should be in the lobby, the blame normally fell on Fiona. It was—and still is, I suppose—her job to make sure everything was spick and span at all times. Mr Potts was particularly hard on her. She never crumbled though, and always took his comments on the chin. She is a strong woman, even stronger after she lost her husband. But some days after work we would head to the pub for a glass of wine, and she would let it all out. It is best not to keep things bottled up for too long and I am always willing to lend an ear to a friend.

As was the norm when we had a wedding at the hotel, there was an influx of suppliers the morning of. Florists, musicians, the cake supplier, the marquee hire company, it all happened in those last few hours. The hotel has its own dedicated commercial kitchen down back, where the chefs make all the food for weddings and events. It is more profitable than bringing in an external caterer, I believe. The couple getting married would usually come in for a tasting about two months before the wedding and sample all the options before deciding what dishes they wanted on their menu. From memory, I think they chose the smoked salmon and vegetable tart for the entrees, and then the pork belly, gnocchi and kingfish for the mains. The wedding cake would be served for dessert and they requested mini beef sliders to come out around 10 pm as a little late-night snack to fuel the dancefloor.

I know the florist, Laurina, quite well. She is the preferred supplier here at Cavengreen, and on the morning of the wedding she turned up with the most beautiful peonies neatly tied into bridal bouquets. All the flowers were white, which I always think looks very elegant. Around 1 pm I went and had a little peek at the wedding set-up, and it looked simply spectacular. But that is what you get when you marry at Cavengreen. It is not a venue for those who are short of a bob or two.

Everything that day proceeded as normal. That was until 2 pm rolled around and Mr Potts and the Americans entered the lobby. The tall fellow, American Dave, had the loudest voice. He sounded like a cowboy, and his brash tone was like nails on a chalkboard in our refined hotel. Or *his* refined hotel, I should say. Mr Potts pointed out various features to the Americans, the two ducklings at the back taking notes. Then they came my way.

'Hector? That's your name, isn't it?' American Dave asked. He placed his giant hands on my counter, leaving smudges when he eventually peeled them off.

I politely confirmed my identity and wondered where this could be going. I would be lying if I said that I wasn't a little concerned after what Fiona had told me about them replacing the concierge system with some new technology.

'A word, Hector?' Mr Potts gestured towards the library, and I followed him and the Americans into the room.

'Hector,' American Dave boomed. 'Pottsy here tells me you've worked at the hotel for over fifty years.' He didn't pause for me to agree or disagree. 'That's a mighty long time. You must have seen some things in your day?'

I nodded but he wasn't looking for a response.

'That may be the case,' he went on, 'but we think the concierge service at Cavengreen could do with a little refresh.'

'A refresh?' I said.

'A refresh. That's right. We want to take Cavengreen into the future and we're going to need your help.' I felt like I was being recruited into the army. 'Do you know what an iPad is?' One of the other Yanks handed him a device.

'Of course.' I withheld my offence as I replied. I might be seventy-three and not able to use a computer, but I am not a bloody imbecile.

'Great!' American Dave thumped his hand down on the mahogany coffee table and I tried not to grimace. Mr Potts gasped a little for both of us. 'Our team back in Dallas has been working hard to develop brand-new software especially for this hotel. Our digital concierge service will now be available in every suite at Cavengreen, allowing guests to make their requests without having to deal directly with you. It will save you time and you won't have to make small talk.'

'I quite like chatting to the guests,' I protested. 'It's no bother.'

But American Dave wasn't interested. 'This is the future, Hector. Nobody wants to speak to a human anymore. The world is all about convenience and this is just part of it.'

'With all due respect, Dave,' Mr Potts began, noticing the horror on my face, 'Hector has worked at the hotel for many years and our regular guests look forward to seeing him. He is part of the experience.'

'And he still will be, Pottsy—he'll just be inside one of these iPads, that's all.' American Dave waved the device in his hand. 'Let me show you the software: you're gonna love it.'

American Dave made us sit either side of him on the sofa as he poked at the screen. The software in question allowed people to request a new pillow from a menu, order room service directly from the kitchen, book dinner at Lavender Plates and make other special requests that would be sent through to the appropriate staff member who could fulfil them. I would have an iPad on my desk through which I would be able to see any guest requests that were relevant to me, he explained. As far as I could see, my new role was that of a donkey. Instead of talking to guests, I was reduced to merely a fetcher and carrier. Most of the requests that I would normally have handled would now go straight to an iPad set up in the porter's quarters. I am no fool, so I asked them straight.

'This is all very well and good for the future and technology, but what does it mean for my job?'

'Hector, relax.' American Dave held up his palms to soothe me, as if I were acting like some lunatic. 'This is merely a trial period to see if it improves guest satisfaction. If they don't like it, we'll take it away.'

'And if they do like it?' Mr Potts asked nervously.

'Then we've done our job right!' American Dave clapped his hands together and his minions all nodded along like those dog figurines that builders have on their dashboards.

After the meeting concluded, Mr Potts pulled me to one side and told me he was going to protect my job at all costs. But we both knew that American Dave and his iPads were likely going to mean the end of my career at Cavengreen. And I will admit it: I was angry.

CHAPTER

6

Normally, I start recording at 7 am, after the morning paper has arrived and I have had one of my two cups of English breakfast. But today, that did not happen, and let me tell you why. That good-for-nothing Paula McDavidson! The newspaper boy flung today's black-and-white at my front door and it landed with a particularly loud thud. I put the kettle on, then stepped outside to pick it up. My heart stopped when I saw my ugly mug on the front page. I haven't read it yet. I just got off the telephone with Helen and she said I should read it to you lot so you can have my real, as-it-happens reaction.

The headline says: CONCIERGE OR CONMAN? Well, I never! Concierge or conman? I haven't devoted the last fifty-odd years of my life to Cavengreen just to be labelled a conman by the local newspaper. Of course, Paula McDavidson is responsible for this. There is a little photo of her next to the word 'journalist'. If she is a journalist, then I am the bloody sultan of Taiwan. A fiction writer is what she is. A make-believe storyteller. On the plus side, the photo she has used isn't the worst I have seen of me. It is from Cavengreen's website. The Americans mustn't have had the chance to update it yet. It was taken about ten years ago now and shows me looking rather smart in my uniform outside the front of the hotel.

Next to the picture of me is a photograph of the twins, Ruby and Oksana. I am not sure what being in a bikini on the beach in Dubai has to do with the murder investigation. The caption underneath the photo says that they are the daughters of a millionaire property investor, and they live in a five-million-pound house in Chelsea, London. They have even put in how much my cottage is worth! It hasn't been sold in over eighty years, so I am not sure where Paula McDavidson has plucked that number from. Why does the newspaper have to mention that? The lower the home value, the more likely the owner is to murder someone? Are people supposed to make judgements on a person's character based on the price of their house? I am already getting riled up and I haven't even started reading the bloomin' thing yet. I am sure this will be a pack of lies, but here goes:

> Cavengreen Hotel may be one of the most luxurious places to stay in the United Kingdom, but recently it was embroiled in a scandal fit for the movies. In an exclusive for the *Yorkshire Sun*, two of the guests staying at the hotel at the time of the notorious Cavengreen murder have decided to come forward. This is their story . . .

Spare me the dramatics! There is no point in me telling my story if the others keep coming out of the woodwork with their made-up nonsense. But then again, I must remember: exposing the truth is why I am doing this.

> Twins Ruby and Osksana Farrinucha are daughters of million-aire property investor Roman Farrinucha and currently reside in

Chelsea, London. In April of this year, the girls were invited to Cavengreen Hotel in the Yorkshire Dales to act as bridesmaids at the wedding of their friend Olive Nixon. During their stay they witnessed the brutal murder of—

WITNESSED? Witnessed, my arse. Not a single person in that hotel witnessed anything. The only people who saw the dead body were me, the police and the murderer. They may have seen the body bag as it was wheeled out of the hotel, but I doubt it; I think I was the only one awake for that. I can't read any more of this nonsense without talking to Helen.

I turned the dictaphone off for a bit. I just needed to gather my thoughts. Helen had to talk me into continuing with this book. Sometimes I think she is the only one on my side. When we first discussed writing this, I told her that if I was going to do it, it had to be the full truth. No fluff or lies. And I stand by that. But it is going to be hard to convince people that this is the true version when there are half-a-dozen other versions out there. Just you wait until American Dave has his chat with the media. We finally got confirmation of that today. Instead of a book, he is planning on releasing a documentary with some American production company and now I feel like it is a race between me and him.

I told Helen I was tempted to just pack it in and let the truth stay hidden forever. But she persuaded me that not only would I be letting myself down by not telling my story, I would be letting her down, after all the effort she's already put into this. She is really enjoying getting stuck into a book project again. It has been a welcome distraction from her recent break-up, so she tells me. Plus, she added, withholding the truth would be letting the victim down.

A good telling-off was all I needed. I'm going to pull myself together and finish what I started. Not today, though; today I need to rest. And as for this pathetic excuse for journalism, this can be tomorrow's fish-and-chip wrapping.

And yes, Helen, that sound was me flinging the newspaper across the room.

Yesterday was a bit rocky but I am in a much finer mood today. Onwards and upwards. It is time to get back to my story. Today we are returning to the hotel and picking up where we left off on the day before the murder. You might remember that I had just been given a lesson in technology from American Dave. It was nice to know that Mr Potts supported me. Whether the Americans would listen to him or not would be another matter.

American Dave left an iPad on my desk so I put on my glasses and tried to have a click around with it. Fiona didn't half chuckle when she saw me. As someone who still has one of those old types of mobile telephones, made just for calls, I am sure I was quite the sight trying to navigate an iPad. Fiona showed me the ropes, and after a few goes I understood the basics. A little pop-up message appeared on the screen reading: TEST TEST TEST. DAVE. TEST TEST TEST. He was just as loud over iPad as in real life. The new devices were to be placed in the guests' rooms during the day's scheduled housekeeping rounds. I was apprehensive to see just how many people preferred to use them.

In the meantime, Alec Maclean, the Scottish writer, called my desk requesting fresh glasses and a bowl of mixed nuts. When I knocked on his door, his voice boomed at me to enter. The curtains in his suite were drawn and just a sliver of bright light spilt through onto his face. There was a humming noise and it took me a few seconds to realise it was coming from Alec. He was sitting at a desk with his laptop open, his hair all in disarray. When he turned around, it was immediately apparent from his grey complexion, drooping eyelids and red eyes that he had spent the few hours since checking in getting very well acquainted with the hotel's complimentary whisky.

'It helps me write,' he mumbled, and then coughed.

'I've heard that Lewis Carroll took hallucinogens when writing *Alice in Wonderland*,' I said, in an attempt to reassure him.

'I don't suppose you have any of those behind that desk of yours,' Alec joked.

'I'm afraid we're all out. Is there anything else I can get you?'

'Opening the curtains might make things a little less depressing in here.'

That seemed like a marvellous idea. A button on the wall next to the fireplace controlled the curtains and with one quick press they whirred open like the beginning of a theatre production.

'How's that writer's block going?' I asked, trying to sound upbeat.

'I thought a little lubrication might help.' He tipped his whisky glass from side to side and watched the liquid sway. 'But I was wrong. Any tips?'

'I could barely read or write when I was at school. It still takes me a while to get through a good murder mystery novel, but perseverance is key in challenging moments. I'd love to be able to write a story one day.

Don't they say everyone's got one good book in them?' I said to him. Irony, that's what that is.

'You could write about life here at the hotel,' Alec suggested.

'And who would want to read about that?'

'You'd have to make it interesting. Every good book needs an event, a twist and a resolution. Get those three, add a few messed-up characters, and there's no reason why you can't write a good book. In fact, I've been writing about some of the people here in the hotel myself. I often do that. I write about conversations or moments I witness, just in case I want to use them later. Not that I know shite about writing a good book. I'm stuck on the twist.' He sighed.

'Well, what have you so far?' I asked.

You might find it odd that I lingered in Alec's room given that, as I told you, I was always the professional, and as such I wasn't in the habit of getting too close to the guests. But this was a funny kind of day, having learnt that my human interaction was about to be replaced with a machine, and since Alec seemed like he wanted to chat, I saw no harm in a little conversation. Plus, the topic was of interest.

Alec ran me through the plot of his book. I don't want to say too much because, like I said before, it is to be published posthumously—by Helen's old firm, as it happens. The story is about a Scottish fisherman who lives on a remote island where strange things keep happening. It's one of those dark and mysterious tales and he uses a lot of adjectives like 'crashing' waves and 'howling' wind to set the scene. He only read part of it to me, but I could tell how cold and miserable it would be in the place the fisherman lived. I guess that is what a good writer does.

In the end we brainstormed three potential twists that could take place to explain the strange occurrences on the island. We quickly ruled out Alec's suggestion of aliens, followed by my recommendation that the fisherman had a long-lost twin brother who had been put up for adoption by their parents and was now back to seek revenge on the family that disowned him. Alec described that as too far-fetched, which I thought was a little rich coming from the drunk who wanted to blame everything on extraterrestrials. But I was pleased with where we landed and happy to have helped Alec overcome his writer's block. When I left him, he was busy tap-tapping on his computer and opening another bottle of whisky. I will say now, with the benefit of hindsight, there is something very dangerous about a man with an empty bottle of whisky—even more so when there is a full one waiting next to it.

I left Alec's room, closing the door behind me quietly, not wanting to disturb his flow of words. A few doors down, someone else was doing some sneaking around too. I saw American Dave zip up his trousers with a satisfied smile on his face as he closed the door to his colleague Tanya's suite. It was my job to turn a blind eye to such dalliances, but I am sure Mrs American Dave won't be best pleased if she ever reads my book. A man like that could convince the Pope that Jesus doesn't exist, though, so I am sure he'll wheedle his way out of it somehow.

'Ready to try out those iPads, my man?' he bellowed as he caught sight of me.

I gave him a thumbs-up, because that seemed the appropriate form of communication with such a man in such a moment. He returned the gesture, seeming completely unfazed by my having caught him in the midst of a tryst. But that goes back to what I was saying before about people feeling like they can be their true selves around me, because it is only the concierge watching—no one important.

Around 3.30 pm, the wedding guests began to arrive in coachloads. The hotel isn't large enough to accommodate hordes of rowdy guests, so we usually suggest that the bride and groom's immediate family stay

in the suites, and that other guests book their own accommodation at one of the neighbouring hotels or bed and breakfasts. I stood by the door with Fiona and the girls from reception, trying to catch a glimpse of the attendees. This lot looked like a very well-to-do bunch as they stepped off the coaches. They were directed around the side of the hotel rather than through the lobby, so as not to bother the regular guests. A rainbow of colourfully dressed women was broken up by the dark tones of designer three-piece suits on well-groomed men who spoke like royalty. One woman seemed determined to outdo the bride in a flowing cream gown made of what appeared to be feathers.

Fiona coordinated some pre-wedding drinks for the groom and his groomsmen in the library. Patrick was complaining that his parents couldn't make it, having been caught up on business in the Middle East. Some people have all the money in the world, but don't put their family first, so what is the point? I would rather have had wonderful parents growing up than millions of pounds. As it turns out, I had neither. That is unfair to my mother, but she was not around that long.

My mother died when I was thirteen. Heart attack. My father found her dead in her favourite chair with a full glass of sherry and an uneaten slice of apple pie next to her. She didn't even get to enjoy her last meal. My mum was a lovely woman. Anna-Elise was her name. She used to paint watercolours of the landscape and sell them at the local pub to tourists passing through. My sister tried to track down some of her work a few years ago. She came close to getting one back for us once, but the greedy seller wanted more than three months' wages for it. Maybe if I sell enough of these books, I could buy it.

Our father's drinking got worse after our mother died. It was a good thing for me, though, because he spent more time down the pub than at home. Then he would pass out almost as soon as he came through the front door, and I would sneak out before he woke the next morning. We were like ships in the night. Sometimes I would get to school three hours early just to avoid him. On the weekends, I would walk up the hill behind our cottage and sit in the grass until I saw him leave for the day.

Anyhoo, after they'd had their drinks, Fiona escorted the groom and his men out to greet the guests. I caught a glimpse of Patrick's face as he passed through reception. Why is it that some grooms look like they are walking to their execution when they are on their way to marry the supposed love of their life?

When Fiona returned, she told me that the groom was having second thoughts. That he wasn't sure if Olive was going to make him happy forever. He said she was selfish, constantly dissatisfied, and always expecting too much. Fiona said she made a joke about divorce that went down like a lead balloon. Fiona has never had the tact for those sorts of situations. I have always found her very funny, though. Nevertheless, it seemed a bit late in the day for the groom to be having cold feet. I have seen a few instances of pre-wedding jitters in my time but I can't recall one single occasion where the wedding hasn't gone ahead. No doubt there are a fair few divorced couples out there now, but a wedding at Cavengreen costs an arm and a leg and no one wants the embarrassment of explaining to a group of snooty guests that a fancy do has been cancelled. I bet Fiona ten pounds that the wedding would still go ahead and later that day she paid up. I tried to refuse—a gentleman never accepts money off a lady from a lost bet—but she tucked the banknote in my breast pocket and told me I could buy her a glass of wine on Friday. That sounded like a good plan to me. Not that we made it to the pub in the end.

Olive's parents were bickering when they came down to the lobby. Something about him not saying her hair looked okay when prompted. Sue's snappishness probably stemmed from mother-of-the-bride nerves rather than a lack of compliments from her husband. Martin was sighing and looked like he would rather be elsewhere. I don't know the ins and outs of the Bainbridge family dynamics, and the whereabouts of Olive's biological father is still unknown to me, so don't expect him to suddenly appear to murder someone. You can cross him off your list of potential suspects.

The bickering stopped when the twins came stumbling along the corridor—a few champagnes in, it seemed. They were laughing loudly and taking pictures every couple of steps. They wore slinky peach dresses with no backs, and had matching half-up, half-down hairstyles. The wedding photographer got some photos of them, and then some more, as they demanded to be shot from every angle. Poor Olive waited in the wings for several minutes before she was called forward for her big reveal. And what a reveal it was. Her mother and stepfather cried happy tears as their little darling emerged in a huge white meringue with a veil that stretched a good way down the hallway. They all posed for pictures on the hotel stairs. Those stairs have been the backdrop for many a beautiful photograph in their day. From newlyweds to celebrities and royals, they have seen it all. You do have to watch out for the odd interruption of a passing guest, mind you. In this case, an inebriated Alec came bounding down, squeezing between Ruby and the bride. Ruby called him a host of offensive names, but Alec ignored her, making a beeline for my desk. It was essential that I join him in his suite immediately to help with the final part of his story, he insisted.

'Are you not going to do something about him?' Ruby shouted in my direction. 'He nearly knocked the bride down the stairs!'

This was a tricky situation for me. I wasn't employed as hotel security and Alec had every right to use the main staircase regardless of their photo shoot. Unfortunately he went about it like a bull in a china shop.

'I am ever so sorry,' I said. 'Fiona will arrange for some more champagne before you make your entrance.'

My words appeased the bride, but the twins weren't satisfied, making it clear that not only was I a silly old man who was beneath them, but noting that it was no surprise to them that I didn't wear a wedding ring given that I had amounted to nothing more than a hotel concierge.

Fiona gave me an apologetic look as she shepherded the bridal party into the library for some champagne and more photographs.

When I look back, it is very clear that the twins were gunning for me from the start. To them, I was an easy target. But I had no time to process the insults because a flushed-looking Alec was practically dragging me up the stairs towards his suite. When I suggested that it might be a better idea if we conversed the following day, when we were both fresher, he shouted something incoherent and spit-laden, then thumped back upstairs alone, tripping once or twice on his way.

The lobby felt like a hurricane had just blown through it and I took three deep breaths to reset myself. Fiona returned to reception, rolling her eyes about the 'twin twits', as she called them. Mind you, this isn't even the half of my experience with the Farrinucha girls. There is more to come, but maybe you're starting to see why I was less than pleased to learn they were telling their story to the *Yorkshire Sun*. Those two girls are menaces.

CHAPTER

8

Paula McDavidson has been round again. This time she wants a quote in response to her interview with the twins. Fat chance of that. I slammed the door in her face and told her not to come back ever again. As if that will stop her. Helen is here today. Something is wrong, I can tell, but she keeps repeating that she is 'fine'. She is sitting in the corner acting all shy because she doesn't want her voice on today's recording. Even when I said pretty please, she folded her arms and looked away. I won't be too pushy. Perhaps when I turn off the dictaphone she will open up.

Helen has come to gauge where I am up to in the story and to give me some helpful tips to make sure I don't forget anything important. She has brought along some vanilla tarts from Maude's Bakery, so excuse me while I munch on one of these and tell you about Bruno Tatterson. I told you I recognised him from somewhere; I wasn't the only one. Fiona said that she knew him from somewhere too. An older movie, she reckoned. Fiona loves her British crime films, and she swore that she'd seen Bruno in one of them. She winced when I cheekily suggested she subtly ask him if he was an actor. At Cavengreen we pride ourselves on our discretion. It is a place where the most famous person in the world can get some privacy.

Bruno spent most of the day in the spa, eventually emerging to head back to his suite around 5 pm. That is what Fiona told me. I wasn't there to see him as Alec had requested a new pillow as a way of luring me to his suite to help again with his writer's block. As it happened, the reason he wanted my assistance so desperately is that he was using me as inspiration for his main character. I already knew he had used little snippets of me in his book, but Helen has since told me I feature quite heavily in his manuscript. The main character looks just like me, she said, and even has many of my mannerisms. He is me but with a Scottish accent. Funnily enough, I do quite a good impression of a Scotsman. Not that you will be able to hear it if I do it for the dictaphone. I did it for Helen earlier and she will not admit it, but I know she was impressed. I even saw a glimmer of a smile as she lost herself for just a moment recalling a Scottish man she dated before her recent on–off relationship ended. In typical Helen style, she caught herself before revealing much more than that.

You've always been a mysterious one. For years we didn't hear from you while you were making books down in London. There are quite a few blanks to fill in, Helen—if that is indeed your real name.

She knows I'm joking. I even heard a little giggle from behind the vanilla tart that is making its way up to her mouth.

Alec wanted me to tell him about a memorable time in my life, so I recited the story of how I changed Mr Thomas's tyre that one time. He smiled and typed as I spoke. He then asked me to tell him about my relationship with my parents, which made me tap my head three times. He noticed and asked what that was all about. I was hesitant at first but then I spoke about my father, about the beatings. I did it without thinking, opening up in a way I wouldn't normally. Not before writing this book, anyway. I told him the head tapping was not the first thing. Just before that, I developed a stammer. That is all gone now. Though when I am very, very stressed, a slight one can creep back in. It used to drive my father up the wall. I suspect that, deep down, he knew he had done that to me. He stopped forcing me to apologise for things because of how long it would take to get the s out when I said 'sorry'. But the beatings didn't stop. It was always three heavy lashes across my lower back.

Realising I had shared too much, I decided it was time to make my excuses and leave. Alec got up hurriedly from the desk. He staggered, then lurched forward to grab me, begging me to stay for five more minutes, to tell him just a few things more. Unfortunately, he tugged too hard and ripped my suit at the shoulder seam. He was apologetic, but not overly so. He knew he had to let me go, though, and I slid out the door, reassuring him that no harm was done. It is an interesting dynamic, that of guest and concierge. Outside the hotel, a man would never imagine he could simply get away with ripping another man's suit. It would only happen during a heated fight of sorts. But because I was the concierge, and he was a paying guest, somehow that made it okay.

Usually, I liked to check in with all the guests at least once a day, whether that meant catching them when they returned from a walk, or when they were on their way to dinner. After what happened with Alec, I was hardly in the mood to make small talk, but I wanted to catch Bruno before I went home. I knew he had a 7 pm booking at Lavender Plates, so around 7.15, right before I was to head home for the evening, I popped my head into the restaurant to say a quick hello. I placed my torn suit jacket, neatly folded, on Fiona's desk on my way past. Excellent seamstress, she is; she said she would have it looking spanking new by morning.

Bruno was engrossed in his mobile telephone and had a bottle of fine Italian wine opened on his table. It was not my intention to startle him, but that's indeed what happened when I coughed to alert him to my presence. The conversation was short and uncomfortable. I got the impression I had interrupted something important on his mobile telephone, so I kept it brief. I advised that I hoped he'd had a pleasant day and to let the nightstaff know if there was anything he needed. I would be back at 6 am, I advised, and then I left. He didn't acknowledge my exit, but I never took such things personally.

Back at my concierge desk, I grabbed my car keys and said goodnight to Fiona, who was leaving herself. No sooner had she walked out the door than Bruno entered the lobby. He apologised for having been so rude, though this was unnecessary, as I had already moved on from our interaction. When you work in hospitality, the sooner you realise that you shouldn't expect an apology for abrupt guest behaviour, the better. Bruno's timing was rather annoying, as I was looking forward to getting home. I told him it was no bother and nothing to worry about, but he appeared angst-ridden, waving his arms in the air erratically as he described how much pressure he had been under recently and expressing regret that he had taken it out on me.

It was at that moment, with Bruno mid-flail, that the twins made their way through reception. They both raised their eyebrows at me as if to say, *Causing trouble again?* Ruby sucked in her cheeks to contain her smirk, while Oksana whispered something in her sister's ear. Those girls may as well have wooden spoons for arms, the amount of trouble they like to cause. Of course, they were gone by the time I had diffused the situation. Had they gawked at us a little longer, they would have seen us shake hands and wish each other a pleasant evening.

And that's it. That was the day before the murder. Yes, I have highlighted some moments of mild disturbance, but these things happened from time to time at Cavengreen. Certainly nothing occurred that would lead me to suspect what was to come the very next day. But before I get to that, this seems an opportune time for me to check in with Helen to make sure I have ticked off all the bits of information necessary for the story so far. We have a little list, you see. I will leave this chapter here, I think.

CHAPTER 9

Helen ended up staying for tea last night. I made chicken tikka masala from a jar, and we chatted about the book, among other things. She told me about her time at the publishing house in London. 'The most exciting time in my life,' is how she described it. And she really did make it sound very glamorous. Fancy dinners with new authors, book launch parties and lots of interesting people. I can tell she misses that world. I even got her talking about her relationship. She never mentioned him on those few times she came to visit Josie and me, but apparently he wasn't someone who wanted to be mentioned. She didn't even tell her work colleagues about him; said they were too up and down. She decided it was easier just to say nothing. Fair enough, I say.

Helen's a bit different from me. She is very outgoing, and I am a tad more reserved, but not shy by any means. What I am trying to say is that I am happy to be around people—that was my job for fifty-plus years—but I also love my own company and I tire easily in loud or particularly busy social settings. Helen, on the other hand, craves social interaction. And she has a lot of stories to share about her time down south. I am sure she won't mind much if I refer to her as a bit of a chatterbox. She is great company for an old soul like myself. If it weren't for Helen, I wouldn't get any social interaction outside of my infrequent visits to the pub with Fiona.

Listen to me, talking like I am surrounded by women. A big part of me misses the company of my mother and sister. My father stole so many potential happy memories away from us.

Tap one. Tap two. Tap three.

It has been a few chapters since I have done any head tapping, hasn't it? Now that we are getting into the sticky part of this story, I fear the tapping may increase in frequency. I hope that doesn't bother you too much.

When Helen was over last night she asked if she could use my computer. Yes, I have a computer. I bought it a while back with the hope of learning how to use it, but I never did. I got as far as setting up an email account—Fiona helped me do that—and that is it. Now it sits upstairs gathering dust. Helen will kill me for saying this, but her telephone died, and she needed to book in to get her greys covered with brown. Apparently you can schedule hair appointments on the internet now. Helen managed to log on with ease and informed me that aside from something called spam, I had one email. It was from American Dave. She wrote it out on a piece of paper for me so I could read it for you today. In your head, you will need to read this in a Texan accent. Helen tried to do her best impression last night but ended up sounding slightly Irish and slightly Russian.

Dear Mr Harrow,

Long time, no speak! As you may or may not know, a production company over here in the States has approached me to make a documentary about the Cavengreen murder. I plan to fly back over to the UK in the coming months to revisit the Dales with the film crew. Since you played such an important part in all this, I would like to ask if you'd be interested in appearing on-screen to tell your story? You'd be paid, of course. I think you'll find £2000 a very generous offer.

What do you say, old friend?

Dave

You can imagine how insulted I was by this. Old friend? We certainly are not old friends. And two thousand pounds! That is considerably less than the book advance Helen is trying to negotiate for me. I will tell you now, I am not going to reply. He can shove his American documentary up his backside for all I care.

Everyone needs my help to tell this story properly. Without me, they are all just guessing at what happened with the scattered jigsaw pieces they have.

Right, I have crumpled up that note. Hold on—I'll have to put it in the bin, otherwise it'll distract me . . . Okay, I'm back.

That squelching noise was the armchair, Helen.

Now I can get into the day I found the body.

Tap one. Tap two. Tap three.

It was just a normal day. Most stories where something unexpected happens start with the words 'It was just a normal day'. Like it was going to be anything other than that. It would be too coincidental if, on the day I found a dead body, my car was also stolen, a man tried to rob me, I nearly got struck by lightning and there was a fire at the hotel. But this was just a normal day.

It started with my usual routine. When I got to work, I was keen to find out if Eric, the night porter, had heard how the wedding went. He had. All the feedback was positive, and the visiting guests were loaded back onto the coaches without a hitch at 11.15 pm sharp. Bruno ordered a bottle of champagne and a club sandwich just before midnight, but there were no other room service requests after that. After he delivered Bruno's order, Eric said there was a brief moment of commotion involving Alec. Apparently, he was drunk and searching for me, but stumbled back to his room once he realised I had taken myself home. I decided that I might need to have a firmer word with him to let him know I couldn't be available in the way he wanted me to be. I was happy to help out here and there, but not if it affected the other guests. Eric told me there was also a complaint from one of the rooms about the bride and groom consummating their marriage somewhat noisily at 11.30 pm and then again at 2 am. There was not a lot we could do about something like that, other than reassure the unhappy guests that we were confident the noise wouldn't last all night. Which it didn't.

Fiona was in a terrible mood that day. That was a bit out of the ordinary, I suppose. She said that guests had been calling the front desk nonstop since the iPads had been placed in the rooms, complaining about unanswered requests and slow service. She had compiled a list that she was going to take to American Dave. Fiona always gets so flustered when she is not best pleased with something. She puffs out her flushed cheeks and faffs about like a headless chicken, not knowing which way to turn. I knew she would be nervous about giving American Dave her feedback, but if there was a chance it would save my job, she would do it.

Mr Potts was uptight that morning too. He had been called back to Cavengreen just after 11 pm by one of the suppliers whose car had been blocked in by the hotel's limousine. It just so happened that Mr Potts had taken the keys home that night by accident. He had dark circles under his eyes and no spring in his step, though he pulled it together whenever a guest walked by. He loitered around my desk longer than normal. The Americans' presence in the hotel had drawn him closer to Fiona and me, as if we had formed an alliance. Mr Potts made it clear that I would not be replaced by an iPad, but he had concerns about the other staff. Everyone working at Cavengreen came from the local area, something I think added to the hotel's charm. But the Americans had plans to fly in the best of the best in hotel management from the likes of Dubai and the USA. Here I had been busy fretting about myself when it turned out the whole team was at risk of being replaced. To say the atmosphere was a little more tense than usual would be true. But we would rise above the disruption and not let our personal problems impact the guests.

None of the wedding party emerged for breakfast. Instead, I sent a room service trolley of eggs, bacon, croissants, fruit and the like, along with some bloody marys, to the bridal suite. The kitchen porter told me that my gesture was greatly appreciated by the groom's somewhat dusty face when he opened the door.

Only the bride's mother and stepfather left their room that morning. They went for a stroll around the garden to take in some fresh air, returning forty-five minutes later with some more colour to their cheeks. They asked if I could make an afternoon tea booking for the whole bridal party, something I had pre-emptively done when they checked in.

Afternoon tea is quite the occasion at Cavengreen. The hotel has won numerous awards for it, in fact, and we would often get journalists and TV crews wanting to experience it for themselves. Afternoon tea takes place at Lavender Plates every other day at 3 pm. Each table is treated to tiered stands arranged with small, triangular sandwiches, homemade cakes and scones with jam and clotted cream. All of it is served with free-flowing champagne, and cigars are available to enjoy on the terrace once all the food has been cleared. It is such a special occasion. During my time, there were some locals who would come every single Sunday without fail. I would always stop by and show my face once all the guests were settled. But that day I didn't get the chance.

At 3 pm on the dot, the iPad on my desk pinged. Suite seven wanted ice; I was to let myself in and put the bucket on the coffee table. It was a simple request. At 3.08 pm I knocked on the door and shouted, 'Concierge,' just as a courtesy. I pressed my ear up against the door and couldn't hear a response, the shower, or the TV. I let myself in and put the bucket down on the table as instructed. When I turned around I saw red smeared across the carpet leading to the bathroom, where a blood-drenched body lay lifeless on the floor.

Tap one. Tap two. Tap three.

It was obvious that they were dead. I remember blinking three times. Three slow blinks. My mind struggled to process what I was seeing. It felt like I was in that room for a lifetime. The mess . . . oh, the mess; it was horrifying. The sight will haunt me for the rest of my days. That dead body was so out of context in my life, in the hotel. It was surreal. Everything at Cavengreen was so perfect. To see pools of blood on the steam-cleaned carpets and carefully mopped bathroom tiles was extremely unsettling.

I didn't get closer; I didn't need to. I could see their face. Their eyes were half open; drooped, you might say. Their expression was vacant, but not peaceful. You always expect dead bodies to look quite peaceful, but this was the opposite. Their mouth was slightly open, as if it wanted to cry out for help. I am sure they tried to in those last moments.

I knew I needed to get help. As I burst out into the corridor, I held my hand over my mouth, trying to hold back the vomit that was creeping up. I could barely draw breath. My skull tingled. Grey clouds muddled my vision. I stumbled down the corridor, running a hand along the wall to help guide my way. I wasn't exactly sure where my feet were taking me, but they were moving fast.

Shamila was the only one behind the reception desk and she was chatting with a guest. She spotted me out the corner of her eye and furrowed her brow as she watched me bulldoze through the lobby. I guess at that point I was probably looking for Fiona. Either her or Mr Potts. I fumbled my way through the lobby, bumping into the centre table, knocking the vase and shaking petals from the display of pink snapdragons.

In a moment that must have shocked everyone, I burst through the double doors of Lavender Plates. Heads turned to look at me. Quite the sight I must have been. The lady at the desk—I forget her name, she was new—held up both hands to try to stop me, but I ploughed on. Waiters dodged out of the way as I staggered across the room to where Mr Potts was standing, following my haphazard entrance with a startled glare. He had just popped a bottle of champagne for the newlyweds and the bridal party; they now sat frozen, eyes wide and mouths agape, as the bottle fizzed in Mr Potts's hand.

I collapsed into Mr Potts's arms and he ushered me to the corridor beside the kitchen. The chefs poked their heads through the kitchen pass to see what was going on; some called out to ask if I was okay, but I couldn't answer. I was in total shock.

Mr Potts upturned a crate and plonked me on it. He asked what was wrong. My ears felt hot and my mouth heavy. That was how I used to feel when my father tried to talk to me.

Tap one. Tap two. Tap three.

I tried to tell Mr Potts what I had seen, but the stammer that had hindered my speech in childhood returned and I struggled to get the words out. Mr Potts told me to take a deep breath. I took three.

Mr Potts asked again what was wrong.

'M-m . . . m . . . murder.' It was the best I could do in the moment.

American Dave and Tanya appeared in the corridor. Mr Potts politely advised them that the area they were in was for restaurant staff only, something American Dave did not appreciate. He reminded Mr Potts that he had free rein over the hotel now that it had been sold. It was neither the time nor the place for him to start throwing his status around, but that is American Dave: tactless and insensitive. He edged around Mr Potts to get a better view of me. 'Has the old man got dementia?' he asked. He came very close and shouted in my face: 'Do. You. Know. Where. You. Are?'

Mr Potts snapped at him to give me some space, then he crouched down to my eye level and told me to ignore American Dave. That was easy enough, since my mind was entirely consumed by the gore of what I had just witnessed.

Tap one. Tap two. Tap three.

Mr Potts spoke so calmly; his face was reassuring in that moment. He needed me to give him more information, and I knew I needed to tell him what I had just discovered. It was just that my mouth and my mind weren't in sync.

'M-m-murder,' I repeated. It took so much energy to get that one word out. I felt exhausted. I rested my head against the wall.

'Who has been murdered, Hector?' Mr Potts whispered. He squeezed my hand and looked intently into my eyes. He had positioned himself in a way that blocked American Dave's line of sight, but I could still see the Yank craning his neck and bobbing up and down to catch a glimpse of me. Behind him, Tanya was trying to look official by extending her arms to block access to the area. Waitstaff were peering down the corridor, wondering what was going on. It must have been quite the exciting bit of drama for those young 'uns.

'Potts.' American Dave grabbed the manager by the shoulder and pulled him backwards. 'Did he say *murder*?'

'Keep your voice down.' Mr Potts jerked away from American Dave's grip. 'If you would just get out the way, I'll be able to find out more.'

'What's taking him so long?' American Dave yelled impatiently. 'Just spit it out, Hector!'

This, of course, only made the matter worse. I knew what I wanted to say. I wanted to tell Mr Potts the suite number and the name of the victim and urge him to call the police. But the thoughts wouldn't translate into words.

With great presence of mind, Mr Potts took a pen and notepad from a stunned-looking waitress and told me to write it down.

Writing isn't something I am good at—you know that—but with a trembling hand I managed to scrawl: *Suite 7. Bruno. Murder.*

Mr Potts seized the notepad and read the words. American Dave lunged forward and snatched the paper from his grasp.

Mr Potts took out his mobile telephone and called the police. I heard him say that one of the staff suspected there had been a murder. I hardly *suspected* that there had been—it was quite clear that a murder had been committed. One of the waitresses offered me a cup of water but I refused it; my hands were shaking so much I wouldn't have been able to grip it.

American Dave sprang into action, shouting, 'Block the exits!' as he stormed past dining guests to the restaurant entrance. He pointed at all the doors and windows. 'No one is to leave!'

The sound of cutlery clinking lightly as it was placed onto china plates echoed around the room. Everyone fell silent and, from where I was sitting, I could see nervous guests sharing confused glances with one another. A few took big gulps of their champagne. Some even laughed, thinking it was perhaps a performance.

'There has been a murder!' American Dave declared. 'Everybody must stay seated until the police arrive.'

Gasps filled the room.

Mr Potts left my side and strode hastily towards American Dave. He gripped the man's shoulder firmly and spoke directly into his ear. I imagine he said something like, 'Stop causing a scene, you American fool.' But that is just speculation. Whatever it was, Mr Potts looked furious. Seeing him take charge filled me with ease, though. My heart rate began to slow. Now that more people were involved, I felt as if the burden of seeking help had been lifted from my shoulders. The tingling in my brain stopped. I put my hands out in front of me and saw that they were no longer shaking. But images of Bruno's bloody body still flashed in my mind, and I sat there tapping my head in repeated sequences of three. To anyone watching, I must have looked crazy. But funnily enough, the tapping helps to keep my mind under control.

'There is no need to be alarmed. The police have been called and are on their way.' American Dave rotated three hundred and sixty degrees as he addressed the room.

Far from acting alarmed, the majority of the guests resumed their afternoon tea. The waitstaff returned to topping up champagne glasses and light chatter filled the room once again. That is one of the things I love about British people; they just get on with it, even in moments of murder or confusion.

American Dave seemed taken aback by the lack of interest in his dramatic announcement. He assured the guests loudly that the police had been summoned, but he had lost his audience's attention.

The floor-to-ceiling windows of Lavender Plates offer a view of the front of the hotel. Through them, I could see four police cars speeding down the driveway, the blaring of their sirens growing louder and louder. They screeched to a halt at the entrance and a swarm of uniformed police emerged. Everyone in the restaurant paused their conversations and turned to watch, some rising from their seats for a better view. A few of the young ones took out their telephones and started taking pictures. I overheard some guests say how exciting it all was, but I doubt they would have said that if *they* were the ones who had discovered a murdered body on a Thursday afternoon. No respect for the dead is what that was.

Meanwhile, Mr Potts had left the restaurant, followed by American Dave, who instructed the hostess not to let anyone else leave. The hostess rolled her eyes but closed the doors behind them and encouraged everyone to continue enjoying their meal.

It felt like an eternity before Fiona reached Lavender Plates. She weaved through the tables as quickly as she could in her heels, her gaze darting left and right as she searched for me. I must have looked a sorry sight, because she gasped and clapped both hands over her mouth when she spotted me. I shuffled about on my seat, straightening my back to try to look less weak and defeated. Fiona tightly embraced my body, then, releasing me, stared deeply into my eyes as if looking for reassurance that I was okay. She shooed some of the nosier staff away and told them to get back to work. Fiona can be very bossy when she needs to be.

She took my hand and pulled me up, keeping a tight grip as she led me through the restaurant, telling me to ignore the stares. As we walked towards the lobby, Fiona told me to prepare myself, that there were a lot of police waiting for me and I would have to be strong. I am not weak, and I wanted Fiona to know that, so I assured her I would be fine.

At the end of the corridor stood a man in a suit. His arms were crossed and he glanced impatiently at his watch like he had somewhere more important to be. When he saw me, he clicked his fingers and a group of policemen appeared behind him. Mr Potts and American Dave stood off to the side; all eyes were on me. Fiona nudged me in the direction of the police. I looked back at her, and she gave me a faint smile and little nod.

The man in the suit stepped forward. 'Right then—Mr Harrow, is it? Show us where you found this body, why don't you?'

CHAPTER

10

It was the longest walk of my life, the walk back to suite seven. My mind was playing all kinds of tricks on me. I could hear my father's voice telling me I was lying, and I could see bloody footprints on the hallway carpet, footprints from when I stumbled out of the room. But there were no footprints, of course. I hadn't got close enough to the body for there to be blood on my shoes. It was all in my head.

The police followed me like I was the Pied Piper, stopping behind me when I nodded towards the door that concealed the deceased guest. I recognised a couple of the officers: Fred and Ellie had worked in the force for many years, and I had seen them around and about my village on the odd occasion. Not that there is a lot of crime around these parts. They would normally be out investigating stolen lawnmowers or missing cats. Mundane stuff. Several of the police looked at me doubtfully, with frowns or single eyebrow raises. Some of them smirked as if they didn't believe me—exactly how my father used to look at me. One of them yawned. Had Mr Potts or American Dave been the one to find the body and report it, then I am sure the hotel would have already been wrapped in police tape, but since it was me, the concierge, the old man, I had to convince everyone I was telling the truth.

When I was younger, my father would always say I was lying about things, even though I never was. Knocks your confidence, that sort of thing. I swear it was just another excuse for the lousy sod to give me a wallop. He owned a panelbeating business: beat by profession, beat by nature. It was very fitting for such a man. He was only ever drunk or hungover, and both versions liked to give me the belt. If I looked at him funny: belt. If I didn't look at him: belt. If I looked at Mum with sympathy after he had beat her: belt. One day, I must have only been about nine or ten, I hid all his belts. In my naivety I thought that would solve the problem. But in lieu of a belt, my father used a plant pot and broke all five fingers on my right hand. He did it in front of Josie, who was only a baby at the time. Mother told the school I fell off my bike. I didn't even have a bike at that point. The purpose of giving you this information is not to forewarn you that I became a violent man because of my father; in fact, I would say I am quite the opposite. I suppose this is just a bit of background that might be useful to explain the little habits that I have—the way my brain works.

In that moment, outside suite seven, I felt like it was me versus everyone else. I could tell what they were wondering: Is the old man cuckoo or is there actually a dead body in there? Their looks of doubt made me question myself, just for a second.

I hung back from the door, not wanting to get too close. That sounds strange, now that I think about it. What was I afraid of? A dead body? There is something haunting about being that close to someone who has been murdered. Bruno's lifeless body was scary because it was unexplained, not because it was no longer breathing.

The unknown is frightening, and there were a lot of unknowns in this situation. I was also afraid that the police would make me go back in there. Once was quite enough.

The officer in the suit asked Mr Potts to open the door. As the rest filed forward, I took a few more steps away, as far as the corridor would allow. American Dave tried to edge his way to the front but was told to stand back, much to his frustration.

Best to introduce the man in the suit now, before I get into what happened next. I had never seen him before, but by the end of this murder hullaballoo, we were very well acquainted. His name is Detective Arjun Raj, and from what I have gathered since, he had been moving quite quickly through the police ranks. He had probably expected to be pushing papers for a couple of years here in the Dales before scoring a plum role back in the big smoke of Leeds—which, for those of you who don't know, is the main city in this county.

His manner was threatening and aggressive; he was not the kind of bloke you wanted to help. He had dark circles under his eyes and a mop of jet-black hair he pushed back out of his face far too often. I would say he was in his early forties, and at one point I noticed he had photographs of two children hanging from his car keys in miniature frames. Not to be rude, but I can't imagine him being a particularly loving father. In fact, I would bet money that his kids fear him, much as I feared my father when he was alive.

Tap one. Tap two. Tap three.

Detective Raj strode everywhere like he was going into battle and had no time for people who he viewed as below him—which seemed to be everyone. There was nothing likeable about him, and in that way, again, he reminded me of my old man.

Tap one. Tap two. Tap three.

Mr Potts unlocked suite seven. Detective Raj pulled on a pair of latex gloves, then opened the door and stepped inside. Everyone's attention was on him as they braced for word that I really had discovered a dead body. Even I held my breath, waiting for confirmation that I had not just gone mad.

Detective Raj came out about twenty seconds later. He peeled the white gloves off his hands and kept his head bowed. We all held our breath. It was uncomfortable. The detective finally raised his head.

'Cordon off the corridor,' he ordered. 'There's been a murder.' Then, raising his voice to be heard above the resulting murmurs: 'The hotel must be put under a full lockdown. No one comes in, no one goes out. Now, move!' Detective Raj clapped his hands together and his officers scattered.

American Dave dodged moving bodies and approached Detective Raj to announce that he had already told the guests in the restaurant that they weren't to leave. I suppose he wanted brownie points. The detective did not respond, instead looking American Dave up and down before concluding that he was not important.

American Dave, clearly desperate to feel relevant, turned to me and told me to go back to the restaurant and await further instruction. Fat chance I was going to listen to him. I started walking towards the lobby to find Fiona.

'Oh no you don't.' Detective Raj gripped my shoulder firmly. 'I've got some questions for you.'

From then on, Mr Potts's office became Detective Raj's office. Mr Potts tried to put up a fight, claiming that the police had no right to take over the hotel in such a way, but he was wasting his breath. Mr Potts was relegated to the holding bay in Lavender Plates for the next five hours, just like the rest of the staff and guests. The only person not in the restaurant-turned-prison was me. Two police officers guarded the door to the library, where I was detained, alone. They were snappy and aggressive, telling me not to try anything. As if I would. I am an old man with a dodgy hip, I was hardly going to make a run for it. Plus, I had nothing to hide. Flashbacks of the body flickered in my mind as I paced up and down.

Tap one. Tap two. Tap three.

I knew I wasn't the murderer, yet I felt threatened by the police. My father's voice echoed in my ears, telling me I was lying and was going to be found out. I feared I was an easy target, and that the police could pin something on me if they really wanted to. I was out of my depth.

Now, I did not know this then, but I do now: while I was locked in the library, the detective was reviewing the CCTV footage of the moment I discovered the body. Obviously, there is no CCTV in the suites, but for safety and security reasons the hotel has cameras in the hallways. I am familiar with the positioning of most of them and can tell you that there is a camera directly above suite six that captures the door of suite seven. The cameras are state-of-the-art and were newly installed at the time, so the picture is really sharp. They would have had a direct view of me letting myself into suite seven and then leaving in all sorts. You would think that would have put me in the clear, but when Detective Raj came back from reviewing the footage, by gum did he give me a grilling.

The detective was just doing his job, I know that. But I am going to say this: there are ways of going about things, and his was the wrong way. Three hours I spent in Mr Potts's office getting interrogated by the detective. I had gone from hotel concierge to prime suspect in a murder case in the blink of an eye. And didn't they just treat me like that! They would not even let me have a glass of water. Stress makes you thirsty, you know? My tongue was practically sticking to the roof of my mouth. I reckon it was dirty tactics to make me talk.

They need not have parched me half to death to do that! Everything I knew I told them in the first two minutes, so why they felt the need to drag me over hot coals for three hours is beyond me. Torture, that's what you would call it.

'What's with the head tapping?' That is the first thing Detective Raj asked me as he paced Mr Potts's office from end to end. He made me sit on Mr Potts's desk chair. It was one of those swivel ones and I tell you what, Mr Potts must sit like a pencil because the back of the chair was as upright as could be. I am all for good posture, but I need a bit of a lean so there is not too much pressure on my hip. That was killing me, in case you are wondering. I must have made too many funny movements in the bother of everything, and now it felt like a dagger had been plunged into my side. And I will tell you what I think of Detective Raj's opening question: rude! That is what I think. Fancy poking at someone's vulnerability as soon as you meet them. His question affirmed that I was not dealing with a nice man.

'It is a nervous thing I do when I have a dark or intrusive thought,' I replied, avoiding eye contact.

'Have a lot of these dark thoughts, do you?'

'Occasionally.'

'And these voices in your head, do they tell you to do bad things?' He had twisted my words.

'They're not . . . not . . . voices. They're . . . they're memories.' I could feel the stammering ghost of my past creeping in. I closed my eyes and lightly tapped the front of my head over and over and over in beats of three. My father's voice yelled at me to stop it. To stop being so ridiculous. To stop being weak.

'What is it that you're thinking about now, then?' I opened my eyes and Detective Raj was leaning towards me, both hands on the desk.

'The blood . . . the b-b-body,' I stuttered.

'Pretty nasty sight, right?'

A nod seemed the only appropriate answer. Looking back, I wish I had been stronger. That is easy to say now that I am out the other side. I don't want you lot reading this to think I'm weak. You have to understand that I had just seen a dead body, a murdered one; I was in bits. At that moment, I was scared. Scared that the memory of all the blood would haunt me forever, scared that I would be blamed for something I didn't do. As this story goes on, I hope you'll see a change in me. This experience has made me stronger, that I know for certain. I don't think you are ever too old to learn, not even at seventy-three. That is many people's downfall in life; they think that they are too old to grow and to change. But not me.

Detective Raj said he wanted to show me something. He opened a laptop and plugged in one of those . . .

Helen, please edit this bit to add in the name of those stick things. They are not something I am overly familiar with.

He plugged in a USB stick *[editor's note]*. The detective pulled up a chair next to me and pressed play on a video. It was me. It was me walking to suite seven, holding the ice bucket. It was strange seeing that version of myself again, the version that had not yet seen a dead body. The version that was just about to have his life changed by a sight that would scar him forever. How innocent I was.

In the video, you can see me knock on the door and then let myself in. Detective Raj paused it there. He got out his mobile telephone and told me he was about to set a timer. He set the timer and then pressed play. My eyes glanced from the screen to the telephone to the screen to the telephone. Ten seconds. Twenty seconds. After thirty seconds,

I knew what he was doing. I knew the point he was going to make. Forty seconds. Nothing. Forty-five seconds. Nothing. Fifty seconds. That is when I emerged from the suite, and that is when Detective Raj paused the timer.

'Obviously, we have just started our investigation and we will need to talk to everyone. But can you tell me why, on entering a room and seeing a dead body, it took you fifty seconds to leave to find help? Seems like something that could have been done in ten, maybe fifteen seconds.' Detective Raj stared at me expressionlessly with his dark eyes. It was impossible to find any warmth in that man.

'Perhaps I should get a lawyer,' I suggested.

'No need for that, Mr Harrow. This is just an informal, off-the-record chat. You're not in trouble.' Detective Raj changed to a more upbeat tone of voice, like he was trying to convince me that what he was saying was true. 'Since you're the one who found the body, we need to get your take on things first.' He bared his teeth in a smile. 'Now, back to those fifty seconds . . .'

'That's just how long it took. I put the ice b-b-bucket down, turned around, saw Bruno, Mr Tatterson, dead in the bathroom . . .'

'You knew he was dead just from looking at him?'

'That amount of b-b-blood . . .' I tapped my head three times. 'It was obvious he was dead. His eyes were open and v-v-vacant.'

'Then what?'

'I was in shock. I stood there in shock. I blinked three times. Then I went to find Mr Potts. To get help.'

You might be wondering about this dialogue; is that how it actually happened or not? But mark my words, this discussion is etched in my memory. It might not be word-for-word accurate, but it is darned well near enough. As much as possible in this story, I will try to re-create the dialogue. In moments where I am unsure of the words, I will just describe what happened in the conversation. I want to be upfront about that because I know you will be wondering.

I asked Detective Raj for some water; he said I could have some once I had explained to him why it took me fifty seconds to find the body and then leave the room. He even timed how long it took him to blink three times. Eight seconds. I told him over and over again, that was just how long it took. The shock of seeing a dead body happened to delay my response—surely that was not too out of the ordinary. But he wouldn't drop it. It was like he wanted this case to be done and dusted as quickly as possible, and that meant extracting a confession from me. I swivelled left and right on the chair as I watched Detective Raj pace the office, telling me I was guilty in not so many words. The hands on the clock jumped like time was flying, except everything felt so slow. I was weary, exhausted, ready to go home. All I wanted was to go back to the day before, when being replaced by an iPad was my biggest problem. Perspective is everything.

'You're lying!' Detective Raj slammed his fist down on the desk after another hour of dead-end questions. He had no idea what he was doing, I see that now. I think he was insecure and desperate for a career win. But in that moment, I thought he was tough and using tactics that he must have learnt from years of experience. In fact, in that moment I thought he was such an experienced policeman that somehow he would get me to break and confess to something I hadn't done. Fear bubbled under the surface, but as Detective Raj continued to provoke me, a side of myself I had not known existed started to emerge. As the clock approached nearly three hours of nonsense, I snapped.

'You're wrong!' I yelled, among other things. I clenched my fists and gritted my teeth. I felt possessed by the spirit of my father; he is the only person I have ever known who would act in such a way. Yet now I understand my father even less than I did before. It took being accused of murder for me to reach the point of losing my cool.

Tap one. Tap two. Tap three.

For him, all it took was looking at my face, it was his own personal worst nightmare. Seventy-three years of life, and I have only just realised that. I still can't understand it, though, and I know I will die wondering how he could have felt that way about me.

When my conversation with Detective Raj finally drew to a close, I felt defeated. I caught sight of myself in a mirror on the wall. I looked hollow, exhausted and hopeless. The detective ordered me to wait in the library on my own. I hadn't given him the easy resolution he seemed to be so desperately craving, and he appeared to resent me for that. That's how I saw it anyway.

The walls of the library felt like they were closing in on me. My hands were clammy and my heart thumped. There was a copy of the Bible on one of the shelves. I have never been a religious man, but I rested my head on the spine of the book and said a quick 'hello' to God, in case He was up there. Religion is not something I was brought up with, but then again, I question a lot of things about the way I was raised. It wasn't my choice not to believe in God; that's just how it happened. If He is up there, I hope He knows I mean no harm. I have always tried my best to avoid trouble. Calmness: that is what I like. And here came murder knocking at my door. And worst of all, the detective was insinuating that I had something to do with it. All I could do in that moment was wait and hope that the truth would come out. Whatever the truth was.

American Dave's voice thundered past the library door, and I jerked my head away from the spine of the Bible. He was telling Detective Raj that he was prepared to do whatever he could to help catch the murderer. Twenty minutes later two police officers came to get me again. They were Fred and Ellie. I have known them for years, just from around and about. Did I say that already? I forget. Anyway, it was nice to see some friendly faces, under the circumstances. They looked sympathetic as they escorted me back to Mr Potts's office for another session with Detective Raj. Fred and Ellie knew as much about me as I knew about them, which was that they appeared to be good people. I reckon you can tell when someone has a good soul; it is in their eyes.

Fred patted me on the back as we walked to Mr Potts's office. It was comforting to know someone was in my corner. At that point, I had no idea where Mr Potts and Fiona were. For all I knew, they had been sent home. Outside Mr Potts's office, Fred whispered in my ear, 'We'll get you out of this ASAP, mate.' I know he meant well, but him saying that put me on edge from the get-go.

Detective Raj made me sit down again even though I would have preferred to stand. There were some notes scribbled on a scrap of lined notepaper that had been ripped unevenly from a pad. The torn edges made me uncomfortable, but it wasn't the time to focus on that. Detective Raj quizzed me on my mood over the last week, claiming that a source had told him I had received some troubling news recently and was, quote unquote, 'angry'. Bloody American Dave and his sodding iPads. The very first chance he got to drop me in it, he did. And now he has the cheek to email me to be in his sodding documentary. You see why I got so worked up about him calling me 'old friend'. And he gets worse as this story goes on. The words that

I can think of to describe that man probably can't be published—as you can imagine, they're not nice ones.

I told Detective Raj that I didn't know what he was referring to, even though I full well did. I added that my mood was fine that week. Yes, it was a shock to hear a new system was to be implemented in the hotel, but I had been at Cavengreen for fifty-odd years; new systems came and went, that was only natural. As the concierge, I had always adapted very well to any changes. I was determined to play down my response to the iPads. Detective Raj didn't need more ammunition.

'You were angry that you were potentially being replaced by new technology.' That is what Detective Raj said. This must have been what American Dave told him. So, the slimy git *was* trying to do away with my job. Those Americans know nothing about loyalty.

'I wasn't angry. I was concerned, but definitely not angry,' I told the detective.

'It's okay if you were angry. We don't use emotions to incriminate people. Sometimes I get angry myself, and that's okay.' Detective Raj attempted a good-cop routine.

The grilling went on for another hour. That makes four hours total, if you're counting. I don't know much about the law, but I am pretty sure he shouldn't have been questioning me for so long off the record. My tongue was like sandpaper the entire time. Detective Raj sipped smugly from a glass bottle of Coca-Cola that he must have taken from my concierge fridge. At one point he even observed that Coca-Cola always tastes better from a glass bottle rather than a plastic one. I haven't touched the stuff since I was a kid. My dad used to mix it with his cheap rum. The smell of it makes me sick, so I could not give a rat's arse about the detective's opinion on the topic. I just wanted to get out of that room and go home.

But the detective informed me that was not going to happen. The hotel was a crime scene and no one was allowed to leave until he had spoken to everyone present. This meant the staff would be required to spend the night. Most of the female employees would share the unoccupied suites; others had to make do with anywhere there was a flat surface to sleep on. But myself and some of the other male staff were told we would be spending the night in the library. It all seemed completely ridiculous. The idea of not being able to leave, not being able to rest my head on my own pillow, in my house, where all my belongings are, a place where I could try to block out the memory of the day . . . It was too much for me to handle.

'This is cri-criminal!' I shouted. 'You let me go!' I stood up and leant forward so we were eye to eye across the desk. I felt myself breathing heavily, glaring at the detective. I wanted to punch him. I have never struck anyone in my life, but I have had plenty of lessons in how to throw a punch, having been on the receiving end of my father's fist many a time. My fingers curled inwards, scraping the desk.

The detective smirked, as if he could tell exactly what I wanted to do to him. But we both knew that would be foolish.

'If you are innocent, then you should have no problem hanging around a while longer to help us solve the case. Isn't that right, Hector?' Detective Raj flashed a nasty grin, his nostrils flaring. He had me exactly where he wanted me: teetering on the edge of a breakdown. And I was so ashamed of my outburst; I was behaving just like my father. Meanwhile the real killer was still at large, and there was a chance they might strike again.

CHAPTER

11

Fiona kindly fetched spare pillows and blankets from the linen room for everyone without a proper bed to sleep in. Myself, Mr Potts, Eric the porter, Dean from the kitchen and Charlie the gardener were consigned to the library. Six-foot-five Charlie took the three-seater, Eric took the two-seater and poor Dean scrunched himself into a ball to spend the night on the armchair. Mr Potts and I did our best to make ourselves comfortable on the floor. Not that the young ones didn't offer the settees up to us. But we both declined, knowing we were unlikely to sleep. Instead, we took the cushions from the window seat and arranged them into two makeshift mattresses on the floor, and tried to make them cosy with blankets and pillows. At the end of the day, though, it was still just the floor, and I was still a murder suspect.

Both still in our work suits, we sat on our makeshift beds, heads and shoulders slumped, defeated by the day. Mr Potts took off his tie and wrapped then unwrapped it around his fingers. He seemed distracted, agitated. Then all at once he sat up straight, as if struck by an idea. He pushed himself off the ground and crossed the room to the globe in the corner. It is one of those old-fashioned ones that spins on its axis and has bumps where the mountains are and dips where there are valleys. He lifted the lid and, careful not to clink anything and wake the others, poured a splash of whisky into two glasses. Like I have said, I am not much of a drinker, but by gum, this occasion called for it.

The snores of the other men were quite soothing. Like there were a few of us in this together. I never went to war, but I imagine what I felt in that room was a tiny fraction of the camaraderie that soldiers feel. At least I was not alone anymore and at least if Bruno's murderer was still in the hotel, they wouldn't risk trying to attack any of us in that room. They wouldn't dare.

From what Fiona has told me since, all the guests were escorted back to their suites. It was their idea to stay in the comfort of Cavengreen rather than go to the police station, at least for that first night, that is. The locals who had just popped by for afternoon tea were eventually allowed to leave around midnight, after it had been confirmed from the CCTV footage that, on arrival, they had headed straight to Lavender Plates with no detours to anywhere else in the hotel. They were therefore off the hook. Recently, there have been a lot of grumblings about the legality of locking down a whole hotel against the will of those inside. The guests had only agreed to stay one night, but remained for four. As it turned out from the report Helen skimmed for me, Detective Raj did put up a sign in an obscure place where no one would see it reading: *Guests are permitted to leave at any point.* That got him out of the woods, legally speaking. The guests may have agreed to stay that first night, but that didn't stop them kicking up a fuss when the police disconnected the Wi-Fi, leaving them with no way to contact anyone outside the hotel. Fat chance getting a telephone signal at the hotel.

Reception is patchy at best all over the Dales. Detective Raj must have been worried about information being leaked to the press. And they were probably trying to avoid the likes of Paula McDavidson snooping around with her notebook of lies before they had a chance to find out who the killer was. Besides, with the number of police roaming the corridors, it didn't feel like we could just casually leave. Cavengreen was like a prison and we were like prisoners. After my interview with Detective Raj, I felt like I was the hotel's most notorious prisoner. Like I was on death row and everyone else was just in for petty theft.

That night, I could tell Mr Potts was consumed with angst. He didn't sleep and nor did I. We didn't speak, though. He leant against a shelf of books—Agatha Christie novels, fittingly. He desperately tried to telephone and text message his wife. He knew she would be concerned when he didn't come home. Quite right. But with no Wi-Fi and no phone signal, there was no way of contacting anyone beyond Cavengreen's gates. We wondered if word had been leaked of my grim discovery, but now I know that it hadn't.

Around 2 am I had to go to the bathroom. Ellie was standing guard outside the library. She must have been dozing off a little because she woke with a gasp when I opened the door. Together, we walked to the bathroom located between the lobby and the entrance to Hugo's cocktail bar. The hotel felt eerily quiet. It had been a while since I had been at Cavengreen so late. Back in my early days at the hotel, I often worked the late shifts. They tend to be the hours that no one wants to do, so the junior staff are rostered on. In those days, there was always a good atmosphere. We would get up to all kinds of mischief, mostly eating leftovers from the fridges of Lavender Plates or racing down empty corridors. There was the odd late-night drink request, and the occasional drunken guest staggering about, but the graveyard shifts were otherwise fairly uneventful.

Ellie was kind to me as we walked the corridor. She and Helen actually know each other from school; Helen told me that earlier. Ellie knew my sister, too, and told me she was sorry to hear about her passing. Ellie would be nearly ten years younger than Josie, but they were friendly nonetheless. Everyone pretty much knows everyone around here. Ellie took a few years off the police force, ended up having five kids. They're all adults now, so I think she picks up the odd shift here and there to keep busy. She's not ambitious, not like Detective Raj, who would be a good few years her junior.

'Make sure you defend yourself, Hector.' That is what she said to me as we headed to the bathroom. 'Make sure no one takes advantage of your kindness, you hear me? You are in a sticky spot, and of course I know you didn't do it, but Detective Raj will be wanting to crack the case, to impress the higher-ups in Leeds. Make sure you don't let him get to you or you'll end up taking the fall for someone else.'

In the bathroom, I hesitated. The bathrooms at Cavengreen are beautiful, but they aren't my cottage, where all my things are, where I have my little routine that I perform every night. I swiped my hand under the tap and water automatically gushed out. And then it stopped. I swiped again, this time filling my cupped hands with water. I felt out of sync with my life. Normally I would be tucked up in bed, a finished puzzle with a pen resting on top on my bedside table, five hours into my nightly eight hours of sleep. I released my hands and let the water splosh into the sink. I filled them up twice more before splashing the water on my face.

I let the water drip off my skin. The man staring back at me in the mirror didn't seem like the same Hector I had known for seventy-three years. The colour had drained from my face, I had dark circles under my eyes, and my hair, which was normally neatly combed, was all askew. As I looked at this different version of Hector, I wondered if his life would ever be the same again. This sort of thing changes people, and I can tell you now, since I have had the time to process what happened, I have been changed forever. The initial shock and pain have eased, but once you have witnessed a murder scene like that, it is like your innocence has been taken from you. I feel I am harder since. Even when I feel happiness or joy, it is more subdued now. Being inside Cavengreen and looking the way I did in the mirror that night felt abnormal. But then again, there was nothing normal about anything that happened over those four days.

Walking back to the library, I noticed the yellow police tape that was cordoning off various corridors. Peering down the hallway, I could see people in white overalls going in and out of suite seven; some held cameras and others had sealed bags, presumably full of evidence. A couple of officers were sitting on the floor, leaning against the wall, typing away on their laptops. The scene was one of organised chaos. You forget sometimes that there are people who see murdered bodies for a living. To me, this was the most out-of-the-ordinary experience, but to them it was just another day. How murder can ever become 'normal' is beyond me, but I suppose it is the same way doctors become desensitised to blood, and I have become desensitised to being treated like a piece of furniture. Even you, the reader, will have a different normal to my normal. Sorry—that was a tangent.

Ellie kindly let me linger long enough to take all that in. Part of me thinks she wanted to have a nosy too and knew I wouldn't mind a quick look at what was going on. As we watched, several men exited suite seven carrying a stretcher with a body bag on top. They were escorted down the corridor by a convoy of police officers. There was a swoosh of air when they walked by; the body bag was close enough for me to touch, had I wanted to. Ellie bowed her head, but I kept staring at that white bag. It was surreal to think that a man who had been alive twenty-four hours earlier was now in a bag. It seemed like an undignified end to his life, being carried out in plastic by strangers. But then again, being murdered was hardly dignified either.

Detective Raj appeared as if out of nowhere. He must have been trailing behind the police officers, out of sight. He clocked me and Ellie and his usual frown scrunched into an even more severe scowl. He carried a takeaway coffee cup which he threw at the wastepaper basket behind my desk, not noticing or caring that he had missed. Ignoring Ellie, he drew the back of his hand over his mouth, wiping away some but not all of the brown stains that had folded their way into the dry cracks of his lips. His teeth were coffee-stained too and when he spoke the smell of stale breath laced with caffeine turned my stomach. He demanded to know what I was doing in the lobby. He appeared dissatisfied when I told him I was on my way back from the bathroom. It was as if he wanted me to tell him that I was returning to the scene of my crime. Ellie corroborated my story but the detective ignored her.

'How convenient,' Detective Raj hissed. 'One last look at the body, eh?' He wanted me to be the murderer and he was acting like I was. It was terrifying to think he was wasting so much time focusing on me when the real killer was potentially still roaming the hallways. When I said as much to Detective Raj, he told me not to worry, that a thorough search of every suite would take place with every guest interviewed over the next couple of days. A couple of sodding *days*? It was about bloody time they got down to business, I thought. The sooner they did that, the sooner they would work out I wasn't the culprit. Although, as you will find out, things would get much worse for me before they got mildly better.

Morning crept in slowly. I hadn't slept, not even for one minute. Mr Potts eventually drifted off around 5 am, but the sound of a horde of police cars pulling up on the gravel outside woke him at six. Ellie said her goodbyes; she was heading home to sleep. Thankfully she made sure that Fred took over her post. It was good to see him.

It wasn't long after Fred arrived that there was a call to his radio from Detective Raj. He barked orders that were hard to decipher. Fred looked confused and held the radio right to his ear to try to work out the detective's instructions. He needn't have bothered, as before long Detective Raj appeared at the door to the library.

'Did you not hear me? I said take this lot to Lavender Plates. We need to use the library for a briefing,' he barked.

Those of us who had spent the night in the library gathered up our few belongings and I put all the cushions back on the window seats. As we tried to leave, dozens of police officers barged into the room. It was like when you try to board the London Underground just as crowds of people are getting off. Not that I bother much with London. Went there once or twice to see what all the fuss was about. Overcrowded, unfriendly and expensive. That is what I think.

No offence, Helen, I know how much you miss it. You're far more cosmopolitan than me, though.

My opinions on the UK's capital aside, it felt good to be out of that library. I heard one of the police officers comment on how the air smelt of disgusting stale breath. Just like school bullies, a bunch of them turned and laughed at us. I want to make this clear: the treatment we received from *most* of the police was nothing short of disgusting.

Lavender Plates felt bleak. It was normally one of my favourite places in the hotel. Even at 6 am, there would be plenty of activity, with the chefs busy preparing breakfast and a few early risers already getting their morning coffee and reading the newspaper. The hotel will pretty much make anything you want for breakfast, as long as they have the ingredients. Even then, if a guest had a particular request and they gave me that information in advance, we would arrange it. Lots of people enjoyed oysters and champagne for breakfast in my day. There is no reason why you can't rise and shine with a little glamour. That is what Cavengreen is all about. But there were no clinks of champagne flutes that morning.

Mr Potts flicked the lights on and brought us out of the depressing shadows. It felt strange to be basking in the glittering light of the chandelier, but then again it felt strange to be anywhere in Cavengreen during such a time. That place is too special for the horrors it endured.

Mr Potts fetched everyone orange juice and bottles of cold water. Then, without even asking for Fred's permission, he started up one of the cooktops and shouted out for us to give him our egg orders. That small action reminded me for a second that we weren't prisoners; we didn't have to ask for permission in *our* hotel. Not that Fred minded, of course. Had any of the other officers been watching us, I am sure they would not have allowed it. Starvation felt like one of their tactics to get us to talk quicker. Or to get *me* to 'confess' quicker, I should say. Mr Potts insisted on making me scrambled eggs and bacon even though we both knew I would not be able to eat. He even made Fred some. It was a funny old sight, seeing Mr Potts with his shirt all wrinkled and his top button undone. His hair was messy, and he was yawning every couple of minutes. This was quite a different man from the one who normally fussed around the hotel making sure everything was spick-and-span. It was nice to see this more human side of him.

Rain pelted down outside, and our small group sat silently by the windows. The three young lads knocked back their food as if they had just returned from being lost at sea. Mr Potts took a few bites, and I politely ate half of mine, despite the knots in my stomach. Fred moseyed around the restaurant, stroking the wallpaper and having a gander in the china cabinets and wine room. I think he was trying to give us some space. Not wanting to sound like a gossip, I chose not to share my experience of seeing the body being taken out at 2 am. Whatever I did or said, I was aware that Detective Raj might find out. So, I kept my head down. Not that I would be able to do so for much longer.

From outside Lavender Plates, I could hear Fiona shouting. She was telling whoever was guarding the door to move out of her way. Fiona's good like that. She's a strong woman who doesn't take any nonsense. The double doors to the restaurant swung open and Fiona scanned the room before beelining towards me. She flung her arms around me and then held my cheeks in her hands, surveying my face for any signs of distress. It was nice to know someone had been worrying about me.

'Ridiculous! All of this is ridiculous!' she shouted. 'Mr Potts, what are you doing about this? Keeping us locked up like wild animals—it's barbaric!'

The young lads held back laughter. I must say, Fiona looked quite the sight shouting at Mr Potts while dressed in one of Cavengreen's bathrobes with her hair in a messy bun on top of her head. I could see the long grey pencil skirt she had been wearing the day before sticking out beneath the hem of the robe, but she had swapped her high heels for a pair of white Cavengreen slippers. Mr Potts was taken aback, to say the least. An angry Fiona was not the kind of wake-up call he needed that morning.

'I'm afraid this is out of my hands, Fiona,' Mr Potts replied meekly—uncharacteristically so.

'Well, whose hands is it in, then?' Fiona waved her own hands impatiently from side to side.

'Perhaps the Americans can advise us on what is going on,' Mr Potts replied. 'They are technically the new owners of the hotel, after all.'

'The Americans! Pfft. They are just a bunch of good-for-nothing—'

'Howdy, everyone!' American Dave waltzed into Lavender Plates, his mistress and two minions following him like disciples. He tipped his cowboy hat in greeting. 'What a day. How did y'all sleep? Fiona?'

Fiona lifted her chin, made a dismissive noise and turned her head away, her arms folded, just like she always does when she's annoyed.

'Any coffee going?' American Dave took a seat and fanned a linen napkin onto his lap. He removed his cowboy hat and placed it on the table. I remember wondering why he was so relaxed about everything. It was almost like he was enjoying the goings-on, unfazed that there was still a murderer on the loose. He bored us with details of the hotel's plans to 'step into the future' and how he was going to suck the soul out of the place. Not that he used those words, of course. He said he wasn't at all worried about how the previous day's incident might impact the hotel's brand because by the time he was done with the name change and renovations, people wouldn't even know it was the same place. Eyerolls swept across the room when he said that. Cavengreen meant a lot to the rest of us, even though it was just a workplace. We were a family and, to me, Cavengreen was like a second home.

Once American Dave had finished his monologue, he turned his attention to me.

'What's the deal with you and that detective, Hector?' he probed. 'Y'all were chatting for a long time yesterday. You're not a suspect, are ya?' He twirled his cowboy hat on his fist.

I chose not to answer and sipped on the cup of tea that Mr Potts had kindly placed in front of me. I avoided eye contact but could see

Mr Potts and Fiona glaring at the American. A very clear line had been drawn.

'I've seen you do this bizarre head-tapping thing a couple of times,' American Dave was snarky in his observation. 'When I asked one of the young guys here in the hotel about it, he told me you do it whenever you have a bad thought. So, would tapping your head three times stop you from murdering someone? Or is it not that powerful?'

His American mistress laughed, and his two minions followed her example.

'No more, Dave.' Mr Potts kept his voice low, but he was firm.

'What?' American Dave scoffed. 'We know someone in this joint is a killer, why shouldn't we suspect him? Just because he's old doesn't mean he didn't do it.'

'You'd better watch yourself, you low-life . . .' Fiona began.

'Or what?' American Dave tilted his head, awaiting a response.

'Or else you'll have me to deal with,' Fiona finished.

The Americans all laughed like hyenas.

'I've changed my mind.' American Dave took a bite of a bread roll and spoke with his mouth full, crumbs flying. 'Hector couldn't have killed someone. Not when he needs some middle-aged broad to fight his battles for him.'

'That's enough!' This was me speaking now. I had stayed quiet long enough. Heat radiated through my hands and that's when I noticed that I had slammed them onto the table and broken a saucer. Blood trickled down my left hand and onto the wooden parquetry.

Fred rushed over from the window. He grabbed my wrist and ushered me towards the door.

'I'll be telling Detective Raj about this. He'll welcome my help!' American Dave bellowed after me.

I turned around and saw him place his cowboy hat onto his head smugly, only for Fiona to knock it to the floor with a quick swipe of her hand as she marched by. She and Mr Potts followed me, Fiona channelling her rage into huffing and pulling her dressing-gown belt into a tighter knot. Things were going downhill swiftly.

We sought refuge in Hugo's.

Hugo's didn't have quite the same feel as Lavender Plates, but the enemy—that is, the Americans—had called dibs on the restaurant, so the moody ambience of the cocktail bar would have to do for our small army.

'Best we don't mention this to the detective, I reckon,' Fred said, nodding at my hand.

'I don't believe we'll have a choice,' I replied. 'The American has probably already told him. Sucking up; trying to feel important. He's all ego that sodding Yank.' I rinsed my wrist in the sink behind the bar, watching the blood swirl down the drain. Flashbacks of Bruno's dead body clanged around my mind. I tapped my head three times with my dry hand.

'I'll tell them that it was an accident,' Fred reassured me.

'But you were looking out the window,' I reminded him.

'I saw what happened.' Fred tapped his nose and nodded his head. 'It was an *accident*.'

I'm not entirely sure why he emphasised the word 'accident' when it truly was an accident, but his support was appreciated. I have never in my life dealt with such conflict. Well, not since my father dropped dead. Although I would hardly describe getting belted every other day as conflict.

By the time I was sixteen and working, my dad left me alone. I had reached an age when I was starting to think about defending myself, and Dad was getting weaker by that point. Then, by the time I was twenty, my father was housebound due to deteriorating health. You might find this odd, but I looked after him. I used to bring him food and turn his chair around to face the TV. Sometimes you just do what you have to do. I arranged for the panelbeating business to go up for sale and used the money to pay for food and bills and so on. Despite my father being a complete prick, he was good at what he did, and the money was enough to last until well after his death.

Tap one. Tap two. Tap three.

But I couldn't just close my eyes tight and count to three over and over until this conflict at the hotel came to an end. As Fiona said, I would have to be strong.

We were in Hugo's for six hours. Mr Potts sat on the floor behind the bar, sneaking swigs of whisky whenever Fred turned a blind eye. I was starting to think he might have an alcohol problem, but that was none of my business and I wouldn't want to start any rumours that might damage his reputation. Lots of people use alcohol as pain relief in dark times.

Fiona paced up and down and got me to repeat my account of what had happened until she was satisfied that the police wouldn't be able to break me. Every so often Fred would swap out with another officer and then return half an hour later with little snippets of information. He told us that Detective Raj was interviewing the guests suite by suite and each room was being thoroughly searched. Nothing of note had been discovered yet, though. He said that a pair of twins were up next.

That reminds me, I must tell you about the fallout from the twins' newspaper article. Paula McDavidson has continued to harass me for my side of the story. If I go to the supermarket, she's there. If I pop out for some milk, she's there. If I am withdrawing money at the bank, she's there. It really is getting quite bothersome. She tells me that the impact of her story with the twins wasn't as powerful as she thought it might be and the feedback from her superiors is that she needs my take on events. I have told her on multiple occasions that she isn't getting it. But it has been uncomfortable to say the least. I have noticed people in the village giving me little looks. Couples nudge each other when I pass and people that I haven't spoken to since school have started coming up to ask how I've been and then grilling me about Cavengreen. The cheek of it! But I keep my mouth shut. And I haven't told anyone about this book. Helen told me not to until everything is signed off and we get a publication date. To be honest, I thought you just wrote the words and then off you go, but apparently there's a whole process of editing and cover design before that. I did get one useful nugget of information from Paula McDavidson. She told me that American Dave has booked his flights and will be landing in ten days. She was very smug when she told me that he had asked her to be part of his documentary. She probably thinks she's going to become a big star in America. Deluded old bat.

Back to the twins. Fred was radioed with instructions to escort them down to Mr Potts's office for questioning. An officer named Tyrone took his place in Hugo's. Tyrone was particularly unfriendly; he had a scowl like one of those ferocious dogs that are illegal in the UK. He looked like a right thug with his shaved head, and I caught a glimpse of a neck tattoo poking out of his collar. I've never understood why someone would want to doodle permanent drawings on their skin. Not that I judge anyone for doing so. Do what you want with your own body, I say. It's just not for me. Tyrone sat in one of the booths and glared at us, biting his fingernails and spitting them onto the ground. It made me sick to my stomach. Fiona was livid; she kept saying, 'If he does that one more time, I'm going to snap.' But she didn't snap. I think it just made her feel better to say that she would.

Fred returned an hour later. Tyrone refused to swap out with him; he was enjoying taunting us with his homemade lunch of sausage rolls, complete with excessive amounts of ketchup. Fiona watched him eat, clearly disgusted by the way he chewed with his mouth open and licked his fingers before pressing them onto the fallen crumbs on the table and sucking them clean. The memory of the sound of meat getting broken down in his mouth is enough to make me never want to eat a sausage roll again. Which is a shame really, because Maude's Bakery does a belting one with a mix of pork and lamb mince.

To get rid of Tyrone, Fred pretended that Detective Raj had specifically requested his assistance on something that seemed important. That got him up and moving. Flakes of pastry fell to the floor as he leapt to his feet and virtually sprinted out of the room, saying, 'See ya later, knobheads.'

We all huddled around the bar, waiting for Fred to share any updates. This might look bad—a police officer sharing confidential information—but Fred was on our side. He knew that we were the good guys and he kept saying how he wanted to go out on the right note. That makes sense now, since he resigned from the police force right after Cavengreen. Swanned off on a round-the-world trip the week after. He sent me a postcard from the Taj Mahal the other day. I have never fancied India; too busy for me.

When Fred had knocked at the door of the twins' suite, they told him they were in the middle of a pamper session and he should come back later. They tried to shut the door in his face but he shoved his steel-capped shoe in the gap so it couldn't close all the way. He told them that it was urgent, and they had to follow him right away. The twins whined shrilly about how ridiculous the whole situation was, how they couldn't check their social media accounts because the Wi-Fi had been disconnected, and how they were one more inconvenience away from calling their lawyers. Detective Raj had no idea what he was getting himself into with those two. We laughed as Fred told us how the detective had looked pale and broken when he finished questioning them.

Fred said he'd had his ear pressed up against the door the whole time. He couldn't tell which twin was saying what, but one was definitely more vocal than the other. That would probably be Ruby, from what I've experienced. And didn't they just have a few things to say about me! Of course, they didn't use my name. That would be beneath them. Instead, they referred to me as 'that old concierge' and 'the old man behind the desk'. Any of you reading this who are around the same age as me, don't be offended by all the references to age that are being thrown around. Some of these young 'uns will label you as 'old' as soon as they see a grey hair. But they'll be seventy-three one day and then they can decide just how 'old' they feel. Personally, I feel a million bucks. Minus a few for the dodgy hip.

Having established that I was the 'old man' in the twins' story, Detective Raj quizzed them on what exactly I had done to get them so riled up. The twins told the detective how, on their way to Olive's wedding, they were ambushed by a drunken guest on the staircase. That would be Alec, in case you need reminding. They complained that 'the very rude old man at the desk' did absolutely nothing to stop the attack and that, on the contrary, it seemed almost like I was encouraging it. What a load of nonsense! You'll recall from my account of the scene that I did nothing of the sort. The incident was over as soon as it had begun, and everyone was sharply on their way.

Fiona huffed in frustration. I peered over and saw her shredding a drink coaster into tiny pieces. Meanwhile, Mr Potts was resting his forehead on the counter and shaking his head in despair. At the time, it was hard for me to process what the implication of the twins' lies might be. Detective Raj had already put me through the wringer and I had come out the other side—or so I thought.

According to the twins, they went back to their suite to change their shoes during the wedding dinner, and they saw me and the victim arguing in the lobby. You and I both know that is not what happened. They described how Bruno was flailing his arms erratically in what appeared to be anger, when in fact, as I've told you, he was just apologising for being rude when I had approached him at dinner earlier. The twins said I grabbed my car keys and stormed out the front door mid-argument. Lies, lies and more lies from that meddlesome pair of rotten brats.

They repeated these falsehoods in their interview with Paula McDavidson. Despite it being proven that I was not involved, those twins are still trying to drag my name through the mud as if I have a case to answer. Having an argument with someone who turned up dead the next day hardly paints me in the best light. When this book is released, it'll be their word against mine. But I've got more of this story up my sleeve than they do.

Fred said he heard Detective Raj tell the twins that he had seen the footage of a heated discussion between me and Bruno, but that even though it looked like an argument, there was no audio to back up their claims. Finally, Detective Raj had said something sensible. However, don't expect much more of that from him.

Detective Raj wanted to see me again. The call came through on Fred's radio. This time, I poured myself a glass of water to take with me. Fred gave me a minute with Fiona and Mr Potts before I left. He must have thought I needed a pep talk. Mr Potts said nothing, instead taking a swig of whisky and then grimacing as it hit the back of his throat. He patted me firmly on the back and then slumped down into one of the booths. Fiona was fiddling with her mobile telephone. She put her finger up to her lips and then slipped the telephone into the inside pocket of my suit, mouthing, 'It's recording.'

I have never been much of a rulebreaker, and Fiona's bold move made me nervous. It felt dangerous, and I am almost certain it was illegal. But then again, as Detective Raj told me, these were just 'off-the-record' conversations. One man speaking to another man, casually. Now that I am writing this book, let me tell you, I am so thankful that Fiona pulled that move. It isn't half useful having a recording of that conversation with Detective Raj to go off. Best thing to do, I reckon, is to get Helen to transcribe that recording here and then I will pick things up a bit later. We will probably have to change Detective Raj's name—for legal reasons, that is—but Helen can advise me on that next time we catch up. This will be the first time I'm listening to it myself, so I am interested to hear just what was said.

Detective Raj: Take a seat, Mr Harrow. Some things have come to light since we last spoke and I'd like to get your thoughts. Two witnesses have come forward with information that

links you to the victim. They claim you were seen arguing
with said victim at approximately 7.30 pm the night before
you found the body. Now, I just want to make one thing
clear: there's a lot of *you* interacting with the victim going
on, and not a lot of other people interacting with him.
Funny that. So, tell me, what were you and Bruno Tatterson
arguing about that night?

Hector: W-w-we weren't arguing.

Detective Raj: Don't give me that, Mr Harrow. We have
CCTV footage of you and Mr Tatterson arguing in the
lobby before you rush off. Here, I'll show you.

[A few minutes pass in silence.]

Detective Raj: Looks like an argument to me.

Hector: It . . . it was a discussion. Mr Tatterson, B-B-Bruno,
was apologising to me.

Detective Raj: And why would a hotel guest that you met hours
earlier need to apologise to you, the concierge?

Hector: I in-in-interrupted his dinner and he w-wasn't happy
about it.

Detective Raj: Why not?

Hector: He was busy on his telephone.

Detective Raj: Busy doing what?

Hector: No idea.

Detective Raj: And for that he felt the need to apologise to you? It's your job to cop it a bit from the guests, is it not?

Hector: That's called customer service, yes. Bruno did not need to apologise to me, you're right. But he did. You can see him doing so in the video. And I accepted, graciously, and then went home for the evening.

Detective Raj: That's not how it looks. Right, moving on. How do you explain this then? The same witnesses said you allowed a guest to attack them on Thursday afternoon. Is this true?

Hector: Not in the slightest.

Detective Raj: So, what happened with . . . Mr . . . I can't read my own writing . . . Maclean.

Hector: Alec. He'd had a few drinks and interrupted the bridal party's photographs on the stairs. It was just a one-minute interaction and then he was on his way.

Detective Raj: And by the looks of the CCTV footage, you did . . . nothing?

Hector: It is not my job to get involved in such things. Alec did not attack the bridal party; he wanted to talk to me, and they were just in his way, I suppose.

Detective Raj: What did he want to talk to you about?

Hector: His book.

Detective Raj: What book?

Hector: The book he is writing. Is this relevant?

Detective Raj: I'll ask the questions, Mr Harrow. And you're saying he was drunk?

Hector: He'd had a couple of drinks.

Detective Raj: How many is a couple?

Hector: I'm not sure. He was in his room.

Detective Raj: We've got CCTV footage of you going into his room.

Hector: I go into a lot of guests' rooms. I am the concierge.

Detective Raj: So I've heard. You've got access to every suite then?

Hector: I'm not the only one. But yes, I do.

Detective Raj: Hmm. And you didn't see Mr Maclean drinking when you went into his room?

Hector: He was having a glass of whisky.

Detective Raj: How many?

Hector: Just the one glass in his hand that I saw.

Detective Raj: You know what I mean.

Hector: There's no way of knowing if he had drunk a glass before or after I went in.

Detective Raj: We're going in circles. I think it's best we keep you separate from the rest of the staff for the time being.

Just until I get all my ducks in a row. Fred—get in here!
[A pause.] Take Mr Harrow to the gardener's shed out back.
He's not to leave until I say so.

Fred: The shed? I heard there's a free room upstairs. I'll take
him up there.

Detective Raj: I need that room.

Fred: Um, perhaps back to Hugo's then?

Detective Raj: No, his friends are in there and I don't want
them setting him up with stories. The shed is the only place
where I can be sure he will be isolated.

Fred: We can keep him in the hotel, and I'll make sure no one
talks to him.

Detective Raj: No, that's too risky.

Fred: I'll take him down to the station.

Detective Raj: I can't be here and there at the same time. The
shed is the best option. It'll just be for a few hours. You
understand, don't you, Mr Harrow?

Hector: Okay.

Listening to the exchange now, I can't believe I heard myself agree to
go out to the shed. I don't remember that. I must have been completely
consumed by panic. It's not in my nature to disobey authority, it never
has been. That must be why I just heard myself agree to ill treatment.
I feel sad for the man who said 'okay' at the end of that recording.

He was scared. Like I've said, I am stronger now. I should have said no. I should have stood up for myself, like Fred was trying to. But I was overwhelmed.

You might be wondering why I didn't tell Detective Raj the truth about Alec's drinking. Well, I didn't believe Alec killed Bruno, so I saw no reason to fuel the fire by explaining just how much alcohol Alec seemed to have consumed that evening. If Alec had drunk too much and somehow ended up killing Bruno—which, mind you, seemed very unlikely to me—then I was sure that would come out eventually. If he was innocent, then I didn't want to get him in hot water by telling Detective Raj that he had drunk at least a bottle of whisky, likely more. I am glad Fiona had the foresight to get that conversation on tape, or on telephone, whatever you want to say. It jogged some memories that will help with the book.

Fred escorted me to the gardener's shed. On our way, I asked if we could stop by Hugo's. Fiona flung her arms around me as soon as she saw me and asked if I was alright. I was not alright, but I told her I was and I slipped the telephone back to her.

She looked at Fred, wanting reassurance that nothing bad had happened to me. He told her about the shed. She kicked off, of course. But he told her his hands were tied.

'It's just for a few hours,' he said.

She is such a mother hen, is Fiona. She quickly grabbed some linen from the staff storage room opposite Hugo's and slipped it into a Cavengreen tote bag. It was just a thin sheet and pillow, but it was better than nothing. She also stuffed some of the minibar items that we put in the suites into the bag. Then she handed Fred two bottles of water and a kettle to carry. Fred was under strict instructions from Fiona to make sure I had food and plenty of cups of tea, as it gets a bit nippy down in the gardener's shed, even during the warmer months. When I looked at her face, it was like I was boarding a train off to war, and she was worried she might never see me again. Mr Potts gave a grave nod of his head. Their attitudes were not exactly reassuring.

CHAPTER

13

The gardener's shed is about the only place in Cavengreen that is not suitable for spending the night. A night on the library floor was sheer luxury in comparison. The shed itself is about as nice as sheds get, but that doesn't change the fact that it is still a shed. It is made of wood and the floor is covered in soil and green clippings. Worms, some alive, some dead, made for unsettling company.

Fred sat on the floor next to me for the rest of his shift. He radioed Detective Raj a couple of times, asking if we could go back inside yet, but the response was always, 'Not yet—soon though.' He didn't go willingly, but ultimately Fred's shift had to end and a new officer took his place. He left me with one of those keyring torches and wished me well. His face when he left was full of sorrow; he knew I was in for a rough night.

And rough it was. The days might have been warming up, but it was bloody freezing out there. My teeth chattered uncontrollably, and I had to resort to warming my hands over the steam from the kettle, which I flicked on at least ten times during the night. The young officer—one I hadn't seen before—who replaced Fred, sat on a wooden stool complaining about how cold it was. He lasted all of eight minutes or so before taking himself indoors to keep an eye on the shed from the warmth of the function room. I asked if I could go inside with him, but he said no. It was only his third week on the job and he was too scared to rock the boat.

Torture is the only word for what happened to me that night. I tell you what, if Fiona hadn't stuffed that sheet and pillow in a bag then I reckon I would have frozen to death. I'm hardly skin and bones, but there's not a lot of fat on me either.

As someone who lives a life of diligent cleanliness, you can imagine the constant state of discomfort and angst I was in that night. My work suit was filthy with dirt and all sorts. I couldn't complete my nightly routine. All I wanted was to read a good mystery book in my armchair and then head up to bed with a puzzle. I felt like my skin was infected with some sort of disease after not being properly washed or in a clean set of clothes in two days. I hadn't even brushed my teeth. Somehow, though, I must have nodded off, or perhaps passed out. One of the two. I awoke to a boot lightly kicking me in the side.

Right-ho, I need to leave it there. Fiona will be here any minute, so I need to get the kettle on and put out some chocky biscuits. She's popping over to help me fill in some of the blanks in the book; things that happened when I was in isolation. This is my story, but it will be helpful for you to have all the information from that evening, as I am told there were quite a few disturbances. I trust Fiona. I trust her to give her voice to my story and that it will be the truth. You should trust her too.

Fiona just left. She wouldn't let me record our conversation on the dictaphone. She said she would have done it if it were just for me to listen to, but she wasn't comfortable with Helen being the one who would transcribe it. They have never met, Fiona and Helen. Hopefully they will one day. They are both very important ladies in my life. But Fiona didn't want Helen to listen in on our conversation; she said she wouldn't be able to be herself knowing that someone she wasn't familiar with was privy to our chat. And I respect that. It does make my job that bit harder, though. My brain is so full of her words. By 'eck she is a fast talker; even with a pen and paper I wouldn't have been able to keep up. So, I'll quickly need to regurgitate it all for you.

Fiona told me that right after Fred led me away, American Dave appeared in the hallway, wearing his cowboy hat. Fiona described the way he strutted down the corridor with his shoulders back and his feet seemingly too far ahead of the rest of his body. Like a rooster, she said. He was cocky.

'Look, no policemen,' American Dave said, doing a quick spin with his arms outstretched. He then went on to bragging about how he had been given full access to the hotel and no longer had to be escorted around. Apparently, he had a solid alibi for the time of the murder. Since then, we've found out that his alibi involved sneaking into the plunge pool at the hotel spa with Tanya, and then stumbling back to her suite with her, wearing nothing but towels. I have heard that a gallery of timestamped photographs on her telephone revealed that they were very busy, only taking a break to order room service for breakfast and then eventually emerging at 3 pm for afternoon tea. Apologies in advance to American Dave's wife. I am sure you deserve better.

Next, Fiona described how, at around 11 pm, she heard a Scottish man—presumably Alec—shouting that this lockdown was preposterous and demanding to leave the hotel. Fiona said he was slurring his words and when she popped her head out of the cocktail bar, she saw him swaying and stumbling through the lobby. As I said before, *technically* anyone was allowed to leave at any time. Not that they made that clear to us when they kept us under police guard and told us not to move from where we were. But Alec was fighting back. He had his car keys in his hands and an overnight bag flung over his shoulder.

'Move out of my way!' Alec repeated, over and over, Fiona said.

Two officers tried to block his exit, but Alec was determined to leave. The officers tried to tell him he had to stay in the hotel until the police had finished their investigation. Alec barged past them and out of Fiona's sight. She could still hear them.

'If you start that engine, we'll have no choice but to arrest you for drink-driving,' the police shouted. 'Come back inside, sir.'

Fiona hoped that Alec would at least decide to leave on foot, to be the first to take a stand against the police handling of the situation. The Scots are known for their defiance. When I asked her if she would have followed him, she said no, not without me. But to her disappointment she saw Alec plod back through the lobby, dragging his bag behind him. The police confiscated his car keys. Fiona said he mumbled something incoherent, staggered behind my concierge desk, took a bottle of water from my fridge and then wandered off down the guest corridor. Alec might have failed in his quest to get out of the hotel, but it was obvious that unrest was bubbling.

After that, Fiona said various guests were paraded through the lobby on their way from Detective Raj's interrogation room, formerly Mr Potts's office. Most grumbled and complained but were compliant, and many were carrying glasses of wine. Fiona said Patrick's two groomsmen were interviewed together and she overheard them talking on their way back to their suite. They were whispering about whether or not they should have confessed that they were both unconscious the night before the murder, having smoked 'a lot of weed' in the hedge maze after the wedding. As it happens, they decided not to and instead flushed the rest of their stash of drugs down the lavatory to hide the evidence. Not that I have ever touched drugs in my lifetime, but I can imagine the sort of impact something like that would have on the brain. Innocent or guilty, I probably wouldn't have mentioned it to the detective either. Fiona joked that a bit of marijuana from time to time might help with my intrusive thoughts, but that's not something I plan on trying tomorrow, or the next day for that matter.

The last thing to note would be the mental state of Mr Potts. It was bad, Fiona told me. Sleep deprivation and the stress of the investigation had really started to get to him. He sat slumped in one of the booths in Hugo's, only looking up occasionally when Fiona huffed and puffed. I'm not telling you this to embarrass Mr Potts or make him look weak. Stress affects everyone differently. I lose my ability to speak properly, Fiona gets all huffy-puffy, and Mr Potts internalises everything. That is just how it is. Before the murder, Mr Potts gave off the impression that he was a strong, confident gentleman. I mean, he would have to be to run an establishment like Cavengreen.

While patchy, Fiona's recollections are relevant to the story, so thank you to her for popping by. It is always nice to see her. Now, let us go back to my point of view.

~

After spending the night in isolation, I was relieved when Fred turned up with a takeaway cup of coffee, two slices of buttered toast and a change of clothes. I can't say I have ever worn tracksuit trousers and a hooded sweatshirt before, but at that point I had to take what I could get. At least they were clean. I must say the trousers looked even more ridiculous with my polished work shoes. Not that I wasn't grateful; I am just setting the scene.

Fred told me I would need my energy because Detective Raj wanted some of the hotel staff to help move sandbags from the gym. I was horrified. Some of those things are packed with ninety or even one hundred kilograms of weight. The hotel has a personal trainer service that can be booked on request. I've seen muscly blokes lug those bags up and down the gym, biceps bulging and the veins in their temples pulsing. Back in my youth I would keep in fairly good shape, but not now, and especially not since I've done my hip in. But Fred said Detective Raj insisted we meet him in the gym, so after my coffee and a quick lavatory break, we headed there.

Expecting to see some of the young 'uns from the hotel staff, I was surprised to find it was just myself, Fred and Detective Raj. Our voices echoed off the polished floors and bounced off the mirrored walls. All the equipment had been stored away and the room was empty except for a few tumbleweeds of fluff that blew across the floor and, of course, the sandbags that needed to be moved. Raj told me that the other blokes were changing and would be along soon, but I was to get started in the meantime.

'This one,' Detective Raj said, kicking a big black bag with *90 KG* written in white on the side of it. 'Come on then. Move it from there to there.' He pointed from one side of the gym to the other.

The hotel was turning into some sort of prisoner-of-war camp. Fred gave me a look that seemed to say, *Pick your battles*, so I moved around to one side of the sandbag and leant my good hip against it to try to shift it with my body weight.

'No, don't push it—drag it,' the detective ordered.

So, I moved to the other side of the bag, grabbed the handle on top and pulled it towards me. It wouldn't budge. And I am not surprised. I am a hotel concierge, not a bloomin' bodybuilder. I gave it a good go, though, gritting my teeth, grunting and everything as I pulled hard on the handle. A little too hard, it seemed. My dodgy hip cracked, and heat rushed through it. It felt like a forest fire was spreading through my bones. The pain was so excruciating it brought me to the floor. My hands clasped my hip as if it was crumbling apart and they could hold it together. I was howling in agony and angry that some detective had pushed me that far. It felt criminal.

Fred rushed over, telling me to breathe.

'It hurts!' I gasped through gritted teeth.

Fred begged Detective Raj to call an ambulance.

Instead, the detective walked towards the door. 'Take him upstairs to rest—suite two is free,' he said over his shoulder. And then he was gone, slamming the heavy door shut behind him.

Fred squatted down next to me on the floor. He breathed along with me to try to help calm my frantic, pained breaths. Inhale, exhale. We did that for a minute or so and it helped, somewhat. He gripped my hand tightly and told me to focus on his grip. I looked at our clasped hands, noticing how wrinkled mine was next to his. Even now when I look at my hands, sometimes I can't believe they are mine. They are older than me, that is how I feel. Fred's effort to distract me worked and I was able to control my breathing. The pain subsided enough for me to shuffle over to the mirrored wall and lean up against it. In a weak voice, I asked Fred what that was all about. It was obvious that none of the other staff members were coming to help. This little game of Detective Raj's had been designed for me alone.

'The dead man,' Fred began. 'He was in the bathroom. But that's not where he died. There was blood smeared across the floor as if someone dragged him from the bedroom. I'd guess he weighed about ninety kilos.'

CHAPTER

A letter arrived with today's post. There is something so special about a handwritten envelope nowadays, when everyone communicates via email or telephone. The only other post I get is bills, bills and more bills, all of them with a printed address in a clear window. A computer most likely autogenerates them. But this letter is special. Someone has taken the time to write my name and address on an envelope, lick two stamps and stick them in the top right corner. There is only one person that this could be from.

Note to Helen: Can you please type out the contents of the letter for the readers?

Dear Hector,

I'm sorry I haven't been in touch sooner. As you can imagine, things have been difficult and I've been focusing on making sure my family is okay. But I wanted to write to you to make sure you are doing well. It was awful what you went through at Cavengreen, and I am so sorry for my part in that. I am doing okay, all things considered. Hopefully you'll come and visit me soon. I'd like that.

Regards,

T. Potts

The letter is short yet it says everything I wanted to hear. I'm glad he's doing well. It is always a worry when you suddenly lose contact with someone. We formed a sort of bond during our time locked inside Cavengreen. Little did I know how brief our friendship would be. I do plan to visit him soon, though; I need to know why he did it.

Let me tell you everything I know and believe to be true about Mr Potts. It will be useful for you to have some background information about him. His first name is Toulouse and I believe his mother is of French descent and his father is English. His wife's name is Isabella, and I think I heard Mr Potts mention once that she is Italian. They have a fifteen-year-old son named Anton. Isabella and Anton visited the hotel once for afternoon tea, but unfortunately I didn't get a chance to say hello. Had I known of the bond that would ultimately form between myself and Mr Potts, I would have taken the opportunity to get acquainted with his family. A man's family says a lot about him and perhaps I would have spotted some red flags if we had met sooner. Although I am not sure what my lack of wife or children says about me. Perhaps that I am unlovable.

Tap one. Tap two. Tap three.

Sometimes I wonder who is going to bury me when I die. It is a luxury to have a family who care for you. If I had my time over, I think that is something I would have prioritised. But time went so fast for me and here I am. Alone.

Mr Potts lived ten minutes from Cavengreen in a renovated farmhouse. I know that because I dropped him home once when his car was having engine problems. It was a lovely house with tall gates and climbing ivy. It is a shame they aren't able to live there anymore. That was the extent of what I knew about Mr Potts before the murder. During the lockdown at the hotel, I learnt that he doesn't manage stress particularly well. Mr Potts might have had silver service and hotel manager training, but there is no manual for how to deal with a murder.

Mr Potts was the first person to come and see me when I was allowed out of isolation and taken to rest in suite two. He burst through the door just as I was getting out of the shower. Luckily I had a towel wrapped around my waist, or he would have been in for a fright.

He wrapped his arms around me, undeterred by my hairy chest pressing against his bedraggled suit. His face was red and sweaty, and the dark rings around his eyes had deepened. He smelt like whisky and peanuts.

He walked over to the minibar and rummaged inside, eventually pulling out a beer. After cracking it open, he told me that according to Detective Raj I'd said that the police should look closely at him, but that he didn't believe a word of it. I couldn't fathom why Detective Raj would resort to such dirty tactics as turning the staff against each other. He told Mr Potts that I said I'd overheard him threatening Bruno the day before he was murdered. If you've got this far in the book, I'm sure I do not need to tell you that I heard and said nothing of the sort.

Mr Potts was horrified when I told him about the sandbag incident. Surely anyone would be horrified on hearing such a story. Although I imagined American Dave would have a good laugh at my expense if he ever heard what I had to endure. Nevertheless, as far as I knew, the sandbag incident had proven my innocence. If Bruno's body hadn't been dragged across the floor after the murder, then I am not sure where I would be now. The sandbag test would not have helped rule out many others. Most able-bodied adults could probably drag ninety kilograms if required, Mr Potts included.

After getting dressed, I joined Mr Potts in the suite's living area. He playfully mocked my overly casual attire, but it was nice to share a laugh in such a moment. Seeing a concierge in a tracksuit is like seeing a fish in a top hat. Mr Potts was sitting on the sofa and had made himself a coffee, but his shaky hands caused liquid to spill over the rim of the mug whenever he tried to take a sip. Clearly, he needed some rest. I suggested he lie down, but first he wanted to tell me about the interrogation he'd been subjected to by Detective Raj. Apparently, the forensics team had found faint bloody footprints on the carpet. Detective Raj said that it wouldn't take long for them to find out who they belonged to. He even insinuated that if Mr Potts wanted to come clean at that moment, then it would save everyone a lot of time. Mr Potts didn't, of course; why would he? We would spend two more nights in the hotel before anyone left in handcuffs.

Mr Potts slept for nearly seven hours. That time flew by. In between cups of tea, I sat in an armchair staring at the puddle of spilt coffee on the table. In seven hours, it did not get any smaller. In any normal circumstance, I would have had to clean the spill up straight away, its very existence making me twitch with discomfort. But I left it because I wanted my mind to focus on something other than my current predicament. While that pool of coffee was in my sight, it was all I could think about. It was a welcome break from wondering who the murderer might be.

As soon as I heard Mr Potts stirring, I grabbed a tissue and mopped up the mess. Mr Potts stretched and yawned, then he swung his legs over the side of the bed and stood up, scratching his head as he walked over to the minibar. He took a bottle of beer and packet of wasabi nuts. He offered me a drink, but he was just being polite. We both knew I wasn't going to crack a cold beverage with him.

It was golden hour at the hotel. That is how wedding photographers refer to the time just before the sun sets. An orange hue lit up the suite and beamed onto Mr Potts's face. Even with seven hours of sleep and good lighting, he still looked weary.

'Who do you think did it?' Mr Potts asked me after a slug of beer.

'No idea,' I replied.

'What do we know so far? We know it wasn't you.'

'And we know it wasn't you.'

'How do you know that?' Mr Potts looked me right in the eye. 'I mean, it wasn't me, but you're just taking my word on that.'

'Your word is good enough for me,' I told him.

'Thank you, Hector.' He swigged his beer. 'We know that Eric, the night porter, saw Bruno when he dropped off champagne just before midnight, so it couldn't have been a wedding guest, because they all left at quarter past eleven. And then the next time anyone saw Bruno that we're aware of was when you found the body just after three the next afternoon. That's a long window of opportunity.'

'I'm the only person that the CCTV shows going into the room. Could he have done it to himself?' I asked.

'And then dragged his dead body across the floor? Unlikely.'

'He could have done it and then tried to crawl to the bathroom.' But a flashback of the body reminded me that there was no way a man could have perpetrated such horrors to his own flesh.

Tap one. Tap two. Tap three.

'Hector!' Mr Potts leapt up with an energy I didn't know he had. 'The terrace doors. There's no CCTV on the terrace doors. That's how the murderer got in undetected.'

'Of course.' It was so obvious. I am not sure why we hadn't thought of it sooner.

'The murderer had to have known that there was no CCTV out there. Hector, it could have been a staff member.'

'Or a guest who didn't care if they were caught.'

Cavengreen has never had CCTV on the terraces; it was always considered an invasion of privacy, which is fair enough. We'd never needed it until then. There are no cameras in the gardens either, but there are a few on the external building, pointing into the car park and onto the restaurant terrace. Inside, there are cameras everywhere. You can't sneeze without someone watching. This is all information that I am sure the police had at that point. Mr Potts said Detective Raj had covered one of the walls in his office in sheets of white paper with names, alibis and question marks all over, just like in the movies. When I quizzed him on what was written down, he said he could not recall. Absolutely useless.

There was a knock at the door that startled us both.

'Move aside, you big oaf,' snapped a familiar voice.

My hip twinged with a lightning bolt of pain as I jumped up faster than I have moved in years. I am very glad Detective Raj did not see that momentary boost in agility or he'd have had me lugging sandbags again.

Tyrone the pit bull was patrolling the hallway, and he scowled as I opened the door and ushered my dear friend Fiona inside. She had a black smear on her face and was still wrapped in a Cavengreen dressing-gown. Her slippers were gone, and she marched around the suite barefoot in search of another pair. Mr Potts and I exchanged glances as we watched a flustered Fiona open up all the cupboards. When she finally found a pair, she slipped them on then slumped in an armchair and rubbed her temples, asking for painkillers, which we did not have to hand.

Fiona was agitated and muttering to herself about how she should have gone for one of the voluntary redundancy packages offered the year before. But she had kept working because she feared loneliness after the death of her husband. There is no feeling worse than loneliness, in my opinion. Loneliness consumes you. It encompasses sadness, shame and regret all in one. Loneliness makes you question your purpose in life. Because if you have no one to share life with, then what is the point? Loneliness digs into your brain and makes you feel unworthy. Once you let it in, it is like a fog that won't lift. And then you find that your physical health starts to suffer along with your mental state. That is why my job at the hotel meant so much to me. The guests, Fiona, Mr Potts—all the staff, really: they gave me the energy I needed to get through each day. Even if I had been given the green light to leave the hotel during the lockdown, I wouldn't have left until everyone else had been allowed out first. This book is giving me purpose now that I am no longer working there, but once I have finished, I will need to fill the void in my life. That is something I am still working on, don't worry. I have not come this far to just give up and start digging my own grave.

That was a bit of a sidestep; let us get back to Fiona. She was questioned during the night, along with the other reception staff. As you can imagine, it was a hostile experience for all involved. Fiona recounted the conversation she'd had with Detective Raj, mimicking his voice and facial expressions for our benefit. At one point she even managed to get Mr Potts to crack a smile when she told of how, when asked to put her finger in some black ink and provide her fingerprint on a piece of paper, she instead smeared a penis and testicles. Needless to say, that did not go down well with the detective, she said.

Detective Raj ended his questioning by granting Fiona permission to move around the hotel as she pleased but not to leave the premises.

If Fiona had been given the freedom to wander the hotel, then Mr Potts and I assumed we had too. In my borrowed hooded sweatshirt and tracksuit trousers, I opened the door to the suite. Tyrone barked at me, asking what we thought we were doing.

So I told him straight. 'We're going for a walk around *our* hotel.'

And that's what we did.

It would seem that we were the last to know that guests and staff had been given permission to move freely around the hotel, including the gardens. Suite seven was still sealed off by yellow police tape, but aside from that and Mr Potts's office, nowhere was off limits. We wandered by Lavender Plates, probably looking like the walking dead. The exhausted chefs were firing up the ovens, promising to do their best with the supplies to hand. Surveying the room, I wondered if the murderer was still sitting among us and if perhaps I could do my own investigating to help solve the case so everyone could go home and I could get back to my puzzles and routine.

The newlyweds, Olive and Patrick, looked tired and despondent. They were sitting at a table with her parents and his groomsmen, no one speaking. They had dressed for the occasion, whatever they thought it was. There was an upside-down champagne bottle in an ice bucket on their table and another, almost empty, in front of the bride. I am sure this was not quite the honeymoon they had envisaged.

Knowing I looked unkempt and unprofessional, I was hesitant to approach them, but I decided that it was the right thing to do. I advised Mr Potts to hang back. He hadn't showered and his eyes looked bleary, not to mention the fact he smelt of alcohol. It was hardly the image we wanted the guests to see, so he opted to go out onto the terrace to try to telephone his wife.

Olive and Patrick feigned delight when they saw me. There wasn't much to be said other than to issue apologies and well wishes. They were very polite and told me they were glad they at least got to enjoy their wedding day. They asked me if I knew anything about the investigation; I told them I didn't.

Olive's mother, Sue Bainbridge, had been frowning at me as I talked; I could see her in my peripheral vision, her arms crossed and lips pursed. Her husband put his arm on her shoulder and quietly advised her to relax but she was a bull, and I was the colour red. You will have to excuse me, because I don't remember the conversation word for word, and I don't want to go putting words in mouths, but Sue seemed to be under the impression that this was all my fault, and that I should just confess so everyone could go home. Considering she believed me to be a dangerous murderer, she was acting rather bossy.

All the other tables of guests had started to look over. A few nodded their agreement. Others rolled their eyes and offered me sympathetic smiles. I had to remember that I was the concierge and confrontations with the guests were not appropriate, but this woman was getting on my last nerve with her accusations. As I indicated earlier, a different version of myself had started to emerge during that time in the hotel; one that resembled my father. My usual approach to customer service had been replaced with a determination to defend myself.

As bluntly as I could, I told Sue and everyone else who was listening that I had been proved innocent and she was more than welcome to ask Detective Raj to confirm that if she did not want to take my word for it.

Sue immediately stood up. Her daughter, Olive, tugged at her blouse, urging her to stop causing a scene, but Sue wafted her away. She strode out of the restaurant, turning to bark her husband's name, snapping her fingers. He scrambled from his seat and followed, clutching her handbag in one hand and a half-eaten croissant in the other.

Olive shook her head and sighed. For a second, I thought she was going to apologise for her mother's behaviour but instead she picked up her mobile telephone and appeared to be absorbed in whatever she saw on the screen.

I raised my hands to straighten my tie, only to find the two dangling tassels of my borrowed hooded sweatshirt. It felt ever so strange to be dressed so casually at the hotel. It's like when you see your local doctor or an old schoolteacher at the supermarket and the context seems wrong. That was me at that moment: completely out of context.

The peace was disturbed moments later by those wretched twins. Ruby and Oksana nearly accidentally-on-purpose knocked me over on their way to exchange air kisses with the bride and groom.

'What is *he* doing here?' the louder one, Ruby, asked as she flung a napkin over her lap and poured the last few drops of champagne into her glass. She clicked her fingers in the air and demanded that another bottle be fetched for her. Not that any staff were officially on service nor paying any attention to her. 'Shouldn't he be in prison or something?'

I remember those words so clearly, and I remember the hatred with which she looked at me as she said them.

Olive must have kicked Ruby under the table then because she yelped and shouted, 'What was that for?'

Through gritted teeth, Olive whispered that they would talk about it later. Everyone at the table looked at me as if I were an annoying insect that they wanted to swat away. It was time for me to exit.

Alec was sitting in a corner of the restaurant, twirling a spoon around a teacup, and chewing the end of his glasses. It was nice to see him drinking tea and not whisky. As it happens, he had added a splash of brandy to his tea, but I was none the wiser until he told me.

He greeted me with a firm handshake that seemed genuine. He thanked me for my book ideas and said that, as a result of my help, he had finished a first draft. There was just one problem: he had misplaced his laptop. We both knew it couldn't have gone far, but Alec couldn't remember a thing about the previous night. He didn't even remember trying to leave the hotel or the police confiscating his car keys. The look of horror on his face when Fiona briefly swooped by to remind him was a picture. That is one of the reasons why I have never been a big drinker. Fancy waking up and finding that hours of your life are missing from your memory. My mother used to try to tell my father off the morning after big night. She would tell him how he hit me, or how he had broken a picture frame or scared Josie, but he would always say, 'I don't remember doing that,' putting a swift end to the discussion. My mother knew better than to argue with a man who was good with his fists but bad with his words.

Alec invited me to join him and, since I wasn't on the clock, I thought, why not? Fiona and some of the other female staff were sharing cake over at the chef's pass, and Mr Potts was still outside, so I saw no harm in sitting down for a warm brew, minus the brandy.

Alec and I speculated over where his laptop could be. He even considered that someone could have stolen it, although he couldn't see why anybody would. There was a moment when I saw in his eyes that he had come to terms with the fact that it was lost. His shoulders dropped and he puffed out his cheeks. He confessed that he hadn't yet backed up his story.

That reminds me, Helen, can you please make a note to back up my book if you haven't done so already? I am sure you have, being a professional at this business, but on the off chance you haven't, please do. I am sure the last thing you want is to have to retranscribe these tapes all over again. What a nuisance that would be.

Alec kept twirling his spoon around his teacup, seemingly mesmerised by the mini whirlpool the movement created. He must have been relaxed, because he chose to open up to me. As I have said before, lots of people confided in me during my time as a concierge. They might have seen me as a free therapist, knowing I would be too polite to tell them to stop talking. It was my job to cater to the guests' every whim, and if that meant listening to them talk about themselves, then so be it.

It was different with Alec. His company was pleasant, and I found what he had to say very interesting. He was someone I would have chosen to be friends with, had the opportunity arisen. Alec told me about his wife, whom he'd had to have put into full-time care when she was paralysed from the neck down after a car he was driving skidded into an embankment one evening. He was consumed by guilt and sadness, mourning the loss of his old life and living with the pain of having destroyed his wife's future. There was no use comforting him by telling him it wasn't his fault, because I didn't know if it was or wasn't. Perhaps it was. Perhaps they were arguing and he took his eyes off the road, or he was otherwise distracted or tired. Without the details, there was no way of knowing. He made it clear several times that he was sober when he was driving. People cram in all sorts of details out of fear of judgement. Sometimes it is better to say something for clarity, rather than sit there wondering what the other person makes of you.

As interested as I was in what Alec was saying, I became slightly distracted by the sight of Mr Potts, climbing from one of the outdoor chairs onto the concrete ledge of the terrace. Jumping off would do nothing but scrape his knees so I did wonder why he was up there until I saw him shaking his mobile telephone up to the high heavens, presumably in an attempt to get signal. It seemed to work and moments later he was talking, or rather, shouting, to someone on the other end. I turned my attention back to my Scottish friend.

Alec had a son named Joseph and a daughter named Hailey; both had children of their own. Neither of them were able to spend much time with their father after blaming him for the car accident. Alec told me he was lonely, something I understood. You can have a family and friends but still feel lonely—for example, you might spend all day surrounded by people but get into bed at night feeling as if you weren't able to have a meaningful conversation or you weren't given the affection you craved.

From that conversation with Alec, I knew he would never get used to feeling lonely. He said that was why he started writing, because when he was writing he felt like he was talking to someone. I understand that now. Even recording this, I feel like I am chatting away to people. Even though you don't know me now, you will soon. I have been as open and vulnerable as I can be in this book. That is a scary but rather exhilarating thing.

Back to Alec; we had a grand chat. We spoke about Scotland and the places he likes and the places I have always wanted to go. He said that after all this was over, he would invite me to visit the Loch Ness Monster. That was the nickname of the landlord of his local pub rather than a mythical sea creature, he added. We had a right laugh about that. Who knows if it was a genuine invitation, but had things turned out differently, I would have made the effort to get up there. One day I will go on my own.

At that point Mr Potts banged on the window and indicated that he wanted me and Fiona to join him outside. He didn't half make me jump. Mr Potts had lost all sense of self and had clearly forgotten he was the hotel manager. Instead of his straight posture and neutral face, he was hunched, frowning and frantic. However, it wasn't the time to remind him of how he should be acting. I mean, there I was in a hooded sweatshirt and tracksuit trousers.

Mr Potts wanted to tell us that, according to his wife, the press had got wind of something happening at Cavengreen. He said he only got to speak to her for a minute before the telephone signal dropped out, but it was enough time for her to tell him that the six o'clock news had announced that Cavengreen was under police guard and an investigation of the staff and guests was taking place. That was all they knew. There was no mention that a man had been killed or that a crazed detective was holding everyone against their will. It wouldn't be long before Bruno's face would be plastered across the newspapers and television, but that wouldn't be until after we all got to go home. Well, most of us.

Fiona grabbed her mobile telephone out of her pocket. She said she was fed up and wanted to tell the media exactly what was going on at Cavengreen. I remember her asking for the number of the TV news, like I would know. I didn't even know it was possible to simply telephone the news with updates and the like. It didn't seem like a good idea. If Detective Raj got wind that the staff were campaigning against him then who knew what horrors he would conjure as punishment. Rumour had it he was close to breaking point and forcing his staff to work eighteen-hour shifts until they solved the case. But Fiona was determined to have her say.

Her long pink fingernails tapped against the telephone screen, and she made an impatient clicking noise with her tongue. Unable to connect to 'the TV people', as she called them, she turned to go back inside to ask one of the young 'uns if they had managed to get their telephones to work. But then she paused. She took a few cautious steps forward and knocked on the glass. Then she knocked again. I turned around, but I could not yet see what she saw. If I had seen, I would have moved faster.

Fiona knocked again, then she ran inside.

Once she had moved out of the way, I could see exactly what had so alarmed her. Alec was slumped against the window, his face slowly sliding down the glass, leaving a smear. One hand gripped his chest.

CHAPTER 16

Mutterings of a man being poisoned spread around Lavender Plates. Patrick, the groom, lifted Alec from his chair and laid him on the floor. He started performing CPR. The chest thumps were particularly violent, but I am told that's normal. Detective Raj, followed by several officers, barged through the crowd. The detective pushed Patrick aside and took over the CPR himself. He desperately exclaimed that another man could not die, especially not on his watch.

After a couple of minutes it became painful to witness. Some of the younger staff moved away and others were crying at the back of the restaurant. Patrick knelt at Alec's side and checked his wrist for a pulse. Then he checked again. He told Detective Raj he could stop the CPR, but the detective only pumped Alec's chest harder. There is no doubt that some ribs would have been broken. The police officers exchanged glances, as if wondering whether to intervene. It was left to Patrick to seize Detective Raj and pull him away.

'He's dead,' Patrick announced, checking his watch, presumably to record the exact time.

My initial thought was of Alec's wife and children. How he never got to say goodbye. How his children might forever regret not having been on good terms with their father in the end. You can say sorry to a dead person, but they won't hear you.

I am not a crier by any means but Alec's death really got to me. The post-mortem would ultimately determine he'd had a heart attack, most likely brought on by stress. He'd had plenty of that to deal with.

Alec Maclean was the second guest to leave Cavengreen in a body bag in forty-eight hours. It was frightening for the guests. We didn't know at that point how Alec had died, so theories of a serial killer on the loose circulated quickly. Most of the guests made a quick exit from Lavender Plates and locked themselves in their suites. Some of the staff started to turn on each other, asking questions that they would never have asked before, like, 'Where were you in the hours before Bruno's murder?' and, 'Did you put anything in Alec's drink?'

Detective Raj stepped outside onto the terrace. We could only see his back. He kicked some gravel and held his head in his hands. He crouched down to a squatting position and then shot back up with a loud expletive. He turned and stormed back inside, pausing in the doorway to look around fiercely at the remaining staff and guests, who stared back wide-eyed. Alec's death had made Detective Raj—

CHAPTER

17

Right in the middle of my train of thought, you will never guess what happened. Just now, I heard some voices out the front of my cottage, so I went to look. I opened the door but no one was there, though a large box with a red ribbon around it was sitting on the mat. An early birthday present was my first thought. Perhaps Fiona or Helen had dropped it off in a hurry. It is my birthday this coming Sunday, so it would not have been completely out of the blue to receive a present, although I cannot say I expect them. But I have got the box here now, and after I describe its contents to you it is going straight in the bin.

So, picture this: I am on the doorstep with a parcel, and seeing as it is a lovely day, sunny and not too warm, I decide to open it there and then. I untie the ribbon, lift the lid of the box and see a card sitting on top of a second box. Written on the card is a single word. It is a word that haunts me and has ruined a whole genre of movies. As soon as you read it, you will know what's coming:

Howdy.

That was the word. In this context, it feels threatening, intimidating and sinister. As soon as I read it, I looked left and right, suddenly feeling unsettled. Then there was the box. This big bloomin' box. Inside it is a tan cowboy hat.

You can imagine what happened next, and if you could hear this audio recording, you would know how flustered I am still. Out from behind the limestone wall next to my house popped American Dave, followed by a grinning Paula McDavidson. They were clapping like seals, so pleased at the execution of their surprise delivery. American Dave was wearing the same cowboy hat he'd worn at Cavengreen. He was dressed in blue jeans and some clunky black boots. This is the Yorkshire Dales, not a ranch, buddy!

Paula McDavidson looked at American Dave in awe as he fired his cowboy jargon at me. I am not even sure what half of what he said meant. And then—you will not believe this—I noticed a man with a camera on the far side of the wall recording our interaction. Here I am, minding my own business in my own garden, when the American and the local busybody appear out of nowhere to ruin my day. I held my hand up to block my face, shouting that I did not give them permission to film me. They will probably just blur me. I have seen clips of those American cop shows before. Everyone from around here will know it is me; even with a fuzzy blob concealing my identity, I still walk, talk and stand like Hector.

As I shouted at him to go away, American Dave smirked. He's obviously had his teeth whitened because I was nearly blinded. He hooked a thumb through his chunky belt buckle and propped a foot up on my wall. All he needed was a piece of straw in his mouth and he would look just like the cowboys in the movies. He introduced his cameraman and producer to me. I don't care to remember their names.

Some local schoolkids cycled by and shouted a very fitting 'Wanker!' at American Dave, which caught him off guard. I'm not one to encourage children to curse, but it was more than appropriate in that moment.

'I know your parents, Joel Umbridge!' Paula McDavidson shouted after them, only to be met with a middle finger, presumably belonging to Joel.

Paula was in her element, enjoying the limelight with an American. She is the type of woman who thinks Americans are all glitz and glamour, and I bet she's thinking that she'll hit the big time after this documentary. I tell you what: there is no way they will make anything half decent without my side of the story. Where was American Dave when Alec died? In his suite with his American mistress. He was not part of the action; he was too busy getting some!

'We need you to appear on camera,' American Dave told me. 'It won't take long. We just want to ask you some questions about Cavengreen.' He explained that some company is interested in streaming the documentary when it is completed. Apparently that means the whole world will see it. I am certainly not going to support the whole world seeing his pack of lies so I replied sternly, 'Fat chance.' He persisted, of course; told me there was big money to be made and maybe even an all-expenses-paid trip to America. I am not interested. And I think I made that very clear by slamming the door in his face, something I am sure will make great footage for their documentary.

You would think I would be used to these bothersome pop-ins by now, but they seem to get worse every time I open my front door. That won't be the last I'll see of American Dave, I would bet money on that. Now he knows where I live, I am sure he and his cameras will be back. They will be sniffing around Cavengreen too, no doubt. Nuisances, the lot of them. Surely I could get them done for harassment.

Well, there's no use getting worked up. That is exactly what he would want. There is a story that I need to tell, so I will fetch a brew, calm down a bit, and resume recording. I really want to finish this part about Alec. And get this bloody great big hat out of my sight!

A cup of English breakfast does wonders for the temperament. I am like a new man after a warm brew. American Dave is not going to throw me off. Him being in the village has lit a fire in my belly. It is a race to see who can get their story out first. And it *has* to be me.

Let us get back to Alec. We all saw him die; there was no obvious foul play at work. It would be up to a post-mortem to conclude if he had been poisoned, like some of the guests were speculating.

While most of the guests had rushed back to their suites, fearful of further attacks, Olive, Patrick and the twins lingered in Lavender Plates, giving me funny looks and pointing out that I just so happened to be the last person who spoke to Alec. The twins made that very clear to Detective Raj. They were like schoolkids telling tales.

Detective Raj was having none of it. He covered his ears with his hands and closed his eyes. The twins clicked their fingers in his face and shouted, 'Hello?' but Detective Raj seemed determined to block them out. They thought this was an appropriate moment to demand the Wi-Fi be turned back on. The detective turned away, ignoring them. The twins stormed off, taking a bottle of champagne with them.

Olive pressed herself against Patrick and he tenderly comforted her by stroking the back of her hair. At that moment, American Dave and his mistress walked into Lavender Plates, their arms around each other's waists. Their timing could not have been worse.

'Who died?' American Dave asked jovially when he spotted our glum faces. He smiled broadly.

Detective Raj looked at him and then tilted his head back, directing an exasperated sigh towards the heavens. Patrick was the one to announce that Alec had died.

American Dave's smile turned to a look of shock. 'Fuck!' he mouthed as he caught sight of Alec's body.

He disentangled himself from his mistress and put his hands on his hips.

'What the fuck is going on here, y'all?' he demanded, his voice raised to a volume not appreciated by those of us who had just been through a traumatic experience. But he was right, it was time to try and get some answers.

We sat around for a few hours, the sky darkening as we sunk deep into the night, waiting for Alec's body to be taken from Lavender Plates. It was a solemn time. May he rest in peace.

Once Alec's body had been collected, Detective Raj and some of his officers, American Dave, Fiona, Mr Potts, and I gathered in the library. American Dave's mistress tried to join us, but he slammed the door in her face, leaving her in the corridor. We each took a seat and looked expectantly at the detective. (Except Mr Potts, who was in the corner of the library, his back turned to everyone. Nobody else noticed, but I guessed what he was up to, and the ever-so-slight clink of the lid being placed back onto the whisky decanter confirmed my suspicions.)

Detective Raj took his place in front of the unlit fireplace. He seemed drained. His eyes begged for sleep and his facial hair, which had been neatly groomed, now looked patchy. There were coffee stains on his white shirt, which was wrinkled and untucked. He agreed to answer any questions we had, as long as his responses stayed in that room. I think he could sense that we had the potential to become a troublesome bunch and that keeping us on side would help maintain control.

Fiona went first. 'Are you any closer to finding out who killed Bruno, and now, potentially Alec, so we can all get the hell out of here?'

'We're slowly ruling people out, so yes, we're getting closer,' Detective Raj responded.

Fiona followed up with: 'Do you think the killer is still in the hotel?'

'Yes. Looking at the CCTV footage, we are positive that the killer is still among us.'

It was my turn. 'Do you realise that there's no CCTV facing the terrace doors of the suites?' I asked.

'We are aware of that and assume that is how the killer gained access to Mr Tatterson's suite.'

'What about the murder weapon?' American Dave leant forward in the armchair, resting his elbows on his knees and twirling his hat in his hands.

'Missing.'

'But it has to be somewhere in the hotel?' American Dave persisted.

'Presumably so.'

'Well, let's all get off our asses and look for it!' American Dave sprung up.

'Oh, sit down you great *arse*!' Fiona snapped. 'We don't even know what we're looking for.'

'A knife, we think,' said Detective Raj, adding: 'We are still waiting for forensics to confirm.'

When you work in a hotel, you have a fair idea of the sort of inventory stored within the building. And knives, well, we had plenty of those. Sushi knives. Steak knives. Fish knives. Gardening knives. Letter openers. Butter knives (although I am fairly certain one of those wouldn't break the skin). I am sure American Dave's documentary will paint him to be a hero because he happened to be the one who eventually found the murder weapon. We will get to that later.

The clock above the fireplace chimed eleven times. We were to spend our third night in the hotel, and we all agreed that perhaps it was best for everyone to get some rest. It was clear that the killer, whomever they may have been, was still hiding in plain sight within the hotel. Either that, or they had just been taken away in a body bag.

Everyone dispersed back to the suites, myself and Mr Potts agreeing to share suite two, him on the sofa and me in the bed. He was very kind to offer me the bed. It is one of the benefits of being classed as an 'old man', even though that is not how I feel. But I accepted gratefully. I was in desperate need of a long rest if when I woke I was to put my energy into helping solve the case so we could all go home.

On the way back to the suite, we stopped at my concierge desk to take a few bottles of water from my fridge. Nothing on my desk was where it should have been. My hands throbbed, desperately wanting to sort and tidy everything. There were empty bottles of water, sweet wrappers and crushed cans of soft drink strewn across my files. The telephone was off the hook and Cavengreen pens were lying lidless all around. Something sticky had collected fluff and dust in a little patch. It was the stuff of nightmares—to me, that is. Of course, being locked in a hotel with a murderer was bad, but it didn't itch at my brain in the same way as a messy desk.

As I surveyed the damage I could sense that Mr Potts was growing impatient. I knew that I would have to clean up another time, though denying my urge to tidy caused me great discomfort.

Tap one. Tap two. Tap three.

Instead, I took a deep breath and bent down to open the fridge. I was surprised to find a black satchel inside. It wasn't mine and I hadn't the foggiest idea why it was in the fridge of all places. I checked over my shoulder; Mr Potts was flicking dead petals off the floral display. I pulled the satchel out and, peering inside, I knew immediately what I had found. It was Alec's lost laptop.

I took it. Part of me felt like I needed to protect it now that its owner was no longer with us. Alec was so passionate about his work. The other part of me was overcome by curiosity. I wanted to read what was on there. In that moment, for all I knew, Alec might have been murdered too, and maybe that laptop held some answers. Mr Potts didn't even notice I was suddenly carrying the satchel as we walked back to our suite. Soon enough I would tell him I had it. Indeed, I would need his help to access its files.

CHAPTER

18

A change of scenery is required for today's recording. Helen's idea. We spoke on the telephone yesterday and I told her all about how I was ambushed by the American and Paula the busybody. Helen thought it was rather funny and told me it would make great content. 'Anything for a good book,' that is what she always says.

I invited her along to Cavengreen with me, so she could see the hotel for herself, to get a sense of the setting. I thought that might help her with the editing. She said she was too busy. Something about paperwork, forms to fill in and all that. I didn't pry.

Fiona was more than happy to set up a little space for me in the gardens at Cavengreen. It feels peculiar coming back here. The last time I was here was the day we were all finally allowed to leave. Well, most of us. A couple of months have passed since then and, while I no longer work here, Cavengreen will always be my second home. Coming up the driveway and seeing the hotel brought back so many good memories. I will never tire of the sight. I mean, in fifty-odd years, I never did. Even after all that has happened, she's still my Cavengreen.

When I arrived, there was quite a bit of hustle and bustle going on out the front. Fiona greeted me with a warm hug and orange juice in a champagne flute. I felt like a guest, and I knew that was Fiona's intention. Isn't she lovely?

I pointed out some scaffolding around the main archway outside the front of the hotel.

'They're changing the sign,' Fiona told me with a sigh.

I'd known this was going to happen, though I haven't mentioned it to you lot. Part of me hoped it might never come to pass. The Americans have officially taken over Cavengreen and given it a new name. With the name of the hotel being plastered over the news the last couple of months, they have decided to rebrand. Fiona said the hotel has been busy enough, but instead of the normal clientele, they have been taking bookings from ghost hunters and those with a morbid fascination. What an odd thing to have as a hobby, visiting murder sites.

The new sign for the hotel was resting against the back of a truck when I arrived. I had to tilt my head sideways to read it. Fiona rolled her eyes and tutted at it. As of today, the hotel is named The Lavender. It is a nice name, I suppose. The Americans have planted lavender in terracotta pots all along the driveway and the front of the hotel. I must admit, it looks lovely—though a nightmare if you have allergies, of course. Still, this place will always be Cavengreen to me, and I'm not about to start using its new name in this book. Not only would that be confusing, it just wouldn't feel right.

The name is not the only thing that has changed around here. Most of the staff are new too. The Americans only kept on Fiona and the kitchen staff. Fiona laughed when she told me that; she was surprised since she had given American Dave so much grief during the lockdown.

He had described her as 'fierce' and 'just like me', which she found highly insulting. She only agreed to stay on because they gave her a generous pay increase. But she did note that the soul of the hotel is missing now that the staff have changed over.

'Ninety-nine per cent of us aren't even from round here now,' Fiona said with a frown. 'There are accents from London, America, all over the place. Not another Yorkshire voice outside of me and the kitchen.'

Inside the hotel, things are different. My old desk is blocked from view by what Fiona called 'touch-screen kiosks', and I saw a man pressing his finger on one to bring up a map of the local pubs. The floral display in reception is larger and more elaborate, and the butlers' uniforms have changed. Instead of classic navy suits and white shirts, the butlers now dash around in pale lavender linen. They look a bit like they're working at an asylum, but that seems to be in keeping with the Americans. It wouldn't be classy of me to criticise too much. But The Lavender does not have the same five-star feel that Cavengreen had. There, I said it.

Fiona led me out into the gardens, where I had requested she set me up for the day. It is still one of my favourite places, despite everything that happened here. Fiona has prepared a table for me with an umbrella for shade. There is a jug of iced water with orange wedges floating in it, and she brought over a plate of tomatoes, mozzarella and basil that I have already eaten most of. The sun is shining, a breeze is blowing lightly through the trees, and I feel calm. A brand-new team of gardeners are busy snipping at stray twigs on the outside of the maze.

I must say, I was not entirely sure how I would feel coming back here for the first time. When I left, I was frazzled, exhausted and numb. But Fiona has made me feel welcome and relaxed. Regardless of the unfortunate goings on here, I have fifty years of happy memories from this place—I'd best not forget those.

The reason Helen thought it might be a good idea for me to write here, and I agree, is because I need to refocus. A big chunk of the story is now out of my head and into this dictaphone, and I have touched on pivotal moments like Alec's death and my experience of being a suspect. But things are about to get more intense. Coming back to Cavengreen today, my mind feels invigorated and ready to tell the next part of the story. Even just sitting here in the garden, I am starting to remember more about how I felt in certain moments.

You might be wondering why I chose this spot and not somewhere a more private. But for this next part of the story, the garden is key.

The garden smells like freshly cut grass and lavender. It didn't that evening, though, on night three. When I got back to the suite with Mr Potts, he sank onto the settee and sat with his head hung low. He told me that the police had decided to turn the Wi-Fi back on to placate the increasingly anxious and frustrated guests. The press had already caught wind of the situation so there was no use keeping it off any longer. A text message had come through from Mr Pott's wife. She was angry because he still wasn't home and she didn't understand what the hold-up was. That seemed fair. From the outside, it must have sounded very strange: a bunch of staff and guests kept under police guard in a hotel where not one but *two* people had been carried out in body bags. Mr Potts had missed his son's football match, apparently, and the lad had scored the winning goal. Not having kids of my own, I couldn't tell him I understood what it was like to miss those key moments in their childhood, but I did tell him that there would be plenty more to come and he would be present for those.

Mr Potts still hadn't noticed the laptop, which I had placed on the bed. He finally took himself off for a shower, with a little push from me.

I sat in a chair next to the bed and stared at the laptop warily. I had seen plenty of people use them around the hotel, but I had never used one myself. Edging closer, the first thing I did was lift the lid, if that is what it is called. The machine whirred and screeched and then a picture of a rocky landscape popped up. It seems safe to assume that it was somewhere in Scotland. A little box appeared asking for a password. That was an obstacle I hadn't anticipated. Was Alec hiding something?

If anything, the need for a password made me even more eager to see what was on the computer. I knew about the book, but what about other notes? Alec told me he often documented interactions with people or descriptions of events, just in case he wanted to use those moments in his work. He had written about me, so perhaps he had observed others around the hotel and written about them too. Clutching at straws, you might call it, but the laptop was the only straw I had in that moment. As soon as I heard the shower stop, I slammed the laptop shut and slid it under the bed. I wasn't quite ready to share my discovery with Mr Potts. I wanted more time to consider if withholding the laptop from the police was the right thing to do.

Around 3 am, I awoke to the sound of voices on the terrace outside our suite. I got up and peered between the curtains, and sure enough there were two people having an argument. Both of them were wearing Cavengreen robes and I had to squint a little to make out who it was in the darkness. Two women, that much was obvious from their hushed shouts. I recognised Olive's blonde curls first and then I identified her mother Sue, short in stature and yappy in voice. Olive kept having to shush her as her volume increased.

I glanced over at Mr Potts on the sofa—he was fast asleep—then carefully opened the terrace door a smidge, just enough to hear what the two women were saying.

'Nobody can know,' Olive said in a sort of shouted whisper.

'Just tell me the truth, Olive,' her mother replied. 'I can help you.' She clutched at her daughter's arms, only to be shrugged away.

'I didn't do it, Mother.'

'You know it doesn't look good, though, don't you?'

'Yes, Mother,' Olive hissed. 'I know exactly how it looks.'

'Let me help you, Olive,' Sue urged again.

'I don't *need* help. I told you: it wasn't me.'

That was all I caught of the conversation before they moved off into the garden. I watched them pace up and down the lawn, their abrupt hand gestures making it clear they were still arguing. So many possibilities rushed around my head, as I am sure they are doing for you right now. When I thought about suspects, I considered staff members, even Mr Potts or, at a stretch, perhaps more so before his death, the drunken Alec, but I'd never considered the bride. Then I remembered the noise complaints from the wedding night; they placed the bride in her suite at 11.30 pm and 2 am. But there were plenty more unaccounted for hours between then and me finding the body. What was the bride hiding? I had to know, and I imagine you lot are pretty keen to find out too.

In the morning, I told Mr Potts what I had seen and heard. I sprang the information on him almost as soon as he opened his eyes; the poor man was quite taken aback. I had been waiting since 3 am to tell him. He rubbed his face as he tried to process the information.

'Coffee,' was his response.

He poured a splash of brandy into the coffee I made him. I was not pleased. I needed Mr Potts to help me decipher the information and crack into the laptop that day; if he was drunk, he'd be useless. He was an adult, though, and my boss, so there was nothing I could say to stop him.

That first sip seemed to revive him, and he asked me to repeat everything I had just told him, but a little bit slower.

I started with the laptop. He didn't share my optimism that we would be able to guess the password of a man we barely knew. He also didn't share my shock that there was a password to begin with. I'd thought that was a sure sign Alec was hiding something, but Mr Potts told me that it was commonplace for people to protect their devices with a password for the purpose of keeping their contents private.

Then I told him about Olive and her mother. He agreed that the conversation sounded suspicious, but it didn't actually prove anything. Looking back, it was obvious he wasn't as keen as I was to find Bruno's murderer. He was too consumed by whatever demons he was fighting in his head. Not that he didn't provide some assistance, it was just that I could have done with a bit more help. Nevertheless, it was his idea to keep what we had discovered to ourselves for the time being. I agreed this was sensible. Going to Detective Raj with a few small pieces of a puzzle would only have angered him. He was already drowning in question marks, and in my opinion, he needed our help. Otherwise, who knows? We could still be stuck in that hotel today.

Mr Potts and I sat in front of the laptop for an hour typing potential passwords. *Alec.* Incorrect. *Scotland.* Incorrect. *Celtic.* Incorrect. *Rangers.* Incorrect. *Author.* Incorrect. *Password123.* Incorrect. We exhausted our options quickly. Not knowing much about a person makes it a million times harder to try to guess their password. Mine is always just my birthday. Although I might have to change it now that I have shared that with you. Mr Potts was getting frustrated by the *Incorrect Password* alert on the screen. He saw the whole exercise as pointless, reminding me that even if we did happen to get into the laptop, the chances of us finding something relevant were close to zero. But the only other option we had was to sit around waiting for the answers to come to us. Fat chance of me doing that, I can tell you that for free.

I don't believe it. Two guests from the hotel just came over and ambushed me with a barrage of questions about the murder. They said they recognised me from the newspaper and wondered what I was doing sitting in the garden talking to myself. I didn't tell them about the book. I don't care if they think I'm barmy; I can't risk American Dave finding out about my secret project.

One of the guests, a man, swung a bottle of red wine in one hand and sipped from a glass in the other. He asked me if I had been to the prison to visit the murderer. I told him no, not yet. The other guest, a woman whose teeth were stained red from the wine, asked if I was going to be in the American documentary. Surely word of American Dave's film couldn't have spread as far as Cavengreen's guests. Trying to sound casual, I asked how they knew about it.

'They're here now filming. We saw them in the lobby.'

Can't a man enjoy his tomatoes and dictaphone in peace? (That wasn't my first thought when I heard of the potential interruption, but it sounds mildly humorous for the book.)

As if on cue, American Dave appeared.

'Hector, my friend! Just the man we're looking for. Let's talk.' American Dave strode towards me across the lawn, his camera crew following behind and Fiona anxiously teetering over the grass as quickly as her heels would allow.

'I had no idea they'd be here today,' she said apologetically.

'Fiona here tells me you're writing a book. Well, fancy that.' American Dave chewed a piece of gum aggressively; seeing it swivel around his mouth made my stomach turn. Never have I ever chewed a piece of gum, and it is one of my pet peeves when people do so, especially when talking. Not that I would expect American Dave to have manners. He sticks out like a sore thumb in this part of the world.

'No,' Fiona began, 'what I said was, Hector has been approached by a publisher to write a book.' Fiona grimaced at me awkwardly, her eyes wide, I could tell she regretted letting the cat out of the bag. She mouthed, 'I'm sorry,' over American Dave's shoulder.

The camera was pointed right at me, so I reminded American Dave's posse that I did not give my permission to be filmed nor for any sort of fuzzy blur to be used to conceal my identity. They kept filming, I expect they wanted to frustrate me so much that I would launch myself at the camera. That would make great footage, wouldn't it? Instead, I started to pack up my belongings. I didn't even manage to get to the part of the story that I wanted to. But there is no use trying to go on with that fool dancing around me with his cameras and loud voice.

'And who gave you permission to sit out here? This area is for paying guests only,' American Dave said with a smirk and a cocky tilt of his hat.

'I invited him to sit out here,' Fiona said, her voice firm.

'Is that so?' American Dave took my napkin off the table and spat his gum in it. Then he put it back, right in my eyeline. 'With all due respect, Mr Harrow, you are not a paying guest and it is not Fiona's place to invite non-paying guests into private areas of the hotel. Please leave.'

Can you believe it? He kicked me out! That Yankee Doodle sod booted me out of Cavengreen. I'm recording this from my car. The bleedin' good-for-nothing is still watching me from the window of Lavender Plates. His cameraman is still filming. I CAN SEE YOU. This is just what they want. *Get the old man all riled up and see his reaction. That'll make great TV.* That swine. He had security escort me to the door. And the icing on the cake: he banned me! He stamped me with a lifelong ban from The Lavender.

He's still standing there. He's shooing me away. Alright, I'm going, I'm going. Squeeze the steering wheel one, two, three times. Sod. Go back to America, why don't you? Swine. I can't believe this is the last time I'll be driving down this driveway. My last time through these gates.

Let me look back at her one last time; a beauty of a building, she is.

Sorry about all that huffing and puffing. I forgot you lot were still there. Not that you're here, but you are there. The dictaphone is on the passenger seat, so I guess you're along for the ride back to my cottage.

You too, Helen.

I am lost for words, to be honest with you. Cavengreen means so much to me. That place rescued me from the darkness of my home life. It taught me that there was good in this world. I have seen more people go in and out of those doors than anyone else and I never thought for a second that one day I would be told that I can never go back. It is my hope that the Cavengreen family read this book and see what monster has taken over their once-beautiful hotel. What a shame. What a damn shame.

Let's end it there, Helen. Any mutterings you hear after this are for my ears alone. I'm driving so I can't turn the tape off. Oh, Cavengreen.

CHAPTER

19

Helen got a right earful when I got home yesterday. She ended up coming for tea. Pie and mash. I told her all about how American Dave banned me from the hotel. Helen has such a rational head on her shoulders, it took her no time at all to convince me that it was okay.

'It is not about the hotel,' she said, 'it is about the memories.' And do you know what? She is absolutely right. All of the good memories I have from my time at Cavengreen are stored in my brain, and all of the bad ones are in this book, to be banished from my mind as soon as the publisher clicks print.

Tap one. Tap two. Tap three.

It is a pity I will never get to take Helen to the hotel. I had planned to take her to Lavender Plates for afternoon tea as a thank you for helping me with the book, but I will have to think of some other fancy place now.

Helen had a listen to some of the audio I have recorded over the last few days. She thinks I should slow down, pad a little. That was an interesting thing to hear, because I feel like all I have done is waffle.

All the interruptions from American Dave and the like have thrown me for a loop, and I feel like I've done a lot of complaining about that and not an awful lot to push this story forward. There is still a lot to be told. It might turn out, when Helen writes all this up, that the murder happens in the first few pages and then you spend the rest of the book trying to decipher my gibberish. If that is the case, then you may as well flick through to the final chapter.

Helen might take that part out. I am sure professional authors don't tell their readers to skip to the end. Fingers crossed Helen salvages some content for the bits in between the murder and the finale.

Beans on toast is my favourite way to start a day. One can of beans, two pieces of toast cut into triangles—never rectangles—and enjoyed with a nice hot brew in my big, comfy armchair. Good old beans on toast picked a peck of pickled peppers.

Sorry, Helen. Just warming up the vocal cords. Feel free to cut that out if you wish.

This morning's newspaper arrived with a thud. I was just having a quick glance when I came across a write-up about you-know-who. COWBOYS AND MURDERERS is what they have gone with for the headline. There is a picture of American Dave, cowboy hat and all, with his arm around Paula McDavidson, who has also donned a Stetson for the shot. His teeth glow even in the grainy black-and-white photo, and Paula certainly looks like the cat that got the cream. The caption underneath reads: *Texan Dave Cleesey stands in front of his newly purchased hotel, The Lavender, with renowned journalist Paula McDavidson.*

Renowned?! Bloomin' renowned? The woman's never written a decent thing in her life. Back in the day she used to do the weekly horoscopes and now she's done one interview and suddenly she is *renowned*. Purely because of her nonsense articles, I learnt that I am a Leo. Paula always predicted I would be coming into a spot of bother soon. It only took ten years for her prediction to come true. Useless good-for-nothing. Maybe she should have read her own horoscope to see that she would become a terrible journalist who should find a new career path.

Right, Helen has just opened the gate. I'd best let her in.

For the sake of the dictaphone, Helen has arrived, and she has brought chocolate éclairs. Perfect timing, I have just brewed another pot. While we get stuck into these, I will tell you the next part of the story. Helen is listening in today. This is an important part, and she wants to make sure I don't miss any of the details.

So, where were we? Mr Potts and I were failing to break in to Alec's laptop. Olive and her mother were hiding something, but what? It was suspicious to say the least.

I put the laptop in the suite's safe, code 1608, the day and month of my birth. (Must remember to update my debit card's pin code soon.) We didn't know it at the time, but that would be our last full day at Cavengreen. Everybody would be going either home or to prison the following day.

We headed down to Lavender Plates just after seven, wondering if there would be anything left in the fridges for breakfast. The chefs were busy defrosting lamb stew, and Olive and Patrick had donated their wedding cake. Cake for breakfast. I suppose it was better than listening to my belly grumble all day. The kitchen's supply of eggs, bacon, and sausage were long gone. The head chef complained that if he had known how long this lockdown was going to last then he would have rationed the food.

The sound of Fiona's heels clip-clopping on the parquetry announced her arrival before we could even see her. She looked like regular Fiona again. She was no longer in a bathrobe and slippers. Her uniform was fresh and pressed, her hair in a slicked-back bun, and her face had a nice glow. She smoothed her skirt with her hands, and then greeted those assembled in the dining room with a 'Good morning' and a smile. She told me she had found a fresh uniform in the laundry room, and she had done what she could with the hotel's amenities and dribs and drabs of make-up that she found at the bottom of her handbag. Fiona was optimistic that we would be let out that day, and if there happened to be media outside the gates, then she wanted to look professional.

I hadn't even considered that there might be media waiting. Cavengreen has such a long driveway, it is impossible to see anything beyond the grounds. Mr Potts had an idea. The hotel is just two storeys high, but above the suites on the first floor is an attic space used for storing Christmas decorations and antiques. The attic is the only place in the hotel high enough to see beyond the gates.

The on-duty police had grown restless and spent a lot of the day outside the front of the hotel kicking gravel, smoking and making jokes. It made roaming around the building much easier. Fiona was reluctant to come at first, but when the twins waltzed into Lavender Plates wearing matching pink tracksuits, she changed her mind and followed myself and Mr Potts, bringing along a piece of wedding cake wrapped in a paper napkin.

The attic was accessible by a narrow staircase tucked away behind a door marked *Staff Only*. I had been up there many a time. Back when I was doing odd jobs at the hotel, I would often be asked to fetch and carry things from storage. It is full of old paintings, sculptures, mirrors, and the like, most covered in white sheets. Many of the items up there are worth a fortune. The ceiling is high enough in the middle that you can stand up, but you have to crouch down as you get closer to the sloping edges. There is a huge arched window at one end of the room where light floods in, revealing tiny dust motes that hover like glitter.

The attic is actually the place where I had my first kiss. Her name was Penny Duckford and she was a maid at the hotel. We were both sixteen—or she might have been seventeen. Well, we were around the same age. Penny had lovely long red hair and cherry-coloured lips. When she spoke, her nose scrunched up, and when she felt shy, she couldn't look me in the eye. There was something special about her.

We were up in the attic one day looking for the Christmas chinaware. It was freezing up there, so cold we could see our own breath. We were pretending to be dragons breathing fire when I puffed out a gust of foggy breath and, on my inhale, she kissed me. Her eyes were closed; it was romantic. It only lasted a couple of seconds. When she pulled away, I was hoping to ask her on a date, but she ran off downstairs before I could. It was a hard knock for a young lad. Worse still, Penny avoided catching my eye after that and we never spoke again. I tried, but she always walked away. Maybe it was me, maybe it wasn't. The moment was nice, nonetheless.

Fiona sucked in her stomach and carefully slid between the dusty boxes, not wanting to soil her fresh uniform. Mr Potts reached the window first and gasped. When I caught up to him, I could see why. Outside the gates at the bottom of the driveway was a crowd of thirty or so people and about half-a-dozen parked cars. We squinted, but it was hard to make out much detail.

Fortunately, I had a solution. Next to me there was a tall object with a sheet over it. If my memory served me correctly . . .

I pulled the sheet off to reveal a telescope that had been at the hotel since before my time. It was old and dusty, but by 'eck, it still worked, and that was all that mattered. We took it in turns to survey the scene.

When it was my go—after Fiona and Mr Potts had each had a good gander—I saw that the media had arrived in force. There were people with cameras around their necks and video equipment set up on large tripods. Some of the journalists sat slumped in those fold-up camping chairs. They must have been there a while.

Then I spotted a man holding up a white sign with a telephone number on it. The others had seen it too. We debated for a minute whether or not we should call. And then we did.

Mr Potts took his mobile telephone from his pocket and dialled, and I watched through the telescope as the man with the sign put his arms down and scrambled for the phone in his pocket.

'Hello?' he said when he answered.

'We saw your number on the sign,' Mr Potts told him. 'We're in the hotel.'

Mr Potts and the journalist discussed what the media knew already about what was going on inside the hotel. They knew someone had been murdered and that another man had died from a suspected heart attack. That was the first we were hearing of Alec's potential cause of death. Thankfully—although that seems an odd choice of word—we were back to having just one murder to solve. The media knew the murder victim was a man. They knew that the killer had not yet been identified. And they knew that all the guests and staff who were present in the hotel at the time of the murder had volunteered to remain locked down until the culprit was found.

'Volunteered?' Mr Potts said, frowning.

The man on the phone—Mick I think his name was—confirmed that the police had released a statement saying that while those in the hotel were permitted to leave at any time, we had chosen to stay. We were flabbergasted to hear this. Three nights we had spent in the hotel by that point, one of which I spent on the floor of the library, one in the gardening shed and the other . . . well, the other was in a lovely suite with Mr Potts.

Mr Potts told the man on the telephone in no uncertain terms that the guests and staff had *not* been given the option to leave and were being held against their will. I watched through the telescope as the man on the other end of the phone moved away from the crowd and into the privacy of his parked car. He offered us money to stay and leak information to him. It would be easy to do with the Wi-Fi back up and running. He wanted videos of the detective, recordings of conversations and pictures of the crime scene. Even hearing the offer made me feel filthy. Not in this lifetime would I ever be someone's rat. But there were three of us, and he only needed one person to agree. Fiona pondered the deal for a minute or two. She needed the money, I knew, especially since her husband's death. I told her I wouldn't judge her if she agreed to the deal, but she might judge herself. Her answer was no. Sweat dripped from Mr Potts's forehead as he grappled with the decision. To be a rat or not to be a rat. He squinted into the sun for several seconds, then he sternly told the man no, that as hotel manager it would be utterly disgraceful for him to act in such a way.

'A hypocrisy,' he said. Then he hung up the phone.

We spent some time up in the attic, sitting on upturned buckets by the window. Fiona ate her cake, offering to share it out of politeness, even though I knew she wanted it all for herself. There were a lot of long sighs. I could tell Fiona was thinking about how the money might have changed her circumstances, but I know her: her soul is too pure to do such a thing. Mr Potts was tapping away on his phone, as usual.

His wife wanted regular updates. I had seen over his shoulder some of the long messages she had sent him.

It was a moment of peace. Some of the old boxes up in that roof must have been there since I'd first come to Cavengreen as boy. I had a rummage, looking for any old bits of uniform or lost property I could change into. Everything smelt musty, but I found a box with one of the old butler uniforms inside. It was a style from maybe a decade ago, when the hotel trialled an olive-green hue. It wasn't a popular colour with the staff, but I didn't mind it. I pulled out a blazer and pair of trousers in my size and thought they would do quite nicely. It might not have been the correct uniform, but by that point the rules were out the window. I mean, some of the staff were still wandering around in Cavengreen robes like they were at a day spa.

We left the loft after an hour or so. The day had only just begun, but the weight of the circumstances were dragging us down already. Fiona peered out from the door at the bottom of the stairs and ushered us out when the coast was clear. She had been staying in suite fifteen, right next to the stairs on the first floor, and she wanted to duck in to grab her telephone. We followed her, and Mr Potts immediately went to the minibar. Behind his back, Fiona rolled her eyes.

Everything in Fiona's suite was neatly folded and organised in logical spots. It was a much calmer place to be than the room I was sharing with Mr Potts, which was littered with empty beer bottles and used towels. The view of the garden from the upper level is nice too. (The gardeners make sure that the maze hedges are high enough that those staying on the first floor of the hotel can't see any of the pathways.) A flock of birds flew in murmuration up above; it was a beautiful sight, the way they created waves in the sky. It was one of those rare events that I wished everyone in the world was able to see at that moment, but while Fiona and I were fixated on the sky, Mr Potts alerted us to some goings-on back on the ground.

American Dave and his mistress were standing at the entrance to the maze, and we had a clear view of him kissing his lover's neck, mouth and chest before, giggling, they slipped between the hedges.

'Our new boss, everybody.' Fiona stuck out her tongue in disgust.

God knows what they intended to do in there. Seems a bit prickly, if you ask me.

Fiona distracted us with a rant about how inappropriate American Dave's conduct was. But whatever it was that the pair of them went into the maze to do, I am sure they had barely got started before American Dave's lover ran from the greenery, screaming. American Dave followed, waving his hands and shouting, 'Help!'

Squads of trained police officers had searched the whole grounds of the hotel over and over by this point. So how was it that, all of a sudden, the murder weapon happened to appear in the centre of the maze?

CHAPTER

20

The maze at Cavengreen has been a feature since the 1970s. A gardener from Spain was flown in to transform the grounds. Her name was Elena, and you might be shocked to hear that, during her time at the hotel, we had a bit of a dalliance.

Helen has just choked on her éclair. Is it so surprising that I might have had a few love affairs in my day? I have been single for seventy-three years, so believe you me, I have got some stories. Helen is blushing; I don't think she has ever thought of me like that. But back in the day, I was quite the looker, and on occasion I would find myself temporarily involved with a member of the opposite sex. Never a guest. I want to make that clear. Not that some didn't try, but I would never have done anything that put my job at risk. That is not to say that when a guest stopped being a guest there were not interactions. But definitely nothing untoward happened in the hotel.

Elena was a beautiful woman from a small town called Cudillero. I believe it is quite the tourist trap now. She had long brown, almost copper hair and her skin was golden. Around here, she stood out. Elena had a gap between her two front teeth, which made her smile all the more alluring. I was drawn to her love of plants and gardening; she knew so much and was happy to share her knowledge with me. She was the one who suggested creating a hedge maze, and I helped her plan the route. I could find my way to the middle with a blindfold on. One day, when we were sketching some potential layouts, our hands touched and then I kissed her. That was the start of something special that ended as soon as she went back to Spain. Postcards were sent back and forth for the next few months, but they gradually were few and far between. Her final message told me she had met someone.

Helen looks sad for me, but it's okay, these things happen. There have been many times in my life where potential love has slipped away. I know Helen understands that, having recently ended a relationship herself. She's looking away.

I didn't mean to upset you, Helen.

She insists I haven't, but I know she is only being polite.

That story sent Helen into a bit of a tailspin. She scrolled through the contacts on her telephone, offering to set me up with this woman or that woman. Set-ups aren't for me. If love is supposed to come my way, it will come. But for now, I have chocolate éclairs, my puzzles, my mystery books, and great conversations with my dear friend. What more could a man want?

Back to the hotel. There was pandemonium after the murder weapon was found. American Dave alerted Detective Raj to his discovery and within ten minutes the entire maze was wrapped up in yellow police tape like a Christmas present. Myself, Fiona and

Mr Potts went downstairs and lingered on the patio, trying to pick up pieces of information from the conversations that rushed by. American Dave did his best to shoehorn himself back into the action; the police had thanked him for alerting them to his discovery but said he was no longer needed. Even after he was dismissed, Detective Raj had to repeatedly tell him to move back so his team could do their job. He ended up being ordered to stand with us and not stir from that spot. His ego took a bit of a bruising, and for a few moments there he was the quietest I had ever seen him.

When he eventually piped up, American Dave told us that in the centre of the maze he had found a steak knife covered in dry blood, one of the new concierge iPads and a pair of women's boots. Everything was bundled up in a Cavengreen bath towel. He described how he'd scrambled to get out of the maze after his discovery, only to get lost in dead end after dead end. I knew exactly where he would have gone wrong. He would have exited the centre of the maze on the opposite side from where he came in. We designed it so that the middle of the maze was perfectly symmetrical, meaning that if you lost your bearings, there would be a chance that you wouldn't know which way was which. Part of me felt smug for having helped design a maze that American Dave had struggled to escape, but I didn't let on.

Helen just told me it is unlikely we will be able to insert a photograph of what was found in the middle of the maze. Apparently, that will increase the book's printing cost too much and requesting permission to use the image from the police could take months. I haven't seen the photograph yet. It is probably being kept in evidence until the trial.

Tap one. Tap two. Tap three.

The good thing about American Dave loving the sound of his own voice so much is that he did an excellent job of describing exactly what he found in the maze. We asked him how he knew they were women's boots and he said it was fairly obvious from their small size. That changed everything for us. I guess we had all assumed that Bruno's murderer was a man, especially since they'd had to drag his ninety-kilo body along the ground. Not that women aren't strong, but—oh, you know what I mean. It just never crossed my mind that the killer might be female.

The police erected a white tent over the centre of the maze, as the evidence couldn't be moved until it had been properly photographed and examined. Prints were taken of the bottoms of American Dave's shoes to rule him out. His mistress, Tanya, was also invited to provide shoe and fingerprints; her hefty size nines quickly cleared her of suspicion.

Then it became a game of Cinderella. Everyone, men and women, were told to meet at reception, where they would have to remove one shoe and prove their shoe size for the police. It was chaos, having everyone in the lobby at once. People leant on the furniture, leaving grubby marks on the wood. Mr Potts helped me empty the dead flowers into bin bags. I had never seen the entrance table look so bare. A queue of guests and staff were ranged around the room. Detective Raj sat in an armchair and invited each person to step forward one by one and have their shoe size recorded. If they passed the test, they were free to return to their room. If further questioning was needed, they would be escorted into the library.

As it turned out, the blood-covered boots were a women's size five. Helen tells me that is quite small, with a size six being considered the average for women in the UK. As you can imagine, all the men were ruled out. Even if they curled their toes, there was no way any of the males could squeeze their feet into the boots.

The first woman to be pulled to the side was one of the receptionists, Shamila. And by God, she looked like she was going to pass out from fear.

Fiona rushed straight over to stand by her side, but two police officers extended their hands to keep her at a distance. I saw Shamila gulp and look plaintively at Fiona, who mouthed, 'It will be okay,' then gave her a reassuring smile. Shamila was led into the library. I can imagine her sense of relief when more suspects joined her, including one of the other reception girls, Chloe, as well as the bride, the bride's mother and the twins. Mr Potts looked at me with raised eyebrows when the bride was taken away. She was fast becoming our prime suspect, but we needed more evidence before we could share our suspicions with the police.

The girls were in the library for an hour. During that time, Mr Potts went to our suite for 'a lie-down', which I think was code for a top-up, leaving me and Fiona to wait anxiously behind the reception desk. We ducked down whenever one of the police officers walked by, not wanting to be ordered back to our rooms. Fiona printed off the reception roster, which proved that neither of the girls was working the day before the murder and both had just started their shifts when I found Bruno's body.

Fiona knocked on the library door, but a voice within shouted, 'Go away!' We both recognised the voice as belonging to Detective Raj. Fiona slid the roster underneath the door.

Behind the reception desk, Fiona nervously wrapped an elastic band around her finger, only stopping when the tip turned a hue of reddish-purple, and then beginning the process again on another digit.

I've always thought Fiona would make a great mother; she is fiercely protective of the people she cares about. Sadly, it wasn't to be. I will get her permission before we put this next bit in the book, so if it makes it into the final copy that means she said it is okay.

I have known Fiona a while, so I was there when she was working through her infertility struggles with her husband. They tried for years to conceive, with no success. We would take tea breaks together and she would cry. The days when a pregnant woman would check in or one of the female staff would announce they were expecting were the worst. Then, when IVF first came about, Fiona and her husband saved every penny they could to have a go. She was working double shifts and I know her husband had two or three jobs at the time. They had their go, it worked . . . and then it just went away. Fiona took a month off work after that, and when she came back she was a much harder, more rigid version of herself. That sort of pain can change someone forever. They didn't do another cycle.

Sixteen minutes after Fiona slipped the roster under the library door, her two receptionists were released. Fiona greeted them with comforting embraces. She told the police that she had the telephone number of a journalist, and if they didn't let the girls go home, she would contact the media and expose exactly what was going on inside Cavengreen. In the end, Detective Raj reluctantly agreed to let the girls leave, but their departure was a strictly confidential exchange to placate an irate Fiona. They left at noon, just before everyone would start causing a fuss about wanting lunch. It all happened very fast. The girls were bundled into the back of a police car and asked to duck down as they passed through the gates, so as not to be seen. From the entrance of the hotel, we could hear the distant eruption of the media shouting as the police car sped by.

You might be wondering why we didn't try and leave too. I guess it is like how a captain will never leave his sinking ship, not until all the passengers and crew have disembarked. Plus, Detective Raj made it clear that wasn't an option for us.

Detective Raj, after seeing off the two receptionists, snapped at Fiona and me to return to our suites and refrain from meddling. His tone was hostile bordering on vicious. That man had not only reached the end of his tether but had gone way beyond it. His determination to solve this case had made him even more impatient, and when he returned to the library, we could hear him shouting at the remaining suspects.

'If you're not guilty then you should have nothing to be afraid of!' he yelled.

Those twins can give as good as they get. They shouted back just as loudly, telling the detective that they came from a very rich and powerful family, that their lawyer was on his way and that they would sue both the police force and him personally. It was nice to hear someone fight back, even if it was the loathsome twins. They burst out of the library shortly after that, demanding lunch and insisting that housekeeping be sent up to their suite *immediately*.

The bride, too, was released from the library, though she looked anxious and tired. I wondered if I should tell Detective Raj about the conversation I had witnessed between Olive and her mother. I told Fiona what I knew but she advised me to hold on to that information a little longer. And so I did.

That was going to be it for today's chapter, but I have a small update to give you. Helen is in the kitchen cooking bangers and mash for us. We are going to have a late night, reviewing some of the pages she has already transcribed. She has a few questions for me on what I meant here and there. While I was waiting for her, I turned on the 6 pm news. That is not something I always do. Quite often I like to read a book or do my puzzles of an evening, but I saw no point starting a crossword only for Helen to interrupt me. So, the news it was. After a story about the royals and rising petrol prices, the anchor announced something that might be of interest to include in the book. I recorded what she said for Helen to insert here.

The Yorkshire Dales will soon feature in a new documentary set for a global release across multiple streaming platforms. The Lavender Hotel, formally known as Cavengreen Hotel, will take centre stage in the documentary, which will include exclusive interviews with some of the staff and guests who were inside the hotel at the time of the murder of Bruno Tatterson earlier this year. The documentary will be hosted by Dave Cleesey, General Manager of the Sapphires Group, which acquired the hotel shortly before the murder took place. Local journalist Paula McDavidson will also appear, as will the hotel's former concierge, Hector Harrow. [Name omitted by editor] confessed to the crime four days after the murder, and it was announced today that they will face trial on the fourth of next month.

This is just getting ridiculous. The Americans know full well I am *not* featuring in their documentary. There is no convincing me. What I really want to focus on is that trial date, which is less than three weeks away. I'll need to get a move on with this book. I want to get most of it onto the tape before the trial starts, because I am not going to have much time to record once it's all go, go, go. It is my intention to head to the courtroom every day, even the days when I'm not standing as a witness. Have I told you about that yet? Well, yes, I'll be giving evidence at some point, unsurprisingly. The courthouse sent me a very official looking letter telling me I was required by law to appear as a prosecution witness—date to be confirmed. Although that is now confirmed by the news report. I am not looking forward to seeing some of the other witnesses take the stand, but I need to see Bruno's killer punished for what they did—to him, to me, and to everyone else involved.

Helen has just come in with the bangers and mash, so I will sign off for the evening. There is a lit candle in the middle of my mashed potato.

That is something new. I have also just noticed a gift tucked under Helen's arm and a cheeky grin on her face. I am not normally one for birthdays, and seventy-four certainly isn't a milestone, but it is nice that she remembered. It is tomorrow, mind you, and I intend to spend the day like I do every year: alone, thinking about my father.

Tap one. Tap two. Tap three.

CHAPTER

21

Helen bought me a book for my birthday. She knows I am not much of a reader of anything other than murder mysteries, and she didn't want to risk getting me something I have already read, so this one is mostly pictures, or photographs to be exact. It is called *Around Australia* and is a collection of lovely snaps from various photographers. The gift someone chooses to give says a lot about them and even more about what they think of you. Although I am not entirely sure why Helen got this for me, I appreciate it nonetheless. The acknowledgements section thanks her for being the *Commissioning Editor*, so she must have had something to do with it. But I don't believe I have ever mentioned wanting to go to Australia; in fact, I think Helen is aware that, as far as flying goes, I prefer to stay within a two-hour radius of the UK, no further. That rules out such places as Australia, which I have heard is a twenty-four-hour journey. How people avoid a blood clot on those long-haul flights is beyond me. And I am sure the price of the fare is through the roof. And that is just for economy. Anything else would be too flash for me, even if I could afford it.

Some of the places in the book look very nice, but it's not my sort of landscape. I prefer rolling hills and big lakes, and Australia is very beachy with big patches of dusty red in between. Tasmania looks more my thing, but I wouldn't go that far to see a place that looks quite like the Lake District. Come to think of it, I remember Helen visiting Australia a few years back, not long after Josie's funeral. It's hard to keep up with all the places she's been. The stamps on her passport would be inked in like sardines. She used to go for work trips all the time, finding new authors and this and that. Always went alone, as far as I know. I daren't ask if she went with her ex-partner. Not after the other night. It wasn't on tape, but I probed her on her relationship—a touchy subject, I know—and she got very snappy with me when I asked if she still kept in touch with him, shouting, 'Absolutely not!'

Sorry, Helen, but you practically bit my head off. I'm not one to take offence, though, so don't worry about me. He must have been rotten to you. I won't ask you any more about him; I don't need to be told twice. Perhaps you gave me the book because you're thinking about going back to Australia and you're subtly trying to convince me that I want to go too, so that I'll visit you.

Helen is always saying she would love to go and live overseas soon.

Don't be going that far, Helen! Even if I make a bob or two from the book, you won't catch me flying twenty-four hours to Australia. Anywhere a bit closer to home and I'll be there to visit you at the drop of a hat.

You might recall me saying yesterday that I always spend my birthdays alone, thinking about my father.

Tap one. Tap two. Tap three.

I can't help that. He ruined birthdays for me. It's all bad memories and intrusive thoughts. The first time he gave me a hiding was on my birthday, like turning eight suddenly made it acceptable. Don't think he always marked my annual milestone like that, as if it was some kind of ritual, because he didn't. But he did make every birthday miserable. He didn't believe in presents. My mother used to hide little gifts wrapped in tinfoil or baking paper behind the bedhead. When my father nipped out to get the paper or more alcohol, we would sit on her bed with my sister and unwrap them. Those are some of my happier memories. It would just be silly stuff, like a wrapped-up onion or chalk, but she loved seeing the look on my face when I got to experience something normal. As soon as my father got home, we would scramble to hide everything and get out of his and my mother's bedroom.

My father made a special effort not to speak to me on my birthday, maybe because it reminded him that he never wanted to be a father. He was much the same with my sister, except that, as far as I know, he didn't lay a hand on her. Josie surely would have told me if he did, and when I asked her again on her deathbed, she still said he never had.

I haven't told you much about Josie, have I? I loved her so much. She was much better at school than I was and used to take part in every extracurricular activity she could. Mainly because she didn't want to come home, I suspect. When our mother died, she took over all the household duties, but when she turned sixteen she moved out with her boyfriend. Freedom at last. Just like her mother, she ended up marrying a not-very-nice man, only Josie divorced him in the end. Two kids; we speak occasionally but I guess they're busy. I understand that. And then Josie died of breast cancer. It happened so fast. I was there when she slipped away. Helen planned the funeral; I think I mentioned that.

Even though Helen was living down south, she came up every weekend to visit my sister in hospital. Helen understands the pain I feel. That is a bond we will always share.

So, happy birthday to me. Later today I will go by Josie's grave with some purple tulips. When I purchased Josie's plot of land, I knew she would want to be next to our mother. It is just unfortunate that our mother is next to our father. At the same time as purchasing Josie's plot, I organised one for myself next to hers. Her two children spent far too long considering if they want to reserve a spot too, so I just went ahead and locked mine in. One less thing to worry about. I may not be close to many people right now, but I know I will rest with my beloved mother and sister forever.

By gum, I didn't intend for the book to take such a depressing turn, but this is just how I get on my birthday. I keep reminding myself that this birthday is different. I am writing, or narrating, a book. Fancy that. It wasn't exactly a birthday wish of mine to be involved in a murder investigation and then write a book about it, but the unexpected twist in my life has brought with it something different to break up the monotony. Not that I want to be disrespectful. I would much rather Bruno was alive than have my name on the cover of a book. On that note, let's get back the story.

Fiona and I went to Lavender Plates to ask the chefs what they could offer the guests for lunch. It turned out Fred and Ellie had brought in some bread rolls and enough ingredients to make a huge pot of pasta. Fred said the other police officers weren't best pleased with them for helping us out. For some reason, the police were acting like we were the enemy and needed to be punished. It was nice having Fred and Ellie around to dilute their us-versus-them mentality.

Fiona donned a hairnet and apron and was straight in the kitchen asking how she could help. It was her job to divvy up the portions. Fred took me to one side and asked if I had heard anything that I wanted to report. Lying to him felt terrible, but I wasn't ready to bring the police in just yet. Fred told me that Detective Raj had been ordered to let everyone go home tomorrow, regardless of whether the case was solved or not. Apparently, the police had been inundated with legal letters from the guests' lawyers. Why they weren't letting us go then and there is beyond me, but I suppose finding the murder weapon that morning had bought the detective a few more hours. No wonder Detective Raj was so frantic.

Fiona pushed the trolley from room to room and I handed food to the guests. We were both enjoying being back in service. During our rounds, Fiona told me that she missed her husband; that she felt lonely not having him to telephone during all this. She just wanted to hear him say that everything would be okay and there would be a nice roast dinner waiting for her when she got home. That is a familiar feeling: not having someone to share things with, whether happy or sad. I told her that she always had me, but I knew it wasn't the same.

The groomsmen didn't want their pasta. One didn't eat carbs and the other was gluten-free. A huge waft of stale air escaped when they opened the door to their suite. From what I could tell, they had spent the last three nights draining their minibar and watching movies on the loudest volume. One of them was doing sit-ups on the floor. The other closed the door in our faces with a rude grunt.

'More for us,' Fiona said with a smile.

We took the lift upstairs and started at the far end of the corridor: the bridal suite. I raised my hand to knock on the door, but Fiona quickly ushered me aside. She put her finger to her lips and then we each pressed an ear against the door. I am not normally one for snooping, but Olive was someone to whom we had to pay special attention. She and her husband were arguing.

'What the fuck, Olive?' Patrick shouted at his bride. 'You've made things so much worse. We could have just explained what happened and it would have been fine. Now you look guilty!'

'Keep your voice down!' Olive yelled back. 'I panicked. I had to get rid of it. You know I had to do it—for Mum.'

'I need to speak to her,' Patrick said.

The suite's door swung open abruptly and me and Fiona smiled like we had heard nothing.

'Pasta?' Fiona offered.

'Just leave it on the side.' Patrick gestured for us to enter. 'Actually, let me take it.' He snatched the bowls from our hands, a blob of bolognaise sauce almost spilling over the rim.

I caught a glimpse of Olive. She had black make-up smeared down her cheeks, and her eyes were red. As soon as she saw me looking, she walked away into the bedroom. Their suite was unusually tidy, I noticed—like housekeeping had been, except the hotel was not offering this service at the time.

Patrick stormed off down the corridor, presumably to speak to his new mother-in-law. We desperately wanted to follow but couldn't risk being caught nosying. Patrick was angry, that much was obvious. My mind immediately went to the murder weapon. Could that be what he and Olive were talking about?

We finished delivering the food and Fiona went to her room for a rest. I returned to my own suite to find Mr Potts in the bathtub, bubbles and all. He was slurping wine from an overfilled glass and seemed to be in an uncharacteristically good mood. He told me that his wife had convinced him to change his outlook and that he had decided to embrace the experience. It was quite the shift in attitude.

Clearly the change in mood meant instead of seeking solace in alcohol, he was now celebrating with it. I filled him in on everything that had happened since the morning, which felt like a lot. I told him how the two receptionists had been sent home and suggested that, if he pushed hard enough, then I was sure he would be allowed to leave too.

'I think I will wait this thing out,' he said. 'No point leaving before the finale.'

It was an odd thing to say, that much was obvious. But I am not one to judge, because I stayed too. Only, I did it because of my dedication to Cavengreen. I knew I was on to something with Olive. My gut told me to stay. Plus, I had no one to go home to. Everyone I cared about was in that hotel.

Except you, Helen, of course.

Meanwhile, Mr Potts had been drowning his sorrows the whole time and calling his wife. So, yes, it immediately struck me as strange that he wanted to stay. Stronger alarm bells should have been ringing about what he could have been planning, but I was too distracted.

I told Mr Potts what we'd overheard outside Olive's room. Rightly so, he said they could have been talking about anything. But when this exchange was set alongside the conversation in the garden, it was as clear as day to me that both Olive and her mother were involved in the case somehow. It was time to tell Detective Raj what I knew.

CHAPTER

22

Mr Potts and I waited in the lobby for Fred to fetch Detective Raj. He appeared from the hallway eating a sandwich. A smudge of mayonnaise sat on his upper lip. It was distracting, but we weren't on good enough terms for me to embarrass him by pointing it out, so I spent the whole conversation trying not to look at it.

'Just the fellas I wanted to see. Where's the third musketeer?' Detective Raj laughed. We ignored his question and his snigger trailed off into a sigh. 'Come to my office.'

We followed him to Mr Potts's office. I have entered it many times before, but on this day it felt unfamiliar. Mr Potts's office was not really Mr Potts's office anymore and, as it happened, it never would be again. Pinned to the wall was a large sheet of paper covered in all sorts of scribbles with various names, including my own, crossed out. Seeing that was a big relief. A few names were circled: Mr Potts, the twins, American Dave, the groomsmen, and Fiona among them.

Detective Raj made us sit with our backs to the wall so we couldn't study the list for too long. He offered us tea and sandwiches from a platter that had obviously been delivered by an outside catering company. We both accepted and thanked him. Then Detective Raj paced up and down behind the desk without speaking while Mr Potts and I exchanged confused glances.

'Here you go, boss.' Tyrone the pit bull entered the room and handed Detective Raj a newspaper. He left, flashing his sharp-toothed grin on the way out. Detective Raj studied the paper for a couple of seconds and then took a long inhale.

'What do you call this?' he asked, slamming the newspaper down on the desk. It was a copy of the *Yorkshire Sun*. The headline read HOTEL OF HORRORS.

'Read this bit out loud,' Detective Raj said sternly.

I put my sandwich down and leant forward to see the paper more clearly as Mr Potts began to read.

'*Cavengreen guests and staff kept prisoner until cold-blooded murderer found,*' the article began.

I was glad Mr Potts had taken it upon himself to do the reading, as I knew I would be unable to do so without stuttering.

'And what's that?' Detective Raj indicated a different part of the page.

It was a photograph of me, Fiona and Mr Potts in the window of the attic. Neither of us answered Detective Raj's question.

'Tell me what you were doing up there,' the detective said. 'And how did you access it?'

'We went up there to get some respite,' Mr Potts informed him. 'And the staircase is behind a door on the first floor marked *Staff Only*. It's hardly hidden. I'm surprised you've not been up there yourselves. No wonder you've got nowhere in this investigation.'

I remember gulping nervously, then reminding myself that there was nothing to be nervous about. The big red line through my name proved that.

Detective Raj summoned Tyrone back into the room. The two of them huddled in the corner, whispering. I could feel anger building up inside me at the police's incompetence, which was stopping everyone from getting to go home. By the time Detective Raj had sent Tyrone off to find the not-so-secret staircase, my cheeks were hot with rage, which in my childhood had signalled I was about to stammer. Except at that moment, the words came easily.

'When will this bleedin' nightmare be over?!' I shouted. My breathing was loud, my chest rising and falling. My top teeth sank into my bottom lip, just as my father's used to do.

Tap one. Tap two. Tap three.

'Calm yourself, Mr Harrow.' Detective Raj leant forward, gripping the edge of the desk with both hands and looming over me, trying to establish his dominance. But instead of finding him threatening and powerful, I saw him as weak and scared. The man in front of me was crumbling, unable to do his job properly and losing control. My temper might have got the better of me, but Detective Raj was in a much worse fix.

'Why should I?' I spat back at him. 'This whole investigation has been a joke since day one. Someone died here, Detective! And you have the murderer at your fingertips but not the competence to find them. How about the bride? How closely have you looked into her?'

'The bride was with her husband the whole time.' Detective Raj folded his arms and turned to look out the window so I couldn't see his face.

'Says who? She and her husband? Because all we know is that they were together at half past eleven and again at two am. And, oh yes, that she and her mother have been having some intense three am conversations in the gardens. But that's what all innocent people do, isn't it, Detective?'

'You're just mentioning this now?' Detective Raj rubbed his temples in frustration. I had planned to tell him more about what I had overheard, but after he made me so angry I didn't feel like helping his cause. 'But Olive's husband places her in bed, asleep, at the time we suspect the murder took place.'

'A husband will lie to protect his wife, Detective.'

Detective Raj turned to me with a pensive look on his face. He called for Fred and ordered him to fetch Olive and Patrick and escort them to Lavender Plates. It was time to get forensics to take a closer look at their suite.

By 2 pm, the hotel bridal suite was completely taped off. The other guests peered out from their doors, gossiping about what could be going on. Olive and Patrick were silent and solemn as they followed Fred down the corridor, like they were walking to their own execution. The bride reached for her husband's hand, but he pulled away. Everybody saw it. Patrick's groomsmen walked on either side of their friend, leaving Olive to continue down the hallway alone. Her mother cried as she watched them descend the stairs into the lobby. To all of us, this felt final. It felt like the police might be on to something. And as you know from my storytelling, there is only one more night in the hotel left to go until someone confesses.

Unfortunately, I was not privy to what happened when forensics swept the bridal suite. Nor could I tell you what sort of conversations were had in Lavender Plates while the married couple and groomsmen waited there. I imagine that there was a lot of tension and probably not a lot of truth-telling. Myself, Fiona and Mr Potts lingered in the lobby, watching a steady flow of police and forensics officers march up and down the stairs like worker ants. Fred was acting coy with me. He didn't pass on any information, either because he didn't know anything, or because what he did know was too grim to share. I tried to gauge which it was from his face, but his expression gave nothing away.

Sensing that our time in the hotel might be coming to an end, Fiona, Mr Potts, and I started tidying up the lobby. We needed something to keep us busy. There was rubbish everywhere and both the reception and concierge desks needed a good wipe down. We got bin bags out of the cupboard and Mr Potts filled them up while

I polished. Fiona logged in to her computer to start issuing refunds to the guests. It felt good to wipe away some of the chaos, and I could tell Fiona was feeling a little more relaxed too as she worked her way through some of her admin tasks.

I took the vase from the centre table to Hugo's to give it a rinse in the sink. The lights were dimmed, as always, and it wasn't until I'd finished rinsing the vase and turned around that I noticed the shadowy outline of a cowboy hat in the back corner of the bar. His head was tilted down and he slowly rotated a whisky glass in his hand. The door was just a couple of metres away, but he uttered a soft 'howdy' before I could make it out into the corridor. A conversation with American Dave was not something I was in the mood for, so I found myself politely saying a 'howdy' back and then taking a few more steps towards the door.

'You know,' American Dave began, his voice still low, 'I kind of hoped you were the murderer. It would have made you more exciting.'

'Sorry to disappoint,' I told him, although I really should not have bothered engaging with such a fool.

'But now, I bet you're going to come out of this looking like the hero. And who am I to you? The big bad American villain who cheats on his wife and doesn't care.' He drained the last few drops of whisky from his glass.

I didn't know how to respond. I was no hero, and he was no villain. I was just a man who tried to do good things, and he was a man who didn't care if he did bad things.

'My wife is going to hear about this somehow, isn't she?'

'Secrets never stay secret for long,' I told him.

He sucked at his top teeth. 'You know, Hector, I'm not really a cowboy,' American Dave said. I thought this might be the start of a monologue about why I should feel sorry for him. Turns out, it wasn't.

He rose to his feet and took a few steps towards me. 'I am a cow*man*. And you'd better stay out of my fucking way.'

He pushed me lightly in the centre of my chest, just enough to make me stumble backwards. It was a coward's move.

'*I'm* going to be the hero of this story,' he said. 'I'm going to solve the case. I'm going to be famous all over the world.'

He threw his whisky glass towards the counter; it skidded across the bar and smashed on the floor behind. He wiped his mouth on his sleeve and then left. He was about as unpleasant a man as they get. But he had achieved one thing: he had further fuelled that fire in me to solve this case before he could.

Back in the lobby, I had an idea. Fiona was still tap-tapping away on her computer. She was focused on the screen, but this couldn't wait. I asked her to pull up Alec's reservation. As I have told you, after anyone made a booking at Cavengreen, I would always telephone them to gather additional information. As soon as I hung up, I made sure to tell one of the girls behind reception what the guest had told me, and they would add it to their file. I figured there could be something in Alec's file that might help us work out the password to his laptop. It was a long shot, but it was all I had.

Fiona did as I requested. She printed out everything on Alec's record and then we went through it together, highlighting key points in yellow. There was plenty to work from and it couldn't wait. With Mr Potts, we headed back to suite two to start punching words into the laptop. We had his address, so we tried the words *Paisley* and *Glasgow*. Neither of those worked. We tried his birthdate in different combinations. Mr Potts worked out what day of the week Alec had been born, so we tried *Monday*. Working our way down the printout, we tried his favourite food, *scallops*, and then *fishing*, *whisky* and *pottery*. Still nothing.

At the bottom of the page was a section for extra details. I'd ask the guests questions about their family or if they were celebrating any special occasion, and we would use this information to personalise their check-in experience. There was a note with Alec's children's names, Joseph and Hailey. Of course. My heart thumped. It felt like the key. First, we tried *Joseph*. Denied. Then we tried *Hailey*. Denied. Then we tried *JosephHailey*. A spinning coloured wheel appeared on the screen. I had no idea what it meant but Mr Potts pumped his fist in the air and Fiona shouted, 'Yes!' We were in.

The screen opened on a white page full of type. There were all sorts of dot points and unfinished sentences, about twelve pages' worth. Fiona elbowed Mr Potts aside and sat in front of the screen, declaring herself a fast reader.

'There are a few bits about you in here, Hector,' Fiona said. 'He describes what you look like and then labels you a "kind man".'

Fiona continued scrolling down the page, sighing when she didn't find anything of use.

Then she cried, 'Aha!' and moved her head closer to the screen. There was a whole paragraph about a bride and her mother having an argument in a garden. Fiona read it aloud, and while I can't remember the exact wording, it was an exchange between two women about an affair one of them was having. It wasn't clear who was the guilty party, however. At one point the bride said, 'He'd better not spoil my wedding,' and her mother replied, 'Don't worry, darling—I won't let him.'

Surely it couldn't just be a coincidence!

There was more, though. In the scene Alec recounted, the mother decided to go and speak to the man, to persuade him not to reveal the affair. She argued with her daughter over whether that was the right thing to do. The discussion became quite heated, with the bride telling her mother to just leave her alone and the mother apologising as her daughter ran away.

If what we were reading was based on events at Cavengreen, which, since Alec told me he was writing about people in the hotel, I believed it was, then we could narrow the killer down to one of just two people: the bride or her mother. One of them was having an affair with Bruno, and one of them committed the murder to prevent him from ruining the wedding.

The scene ended there. Mr Potts poured a drink, while Fiona sat at the end of the bed, recapping what we had read and piecing it together with what we had overheard ourselves. It all fit together so neatly. Bruno was killed because he was going to expose an affair. But who was the murderer?

Laptops, gadgets, and the like are not really my thing. I don't trust them. I keep all my bills and important documents in a locked cupboard, and I use my puzzle book or a good murder mystery for entertainment rather than those video games that the kids are hooked on. Nevertheless, I had a go and clicked just off to the side of the page we were looking at, which made the screen behind it pop in front. It was the *Yorkshire Sun*, but an online version. I had no idea that they had gone on the web. Not that I will be switching from paper to screen anytime soon. Although, saying that, it was a lot easier for me to read the words in the larger font on the laptop. Normally it takes me quite some time to read the articles in the paper.

Mr Potts leant over me and hit a button that refreshed the page. He used that word: 'refresh'. A new selection of articles popped up. At this, Mr Potts panicked suddenly and slammed down the lid of the laptop. He picked it up and insisted that we should go and tell Detective Raj what we knew without delay. Fiona marched towards him. It was clear that there was something on there that Mr Potts didn't want us to see. Of course, that meant we had to see it.

'Give it here, you silly man,' Fiona demanded.

Mr Potts dodged from side to side, as Fiona snatched at the laptop. She was able to grab it, and there was a bit of a tug of war, but Fiona eventually managed to wrest it from his grasp, with a heave that made Mr Potts overbalance and tumble to the floor.

Fiona raced into the bathroom and I followed. We locked ourselves inside as Mr Potts hammered on the door. We punched the password in again and clicked on the headline article. There was a video. Fiona pressed play.

There was a lot of movement, and the view wasn't great, but I recognised my green uniform immediately. And then I recognised the room. It was Mr Potts's office. I heard myself shout, 'This whole investigation has been a joke since day one.' It was a video of my exchange with Detective Raj from only a couple of hours earlier. I looked angrier, more like my father, than I had remembered being. My face was red, my jaw tense and my fists clenched, just like his used to be. I was shocked at the sight of myself.

Whoever had made the video had a perfect view of me, as if they were sitting right by my side. Every so often a finger or smidge of jacket covered the screen. It was clearly filmed by someone who didn't want to get caught. Someone sitting right next to me. And that person could only have been Mr Potts, also known as the man who sold out his friend for a bit of fast money.

There is no point hanging on to ill feelings; I am not like that. Mr Potts did what he felt he had to do in that moment, for reasons I am sure I will never understand. But just because you don't understand someone's actions, doesn't make them wrong. Personally, I am not motivated by money, but then again, I only have myself to spend it on.

One day I hope to visit him and ask questions about a few things he did over those four days, not just about the video.

Now, those are my feelings about the situation *today*. But let me tell you, when me and Fiona first realised what was going on, we were not so forgiving.

'You drunken idiot!' Fiona shouted when she stormed out from the bathroom.

Mr Potts was sitting on the end of the bed with his hands supporting his slumped head. I am not sure if it was the shame or the alcohol that made him look so pathetic, but for a second I pitied him. Fiona, on the other hand, walloped him across the back of the head with one of the bed cushions and demanded he explain himself.

It wasn't much of an explanation. At first, he claimed it wasn't him, but he quickly backtracked when he realised how stupid that sounded. Then he offered to split the money from the newspaper with us. The cheek of it! I wasn't going to give up my morals for a measly few thousand pounds. And any interest Fiona might have had in the money beforehand had gone out the window. She made it clear that even if she needed the money desperately, she would never betray her friends.

I felt sick to my stomach. Mr Potts had been my comrade throughout the whole ordeal. I trusted him. I thought we were a team. Clearly the friendship I thought we had meant nothing to him.

Mr Potts scooped up the few belongings that he had. He told us he was going to ask Detective Raj if he could leave. A single tear dripped from his eye as he apologised. He said he wished he had never done it. But judging by the sound of a fist banging on the door to our suite, the damage had already been done.

'Hector Harrow, you get out here RIGHT NOW!' the bride shouted.

Helen has been thinking about the trial date and says the publisher wants the book ready to go by the time the jury give their verdict. She said that would be best from a marketing perspective, and I suppose that makes sense. I'd better shake a leg then. Especially now that I've been prepped to be a witness. I met with the prosecution team yesterday; didn't think it appropriate to take the old dictaphone along. First up, they reckon I'll be. We went through what they'd ask me and potential questions the defence team might throw my way during the cross-examination. It's a lot more rehearsed than I would have imagined. I've got the list of questions here, and notes for my responses. Like a script.

I telephoned Helen after the session. She's not best pleased that I've been called as a witness, mind you. It means that I can't watch the trial until after I've done my bit in the stand, and even after I've given my testimony I have to get the judge's permission before I can return to the viewing gallery. And that permission might not be granted. It is all such a kerfuffle, but there's not much that can be done about it. Best not to think about all that right now though, eh?

Fiona knows I am not a birthday person, which is why she dropped round a belated 'just because' lemon tart this morning on her way to work. It is always nice to see her, although now I am worried that she is not being treated well by American Dave. Fiona told me that he plans to hang around until after the trial has finished. That could be months! She says he is making her life a living hell, bossing her around and insisting she perform menial tasks like making him coffee and tidying his desk. He's redecorated Mr Potts's old office. Fiona laughed when she told me how he has nailed a hook to the wall just for his cowboy hat and put up photos of himself riding a horse in just his jeans, no shirt. A topless cowboy is not quite the look that Cavengreen used to go for, but I suppose it is The Lavender now.

A lot has changed at Cavengreen since it traded hands, and now that American Dave is in town, Fiona said the hotel has turned into a film set. All staff were sent an email saying if they weren't happy to give their permission to appear in the background shots of his documentary then they had to stay home and miss their shifts. Fiona can't afford not to work, so she has resorted to dodging the cameras as much as she can. The producer has been badgering her for an interview, which she has been avoiding like the plague. But I am not sure how much longer she will be able to get away with that. I advised her to do the interview but make herself seem so incredibly boring, with short, vague answers, that they can't use it. She is not a woman you can dull down easily, but when she left here she was quite giddy about her potential acting role.

But back to talking about Cavengreen, not The Lavender. You will remember me describing how the bride was hammering on the door.

Mr Potts opened it, with Fiona quickly snatching his telephone from his hand before he could take any more secret videos.

Olive stood there, arms folded, tapping one foot impatiently. She looked tired. Her mother was by her side, seething with rage. Their husbands had accompanied them, but seemed content to remain in the background. The twins and groomsmen, all dressed in Cavengreen robes and carrying glasses of champagne, rounded out the party. It was quite the ambush.

Mr Potts snatched his phone back from Fiona and slipped through the crowd and out of sight. I squinted to see if I could see him filming from the back of the group, but it seemed he had learnt his lesson.

'You made it look like I'm the murderer!' the bride shouted, her voice shaky and face tense. She looked like she was holding back tears.

'My daughter did not kill anyone!' her mother added.

'You're a liar!' the twins joined in. 'You're probably trying to cover up your own actions.'

Fiona looked at me. This was a battle I had to fight myself, and she knew that. I took a deep breath. I explained how I had overheard Olive and her mother Sue arguing the previous night, that Olive had claimed she didn't do it, but that her mother had sounded unconvinced. I watched the faces of their husbands change when I mentioned the note on Alec's computer. This was the first they were hearing about it.

'You were sleeping with the dead guy?' the bride's stepfather shouted at his wife.

'No—I swear I wasn't,' Sue replied.

'Then what? Olive was?'

'This is nothing to do with me,' Olive interjected.

'Then what is this old man talking about?' Patrick demanded.

'He's lying!' Olive answered defensively.

'Yes! The old man is lying!' piped up one of the twins—Oksana, I think. 'He's the murderer and he's making up stories to frame you.'

'How do you explain the women's shoes in the maze with the murder weapon then?' Fiona interjected.

'He planted them there to throw the police off,' the other twin said dismissively.

The conversation went round in another circle or two. Each husband quizzed his wife on the bomb I had just dropped. The other guests began to poke their heads out of their suites to see what all the fuss was about. One of them used his camera telephone to film the argument, the footage ultimately ending up on the news.

[Editor's note: The following content has been inserted during editing and was recorded out of sequence.]

Hector here. But you know that. Helen suggested we revisit this part of the book. She said it would make a great scene if we went back and found the footage that ended up on the news. She's here now, laptop open and all. She picked up some raspberry cheesecakes from Maude's Bakery on her way over. I can't say I would normally opt for a cheesecake but this one looks delightful. First bite. Yes, delicious. Thank you, Helen.

Right, Helen tells me this website she is on stores videos from all around the world. Somehow, she has managed to find the footage of the argument in the hallway. I haven't seen it since it was on the news, and even then, I half-hid behind a pillow, not wanting to relive the moment. Now that the dust has sort of settled, I will watch it again, for the sake of the book. The video is titled 'Posh people gone wild after

Cavengreen Hotel murder'. I am sure they aren't referring to me with the word 'posh'.

Right, I'm ready, Helen. Should I talk over the video, or should we watch it first and then I'll make my comments? Okay, I'll tell you when to pause. It looks like it's only a twenty-second clip anyway. Press play.

[The video plays.]

Right, pause. See there, you can tell from the angle that it was filmed from the door of one of the suites. They got a good view, mind you. That's Patrick you can see. Do you hear how he is yelling at Olive? Because they're all shouting over each other, it is hard to make out what they're saying. Then that is Olive's stepfather, there, and her mother Sue. I remember he was telling her off about the affair. That was the most I heard him speak the whole lockdown. Press play again.

[The video plays.]

Pause here. Those two gormless puppies there, those are the groomsmen. They're just standing to the side watching things unfold. And those two girls are the twins. That one is Ruby, and that's Oksana. Press play.

[The video plays.]

Pause. We just saw Patrick grab Olive by the arm. It was a bit rough, wasn't it? Much more so than I remember. Then again, there was a lot going on. He's started dragging her down the hallway, in the direction of the camera. He hasn't seen the camera yet, but from what I remember, he will in a second. Press play.

[The video plays.]

Pause. See how close they are to the camera? The man filming was obviously trying to hide it; you can see his hand smudge across the lens a few times. The sound is a bit muffled, but you can just about hear Patrick demanding—quite aggressively, I must say—that Olive tell him the truth. He is looking intently into her eyes, one hand gripping each of her shoulders so she can't get away.

In the background, you can see the twins moving in and out of the shot, trying to get a better view of Olive and Patrick. Nosy parkers. If you look closely, you can see they're smirking. Rotten, the pair of them! Press play.

[The video plays.]

And that's it. Not long, was it? In the end, Patrick spots the camera and lashes out at it, his face filled with anger. The video ends on a freezeframe of his hand, complete with a shiny new gold wedding band, about to snatch the telephone from its owner.

Thank you for that, Helen. You can insert this bit in just before Fred appears saying he'd been looking everywhere for us.

[Editor's note: End of out-of-sequence scene.]

'There you all are,' Fred puffed, his cheeks red. 'I've been looking everywhere for you. I turn my back for one second and you're all out of Lavender Plates like the clappers.' He smiled, completely oblivious to what was going on. 'What's everyone doing up here?'

The argument erupted again as everyone spoke over each other, trying to explain what was going on and whose fault it was.

Fred looked stunned, to say the least. He glanced over at me, and I shrugged, not knowing how to begin to describe the situation. Turns out, I didn't need to. Detective Raj came storming down the corridor, four police officers marching behind him.

'QUIET!' he ordered.

One of the officers accompanied this demand with a loud whistle, one of those ones you make with your fingers in your mouth. I have never quite figured out how that is done. Nevertheless, it worked. Everyone stopped shouting.

'Library,' Detective Raj barked. 'All of you. NOW!'

The atmosphere in the library was tense. Fiona and I sat in the window seat. That was our territory. The husbands both sat in silence on one settee, while their wives whispered to each other in the corner of the room. The twins were glued to their phones, their fingers frantically tapping the screens. The two groomsmen, meanwhile, were sniggering by the bookshelves.

Detective Raj paced back and forth, his hands thrust into his trouser pockets, glaring from the window seat to the sofa to the corner to the bookshelf. 'I don't know what that commotion was all about, but you're going to tell me—no lies, no cover-ups, no evasions. You first, Harrow.'

So, I told him what was on Alec's laptop, about the conversation on the terrace between Olive and her mother, and the fight I'd overheard between Olive and her husband. The detective wasn't impressed. I had discovered more about this murder case in one day than he had in three. He threatened to have me arrested for withholding evidence, but I assured him that Alec's laptop had only become evidence about half an hour earlier, when we'd managed to crack the password. That shut him right up.

Fiona's version of events was the same as mine, but things took a turn when he asked the others to give their account. In fact, the twins kept saying 'no comment' to every question, even if it wasn't directed at them. As soon as they'd done that a couple of times, everyone else followed suit. Detective Raj clicked his neck from side to side in frustration. No one was going to talk. And it was my word versus the rest of the room.

We had reached a stalemate when there was a rap on the library door.

'Enter!' Detective Raj snapped.

The door opened and a man with a briefcase walked in. His name was Leon Black, he informed us, and he was the twins' lawyer. He thanked the detective for giving him the clearance to enter. Detective Raj replied that after the threats he received from Leon's employer, they didn't give him much choice. Leon looked very young. My guess is that their family's regular lawyer was unavailable, so the firm had sent this guy instead. He had a flop of brown hair and bushy eyebrows. His teeth were crooked and his belt struggled to contain his belly. He was already flustered, sweaty, red, and wide-eyed when he entered. I could tell he was out of his depth.

He pulled Detective Raj to one side and they had a muttered conversation, Leon umming and ahhing every so often. I heard the lawyer ask if detaining guests in the hotel would be classed as 'normal protocol' or not. By that point we were all aware that there was nothing normal about the situation. Detective Raj instructed Leon to take a seat.

As if we didn't have enough egos in the room, American Dave chose that moment to barge in. He wanted to know what was going on; in his words, it was his hotel and therefore he needed to be across everything. He looked most put out on spotting me among those present, clearly miffed that I was involved and he wasn't. I would have gladly given my place to him. I was being dragged into this ruckus from all directions, when all I wanted to do was help find out who the murderer was so I could go home, have a brew, and get into bed with a puzzle. Yet there I was.

Never in my life has anyone been jealous of me. I mean, why would they be? What is there to be jealous of? I live a simple life. But American Dave has always had a bee in his bonnet about me, because I was on the inside of the investigation and he was left on the sidelines. I tell you where I would rather be and that's nowhere near the action. I'd rather have been ten thousand miles away. American Dave would have loved to have been the one to find the body.

Tap one. Tap two. Tap three.

He wouldn't even be scarred by that memory; he would probably use it as an anecdote to pick up women in one of his cowboy bars.

American Dave elbowed his way onto the sofa, taking the position next to Leon the lawyer. They shook hands. Then everyone looked towards Detective Raj as if he were teaching a class.

'Does anyone want to confess so we can all go home?' Detective Raj wearily drawled.

'No comment,' the twins replied in unison.

Even their lawyer looked embarrassed at this. Glances were exchanged between everyone else in the room. Someone in the group was going to leave in handcuffs very soon.

American Dave took it upon himself to go around the room, staring us all in the eye one by one and asking if we were the murderer. I must have blinked when he asked me because he declared that I looked guilty. This was enough to start the twins yapping on about my supposedly threatening behaviour towards them. Their lawyer pinched the gap between his eyes and raised a hand to shush them. He had only been at the hotel for ten minutes, yet already he seemed more exasperated with the situation than the rest of us.

'Get fucked,' Olive said when American Dave asked her the question.

'We got a live one here, Detective!' he called, pointing at Olive.

Olive slapped his hand away and spat in his face. American Dave wiped the saliva from his cheek and called her a bitch. Olive lurched forward to hit him, her mother grabbing her arm and her husband coming forward to intervene. The situation was deteriorating, fast.

Olive sobbed into her husband's chest, seemingly ashamed of what she had done. I can't imagine she had ever spat in someone's face before. I am not trying to defend her, but that hotel was a pressure cooker, and as I have admitted to you, at times even I acted in a way I am not proud of. Besides, I was quietly pleased that someone had put American Dave in his place.

American Dave demanded Olive be charged with assault, but Detective Raj only rolled his eyes. He said that he hadn't seen what happened, and everyone else in the room nodded their agreement. For the record, the twins' lawyer didn't nod, but he genuinely hadn't seen, as he'd been staring at the floor in despair. American Dave tried to hire him to sue Olive, but Leon declined, claiming it would be a conflict of interest.

Meanwhile, time was creeping on. It was 11 pm; by midnight the murderer would declare themselves. So, I think I will pause here. For dramatic effect. By all means, go to sleep, make some lunch, whatever it is that you need to do. I will see you back here soon.

CHAPTER

25

For those of you who moved straight from the last chapter, I am glad that you are still interested in what I am saying. I do worry. I know I waffle and ramble; it is the only way I can get the story out. It is down to Helen to tidy it up, but then again, I have told her to leave it as close to my original words as possible. I am still hoping that the final version of the book, the one that you're reading, is a little less all over the shop than what is on this dictaphone. Perhaps I will release the audio tapes one day. If the book sells well and people are interested, that is. Helen says that would be called an audiobook. I have made a note here to record one of the editing sessions with Helen, if she'll let me. She hasn't been too keen in the past. That way, you can hear, see, whatever, for yourselves just how that process works.

But I am sure you are not interested in that right now. You are here because you want to know who the murderer is. It is time for the big reveal. I am not sure if it is a good or bad thing if you guessed it right. I mean, there were clues along the way, so those of you who got it right did well to pick up on those little breadcrumbs. But Helen also said that, for the sake of writing a good book, it can't be *too* obvious who the murderer is, so I've tried to throw you off here and there. Maybe when the book comes out, I will do a bit of a book tour. Then you can all tell me if you guessed right or not. I would like that.

Returning to the hotel. As you can imagine, by this point everyone was growing tired. American Dave was going on and on about how the murderer needed to confess. His tactic was wasted on this lot. In *Cluedo*, you don't see one player simply shouting in the others' faces until someone owns up to being the killer. This was much the same. We had most of the pieces of the puzzle. The crime was committed with a knife, in suite seven. We just needed the who.

As it turned out, the forensics team had already decided the who for us. A sweaty man in one of those plasticky suits entered the library. He gestured to Detective Raj to join him out in the lobby. They must have found something in the bridal suite. Patrick placed his arm around his wife, pulling her close. Despite everything that had been said, he still wanted to protect her.

Detective Raj re-entered the room, some of the colour having returned to his tired, washed-out face. He stood in front of the fireplace and slowly pulled a set of handcuffs from his back pocket. Two officers stood like guard dogs at the entrance to the library. All eyes were on Detective Raj. He didn't say anything. He just held up the handcuffs, taunting us. And then suddenly he turned his head in the direction of his target.

'Olive Nixon, I am arresting you on suspicion of the murder of Bruno Tatterson. You do not have to say anything, but it may harm your defence if you do not mention when questioned something which you later rely on in court. Anything you do say may be given in evidence.'

Olive was handcuffed. She screamed that she didn't do it. Patrick had to be held back by his groomsmen; there was no rescuing her. Olive cried out for her mother, who looked panicked, as though a million thoughts were racing through her mind. Detective Raj held Olive's forearm and escorted her into the lobby. Olive kept looking back. We all stood at the library entrance and watched her leave. Her mother cupped her hands over her mouth. She kept looking between her husband and her daughter. Her feet edged forward. And then she went for it.

'WAIT!' her mother shouted, hurling herself into the detective's path. 'IT WAS ME! I killed him.' She spoke through tears. Her hands were shaking as she held out her wrists for the handcuffs. Then she lifted one hand to her daughter's cheek and stroked it tenderly. I couldn't hear her words, but I could tell by the movement of her lips that she said, 'I'm sorry.'

'Mum, no,' Olive sobbed.

Detective Raj looked taken aback. His gaze kept shifting from one woman to the other. American Dave laughed and called out, 'Oh, boy,' before opening the globe bar and pouring himself a whisky. He smiled into his glass as he took his first sip. Then he raised his glass to Olive and tilted his cowboy hat down, saying, 'Well played, y'all.'

Detective Raj didn't know what to do, that was obvious. But there had been a confession. He gestured for the two police officers to restrain the hysterical Sue. They used what I would call unnecessary force to drag her away from her daughter. It was painful to watch how she wailed, her heart breaking as she confessed to being the one who killed Bruno, knowing that her life and family would never be the same again. Her husband, Martin, looked on in disbelief.

'How could you?' he asked quietly. Pulling a handkerchief from his pocket, he dabbed his eyes. Sue mouthed, 'I love you,' to him, but he turned his back on her. She called his name as she was handcuffed. She fell to her knees and the police forced her back to her feet. Olive tried to reach her, to help her, but her husband held her back. She buried her face in Patrick's chest again and he stroked the back of her head, watching, gobsmacked, as his mother-in-law was taken away. So there you have it: Sue killed Bruno. I wonder how many of you guessed that.

Blue lights flashed across the front of the hotel. We followed the procession outside and watched the police escort Sue into one of the cars. Her terrified face peered out from the window. Olive broke free of Patrick's hold and ran to the car. Sue placed her palm against the glass, Olive doing the same from the outside. Then the engines started and a convoy of whirring vehicles headed down the driveway. We could hear shouting and see camera flashes from beyond the gates, before they closed again.

Olive sunk to the ground and knelt in the gravel. Patrick crouched down and cradled her. American Dave yelled, 'Yeehaw,' as he tossed his hat up into the air. Classless. Fiona leant her head on my shoulder and linked her arm through mine.

It truly felt like the end of something momentous. The hotel seemed emptier than ever. Some of the other guests and staff started to spill out through the front doors, asking if it was over.

'Go home, everyone!' American Dave shouted gleefully. No one quite trusted him, and they looked towards me and Fiona for confirmation. We nodded; it was indeed time for everyone to go home.

The sound of a car boot slamming drew our attention. It was Mr Potts; God knows where he had crawled out from. He turned back to look at us for a moment and then got in his car. That was the last time I saw him. Later, when I was putting my own retirement notice in, I found his resignation scrawled on a bit of scrap paper on his desk. It was not quite the ending I had hoped for at Cavengreen, but it was definitely time to draw a line under my time at the hotel. Not that I knew it then, but Helen would soon convince me to write this book, and that would take up most of my days.

CHAPTER

26

Sue has been in prison for a couple of months now, ever since that fateful day. As it happens, she has pleaded 'not guilty' to murder. I am sure she has a good lawyer on her side who will put a case forward for lack of evidence. I don't know how they will wriggle their way out of the fact that she confessed, but I am certain they will come up with something; they always do, these lawyer types.

I am not surprised that I have been called as a witness for the prosecution. A lot of the evidence against Sue relies on things I heard and saw. Fiona has been warned that she may be called too, although nothing has been set in stone and she hasn't been prepped to quite the same level as me. A couple of the others from the hotel have also been notified. It's nerve-racking, to say the least. It's just as well I've got this little book project as a distraction, otherwise I'd be in bits thinking about the whole ordeal. Helen is coming over soon to run through some of the last chapters. I will ask her if it is okay to record this editing session and insert it here, so you can get an idea of what we are up to.

Helen: Good afternoon, Hector. Now, I know you don't always fancy a chocolate cake, so I got you a vanilla slice and then I got myself some chocolate mud cake. A bit cheeky, I know, but who am I hurting?

Hector: You're too good to me, Helen. Just quickly, before we get settled . . . Actually, first things first, do you want a brew? Kettle is already boiled.

Helen: Yes, please. Thank you.

[Pause.]

Hector: I was thinking we could record today's editing session and insert it into the book as a little behind-the-scenes for the readers. What do you think?

Helen: I see no harm in that. However, I'm not sure how interesting it will be.

Hector: It is just a bit of extra content.

Helen: Where did you get to with this morning's recording session?

Hector: I finally revealed the murderer.

Helen: Oh, wonderful! I'm sure the readers will be shocked.

Hector: I hope so. I tried to lead them astray, like you told me to.

Helen: That reminds me, I can't make it to the trial with you. I'll be in London that whole week doing the final edits on your book with my old colleagues. We've got to get this on the shelves sharpish.

Hector: That's okay. I'll be sure to take my dictaphone to the courthouse, and in the breaks I'll record as much as I can remember about my time on the witness stand. What happens then? Should we just add those bits into the book at the last minute?

Helen: Yes, if we have everything else ready to go, then we'll add the details of the trial in as more of an epilogue.

Hector: What does that mean?

Helen: A section at the end of the book that concludes the story. It'll be nice to finish by saying something like, 'And Sue Bainbridge was found guilty and sentenced to x number of years in prison.' Something like that, just to tie it all together.

Hector: I see. Yes, that sounds good.

Helen: Okay, let's get started on today's edit. I'm looking at chapter nineteen, the part where you talk about American Dave and his mistress going into the maze for a bit of you-know-what. It is a shame there was no CCTV out there! . . . Sorry, I shouldn't laugh. I have some questions.

Hector: Ask away.

Helen: Do you think you should add some more colour in about the gardens? I like your little side story about the Spanish gardener in chapter twenty. Every book needs a touch of romance. I can't believe you told the readers that I was blushing while you were telling that story. I must have missed you saying that.

Hector: Just trying to give the readers a little insight into you, Helen.

Helen: Well, they'll just think I'm some sad, single old bat.

Hector: Never. Are you blushing again?

Helen: Oh, give over. Let's get back to this. I loved the background about the maze. Did the Spanish lady plant the rose garden too?

Hector: She did. I helped dig the grass up for the beds.

Helen: Let's paint more of a picture here then. The roses were trimmed back to their stems when the murder happened. Let's add that in so people don't have a picture in their mind of some long, beautiful roses. Because that wasn't the case.

Hector: Ah yes, *Botrytis cinerea*. I think that's what the fungus was called.

Helen: I'll make a note to add that in. And then remind me again why there was an iPad with the murder weapon.

Hector: Presumably it was the one Sue used to message me to come to suite seven, so I'd find the body.

Helen: Yep, got it. And then, this part here: I've typed some of this newspaper article out, but I just need to clarify if I should leave the whole part out about the court case or if I should just omit Sue's name.

Hector: Just take out the name, I reckon.

Helen: Okay, done. Now, there's a bit on the tape that I need you to translate for me. When you've been talking for a while, you tend to turn your head away from the dictaphone and your voice drifts. It makes some bits hard to hear. Try to keep the recorder just below your mouth at all times.

Hector: Sorry, Helen. I don't even realise I'm doing it until it's done. And then I can't remember what I've said to repeat it. Can you hear most of it?

Helen: I can hear it; it is just a little faint. Listen.

Hector: First let me turn this off. It probably won't make sense to the readers if we have a transcript of us recording a recording. I'm sure they get the gist by now anyway.

CHAPTER

It is day one of the trial. I am recording this from inside the men's lavatories at the courtroom.

Apologies Helen for the slight echo. Echo. Echo.

The floor and walls are covered in yellow tiles and my voice seems to bounce off them. All the wooden stalls are empty, so there is no one listening. If anyone walks in, I will pause the tape.

I have arrived at the courthouse a bit early—nerves, mostly. I was told to come down here just in case the prosecution needs me as a witness, but it is unlikely they will. Twiddling my darned thumbs is what I'll most probably be doing all day. It would be far more productive for the book if I was allowed into the public gallery. But that's against the rules. Apparently, it is detrimental for me to observe the trial before being questioned as a witness, as I may be influenced by the arguments presented. There are pros and cons to standing as a witness. The only pro I can think of is that it will be useful for the book, these behind-the-scenes insights. Oh, and I suppose if I can help get a murderer locked up then that is a good deed. But the con is that it's far too much pressure. What if I start to stammer? I've got my notes here from my preparation session with the lawyers. Helen kindly typed them up and printed them out for me. I reread them over and over again on the train. The facts are as clear as day in my head but I'm still nervous. I won't be allowed to read off this piece of paper when I'm on the stand, and my brain gets so frazzled when I try and communicate under stress. You and I both know that by now.

None of Sue's family are here yet, as far as I can tell, although I am expecting to see them around the hallways. I have been told that there might be a bit of a delay getting things started while they select the jurors. I have always wanted to do jury duty, but I have never been called for it. Josie was called twice but got out of it once because of the cancer. The first time she sent a man to prison for ten years for smuggling drugs in from Thailand. In noodle packets, I believe it was. To me, jury duty would be something interesting to do. Especially now I am retired, I wouldn't mind doing my public service. I would like to see how it all works. There is no use watching those American courtroom dramas to get an idea. I have heard it's not quite like that.

That reminds me, I am sure American Dave will show up at some point. I'll do my best to avoid him. At least he's not going to be allowed to bring his camera crew in here with him. There have been a couple of complaints to the local council about him turning up in various locations with his camera and filming without permission. There is no need for that. I am sure the council would give him permission to go wherever he likes if he just bothered to ask. Making the village a tourist attraction would be good for the locals, however annoying those of us who don't run businesses would find it. The Cavengreen murder has put the village on the map, so we may as well take advantage of that and get some money flowing through.

I am not in the village today, of course. I took the 6 am train to Leeds, where the trial is being held. This is where the big courts are. I have been here many a time—to the city, that is, not the courts. Normally when I need some new casual clothes. About once a year I take myself to Marks & Spencer to stock up on polo tops and shirts. I usually get the same top in every colour and rotate between them until they get holes under the armpits or a stain that won't budge.

I am in a suit today. It is the same one I wore to my dear Josie's funeral; the only suit I own. Outside of Cavengreen and the odd funeral here and there, I have no use for suits. But it seems appropriate attire for such an occasion. I am going to head back to the courtroom now and see if they are letting people in.

By 'eck, that was a long day. They made me wait around in a poky, windowless witness room until 3 pm, which is when the judge sent the jury home for the day. As expected, they didn't need me. It is now 3.45 pm and I am on the train, heading home. I have the carriage to myself, so I will get all my thoughts out while they are still fresh.

Okay. When I left you, I was in the men's lavatories. I went to see if they were letting people into the courtroom, and they were. At first, I didn't see anyone I recognised, until I spotted Martin, Sue's husband. His wife being locked away and the revelation of her affair had left him gaunt and weary. He looked like he was trying to blend in, opting to wear a very casual grey jumper and jeans, but everyone knew who he was. There were whispers in the hallways identifying him as the husband of the murderer.

Olive was nowhere to be seen. Perhaps she has been told to stay away. Perhaps she is too angry at her mother to attend. I am not sure how I would feel if my mother was on trial for murder.

Disappointed, I suppose. Unless she murdered my father; then perhaps I would be in the front row, cheering and clapping.

Tap one. Tap two. Tap three.

Once everyone had entered the courtroom, I had a quick peek in through the small glass panel on the door. From that glance I got a bit of a sense of what the room was like. All this helps in my mental preparation for having to stand as a witness. Now I can visualise the room, so I can visualise myself in the room. It's just one less thing I have to wonder about.

The courtroom wasn't how I expected it to be. For some reason, I thought it would be huge, with wooden benches and portraits of old judges. But it was modern. The judge sat in the middle, elevated on a platform against the back wall. To the left was the jury box, with big grey seats that had armrests. Less comfy-looking brown seats made up the public gallery, which appeared to be just on the one level, instead of the two that I had envisaged. The lights were bright, unflattering and clinical. The sort of lights that make your eyelids droopy after a while.

There was a witness box off to the right. It was empty, of course, given that I was outside in the corridor and not giving evidence at that moment. There was no sign of Sue, but I imagine she was tucked away out of view.

And that was day one in a nutshell for you. I spent the rest of the day sitting on a vomit-green settee, alone in the witness room, waiting to be called but knowing I wouldn't be. On my way out of the court, I overheard someone on their telephone complaining that it was a boring day that consisted of opening arguments and little else. I can see how this might drag on for a while.

I heard all sorts of accents chatting away as we filed out onto the street. The trial is big news, not just in Yorkshire but all across the UK. You may have heard about it; perhaps that is why you purchased my book. There were locals in the crowd, but I also picked up lots of accents from down south—presumably press wanting to cover the story. Sue is from a wealthy family and the murder happened at one of the country's best hotels, so it is no surprise the story is of interest.

Hopefully I'll have a more exciting day to tell you about tomorrow.

Bleedin' hell, I forgot to take the lamb hotpot out the freezer this morning to defrost for my dinner. Fingers crossed there's some emergency eggs in the fridge when I get home. Goodnight then.

I was going to leave this chapter here, mostly because I have regurgitated everything that I can remember from the trial. Just quickly, though, I have had an update on the book. I am back home now, by the way. Helen telephoned me just after dinner—emergency soft-boiled eggs with dippy soldiers—to run me through a few of the discussions she has been having with the publisher. As it turns out, they quite like what she has presented them with so far. 'Unique, raw, and joyfully imperfect,' they said. Helen wants to send me some of the sample chapters she has written up, but I trust her to transcribe everything as she sees fit. I don't need to relive it again. This entire process has been therapeutic for me, and once all the words are out and the story is complete, I fully intend on parking the memories in that dusty corner of my brain where I keep my father.

Tap one. Tap two. Tap three.

Helen was as patient with me tonight as the desert waiting for rain. She had to talk me through how to get on to my computer and access the email address that I forgot I had. The publisher has created three mock-ups of the cover art for the book and Helen wanted to know my thoughts. Ultimately, the decision will be down to the publisher's marketing team, she said, but my opinion will carry some weight.

The first one was terrible. It was one of those 'Do Not Disturb' signs. Except this one had a bloody hand hovering next to it, with red blobs dripping off a doorknob. The shade of red for the blood was a bit too red-red, if that makes sense.

Helen told me that the second cover was everyone's favourite, and I agree. It is striking and colourful, yet subtle. It would stand out in the window of a bookshop.

And then there was the third one, which I also liked but Helen said was too clichéd. It is a photo from the back of a man wearing a butler's uniform, holding a silver tray with a bloody knife on it out to the side. Although that makes it look like I am the murderer. If you are reading this, then you will know exactly which one was chosen. Hopefully you agree it is the right choice.

Then we ran through title suggestions. The creative team sent through a whole list of options. I will read a couple of them out for you: *The Cavengreen*; *A Deathly Wedding*; *Check In But Don't Check Out*; *Travel Bags to Body Bags* . . . the list goes on. Since the start of this process there has only ever been one title I have wanted for the book. It was Fiona's idea, actually. She said it is my story, and I agree.

I told Helen, 'I don't care what artwork you put on the cover, or what percentage of the sales I get, but this book has to be called *The Concierge*.'

She agreed.

CHAPTER

28

Day two in court. This morning I remembered to take the lamb hotpot out the freezer, so based on that I reckon it's going to be an okay kind of day. At least, that's what I'm trying to convince myself. I suspect I may be called as a witness at some point this morning.

I am starting my day recording a quick introduction in the men's lavatories, like yesterday. Maybe this will become part of my routine. I always like a routine. I am wearing yesterday's suit but with a fresh shirt underneath. And I've swapped to a green tie. One that Fiona says makes my eyes 'pop', whatever that means. Not out my head, I hope. I don't need nonsense like that today. If I'm allowed back tomorrow after giving evidence, I'll opt for more casual attire, like everyone else. But only a suit will do for an occasion when all eyes are going to be on me. Gulp. I said 'gulp' for your benefit. That's not something I normally do to accompany a hard, nervous swallow.

There was already quite the crowd gathered outside the courtroom when I arrived at eight, though the doors don't open until nine.

Some buzz must have spread since yesterday, and more people have shown up either to have a nosy or to write about the day's events for whatever media outlet employs them. Sue's husband, Martin, was the only person I recognised in the crowd. He spotted me and I caught him looking, but he quickly glanced away. That's okay. We are hardly friends, merely two strangers who will forever be linked by this awfulness. He might feel awkward around me because I know he is standing by his wife through not only a murder trial but an affair too. I am not judging him. Marriages survive worse blips than that. My father used to beat my mother to a pulp, but she would still defend him if she needed to. Loyalty knows no bounds sometimes.

It is time for me to head to the witness room to reread my preparation notes and wait to see if I am called or not.

It is lunchtime, and plenty has happened since I last spoke to you. I have found a cosy cafe serving toasted sandwiches. Ham, cheese and tomato with a bit of mustard, that is what I have gone for. I barely have an appetite but the courthouse covers expenses for food so I thought I may as well order a little something. They also pay for travel expenses and any loss of income incurred by being here. Not that I am currently employed. Train tickets and the odd sarnie aside, I'll be a cheap witness in the court's eyes.

The witness care officer— that's the person who tells you the who, what, where and when of what's going on while you're waiting at the courthouse—let me know that I'll likely be called up after lunch. I'm trying to play it down for you lot, but by gum, I'm nervous. You'll never guess—although maybe you will, the options are few and far between—who waltzed into the witness room this morning while I was making a brew and browsing the rather bleak selection of biscuits.

None other than Mr Potts. The room is only about four-by-four metres in size, so to say it suddenly felt crowded with the two of us in there would not be an exaggeration.

Mr Potts sheepishly walked around me and took a seat in an armchair in the corner. As far away from me as possible, which wasn't very far. He quickly opened the book he arrived holding and didn't move his gaze from the pages for two hours. The pensive gentleman on the cover led me to assume it was a self-help guide. Lots of the pages were dog-eared.

Not a word was spoken between us. I'd rather not make such a cliché remark as, 'you could cut the tension with a knife,' so instead I'll go with, 'you could hack the intensity with a chainsaw.' That sounds more colourful for the book. Needless to say, we both leapt to our feet to escape our cage of unsaid words when the witness care officer popped his head in to let us know it was time to grab some lunch. I'm not sure what would be worse, spending the afternoon trapped in a room with Mr Potts, or taking the stand in a murder trial.

Taking the stand in a murder trial was far worse than sitting in tense silence with my former colleague. I can tell you that for free.

Tap one. Tap two. Tap three.

The whole thing was a blur. I feel like I blacked out. I thought it best to return to the men's lavatories and record this sharpish before the stress erases it forever. I will have to rack my brain and do my best to recap the information for you. My preparation notes will help jog my memory.

As soon as I sat back down in the witness room after lunch, the witness care officer came in and told me the prosecution team was ready for me to take the stand. Mr Potts glanced up from his book but said nothing.

When I got to the courtroom, there was no one to greet me except an usher. My heart thumped so loudly that it muffled my hearing. I stared at the court usher's lips as he gave me instructions on what to do once inside the room. I was to head to the right-hand side and into the witness box. He told me to leave all belongings in a plastic tray. He was a young fella and laughed when he saw my old mobile telephone and dictaphone. In fact, he had no idea what a dictaphone was.

Heat rushed to the tips of my body, including my ears, toes, fingers, and the end of my nose. And then my father's voice popped into my head. The timing couldn't have been worse. He told me I was useless and deserved another beating.

Tap one. Tap two. Tap three.

Even though he wasn't there to hurt me, I felt my hands start to shake as if he was waiting inside the courtroom with a belt. I tapped my head three times, but my mind was flooded with his voice. I tapped my head three more times, but he was still there.

Call it paranoia, but I felt like the usher was looking at me funny. I moved away and stared out a window at the traffic below. With my full palm I hit my head lightly three times. I closed my eyes, took a deep breath, and pushed my father out of my mind. He dragged his heels and cracked his belt on the floor as he went, but he *did* go. Then the usher called my name. It was time to go in.

It felt like all eyes were on me when I entered the courtroom— not that I looked anywhere except where I had to go. I followed the usher's instructions and walked along the right-hand side of the room to the witness box. I stared straight ahead. I didn't meet anyone's eyes. In my peripheral vision I could see American Dave smirking and chewing gum. I can only assume he was trying to put me off when he started whispering in Paula McDavidson's ear. She giggled and nodded in response. Whatever they were saying, I am sure it was something cruel about the way I walked, looked, or simply existed. Paula has always been an annoying busybody, but American Dave's nastiness was starting to rub off on her. Her personality can't afford to get any worse, but it looks like it has.

The first thing I was asked to do was to confirm my name and repeat a promise to tell the truth. 'I, Hector Harrow, do solemnly, sincerely and truly declare and affirm the evidence I shall give shall be the truth, the whole truth, and nothing but the truth.' That would have made a grand opening line to this book.

Helen, let's discuss later. Although I remember you saying how much you liked the current introduction so I might be fighting a losing battle here.

There was no 'so help me God' tagged on at the end of all that. Maybe because I am an old man, they assumed that I would want to swear an oath on the Bible. I told them that's not for me.

Then the prosecution started their questioning. The prosecution lawyer is a lady called Marie Habib. I met her at my preparation session and boy, is she a real tough nut. Today her black hair was scraped back into a long ponytail that swung around hypnotically as she spoke with conviction. Every word she said was perfectly articulated, and each moment of particular emphasis was accompanied by some very animated black eyebrow raises, almost like a cartoon.

'She confessed. She confessed. She confessed. She *con-fessed*,' Habib repeated over and over. I remember she said it four times, because I wanted her to stop at three. She locked eyes with each juror as she said it. Some of them bobbed their heads in agreement, probably subconsciously; others looked down shyly.

'You heard the confession, didn't you, Mr Harrow?' She looked me straight in the eye.

I nodded.

'If you could answer yes or no, Mr Harrow.'

'Yes,' I said hastily.

'Can you tell the jury what exactly you heard Sue Bainbridge say?'

I looked at the jury and told them exactly what I had rehearsed, that Sue said, 'It was me. I killed him.' Some of the jurors scribbled down notes.

'Thank you. And going back, what day did Sue Bainbridge check in to Cavengreen and who was she accompanied by?'

A quick glance at some of my early chapters and you will know exactly what I said. I stuck to the facts. Everything was going as planned, that is until my mind got the better of me and I began to go off script, much to the prosecution team's horror.

'How would you describe Sue Bainbridge's temperament during her time at Cavengreen?' Habib asked me.

You know, because I told you, that I had read and reread my preparation notes umpteen times. I knew what to say. I was supposed to tell the courtroom about that one single incident in Lavender Plates in which Sue Bainbridge shouted at me and told me I should just confess so everyone could go home. Well, I started by saying that. Habib nodded along, acknowledging I was following our choreography; setting the scene that Sue was desperate to pin her actions on someone, on me. But the nods of approval soon stopped.

'I'm not convinced she was acting like a murderer would act though. She was just stressed, like everybody was. Even I had my moments.'

The defence team scribbled something down.

'It's the conversation in the garden that we should be focusing on here.' I continued, off script, stupidly. I can't explain what came over me.

'Yes, thank you, Mr Harrow, I was just getting to that.' Habib skipped ahead a few pages in her yellow notepad. I had unintentionally thrown her off. She ran her finger down the page as she tried to catch up to my train of thought. 'Mr Harrow, if you could tell the court about the conversation you overheard in Cavengreen's gardens. Who was it between?'

'Mrs Bainbridge and her daughter, Olive. They were . . .'

'Thank you,' she interrupted me. 'And what time of day did you see Mrs Bainbridge and her daughter having this conversation?'

'Three am.'

'And what did you hear Mrs Bainbridge say to her daughter?'

I returned to our rehearsed script, telling the courtroom how Sue was asking her daughter to tell her the truth, repeating that she could help her.

Habib flicked back a few pages in her notepad, to fill in the gaps that I had forced her to skip.

'Just returning to the alleged day of the murder, you were the one who discovered Mr Tatterson deceased in suite seven, is that correct?'

'Yes.'

'And what time was that?'

'About three pm.'

'And to your knowledge, where was Mrs Bainbridge at that time?'

'I had made a booking for her in Lavender Plates, and she was there with her family.'

'And do you know the whereabouts of Mrs Bainbridge before her Lavender Plates booking?'

'I saw her and her husband head out for a walk around eight am.'

'And how did she seem?'

'Fine.'

'And then after that, did you see her again?'

'Only when she returned from her walk around eight forty-five, and then in Lavender Plates, after I'd found the body.'

'That was around three thirty pm, is that correct?'

'I'd say so.'

'So, you didn't see Sue Bainbridge between eight forty-five am and three thirty pm on the day you discovered Mr Tatterson's body?'

'That's right.'

'No further questions, your honour.'

Habib huffed and sighed when she sat down. The defence team were invited to cross-examine me, a moment I had been dreading.

There was a bit of admin to get through at the start as I reconfirmed who I was and the position I held in the hotel. We ticked off a couple of points as I clarified what I had just said to Habib, and then they got into it.

'Would you say you have a good memory, Mr Harrow?' Why I never. The cheek.

'Um . . . most of the time, yes.' Was what I really said.

'But not all the time?'

'Not all the time, no.'

'How old are you, Mr Harrow?'

'Seventy-four.'

'And this event happened several months ago?'

'Yes.'

'Do you often remember conversations that have happened several months ago word for word?'

'Not normally.'

'But you remember Mrs Bainbridge's conversation in the garden with her daughter?'

'I remember the gist.'

'Ah okay . . . the gist.' With raised eyebrows the defence lawyer turned and smirked at the jury. 'No further questions, your honour.'

I feel deflated. Like I have just played the part of the unreliable, old witness. Like I have been made to look a fool. This whole book, all of your reading it, you're doing so because you have faith in my retelling of this story. Don't listen to that silly defence lawyer. The sort of things that happened at Cavengreen are the sort of things one doesn't forget. Old or not old.

On my way out of the courtroom, I asked the witness care officer if I was allowed to sit in the public gallery this afternoon and for the rest of the trial. He said yes. At least Helen will be pleased.

❧

The court took a twenty-minute break, enough time for me to record that last part in the lavatory. When we resumed, I loosened my tie and took a seat in the gallery. I could see things a lot clearer without all the stress blurring my vision. American Dave was there still. I could hear him before I could see him. I found a seat in the third row, and as people were filing back in I heard a familiar voice arguing with the usher. I turned to look. American Dave was being told to remove his cowboy hat or he would not be permitted in the courtroom. He was not best pleased, having been allowed to wear it that morning. He huffed and puffed and eventually snapped, 'You better not lose it.' He ruffled his hair as if he was self-conscious about it. He took a seat directly behind me and leant forward to whisper, 'Howdy,' over my right shoulder.

'No film crew following you today?' I asked him.

'Not allowed in the courtroom,' he replied. I could tell he was still chewing gum without even looking at him, just by the sound of something sticky chomping between his teeth.

Every seat in the gallery was filled, with another row of spectators huddled in some standing room at the back. Sue entered in handcuffs. She scanned the room, presumably looking for familiar faces, and she smiled faintly at her husband. I leant forward to see his reaction; he smiled softly back at her.

It was the first time I could get a clear look at her. She was a shadow of the glamorous woman who had first entered Cavengreen. Instead of high heels and a designer dress, she was wearing an ill-fitting grey trouser suit. Her brown hair was sprinkled with wiry grey. Without make-up, her skin looked dull. She appeared frail and exhausted. I imagine she hasn't been able to eat much because of stress. Saying that, I lost half a stone over those four days at Cavengreen.

Patrick, the groom, was sitting next to Sue's husband. There was no Olive. Behind them sat the twins, both dressed like they were going to a celebrity's funeral, with black suits and ridiculous dangly gold earrings. I locked eyes with one of them—Oksana, if I remember correctly. She poked her tongue out at me before turning away and whispering something in her sister's ear. They both turned and glared at me, but I looked away. I am not here to be part of their foolish gossiping. I am here for the trial, so I can finish my book.

It was impossible to tell who in the room might have been a friend or family member of Bruno. You'd think there would be a few people there from his side. Perhaps as the trial goes on, I will be able to identify those people for you.

When they brought the jury out, I studied them to try to imagine which way they would sway. There were eight men and four women, all of them stony-faced. One of the men—the oldest-looking, in my opinion—identified himself as the foreman. It is his job to ask any questions the jury might have and, ultimately, he will announce the verdict. Like I said, I would be quite interested in doing jury duty, but I don't think I would raise my hand to be the foreman. Reading out the verdict, changing someone's life forever like that, that doesn't sound like it would be for me.

I thought they might have brought Mr Potts out to stand as a witness, but they didn't. The confession continued to be the main theme of the prosecution's argument the rest of the day, but Marie Habib also added a few other bits and pieces in there. There was no evidence of an alleged affair with Bruno. Only a single text message from Sue to Bruno on the morning of the wedding, saying, *Don't you dare ruin today*, connected them.

'A clear threat,' was how Habib described it.

The message was shown on a TV screen, with paper copies handed out to the jurors. Habib then put forward a theory that Sue had to kill Bruno to prevent him from telling her husband of their affair. The defence yelled, 'Objection,' at that point, citing speculation. The judge asked for that moment to be removed from the transcript and dismissed by the jury. Surely the seed had already been planted in their heads. The judge seems like a smart man. I mean, I am sure you have to be very smart to be a judge.

The prosecution brought up a photograph of the items found in the maze; it was the first time I had seen the murder weapon. Journalists frantically scribbled in their notepads. The photograph showed the bloody knife, the iPad and a pair of boots on the muddy ground.

The argument was that the boots *could* have fit Sue, despite being one size too big. They argued that using boots that were too big would be a great way to throw the police off her scent.

Sue kept her head down the whole time, not showing any emotion or giving anything away. Everything hangs on that confession. I am presuming that the defence will try to explain that away tomorrow.

CHAPTER

29

Yesterday was a complete disaster. I missed a full day in court and a full day of recording. You will never believe it: I got to the train station at 6 am and American Dave was there waiting for me with his camera crew. There was no reason for them to be there at that time. Leeds is two hours on the train and court doesn't start until ten. I like to go early and have breakfast and a coffee at my regular spot before heading to the courthouse. He had left his cowboy hat at home, but that didn't stop him from turning up in denim jeans tightened by a chunky belt buckle with a picture of a horse pulling a cart engraved on it. He had a black shirt with tassels on the back. Round here, he looks like he is in fancy dress. This is Yorkshire, not the Wild West.

American Dave was with Paula McDavidson, who immediately started boasting about the cowboy hat that American Dave had ordered her from the States. Apparently she has quite the collection now, she bragged. She told me she intends to wear them in her to-camera interviews for the documentary. I told her I didn't care.

The platform in our village is not big, so it was hard to avoid them. There is a small ticket booth, one bench, and that's it. If it rains, you get wet. Those big trains that pass through on their way to Leeds make the whole platform vibrate, it's that old. Those that do stop only open the doors to one carriage, since that is all that fits on our platform. There was no escaping American Dave and his gang. Every time I edged away, they moved closer.

'Behind the yellow line!' Paula McDavidson shouted at me when part of my foot touched it. She howled with laughter like a school bully, the camera capturing every moment of it. I am sure she is very proud of her behaviour.

I ignored and ignored and ignored them, biting my tongue and breathing deeply at their provoking remarks. American Dave was quizzing me about why I needed to be in the courtroom every day, whether it was because I was writing a book, like Fiona had mentioned. He told me that he was going to tell the story of Cavengreen and I had better watch out, because he wasn't going to let my book come out before his documentary. I didn't react. You lot should know by now to take whatever is in his documentary with a pinch of salt. Yes, I want my book to be released first, but what will be will be. My story is the truth, and his is a load of cow dung.

But then he went a step too far. 'How 'bout this, Hector? If you attend court today, I'll fire Fiona,' American Dave said, a smirk plastered on his face and chewing gum rolling around his mouth. This man has sunk to a new low. He said I could come to court the next day, but that day I had to stay home. He knew that missing the defence argument would be detrimental to my storytelling. That was his plan.

My face burnt as I tried to hold back my anger. Paula McDavidson sucked in her cheeks and bounced on her heels as she giddily waited for me to respond.

'He's serious, you know, Hector,' Paula felt the need to add.

'As serious as a murderer, that's me.' American Dave winked. 'Come to court, your friend gets fired. Stay home today, and she keeps her job. I reckon she needs the money, don't you?'

There was no use bargaining with him. To bargain with a fool would make me an even bigger fool. I gathered my things from the bench and left the station, the sound of their howling laughter following me.

I can't tell you how defeated I felt when I got home yesterday. That is why I couldn't record anything for you.

Fiona telephoned around lunchtime to leave a message about catching up for a coffee on the weekend. She was shocked when I picked up the telephone, and instantly knew something was wrong. But I chose not to tell her what had happened. As far as she knows, I have got a migraine. There was no use worrying her; she has been through enough and no book is more important than our friendship.

So, that was yesterday. That is in the past and now that I have told you about it, I fully intend to move on. Today is a new day and I am back in the men's lavatories recording my introduction. I will chat to some of the court watchers today and see if they can fill me in on yesterday's proceedings.

Hang on a tick.

Sorry about that, Helen. A gentleman needed to use the facilities. That flush must have made a right racket on the tape.

Where was I? Oh yes. Court watchers are people who sit in the public gallery at trials as a hobby. There are only two types of people who I can imagine doing something like that as a hobby: nosy buggers like Paula McDavidson and people who get their energy from other people's misfortunes, like American Dave.

From listening in on conversations, I have identified a few court watchers in the crowd. There is a woman—mid-fifties, I would say—who looks tough, judgemental and unforgiving. I don't think I'll talk to her. There is a young woman in a headscarf who doesn't look a day older than nineteen. Imagine being interested in murder trials before you hit your twenties. Perhaps she is studying law at university. Then there are two other women, both of them around thirty or forty. There are a few men, too. One of them stood out to me: he has dark skin and orange glasses. He looks eccentric and wears a jumper with a picture of a dancing pig stitched onto it. This is not to say he will be a big part of my story; I just want to set the scene, and this man certainly looks like quite the character.

This is a place where bad people come to get punished and innocent people come hoping for the best but expecting the worst. If these walls could talk, I am sure they would cry. I am not sure what to expect today but, as usual, I shall fill you in later.

The days must feel so quick to you, with me leaving you in the morning and then returning hours later. But I tell you what, they drag for me. On the positive side, I was completely wrong about yesterday's court agenda. It wasn't the defence argument at all. That shows how much I know. Yesterday was a continuation of the prosecution's argument, where they addressed some bits of evidence. That is what one of the court watchers told me, the young girl who, despite my assessment, is not studying law. She just likes having a nosy at particularly high-profile trials. She said the court only sat for two hours yesterday before the judge sent the jury home for the day. I can't tell you how happy I was when the watcher told me all that. American Dave must have been seething when he realised I didn't miss too much. Nevertheless, a day not in court is a day missing from this story.

Today was jam-packed and did not end quite as I had expected. In fact, it couldn't have gone any worse. I'll get to that.

I was surprised that it was *still* the prosecution's turn to present their argument. There were no new faces in the gallery; it was filled with the same journalists, court watchers, and friends and family as before. The twins seemed to think it was a fashion show and were wearing matching bright pink trouser suits. Hardly appropriate for the occasion. I know full well they are dressing up because photographers spend the day camped outside the courthouse. Me, I always sneak out through a side exit, but the twins strut out through the front as if they are stepping onto a runway. They pretend to shield their faces from the camera lenses, but I can tell they are loving every second. American Dave also gives the cameras a good show. One time I saw him pretend to throw an invisible lasso over Paula McDavidson and she played along as if she were being dragged towards him.

It is just me and Martin Bainbridge who use the side door. Not at the same time, of course. He holds back so as not to bump into me. It is a well-rehearsed routine now. I am sure he was somewhat thrown off when I didn't make an appearance yesterday. People like consistency, especially in moments of chaos like this. It is obvious he doesn't want to speak to me. Not that I would hassle him; I would probably just tell him I hope he is okay. His wife might be an adulterous murderer— although still innocent until proven guilty—but that doesn't mean the poor bloke should be dragged through all this.

That is another tangent I have let myself go off on. Back to the courtroom. I am yet to identify any of Bruno's family members, which is bothering me. Surely someone cares that he is gone. A couple of the jury yawned as the prosecution began their argument for the day. They looked bored to tears. The judge even made a joke about it at one point. He asked if they would like him to sing them a lullaby. There were no more yawns after that. It is funny how you would think a murder case would be fast-paced and exciting, but as it happens, it is a lot of admin and going through the same details over and over.

The prosecution spent the morning reminding the jurors once again that, well, Sue confessed. I'm sure the defence will blame stress and exhaustion for a moment of madness designed to save her daughter. A few of the jurors nodded along as the prosecution joked about how the defence would have a hard time arguing that the confession was false. One of the female jurors smirked, scoffed, and folded her arms.

In the afternoon, the prosecution announced that they were going to call another witness. That's right: second up in the stand was none other than my old pal, Mr Potts. I was wondering when he would show up again. He entered the courtroom looking just as exhausted as he did on that final day at Cavengreen. He had spruced himself up with a tailored suit and tie, but that didn't disguise the fact that he looked like he might have had a tipple or two that morning. Only I would have noticed, though. I am more familiar than everyone else with how Mr Potts's face changes when he has had a drink.

A woman who could have been his wife sneaked in and stood at the back of the public gallery, stress plastered all over her face.

The prosecution started their questioning. That's when I made the down-right stupid mistake that would cost me, and you for that matter, the next part of the book. The classic fool that I am. At the time, I thought I could get away with it. I should have known better than to try and be sneaky. I just wanted to be able to deliver you the most accurate information.

My dictaphone was tucked in the inside pocket of my jacket. Slowly, subtly, I reached inside and fiddled for the record button.

Doubting whether I had my finger in the right spot, I peered inside and lifted the dictaphone ever so slightly up and out of my pocket.

'He's recording! Stop everything, y'all!' An outstretched finger attached to the hand, arm and body of that meddling American Dave pointed in my direction.

'What is going on over there?' The judge snapped, rising to his feet. Everyone looked at American Dave and then followed his finger to me.

'This man, Hector Harrow, has a recording device in his pocket. I just saw him y'all. That is prohibited. There's a sign out in the hallway saying so.' American Dave proudly looked over at the judge awaiting his congratulations.

'Is this true, Mr Harrow? Are you recording inside my courtroom?'

My mouth hung open, wanting to say something, but not able to find any words.

'Both of you, step outside.'

'Why me? What did I do?' American Dave barked.

'Leave my courtroom!'

Outside in the hallway, the usher asked me to turn out my pockets. He saw the dictaphone. American Dave triumphantly shouted that he was right. He wasn't allowed back in the courtroom, though. The usher was joined by someone else from the courthouse. A suited man with an angry face. He asked me to play what was recorded on the dictaphone. I begged him not to make me, but he insisted. American Dave leered over, practically resting his chin on my shoulder as I was forced to rewind and press play. The tape started with me, in the men's lavatories, demonstrating how echoey the tiles are. My face went red with humiliation. American Dave sniggered behind me, his warm breath hitting the back of my neck, making me squirm. After the longest fifty seconds or so of my life – apart from when I discovered Bruno's dead body . . .

Tap one. Tap two. Tap three.

. . . I was permitted to turn the recording off. American Dave let out an over-exaggerated laugh as he punched me in the arm.

'Let's just say I'm not worried about what will be better, my documentary or your book.'

That man is a hero in his own mind, and his mind only. 'Who on earth would want to read a book filled with your jibber-jabber?'

Embarrassment consumed me. It was like someone had just read my diary. I felt completely exposed, vulnerable.

'Ah, see you later buddy.' American Dave slapped me on the back and then walked off down the corridor, still laughing. After a few strides he jumped up and clapped his feet together in a leprechaun kick. I'm surprised he didn't accompany the move with a 'yeehaw'.

The court officials instructed me not to return to the courtroom. They banned me. Getting banned from places is becoming quite a habit of mine all of a sudden. After seventy-four years of not causing a fuss, it's a little overwhelming to suddenly be considered a disruptive old man.

So, please forgive this bump in the road. It was my intention to bring you all the insights from inside the courtroom, but it seems that won't be the case. I hope you aren't disappointed.

CHAPTER 30

I am at home in my dressing-gown. My mood is low, I must admit. It seems I have become a nuisance. And I am worried about the book. Perhaps I have bitten off more than I can chew. I want to give you the ending you deserve, but I am not sure finishing the book with a vision of me sipping tea in my dressing-gown will suffice. It is chamomile, in case you are wondering. Helps calm my nerves.

Helen is coming over this morning, to join my 'pity party' as she described it with a little giggle. Hopefully she turns up with cakes and distractions. She wasn't planning on paying me a visit, but when I got off the telephone with her this morning, she called me right back and said she would be over at ten to cheer me up. Best get some proper clothes on then, for Helen's sake.

Helen is here. She says she's worried about me, because apparently I seem sad and look like I have lost weight. I keep telling her I'm not sad, I'm just flat. And a bit of weight loss isn't going to harm me, what with all these cakes she's been bringing round.

As soon as she walked through the front door she started faffing about, tidying things that didn't need tidying and fluffing already-fluffed cushions. Not to sound ungrateful, but she need not fuss around me like that. These Danish pastries with flaky almonds are quite enough. Thankfully she brought over a whole cake box full, and we have a pot of English breakfast to enjoy them with.

The sun is shining, so we are sat at the garden table—in a shady spot, of course. Two minutes in sun like this and I would be lobster red. It is one thing getting kicked out of the courtroom at a murder trial; it is quite another having to bear the points and stares that come along with causing such a scene looking like I've been turned inside out. A recapping of my antics was broadcast on the six o'clock news.

Helen has brought over pretend books bound in the cover the team has chosen. I am pleased to see that they went with option number two. It looks good. To be honest, it is probably not the best day to show me this. On any other day I would be chuffed to bits to see this project of mine come to life, but today I feel like a right grump. Poor Helen has to endure my company, although she is too nice to say anything other than that she's happy to be here. You can't see her, but she just mouthed, 'I *am* happy.' That is the sign of a good friend, eh? When they still want to be around you even when you are being a miserable git. She thinks the stress of the trial and the book have finally got to me. I am too stubborn to agree, but Helen is smiling behind her teacup because she knows she is right.

We should have asked a court watcher to take notes for us inside the trial today. That was Helen's idea just now. Bloody brilliant, isn't she? I will get on to that tomorrow. At least that way we will have some sort of connection inside the room. That is what you lot want to hear about, not me blabbering on about the weather. I will offer someone fifty pounds . . . Oh, wait, Helen is shaking her head and gesturing upwards.

Are you bloomin' joking? Okay, fine, one hundred pounds per day to take notes for us. It better be good stuff at that price. How many copies of the book will I have to sell just to get back—

Who the devil? Someone is at the front door. Who the heck could that be? Everyone I can tolerate right now is sitting in this garden. I am not answering it.

Helen has gone to get the door. She probably just wanted a break from me. She can be a bit hippy dippy sometimes, and she says I am putting too much negative energy out into the universe. That is a very London thing to say, I reckon. No one in these parts talks about energy or juju. My juju is bad today, in case you hadn't guessed. This is very unlike me. I am not the type to be full of beans, bouncing off the walls, like some people are, but I am normally happy, or at least content. Today I am grouchy. That is a good word for it. And I tell you what, that level of grouch is about to get a whole lot worse now that Mr Potts is standing in my garden.

Mr Potts said he didn't want to be recorded. That is a bit bloody rich coming from him. Although, I'm not really one to comment either now, I suppose. He popped round armed with a few things he wanted to say. The first was an apology, which I accepted. It is my belief that whenever anyone comes to you, hat in hand, and makes the effort to apologise, as long you believe it to be genuine, you should accept it and move on. Now, that doesn't mean you have to be all buddy-buddy with that person, but it does mean that you can put them out of your mind.

He seemed genuine enough to me. He told me he had reached out to a counsellor and was working on his relationship with alcohol. He's reading self-help books too. Told you so. He doesn't want to make excuses, but he believes that is part of the reason why he did what he did with the camera inside Cavengreen—he was not in his right mind. That and the money, a wad of which he had stuffed in an envelope and tried to hand to me. I didn't want it. I told him to take it with him when he left, but I have just found it wedged behind the clock on the mantelpiece. I will donate it to the local dog shelter—or to Bruno's family, if I ever identify them.

Mr Potts said today was day one of no alcohol. Even this morning he looked better than during those four days at Cavengreen. His face looked freshly scrubbed and he was wearing a nice casual shirt and chinos. He almost resembled the man he used to be. He told me that his relationship with alcohol was already dicey before the murder; he just hid it better. That is none of my business, and I certainly don't want to embarrass him any further. He is on the up, that is all that matters. He sold his house and is renting a flat in Leeds with his wife and son until he can find a new place to work. He said he was on his way to a job interview at a hotel in Manchester. The move will do him good, I think. They always say the best time to break a bad habit is during a big life change. It gives you an opportunity to reset your routine, something like that.

The main thing Mr Potts came here to discuss was Olive, the bride. He told me he has been replaying everything that happened at the hotel in his head, and he firmly believes Olive was somehow involved in Bruno's murder. I must admit, I agree. I keep revisiting the conversations I overheard, and something doesn't quite add up.

Mr Potts said he saw Olive lurking around the back of the courthouse with her husband yesterday. They were arguing. Mr Potts claims he heard Patrick say, 'You hid the murder weapon. I am not going in there with you and pretending we're not involved.'

Helen interrupted at that point. She thinks it is very likely that Olive killed Bruno because *she* was the one having the affair, and then her mother felt the need to confess to protect her daughter from a lifetime in prison. It makes sense. Why would Bruno be at Cavengreen on Olive's wedding day when he was having an affair with her mother? He must have been there to stop the wedding.

The three of us speculated like old friends. Every so often I would remember that Mr Potts is no friend of mine and scowl a little at his presence, but he had brought up some useful information. That is, if it is true. Mr Potts can hardly be trusted; he has proven that in the past. But what business would he have giving me false information?

We explored the idea that Olive murdered Bruno to stop him ruining her wedding. Or perhaps Patrick is the real murderer, fuelled by jealousy after finding out about his wife's betrayal. The jury has all the evidence it needs to send Sue to prison, but what if we have it all wrong?

Shh. I am trying to be incognito. That is why I am whispering. Not that you can hear, and not that it's necessary. There is no one around. I made it into the courthouse, and I am back in the men's lavatories, recording an introduction to my day. My outfit consists of a very un-Hector-like combination of a black jumper, black pants, black shoes. Like a cat burglar, but a less agile one with a dodgy hip. Technically, I'm not breaking any rules. The court officials said I wasn't to return to the courtroom. They didn't say anything about me being in the building. I breezed through security. Admittedly I was nervous. I imagine it's how drug smugglers feel at airport security. But the show, or the book, must go on.

Helen encouraged me to head down here to engage a court watcher. I told Helen it would be easier if she came down here and took the notes herself, but she doesn't want to muddy the lines between creator and editor. It would have been good to have someone I trusted on the task, but I get where Helen is coming from. She doesn't want to meddle too much in *my* story.

Nerves. I have lots of them. My plan is to observe the crowd gathered outside the courtroom from afar, lock in my target, and then quickly approach them with my offer before word of my appearance spreads. I have a notepad and pen in my bag to give the court watcher, plus one hundred pounds in cash. If they don't agree to help me, I will ask a couple more and then leave it. I don't want to draw too much attention to myself, and I am not entirely sure what I am doing is legal. At the very least, I am confident it would be frowned upon. However, the way I see it, it's no different to the journalists coming in and scribbling notes.

Right, I will be back shortly to let you know how I go. Wish me luck.

'Weren't you banned?' the court watcher said when I approached her with my offer. I politely told her to keep her voice down, but a few heads had already begun to turn. She abruptly dismissed my proposal, emphasising that this was her hobby; things like taking notes for other people turned it into a job and that was not what she wanted.

Acting fast, I quickly beelined for that eccentric court watcher I told you about, the one with the dancing pig jumper. He described my offer as 'scandalous' and was happy to accept my money in exchange for notes on the day's proceedings. Hopefully this system works well. I'm interested to hear what is said in that room today. After my chat with Mr Potts, I am not wholly convinced that Olive wasn't involved as well as—or even instead of—her mother. But that decision is the jury's job at the end of the day. Beyond reasonable doubt and all that.

I am recording this in the back alley behind the courthouse. This is the place where I have agreed to meet the court watcher to exchange the goods and money in a few hours. Now that the wheels are in motion, it all makes me a bit giddy. I've a few hours to kill between now and our rendezvous. Might pop to Marks & Spencer for a polo . . . why I never . . . what is she doing here?

Back home, in my dressing-gown, cup of tea in hand. I have got to record this tonight. You need to know what happened earlier.

At the back of the building, there were cars parked half across the pavement and plenty of traffic noises from the surrounding streets, but there were only two people: me and Olive.

She wore a long green dress and, when I first saw her, she was kicking stones with the side of her sandals. Her blonde hair was pulled back in a ponytail. Her eyes were red and puffy. When she saw me, she frowned and looked away. That didn't stop me walking over to say hello. In my eyes, today was the last chance I would be able to get some first-hand content for the book.

As I approached, she turned and walked in the opposite direction.

'Olive, wait!' I called after her.

'Just leave me alone,' she shouted back, picking up her pace until she was moving quite fast. If it weren't for the uneven pavement, I never would have caught up, but her sandal was snagged by a dip in the concrete, and she landed on the ground, her handbag skidding ahead of her, spilling its contents everywhere.

When I got closer, I noticed a bloody graze on her knee and a few cuts to her palms. She ignored me when I asked if she was okay and again when I offered a hand to help her up. Instead, I bent down to collect the belongings that were scattered on the road. I managed one lipstick and was going to pick up a pen when my hip locked in place and I rolled to the side, landing with a thump between two parked cars.

Olive sprang to her feet and helped manoeuvre me onto the pavement, where we sat side by side on the kerb, nursing our injuries.

'My mother is innocent, you know,' Olive said, her voice defeated.

'But she confessed, Olive,' I reminded her.

We both stared at the road ahead instead of looking at each other.

'She confessed to protect me.'

'So, you killed Bruno?' I asked her. It felt brash in the moment, but I knew I would never have another opportunity to speak to her.

'No,' replied Olive, 'but neither did she. Someone else did and they are getting away with it.' A slightly angry tone had crept into her voice.

'Who was having the affair?' I asked.

'I was,' she replied. 'But it ended when Bruno's wife Deborah found out. Listen, you can't help us, Hector. Not unless it was you and you want to confess.' Olive turned to face me as I shook my head from side to side.

'You must know how it looks, Olive.' That is what I told her.

'If I had killed Bruno,' she said, 'I would never let my mother take the fall for it. Someone else in that hotel killed him, and I am going to find out who.' She shoved the rest of her spilt belongings into her handbag, stood up, and stormed off down the street.

I sat on the kerb a while longer.

'There he is!' It was the twins, suddenly appearing around the corner with a swarm of photographers following them. They marched towards me.

There was no use trying to escape. My hip had buckled and I couldn't get up without assistance. I sat on the pavement, helpless, waiting for the cameras to be shoved in my face.

Then I spotted one of Olive's lipsticks wedged under a car wheel. The top of it had rolled off and was nowhere to be seen. The sound of cameras clicking and people shouting in my face got louder and louder.

'What are you doing here, Mr Harrow? Didn't they kick you out?' One of the photographers yelled as he clicked his camera.

The twins hovered behind me, making sure to be in every shot. But my eyes were focused on something else. Leaning forward slightly, I pulled Olive's lipstick out from under the wheel. And then a revelation hit me like a tonne of bricks.

I need to speak to Fiona tonight.

CHAPTER

32

Fiona just breached hotel protocol. I told her I needed Olive's telephone number from the reservations system, and she wrote it down and dropped it off for me. It is absolutely against hotel policy to share guest information, but when I told Fiona what I thought I knew, she gave it to me straight away. And she wished me luck. By gum, do I need it.

The telephone number has sat on my bedside table for the last two days while I have mulled over what to do. If I play this right, an innocent woman will avoid prison. To be honest, I haven't been keeping up with the court case. In my eyes, none of that matters anymore. They are clutching at straws, and I am grabbing at solid rocks. I have seen bits and pieces on the news about the defence's argument. They are relying on the lack of physical evidence—fingerprints and the like. Surely that will cast enough reasonable doubt in the minds of the jury. But the clock is ticking. Depending on my next move, I could get the whole case thrown out before the jury even starts deliberating.

That will save Sue the stress of the verdict. She is innocent, I know that for sure now. But who would believe the wild ideas of an old man who gets kicked out of courtrooms? Nobody, especially not when the woman on the stand has made a verbal confession in front of witnesses. I need concrete evidence to take to the police.

I just got off the telephone with Olive. As you can imagine, I was nervously pacing up and down the garden in my dressing-gown, cup of peppermint tea in one hand, telephone in the other. It rang three times before she answered. Lucky. My words came out in a splutter; in fact, I am not quite sure what I said was proper English. I took a moment to compose myself then, after a deep breath, I said, 'It's Hector, from Cavengreen, I need to speak to you.'

Olive was angry at first. She told me to leave her alone. But she didn't hang up. Surely if she really wanted me to leave her alone, she would have hung up. I persisted. I told her that I wanted to help get her mother out of prison. Of course, she was interested in my proposition. But we couldn't talk about it over the telephone. I told her to come over. This was a conversation we needed to have in person.

Like I said, I need concrete evidence. So, I am going to record my conversation with Olive. That poses one problem, though: I need Olive to agree to being recorded. Fiona was adamant about this. She told me it is illegal to record someone without their permission, and for that reason the recording could never be used as evidence. Even if I did record Olive confessing to the murder on tape, the police could never use it.

Fat chance she would confess to anything if she knew I was recording. It is going to be tricky, but Fiona had a good idea: She told me to say the words, 'I'm recording you, is that okay?' but to make it sound like a silly joke relating to my recent courtroom antics. That should throw her off thinking I might actually have a recording device hidden under my puzzle books or in my teapot. She is coming over at eleven. That gives me just enough time to take a shower. All going well, this could be the last chapter in my book.

Olive should be here any minute. It is rather exciting, don't you think? And nerve-racking at the same time. All my eggs are in this basket, and if it doesn't play out right, then I am in more than a pickle. In fact, if this goes arse up, there will be no book. I am not publishing something that ends with the wrong woman behind bars. You lot can watch American Dave's documentary for that. Mine will be the full, complete story. Helen will transcribe my conversation with Olive for you.

Hector: Eh up. Hello, I mean.

Olive: The taxi had no idea where he was going on these small lanes.

Hector: Happens all the time. Come in. Come in.

Olive: I'm a bit overdressed; I'm meeting Patrick and the twins for lunch back in Leeds later.

Hector: Well, it's a lovely yellow dress. Take a seat. Can I get you a brew?

Olive: Brew?

Hector: Cup of tea.

Olive: Sure. Thank you. Your home is so . . . cosy. And quaint.

Hector: I'm sure it's tiny compared to where you live down in London. Do you have one of those rooms just for wine, like Cavengreen had? Me, I've had the same bottle of red tucked behind my breadbin since last year. Not to mention, you get much better weather down south.

Olive: I was surprised how much chillier it is up here, even during summer. There have been some lovely days, though. Like today.

Hector: I bet you can't wait to get home.

[Pause.]

Hector: Biscuit? Those ones are Hobnobs and those ones are chocky digestives.

Olive: No, thank you.

Hector: I just want to let you know I'm recording this conversation, is that okay? . . . Oops, I've got crumbs all over my trousers.

Olive: Uh . . . sure. Oh, I get it. After what happened in the courtroom.

Hector: Not my finest moment.

[Pause.]

Olive: Why am I here Hector?

Hector: I need to tell you some information that I think, actually, I know, will free your mother.

Olive: Go on . . .

Hector: That you killed Bruno.

Olive: Not this again. I thought you had something concrete to help prove my mother's innocent.

Hector: I do.

Olive: Well, what evidence do you have then?

Hector: Your guilt is my evidence. Come on, Olive. Why did you kill Bruno?

Olive: I . . .

Hector: It's time to tell the truth, Olive.

Olive [sniffling]: You won't understand.

Hector: I don't need to understand. But if we work together, we can free your mother. You can't let her take the fall for your wrongdoing. It's not right.

Olive: I know.

Hector: Why don't you tell me what happened?

Olive: Well, okay—but try not to judge me. It all started five years ago. Bruno was one of my professors at university. Despite the age gap, we struck up a friendship over our mutual passion for classical poetry. That friendly bond over poetry quickly evolved into a friendly bond over poetry and fine wine. We would meet on Thursday evenings at a small

wine bar with just ten seats and dim lights. We would share
a bowl of truffle fries and a bottle of whatever we fancied.
My favourite was chardonnay, his was pinot. I always let
him choose the wine.

After wine, we would go to a jazz bar, where we would
get lost in the sultry sound of the saxophone and each
other's eyes. The connection between us was electric. Not
to mention, I found him so handsome. We used to talk and
kiss in the corner of the jazz bar. I would try to tempt Bruno
back to my flat, but he always said no. He made sure he
was home by ten at the latest. Instead, we would have quick
encounters between lectures in his office.

I was well aware that Bruno was seeing someone at the
time, a woman named Deborah. He said it wasn't serious
and that he had no intention of proposing. He and Deborah
shared a flat in Camden, but they lived mostly separate lives
during the week and then were busy socialising with friends
on the weekends. It was rare they spent time alone, just the
two of them.

At the time, I was single and, I must admit, I put
pressure on Bruno to leave Deborah for me. But he
questioned our age gap. Being some forty years older than
me, Bruno told me he would never give me children, and
he feared one day I would tire of him and meet someone
else . . . And I did.

I met Patrick when we were university graduates
working for *[name of bank redacted for legal reasons]*. He was
handsome and charismatic, and I was instantly attracted
to him. I didn't rush into anything, though. Bruno still

made me happy, even if he couldn't give me his whole self. Instead, I teased Patrick, rejecting his advances but flirting outrageously. He followed me around like a puppy dog. Until one day, a year or so after we'd first met, Patrick told me he had met someone. Before that, I had never considered how I felt about him. He was always just there when I wanted him to be. That day, I dragged him into the filing room and kissed him. We moved in together six months later, and he proposed one year after that.

I'm sure this all sounds very romantic, but just to remind you, I was with Bruno that whole time. In fact, it wasn't until the day Patrick proposed that I ended our affair. Bruno was wildly jealous and tried to win me back. He told Deborah everything, and left her. It was too late, though, and I told him repeatedly that it was over. But then we started meeting up in secret, trying to find closure, and those moments always led to a shared kiss.

Every time it happened, I felt so guilty. I honestly wanted to spend the rest of my life with Patrick. I still do. He makes me happy. He's from a good family, he wants to be a father and he has a promising career. But it was so hard because, despite all the great things about Patrick, he still wasn't Bruno.

As the wedding day approached, I became increasingly anxious about my relationship with Bruno. I stopped answering his calls and didn't respond to his texts. He threatened to turn up at the wedding and tell Patrick everything. I hid my anxiety from everyone—except my mother; I confided in her. Only my mother knew of the mess I had got myself into.

We were both on high alert when we arrived at Cavengreen, fearful that Bruno would appear at any moment. I tried to push the thought to the back of my mind, dismissing his threats as nothing but that. I hadn't heard from him in a week and hoped he'd come to his senses and calmed down. But the morning of the wedding, I was beside myself with stress. I had no idea he was even at the hotel until that evening.

Right before my first dance with Patrick, I received a message from Bruno, telling me he was at Cavengreen, in suite seven. He said he wanted to see me. I replied, asking him to wait. But he threatened that if I didn't go to him, he would crash the wedding. So, I told him I would sneak out later to see him. He was to leave his terrace door unlocked for me.

After . . . you know . . . consummating my marriage, I put on a dressing-gown and slipped out while Patrick was asleep. I went down to the terrace and opened the door to suite seven. Bruno was waiting inside with a glass of champagne in his hand. He said a sarcastic congratulations before drinking the whole glass in one go. I remember him wincing from the bubbles.

We sat on the end of the bed and Bruno tried his best to win me back. He looked at me with those eyes of his and, foolishly, I let him kiss me. But I stopped him before we got carried away.

To me, Bruno felt safe and masculine, while my husband was young and inexperienced. Bruno begged me to run away with him. He grabbed my hand and pulled me towards the door. I snatched my hand back and fled for the terrace. He tripped me up from behind and I fell to the floor. He flipped me over and pinned me down. I struggled, but he was too strong, so . . . I gave in.

In that moment, I knew I had to play a different game. I told him I would leave with him, but only if we made a proper go of things. No Patrick, no Deborah. Bruno agreed: he had finally got what he wanted.

He kissed me on the lips. That final kiss made me feel sick, but I tried not to let my true feelings show. There was a knife resting on Bruno's minibar; I had noticed it when I first entered the room. It was a steak knife that Bruno had obviously used for his dinner. I edged closer to it, smiling sweetly at Bruno as he gathered up his things. I grabbed the knife and held it behind my back. Bruno opened his arms out wide for a hug. He was so happy.

My hands were shaking as I walked towards him. I knew I had one chance. I waited until I was the perfect distance away and then swung my arm around and plunged the knife into Bruno's heart. His eyes widened and he gripped his chest as blood spilt everywhere. I leapt backwards to avoid the splatter. My heart broke as my first love dropped to the ground.

There was no time to lose. I grabbed Bruno by the arms and dragged him backwards into the bathroom. I can't explain what was going through my mind; perhaps I thought if anyone entered the suite to look for him they'd just think he'd gone out. Then I took the iPad and knife and slid out the doors.

Back in my suite, I panicked. I ran into the downstairs bathroom and wrapped the iPad and knife in a towel, placing them in the bath. Then I slid back into bed.

That's when Patrick woke up, wanting to consummate our marriage again.

Hector: And that was it? You thought you'd get away with murdering a man?

Olive: I hoped. Patrick snored away next to me, but I didn't sleep at all that night. I kept thinking about going to prison. I wouldn't cope very well. Not with the way I speak and look. I was determined not to end up there, so I started to think of a plan to dispose of the murder weapon.

Hector: But first, afternoon tea?

Olive: But first, afternoon tea. I felt completely numb as I slipped into a flowing white dress, straightened my hair, and applied some pink lipstick. Each moment felt undeserved now that I had killed someone. Patrick was hungover, searching for painkillers. I knew they were in the downstairs bathroom, so I went down to fetch them for him, telling Patrick that I wanted to spend the rest of my life looking after him.

It's while I was down there that I used the iPad to message you at the concierge desk, asking for ice for suite seven. Guilt had overwhelmed me. I wanted Bruno to be found by someone, so at least he wasn't alone anymore.

Hector: And tell me, what went through your head when you saw me burst into Lavender Plates in such a terrible state?

Olive: You were so frantic; you could barely breathe. I was the only other person in that room who knew why. I was concerned for you, but most of all I was relieved that Bruno was no longer a hidden corpse but a poor murdered soul. It comforted me when a whole team of police showed up to seek justice for my old lover. But I had to make sure they didn't find out it was me.

When afternoon tea was over, I confided in my mother. Like most mothers would, she vowed to protect me—no matter what. Together, we came up with stories of self-defence, but I knew there had been no struggle. I told my mother that I killed Bruno in a moment of madness.

[Helen stops the recording and asks Hector about the moment when he overheard Olive telling her mother that she didn't do it. Hector replies that he doesn't know what Olive meant by that. He suggests they might have been rehearsing the lies they were going to tell.]

Olive: Things got complicated when Mum and I returned to the bridal suite. Patrick had discovered the murder weapon in the bathtub, and I had to think fast. So, I told Patrick that my mother had killed Bruno in self-defence, because he was threatening to expose their affair. Mum looked alarmed when I said that, but she went along with it. So all this time, Patrick has believed that my mother was the one having the affair with Bruno. And as my new husband, he promised to help protect us both.

Hector: And how do you feel now, knowing that coming forward to save your mother from prison will mean that Patrick is going to find out about your affair?

Olive: Devastated. I loved both men, and now I've lost them both.

Hector: Any regrets?

Olive: Many. I wish I had ended my relationship with Bruno before it had really begun. I wish I had been wiser, and realised he would never leave his partner for me. I wish I had cut him out of my life when I met Patrick. But most of all, I wish I hadn't killed him. At the time, it seemed like the only way I could escape him. He didn't want to let me go and I thought killing him would get him out of my life without Patrick having to find out about the affair. But now he is going to find out anyway.

Patrick wanted to call his lawyers to help us out of the mess we had found ourselves in, but I managed to convince him that we couldn't tell anyone. My mother went along with everything, but I am sure she regrets that now.

The plan was to act normal for as long as possible. Tell the police nothing. But we still had the murder weapon. On day three, the police were getting closer to searching our suite. We needed to make our move. Patrick made sure the coast was clear so Mum and I could hide the knife. I am sure he will feel foolish now for helping me. I just hope the police don't come down hard on him.

In the early morning, Patrick went out into the garden, dressed in his bathrobe to check that no one was about, and when he gave us the signal we took the knife, iPad and boots, all of which we'd wrapped in a towel, and made our way to the centre of the maze, fearing that we would bump into another guest at every dead end or blind turn.

When we reached the centre, I put the bundle down, grabbed my mother's hand and, flooded with adrenaline, together we ran out. I was relieved to have got rid of the evidence and my mother seemed to be too. Looking back, I know now my mother was scared of what she had got herself into. I feel so selfish. But I didn't think it would come to this.

Well, now you know the whole story. What happens now?

Hector: Let's get this book published and on the shelves, and then we can put the right woman behind bars, where she belongs.

The End.

B elieve me, I can imagine how surprised you are to be here. But you see, I had to make it look convincing—the end of the book, that is. Helen sent the final draft off to the publishers last week. But I am afraid the book is not finished. Helen is on her way over now to chat about things and help me piece together the real ending to this story. Helen has done a wonderful job this last month. We were joking the other day about how funny it is that some of you will be reading this next to a swimming pool while on holiday, or on the train to work, when for me it was such an intense time in my life. For you, it is just another book that you will forget about soon enough.

Let me tell you where we are up to while I wait for Helen to arrive. Not that much time has gone by since I last spoke to you. In fact, Sue's trial is still ongoing. From what I have seen on the news, the closing statements are due to happen later this week. But that is neither here nor there. It is only important because I want *The Concierge* to be on the shelves sharpish after the case is wrapped up, if not before. I haven't heard anything more from Olive, not that I expected to. For all I know, she has done a runner to Spain, but that will not stop the truth from coming out in this book.

Everything you have read so far has already been typed up by the lovely Helen and has gone through a hefty edit. The team at the publishing house have been working day and night to get it done, bless them. They liked the ending. They thought it was quite the twist, exposing Olive as the real killer, and the fact that my book has that exclusive should make it pretty popular. Even if I sell one copy, as long as it is to Detective Raj or someone else at the Yorkshire Police, then I will be right chuffed.

Helen told me she really enjoyed working on a book again. Now that she is retired, she misses her old life. I understand. Helen has been the one spearheading this whole process. I think she thinks I need the money, pronto. So, best to get it onto the shelves as soon as possible. I always thought a Christmas release would be nice. I like the idea of being a stocking filler. But this will be out way before then.

Helen is here; I can hear the gate. I will tell you what I will do: I will pop the dictaphone on the table, so you get to read exactly what is said between us. It is easier than me explaining it all later and forgetting bits.

Hector: For the purpose of the dictaphone, I would like to announce that Helen has arrived. That made Helen giggle a little. Are you happy for me to record this?

Helen: That's fine, Hector. And good morning.

Hector: To set the scene, Helen is wearing a lilac blouse and a pair of light blue jeans. I am pleased to see she is holding a box from Maude's Bakery.

Helen: Very good Hector. Setting the scene. You're quite the pro now, aren't you? I've brought along my laptop, but I really can't imagine what kind of alternative ending you're considering. The publishing house love it as is. Everything is ready to go, so what's this all about?

Hector: I know, I know, I'm sorry to be such a nuisance. But I've remembered a few more details that are crucial to the story. I need your help piecing everything together, as it is all a bit muddled in my brain.

Helen: Well, spit it out then, Hector. Come on. Time is of the essence. Can you get me a knife for these cakes? I thought we'd share a passionfruit tart and slice of lemon meringue pie today.

[Pause.]

Hector: Here you go. Thank you, Helen. Thank you for all your help telling my story. You and I both know I couldn't have done it without you.

Helen: You are very welcome, Hector. It has been an absolute pleasure.

Hector: Let's sit over here on the settee. Tea?

Helen: Yes, please. That'll be lovely with a little sliver of lemon meringue. You know it's one of my favourites.

Hector: I know.

Helen: So, what have you suddenly realised that you've left out of the book?

Hector: This is a tough one, Helen. We've been friends for a
long time. But over the past week or so I've realised, I wasn't
writing *my* story after all.

Helen: What on earth do you mean, Hector?

Hector: I realised that I was writing *your* alibi.

[Pause.]

Hector: For the purpose of the dictaphone, Helen has stopped
cutting the cake and is frown—

Helen: Oh, shut up with the dictaphone, Hector! I haven't the
foggiest idea what you're talking about. *My* alibi?

Hector: Yes, *your* alibi. There's a reason why you were so insistent
that I write my book, that you would be the one to help me,
and that once it was finished, you'd do everything in your
power to get it published, to expose Olive as a murderer.

Helen: Yes, because we're friends, Hector. I'd do anything
to help you and I thought you would be excited by the
opportunity. You know how much I love books; this seemed
like it would be a wonderful story.

Hector: That may be so, Helen. But to spend so much time
with an old grump like me for no benefit to yourself . . .

Helen: I enjoy your company, Hector. And I enjoy helping new
authors find their feet.

Hector: And I've really enjoyed this process too. But I have said
it all along: this was to be a *true* story. And right now, it's not
that. The book is unfinished.

Helen: I'm sorry, Hector, but you've completely lost me. The book *is* finished. Sue is on trial. She confessed to the murder to protect her daughter, the real killer, who has been exposed in the final chapter of your book. It couldn't be a more perfect ending.

Hector: Except that Olive didn't kill Bruno.

Helen: She . . . she didn't?

Hector: No. You did.

Helen: What are you talking about, Hector? You've completely lost your marbles.

Hector: I was beginning to think that too. But it was after something you said during one of our last editing sessions that everything started to make a little more sense. The conversation I witnessed between Olive and Sue, when the bride was insisting she had nothing to do with this murder: she was telling the truth, but her mother didn't believe her.

Helen: And what exactly did I say that makes you think you can point the finger at me? I wasn't even there.

Hector: Except you *were* there, Helen. Two Tuesdays ago, we were sitting here discussing some details about the book. I had a vanilla slice and you a chocolate mud cake. We were talking about the hotel's gardens, setting the scene, and you suggested we include a detail that I know for a fact I hadn't spoken about. You said we should mention that the roses had been clipped back to their stems.

Helen: And suddenly I'm the murderer? Because I told you about the roses?

Hector: There is no possible way you could have known that the roses had to be clipped back the previous morning because of a type of fungus called *Botrytis cinerea*. The fungus is believed to have been the result of particularly humid temperatures in the weeks leading up to the wedding. It isn't possible that you could have known that. Only myself and the gardeners knew. But somehow, you *did* know.

Helen: This is ridiculous, Hector. I'm leaving. Let me know if you'd like to proceed with the book or not.

Hector: I thought nothing of it at first, but after Olive mentioned Bruno had been in a relationship for ten years but never proposed, I remembered that was exactly the case with your ex-partner. You always complained to Josie about how he had never proposed—she told me all about it. That sparked another memory. A memory of you and him staying at the hotel.

Helen: Nonsense. I've never been to Cavengreen.

Hector: You have. Fiona confirmed it for me on the system. The records say that you stayed at the hotel for two nights about eight years ago. You were celebrating your two-year anniversary with your partner.

Helen: Oh, of course. I remember now. Hector, it's not a big deal; I'd just forgotten, that's all.

Hector: Nobody forgets Cavengreen. That's when it occurred to me: I never forget a face, but I do forget where I know people from.

Helen: What are you talking about?

Hector: The victim, Bruno. You were in a relationship with him.

Helen: You've got it all wrong, Hector.

Hector: I remember meeting Bruno back then. This whole time I thought he might have been a celebrity or someone off the telly. When I realised who he was, I knew I had to speak to Olive again.

Helen: But what about the conversation you had? She confessed to being the real murderer.

Hector: That was staged. Fake.

When I first thought about inviting Olive here, it was with every intention of exposing her as the real killer and getting our ending. But after Fiona confirmed your stay at Cavengreen, and the memories came flooding back to me, I devised a new plan.

When Olive arrived, I told her what I knew and showed her a photograph of you. She confirmed that you were Bruno's partner and had been to see her, threatening to expose her, the week before the wedding. You knew that their affair had started up again last year, and when Bruno left you for her you were angry. You knew he was going to try to stop Olive's wedding, so you sneaked into his room that morning at Cavengreen and killed him.

You knew there was no CCTV of the terrace doors.
You encouraged me to write my story to solidify your lies
in the pages of this book. This was your alibi. That is why
you asked me to change your name so you could be a
ghostwriter, isn't it, Deborah?

*[Note from Hector: I should probably add that this last chapter has been
written up by Fiona. A big thank you to Fiona. She very kindly offered to
help me finish my book. And I would also like to add that I asked Fiona
on a date last week, and she said yes. That part is not really relevant to
the story, but I thought I should let you readers know that my life after the
murder is looking up. There is no need to worry about me. I am fine.]*

Helen (Deborah): But Olive confessed! It's on the tape that
we're going to hand to the police.

Hector: Like I told you, none of that was real. It was staged.
Olive agreed to help me if it meant we could expose you
as the real murderer. She told enough of her own story to
make it believable; the truth about her relationship with
Bruno, how she sneaked into his suite to see him the night
of his murder, and how she had to dispose of the murder
weapon that you planted in her room, fabricating a story
to her husband of her mother's affair with the victim so he
would help her. But I ran another dictaphone at the same
time, and that one has the full conversation on it, including
the part where we discussed faking our conversation for you.
She recorded it on her telephone too. You had to believe
that the book was finished, that nobody was on to you.
Olive helped me with that.

Helen (Deborah): I can't believe you would do this to me.

Hector: Surely you must have been wondering why Olive
confessed to a crime that *you* committed. I can't believe you
didn't raise all the inconsistencies and holes in her story. As
the editor, you should have asked. But you didn't. You were
too desperate to type 'the end' and have Olive's confession
committed to these pages forever. You didn't even ask
why she couldn't explain what she was thinking when she
dragged the body to the bathroom, not to mention why she
didn't make sense of the boots or the iPad. Perhaps you can
fill in those blanks for the readers.

Helen (Deborah): You deceived me, Hector!

Hector: I'm sorry, Deb. But it is time to tell the truth. The
police are on their way, so how about you start now? Come
on. Give *The Concierge* the ending it deserves.

Helen (Deborah): He left me, Hector. The love of my life left me
for a woman forty years his junior. I was heartbroken and
humiliated—and *furious*.

When he said he was going to Cavengreen to stop the
wedding, I knew it was my opportunity. I went there with
the intention of killing him. I remembered you telling me
once about the lack of CCTV on the terrace, so I hid in the
maze garden from five in the morning, knowing that Bruno
always, without fail, has a cigarette at six before showering.
For one long hour I stared at those clipped roses. And then
Bruno stepped outside and smoked his cigarette, at the same
time revealing which suite was his. I waited a while longer,

then made a dash for his room. When Bruno got out of the shower, I was waiting there with the knife. He didn't even have a chance to say anything before I plunged it into his chest, aiming for his heart. He tried to grab my wrists and fight me off, but it was too late; he was already growing weak.

As he fell to his knees, he looked at me despairingly. I stared into his eyes for the last time, feeling nothing as I watched the life drain from him. I took great comfort in knowing that he was gone. But then I had to make sure I wasn't caught.

Hector: So, you framed the bride?

Helen (Deborah): I wanted her to suffer like I had done. I knew it wouldn't be hard to make it look like she had done it. She had a motive. However, I didn't anticipate that her mother would take the fall for her. That's not what I wanted.

Hector: Tell me how you did it, Deborah.

Helen (Deborah): Hector, I'm not sure I'm ready . . .

Hector: You've been holding on to this secret for long enough. Don't you want to get it off your chest?

Helen (Deborah): Well, I have no choice now that you've caught me red-handed. Sorry, I suppose it's not funny.

Hector: We're at the pointy end of the story, Deb. Why don't you fill in the blanks?

Helen (Deborah): I put the *Do not disturb* sign on the door and planned to wait in the room until 3 pm, when I knew the hotel hosted afternoon tea in Lavender Plates. I'd attended

myself when I stayed all those years ago. And I knew I
needed to wait longer than eight hours, to make it harder for
the forensics team to determine an exact time of death. That
was necessary to help me frame Olive.

I sat on the end of the bed, staring at the body, for over
two hours. I dragged it to the bathroom after rigor mortis
started to appear in his face. I just couldn't bear to look at
him like that. And you're lucky I did. If I hadn't dragged his
body, you might be in prison now, Hector.

Hector: Lucky? Hmph.

Helen (Deborah): Do you know what it's like sitting in a room
with a dead body all day? No, I don't suppose you do. Well,
it's horrible. It feels like you're being haunted.

Hector: You had just murdered someone, Deb. I wouldn't be
surprised if Bruno *was* haunting you.

Helen (Deborah): Just before three, I heard everyone chattering
as they walked past the suite on their way to afternoon tea.
Through the peephole I saw her—Olive—passing by with
her new husband and what I presume were his groomsmen.
Part of me wanted to dash out and kill her too, but I had to
control myself. I waited another fifteen minutes, and then
I took the *Do not disturb* sign off the door and used the iPad
to message the concierge service asking for an ice bucket.
I knew you'd be the one to find the body.

*[Note from Hector: It was at this point that I paused the dictaphone
and left the room. I took it with me, of course, just in case. I needed to
take a few breaths in the kitchen. The kettle was still hot, so I made*

another brew. Deborah—that's Helen to you—meant and still means a lot to me, but this was when I realised that she was no friend of mine. To put me in a situation where I would find a murdered body, a sight that will haunt me for the rest of my life—she knew what she was doing, and she didn't care. I half-expected Deborah to have done a runner while I was brewing my tea, but when I returned to the lounge room she was still there.]

Helen (Deborah): I'm sorry, Hector, but it had to be you that found the body. I knew that they'd never suspect you, and that with everything you see and hear at the hotel, you'd somehow lead them to Olive.

Hector: But they did suspect me, Deb. They made my life hell for those four days. They called me a murderer. In the hotel that I've dedicated my life to for the last fifty-odd years.

[Hector taps his head three times.]

Helen (Deborah): Stop doing that, Hector. The tapping won't make it go away. And it was never my intention to get you in trouble.

Hector: So how did you go about framing Olive?

Helen (Deborah): The last time I saw Bruno, he asked to borrow my laptop for a business call. Somehow his phone linked to my device and I started getting his emails. It was mostly boring stuff, work updates and bills. But on the evening of Olive's wedding, emails started come through with her name on them. Bruno and Olive were exchanging messages. He told her he was at the hotel and wanted to see her. She begged him to leave but, when he refused, she said she would visit his room after midnight. Around 1.45 am, Bruno got another email from Olive saying it was nice to see him but that he had to move on. She ended the email with: *I will always love you.* It was set up almost too perfectly. I thought the police would find the emails, arrest her and be done with it. I didn't expect Detective Raj to be as incompetent as he was. The way I planned this, it should have been an open-and-shut case. Thank God I planted the murder weapon in her room.

Hector: Oh, Deb.

Helen (Deborah): I know. I knew I'd only have minutes before you would be at the door, so I quickly grabbed the knife and iPad and raced out onto the terrace, then I ran over to the bridal suite and peered through the window to make sure there was still no one around. Fortunately the door was unlocked. I slipped my bloodied boots off and went inside. I placed the boots, iPad and murder weapon in the bathtub and threw a towel over them. The items had to be easy enough to find eventually. It was the perfect place in which to hide the weapon in plain sight. Then I ran shoeless across the gardens. I'm surprised nobody saw me, but I managed to make it out the back gate completely unnoticed. It couldn't have gone better.

Hector: Until now.

Helen (Deborah): Until now.

Hector: Didn't you think your friends at the publishing house would put two and two together when they realised that my book, the book *you* helped me write, was about your partner's murder?

Helen (Deborah): They never met him. No one did. We led very separate lives.

Hector: You could have just let him go. You didn't have to kill him.

Helen (Deborah): I know that. And believe me, I tried to stay away. But I was consumed by this desire to make him pay. Once I got it in my head that I wanted to kill him, I knew I was going to. He'd made me look like such a fool.

Hector: That's not a reason to take someone's life.

Helen (Deborah): Not always. But on this occasion, it was. To me, at least.

Hector: And who would have thought it would be me—just an old concierge—who would figure it out?

Helen (Deborah): You're more brilliant than you think, Hector.

Hector: I believe I just heard a car pull up outside. It looks like our friends have arrived.

Helen (Deborah): The police. Ah, yes. Well, I guess this is it then.

Hector: I guess so. Take care, Deb.

Helen (Deborah): It has been a wonderful adventure, Hector. I think you've got a bestseller on your hands.

Hector: I'd better go let them in. Ready?

Helen (Deborah): As I'll ever be.

Hector: One last thing before you go, Deb. Why are you being so open with the truth now?

Helen (Deborah): You know I'll do anything for a book, Hector. And now this one certainly has the ending it deserves.

The End. Seriously.

NOTES AND ACKNOWLEDGEMENTS

If only I could tap into your imagination and see your version of Cavengreen. I would love to have a nosy at how you set out the tables and chairs in Lavender Plates, and what your lobby looked like. For those of you who are curious, the closest place I could find in the real world to the world in my head is a rather lovely hotel in the Yorkshire Dales called Grantley Hall.

Your version of American Dave would also interest me. For me, he has actor Stephen Dunham's face with Matthew McConaughey's voice. Topped off with a big cowboy hat, of course.

There is a little nod to Manchester in the book. That is where I was born and raised. The people of the north of England have so much personality without even knowing it. Thank you to my parents, Jackie and John, for bringing me up in a place filled with future book characters.

You may also have spotted the nod to Australia. My UK family would agree with Hector when he says it is too far away. I live in Melbourne now with Philip and our daughter, Sienna. And by the time you are reading this, our second daughter, who is kicking my insides as I type, will have arrived.

I want to say a never-ending thank you to Robert Watkins from Ultimo Press for taking a chance on the first unsolicited manuscript of his career. I am grateful he saw something special in it. Which brings me to my beta reader-turned copyeditor (who I found on Airtasker of all places!), Sophie Bellotti, for helping me get my submission ready.

This story is time-stamped in my mind as being created while on maternity leave. This is the book of Sienna. Thank you for being a wonderful napper so I had the time to get this done.

Abby Corson has been a luxury travel and lifestyle writer for over ten years, with her work featuring in magazines and newspapers including *Vogue Australia*, *The Age* and *The Herald Sun*. Born in Manchester, England, Abby now lives in Melbourne. *The Concierge* is her first novel.

THE HISTORY OF RYEDALE
From the Earliest Times to the Year 2000

by

JOHN RUSHTON

BLACKTHORN PRESS

Blackthorn Press, Blackthorn House
Middleton Rd, Pickering YO18 8AL
United Kingdom

www.blackthornpress.com

ISBN 0 9540535 1 6

Illustration Credits

The publisher and author are grateful to the following for help with
providing illustrations: York Museums Trust (York Art Gallery),
John Ireland, Elizabeth Lester, Ampleforth Abbey, Tom Todd.

Printed by The Cromwell Press
Trowbridge, Wiltshire

AUTHOR'S PREFACE

This volume is dedicated to the memory of three men who opened up north east Yorkshire history: Bert Frank, Raymond Hayes, and Frank Rimington.

Bert gathered up the relics to create the Ryedale Folk Museum, Raymond widely explored Ryedale archaeology and recorded the discoveries of others, while Frank combined scholarship with the spade, giving leadership to younger menbers of the Scarborough and District Archaeological and Historical Society. Each was a volunteer, each was a good listener and each freely shared his knowledge with others.

History is a changing story. What is written develops as work is done by many people, discovering, interpreting and re-interpreting evidence about the past. All who attempt it, rely on the diligent work of scholars, past and present, who transcribe and translate records, into accessible volumes on library shelves, or who preserve and make them available in archives. We all owe debts to those scholars, past and present, who fill the record publications, transactions and journals of the Yorkshire Archaeological Society, the Surtees and Camden Societies and similar publications. Another debt is owed to those who have written earlier Histories whether of a place, a person, a family or a subject. A new age dawns, with more records and histories becoming more readily available, via fresh means of communication.

I am particularly grateful to the ever helpful librarians at Pickering, Malton, Kirkby Moorside, Norton, Bridlington, York, Scarborough, Northallerton, Beverley and Hull public libraries, at the Universities of Hull and York, and at the Yorkshire Archaeological Society at Leeds, York Minster Library, the Borthwick Institute libraries and the library of the Whitby Literary and Philosophical Society. I do thank the archivists at Hull University, the East Yorkshire County Record Office at Beverley and North Yorkshire County Record Office at Northallerton, York Minster, and the Borthwick Institute of Historical Research at York. A particular debt is owed to Bryan Berriman, the Scarborough Librarian and another to Michael Ashcroft, the County Archivist, for encouragement and help over many years.

History is also a personal view; a personal impression of past changes, most of all when thinking of recent times. It has been my good fortune over many years to hear the impressions of many others and to discuss past changes, as a tutor of courses on history for the Workers Educational Association and the University of Hull, with many adult students. They have contributed a great deal. A lively adult class is a great place for discussing history and discovering that there are other opinions besides your own.

Of the world that has gone, there is much to lament. But 'cheerfullness does break through'. It is over a hundred years since Robert Dennis of Cropton moved a motion against councillors drinking the rate money. It is re-assuring that when elections were chiefly about the price of bread and the relative merits of protection and free trade, a Ryedale candidate stood as an 'Independant, Liberal, Conservative'. If the last two decades seem to overwhelm us, with new technology and high living, it steadies the mind, to hear a student say with conviction in 2003, that 'the two great comforts of life are a hot water bottle and a nice cup of tea.'

I am grateful for recent help and information to Barbara Aconley, Madge & Johnathan Allison, Carol and Jeff Andrews, Michael Ashcroft, Alan Avery, Bernard Barr, Jenny Bartlett, Bryan Berryman, Diana Beswick, Eric Blades, Jack Binns, Malcolm Boyes, Bill Breakell, R. C. Bygott, Mr. & Mrs C. Chuler, Jim Clarke, Kenneth Clegg, Gordon Clitheroe, Edwin Cooper, Richard Crocker, Peter Croot, Ella Cuthbert, Howard Dalton, Mark Dodsworth, John Ellis, Janet Dring, Chris Evans, Bryan Found, Brenda Green, Robert Green, Barry Harrison, Brenda & John Harrison, Edward Harrison, Judith Harrison, John Hobson, June Hall, Jim Halliday, John Hobson, Vince Hollowes, Betty Hood, Dianne Hughes, Keith Johnston, Colin Langford, G. Stuart Leslie, Alex Marwood, Isobel McClean, John McDonnell, Sheila McGeown, Mrs.E. Morgan, Dorothy Morrison, Ted Moxon, David Neave, Mrs. J. Nutt, Moreen Ogden, Geoffrey Otterburn, Veronica Piercy, Christiana & David Pybus, Richard Robertson, Peter Robson, Ron Scales, Mr & Mrs T. Schofield, Linda M. Smith, Keith Snowden, Mrs. D. Speed, Sarah Stocks, John Stone, Albert Sykes, Charles Taplin, Mrs. J. Varty, Ian Walker, Robin Wardle, Martin Watts, Steven Welford, Chris Wilson, Martin Wood, Sidney Woodhams and Peter Woods.

May I thank Sheila for the help that has made the book possible and my daughters Geraldine, Erika and Emma for the support and encouragement that enabled it to be written.

John Rushton

CONTENTS

3. THE LATE MIDDLE AGES

4. THE TUDORS. 1485 - 1603

Revolution in Industry 187, High and Low Governance in the North 189, The Wings of Extreme Opinion 192, Armada Days 195, The Perils of Hard Lives 196, Education in Strange Matters 199, Town Life 200.

5. THE STUARTS. 1603 – 1714

6. THE EIGHTEENTH CENTURY. 1714 – 1803

7. THE NINETEENTH CENTURY. 1803 – 1900

8. THE TWENTIETH CENTURY. 1900 – 2000

GUIDE TO FURTHER READING

INDEX

Front endpaper, *Thomasin Foss, Goathland* by David Baumforth
Back endpaper, *Ryedale District Map*

PLATES

1. The Roman Road on Wheeldale Moor. *Photo, Andy Avery*
2. Helmsley Castle. *Photo, David Ireland*
3. Rievaulx Abbey. *Photo, Andy Avery*

4. 15th Century Wall Paintings at Pickering Parish Church. *Photo, David Ireland*

5. Gilling Castle, The Elizabethan Room. A watercolour by Edwin Dolby, 1875 *Photo, Ampleforth Abbey trustees*

6. Castle Howard. *Photo, Andy Avery*

7. The York to Pickering train passes through Sinnington station, 1953. *Photo John Armstrong*

8. John Prescott, Deputy Prime Minister, visits Malton during the floods of 2000. *Photo, York and County Press*

MAPS

TABLES

ILLUSTRATIONS IN THE TEXT

INTRODUCTION

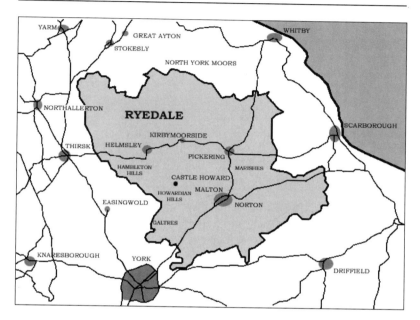

North Yorkshire, Showing the Boundary of Modern Ryedale

The Yorkshire valley of the river Rye gave name to an ancient district known as Ryedale. The name is now applied to a wider administrative area created to serve the needs of modern local government. The new Ryedale stretches west into the Black Hambleton hills, and crosses the south westerly Howardian Hills into the low Galtres district, which in turn approaches the city of York. The mires and carrs of Galtres were poorly drained wet land. A gap between the Hambleton hills and the Howardians was called the Vale of Mowbray, named after a Norman lord who had estates at each end of it. Modern Ryedale extends eastwards into the valley of the river Derwent, often called the Vale of Pickering and south east into the chalk hills and dry valleys of the Wolds.

The lower grounds of Pickering Vale and Ryedale included the wetlands known as the Marishes and ill drained carrs around slow moving and floodable rivers. The Wolds have few streams. The rain sinks through the chalk until it reaches an impermeable layer and forms a vast underground reservoir. This breaks out in springs at the foot of the hills. A dry valley in the Wolds once known as Grindalythe, holds the intermittent stream called the 'Gipsey race', or 'woe waters', the appearance of which was once believed to forecast disaster. North of the chalk hills between Filey and Malton, was Haverford Lythe, which included an unusual strip of light wind blown sands and loams. Another narrow belt of limestone outcrops from beneath the chalk scarp, at the west end of the Wolds.

Within and beyond northern Ryedale, a wider landscape of hills and dales was anciently called 'Blackamore' or Blakey Moor. Much of this terrain now falls within the North York Moors National Park. The moor was once far more extensive and dominant to the eye than it now seems. The name meant black hill moor and that was how it looked. In the right season, in our time, the moor becomes tinged with the purple of the heather.

Much of this great upland plateau, thirty five miles from east to west and twenty miles from north to south, is formed of gritstone and sandstone rocks, which have bold north facing scarps, and which make thin acid soils favouring heather and bracken.

The scarps of Blackamore over look 'Whitby Strand' and Cleveland, which was called 'Clifland' in the sagas of the Norsemen. The modest narrow dales amid the moors have fast running streams called 'becks' and enjoy a better fertility. The more southerly limestone rocks of the lower moors, have lacked a name but have lately been called the 'tabular hills'. They slope gently southwards from their own striking scarps towards the Rye and Derwent valleys, offering a few miles of dry but better soil, from which the moor, in recent times, has had to retreat.

CHAPTER 1
PREHISTORIC TO NORMAN

Early Days

The Ryedale landscape has been used by men and women for thousands of years. The earliest people lived by what they hunted and what they found. Evidence comes from many places extending from the heights to the swamps. This is chiefly in the form of tiny microliths, the small flint flakes used as arrow heads and as blades for other early implements. A hunter's camp from six thousand five hundred years ago has been found at West Heslerton in the Vale of Pickering. Those early hunters and gatherers gave way to the incoming farmers of what we call the Neolithic or New Stone Age some six thousand years ago. They pioneered small permanent settlements, around which they managed domesticated animals and cultivated crops, as well as hunting and fishing. Over two thousand years, much of the ancient woodland was cleared.

These farmers left a few long burial mounds, some standing stones and curious "cup and ring" markings on rock outcrops, mostly in the higher grounds. Their long barrows were huge monuments, used as covered chambers for human remains. The Yearsley Moor long barrow, one hundred and fifty feet long by forty feet wide, and eight feet high, held sand and stone which must have been brought some distance. The late Neolithic round barrow called Duggleby Howe was on a similar scale and stood at the centre of a huge round ditch. Construction of this impressive feature will have needed the efforts of a great many people over long periods. They used a wide range of stone, flint, bone and wood tools and made a distinctive kind of pottery. Their finely polished stone axes have been found in some quantity, scattered over the limestone hills and the chalk Wolds, as well as in the lower grounds. Occasionally, they are still found.

The great 'Adderstone', miles above Allerston village but within the Allerston township to which it gave name; and the several natural Bridestones of Blackamore may have served for gatherings and ceremonies in these and later ages, similar to those attributed to the large

as at ILKLEY MOOR

Flint arrow heads found at Yedingham, Allerston and Wrelton

monolith at Rudston, in the far Wolds. Ancients claimed that the Devil threw this at the church, but the stone was there first. The 'Roodstone' was cut ten or more miles away and moved to its resting place amid a group of four widespread 'cursuses'. These were long pairs of parallel banks with outside ditches, of uncertain purpose. People in much later times used such names as the Devil, the Bride and the Old Wife to speak of impressive features that were already there. An 'Old Wife's Trod' is on the high moor near Saltersgate. 'Old Wife's Stone' is on Bilsdale west moor. 'Old Wife's Well' is at Stape but another 'Old Wife's Stone' stood down in the Marishes.

Men of Metal

The people of the 'Bronze Age' seem to have been more numerous than their predecessors. They too had many centuries of local life, perhaps from about 2000 BC to around 600 BC. Their clearance of woodland went much further, probably as a result of more settlement, both in single farms and villages, with increasing arable cultivation and the formation of extensive managed pastures for raising cattle, sheep and pigs. Long earthworks called dykes, as well as lines of pits in some places, demarcated larger pastoral farms. The high landscape with merely a few monuments gave way to a scene dominated by farms.

The upper chalk and limestone grounds still reveal some of the small cairns, pits and dykes of the Bronze Age, dividing a landscape of small farm cultivations amidst broader pastures within bounded territories. The dykes involved great labour over generations. Some of the better drained soils of the limestone slopes and dry islands in the lower grounds were converted into arable fields and improved pastures

Tumulus at Whinny Hill Farm near Kirkby Moorside

near to the settlements. Excavations on the north Wold scarp revealed palisaded farmsteads containing houses and grain stores at Staple Howe near Knapton and at Devil's Hill, Heslerton.

The York, Hull, Hutton le Hole and Malton Museums show the worked flint, stone and bronze tools and weapons, the loom weights and spindle whorls, the bone pins, the pottery and the jet beads of people from the Bronze Age. Dalby forestry workers, fifty years ago, reckoned to find an arrow head a day. Bronze founders left small hoards of the socketed axes they had cast in bronze at Keldholme and Gillamoor. Weapons have come from several sites. These people erected many round mounds or barrows, locally called 'howes', over single burials and over cremations contained in small pottery vessels. Sometimes, there were stone walls and cairns inside the howe and kerbs outside it.

Loose Howe is a round barrow on moor land, nearly fifteen hundred feet above sea level. This contained a bronze dagger and remnants of leather clothing which were part of a tree trunk burial. The tree was believed to have been used as a boat because of a T-shaped slot at the rear. Another boat was once found at South Holme in lower

3

Ryedale. A road in the centre of Kirkby Moorside is known as Howe End. This circles the site of the howe, a large, round, mound, which contained several burials. Seven more small barrows on low Appleton common were ploughed up during twentieth century wars. Howes survive in clusters and individually on the high moors. Many are on later township boundaries. This was a function that they may already have served.

The Parisi People

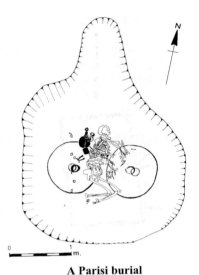

A Parisi burial

The "Iron Age" farmers from about 600 BC, left evidence in the Wold country of settlements of good round houses, set amid inclosed cultivations, with routeways through them for cattle and sheep to reach their pastures. The great estates of the 'Parisi' had ditch and bank boundary earthworks for their pastures, but these features are more evident in some areas than others. Borings at Fen Bog in a moorland dale suggest that the Blackamore woodland was further reduced. These farmers probably used the entire landscape.

The tribes of the 'Brigantes' occupied the west and north parts of what would one day be Yorkshire. The Parisi tribe who held the present East Riding seem likely to have extended over most of the Ryedale district, well towards old Blackamore and westwards to the hills that overlook the vale of York. Evidence for a separate 'Gabrantvici' tribe has yet to be found. Tribal gathering places, sometimes called hillforts, included Boltby Scar in the Hambleton hills, overseeing York Vale, and perhaps also the rock that now carries Scarborough Castle.

Their distinctive "square-barrow" cemeteries have been found most numerously on the Wolds. Similar, if rarer survivals from the limestone hill slopes and moorland fringes suggest that those terrains were also well used but that later agriculture and forestry has destroyed much of the evidence. The small burial mounds set within a ditch of square plan covered crouched burials, sometimes interred with personal belongings and a joint of meat. Concentrations occur in the Wold Valley and south east of Norton.

Heslerton has revealed long settlements of small enclosures for stock breeding and growing crops, nearer the edge of the wetlands than later villages. Near the source of the prolific river Costa, west of Pickering were found extensive water side and cross-water structures at several places. Wooden piles have also emerged at the site of the Kirkby Moorside Glider factory.

The Iron Age people used heavy upper and lower stones worked together to grind grain, which they stored for long periods in pits. Small, carved chalk figures from Malton and Heslerton could even be the toys of Iron Age children. The iron rims from the wheels of carts, sometimes called chariots, have been found in high status burial mounds near Thornton Dale, and at Cawthorne on the low moors, but also at Seamer, Wetwang and Hunmanby in the Wolds. There was no iron to be had on the Wolds but these carts had iron fittings. At Levisham moor and at Spaunton, sites have been found where the iron was extracted and worked.

The Fringes of the Roman Empire

The Roman Empire stretched from Spain to Syria, in 43 AD. when the Emperor Claudius brought forty thousand men in four legions, with extra auxiliaries, to make Britain south of the river Humber into a Roman province. The south eastern Iron Age kingdoms were conquered and absorbed, although some resistance continued for a time. Forts built along the Foss Way looked towards the more northerly lands of the Brigantes, who were ruled by Queen Cartimandua. There was trade between the Romans and the Parisi across the waters of the river Humber, but the Brigantes increased their hostility to Rome after the Queen surrendered the southern resistance leader Caractacus to the

Romans. She was driven out by Venutius, the husband she had rejected for her standard bearer. There was border raiding and more than one incursion by Roman units northwards and some forts were built in the Pennines.

A new Roman governor Petillius Cerialis in 71 AD advanced to occupy a swathe of Brigantian and Parisi territory. The character of this conquest is a matter for speculation. One theory suggests an initial advance by elements of the Ninth Legion, from Brough near Humber into Parisi lands, to ford the river Derwent. They sited a large camp, later altered to a major fort, on the sloping land of the north bank of the river, just east of the site of modern Malton. Separate advances may have taken place into westerly Brigantian lands. Another line of advance has been suggested east of the Vale of York to a river crossing at Stamford Bridge, where another fort was built.

The site chosen for the most important permanent fort for the Legion was further west on a land strip left by the glaciers, which links east and west Yorkshire across the shallow grounds of Galtres. We know it as York. This was also athwart the cross-country route of a major road built across Britain, linking the coast at Filey with the Malton fort, the York fort, the Tadcaster fort and Manchester. Julius Agricola in 78-85 took the Legion campaigning further north, through and beyond the lands of the Brigantes. His forces possibly established the military road system, which was equipped with small forts for police units to supervise the conquered lands. Hadrian's wall was made about 122-130 to separate the conquered from the unconquered areas further north.

Roman Forts

The Romans were here for about three hundred and fifty years and a Romanised society remained even after their military occupation ended. This was time enough for many changes, of which few can yet be known. They added forts, settlements and a road system to an already developed landscape. The larger forts were permanent bases for legionary troops. Their principal fort in the shire remains as ruins which are buried within the county capital at York, but the fort at Malton is beneath an empty field, away from both Old and New Malton. The Stamford Bridge fort is at Burton near the village named from the ford which it commands. Two more small first century forts and two other camps remain on old common overlooking the limestone scarp edge at Cawthorne, near the Wade's Causeway road which runs north-eastwards across the moors. The road goes through another small fort at Lease Rigg, overlooking Eskdale, deep in Blackamore. The earthworks of small practice camps have been found in low ground north east of York.

The large Malton fort has only seen modest archaeological excavation within its sloping site. Some of the great earth banks were even reduced as part of a scheme for keeping unemployed workmen busy. The archaeologists revealed a small part of the regular military layout of the fort. This will have included a head quarters building, and commanding officer's quarters, with regimented ranks of living quarters, stables and granaries. These were laid out between the cross roads leading to the four gates, set within not quite rectangular walls. The eight acre site initially had wooden buildings within a timber palisade, as well as outer earthen banks and ditches. The gates led through thirty feet of rampart and a six feet outer ditch. Outside the walls was a bath-house block.

Over its long life, the fort saw a complex history, with periods of civilian use and military re-occupation. Only serious new excavations will ever reveal its story. There was trouble in the Brigantian territories and further north, in several decades of the late 2nd century. There was some damage to the Malton fort. A dressed stone wall, four to ten feet across replaced the palisade in the rampart and was given a wider ditch. Internal roads showed signs of six or seven reconstructions. Buildings had been rebuilt up to four times, with a progression from wattle and daub on earth floors to stone and then cement. A layer of corn was burnt inside the north east part of the fort in the late 3rd century. A retired trooper from the Imperial Household Cavalry was remembered by a distinctive tombstone. The north east gateway was rebuilt in the early 4th century and the rampart was heightened. In this period a new unit, the 'Numerus Supervenientium Petuariensium' was stationed at the fort. The gateway was thrown down about 367-68 but rebuilt a few years later.

Roman Towns

Urban settlements grew up near the York, Malton and Stamford forts. The town on the west bank of the river Ouse, opposite the York fort, became a significant Roman provincial capital, known as Eburacum. This was given the high status of a 'colonia'. It is presumed that an elaborate palace was built, because the Emperor Severus resided for three years, and the Emperors Constantius I and Constantine I lived here for shorter periods.

The relative significance of the Malton and Stamford towns is debated. One or the other is probably 'Derventio'. The Antonine Road Book listing towns and distances between them gives seven Roman miles from 'Eburacum' to 'Derventio', and thirteen more to 'Delgovitia'. The Roman mile was a thousand paces, or about sixteen hundred yards, which doesn't suggest the identification of Malton with either place. Another substantial town called 'Isurium Brigantium' was formed as an urban centre for the Brigantes at Aldbrough in York Vale while 'Cateractonium', now Catterick was a significant place near a road junction further north, where routes led to each end of Hadrian's wall. 'Calcaria' or Tadcaster, 'Danum' or Doncaster and 'Petuaria' or Brough were urban settlements further afield.

The Roman legions included craftsmen, active within the forts and elsewhere making nails, shoes and pottery, or performing such tasks as the maintenance of iron edged tools, scale armour and lead piping. The towns that grew outside the forts were also centres of civilian trade, of industry and service occupations. There was a military demand for foodstuffs, woven cloth, horses, drink and much else. The towns held the buildings of amenity, amusement and civilian administration. Taxes were collected to maintain the army and the imperial power. At Malton, small finds come from outside the fort in each direction, but so far excavation has been largely confined to one side, leading to the conclusion that the town developed mainly outside the southern gate.

Roads have been found towards the river, lined with buildings including a goldsmith's house and shop. A good town house had wall paintings and a mosaic showing hunters, dog and deer amidst scenes of the four seasons. One room had deposits suggesting up to ten different levels of use. One shop had a large deposit of oyster shells. There was a stone and timber toilet, with a flush through narrow pipes. Open drains ran down beside a fifteen foot wide road, which crossed the river into the site of modern Norton. This was apparently the focus for a star of other roads, a ring of burial grounds and six clusters of pottery kilns, with more scattered settlements. The road had six feet of depth and had several times been rebuilt. Other roads around the fort below Castlegate were found in the 19th century and several buildings have lately been discovered along another road, some distance north east of the fort.

The Romano-British Economy

The Roman wall garrisons, the forts, and the towns themselves created a new demand for farm and industrial products. Local finds include a wide range of manufactured and imported goods, including early Samian pottery at many sites. Pieces of toilet sets come from Foxholes and Gillamoor. Bronze statuettes of Venus and Hercules, as well as a ring dedicated to 'Hygeia' have been found near the Malton fort. Both Malton and Norton continually produce fresh discoveries. From elsewhere have come thousands of coins in a black vase found at Cowlam, a command baton from Acklam, bronze vessels from Stittenham, glass beads and bronze brooches from Sledmere and Thornton Dale. Bridle bits and jet rings have been found at Broughton, a bronze arm-purse on a high moor track above Farndale, a brooch at Hildenley and a Frisian comb at Beadlam. A York tombstone shows couches, tables and stools. The toes of a bronze statue, apparently twice life-size, were found at Bulmer in 1984. Small finds of coins and pottery from an ever widening number of settlements suggest the long reach of the Roman cash economy.

Discoveries of spindle whorls, carding combs, bone shuttles, braiding tablets and bone needles speak of cloth manufacture. A Hovingham hypocaust had brick pillars and Earswick was the site of a Sixth Legion tilery. Jet from the Whitby coast has been found at Malton and scraps of coal at Langton. The Norton potteries produced a familiar grey ware. Another rural pottery industry on some scale was at Crambe, on the Malton to York road from which fine ware was widely distributed in the 4th. century. Other pottery kilns have been found at Knapton, Oldstead and Crayke.

Quarries were opened near the Malton fort and probably along the approach roads, while the Hildenley and Pickering quarries were easily accessible from the Wade's causeway Roman road. Langton villa had evidence of iron working and the moulding of pewter, as well as wool washing tanks and a corn drying oven. An early expansion of grain and meat production in the countryside would be expected if only to pay taxes. Some native farms show new linear and right angled features but others reveal little evidence of change. Two or three farms with Roman finds were found in close proximity to each other at Wharram Percy

Roman Villas

The Roman villa in the Parisi country was a more elaborate farmstead, veering towards the country house, with separate workers' accommodation. Some but not all villas developed out of native timber farmsteads. Some villas had painted and plastered stone walls, window glass, good mosaic floors, heating systems fuelled by cellar furnaces in the house, a separate bath suite, water supply from wells, as well as horse mills, drying kilns, storage pits and workshops.

A group of villas were easily reached by roads from the Malton fort and town including those at Musley Bank and Roughborough, quite close to Malton on the west and another further out at Hovingham. South of Malton there were villas at Langton, Wharram Percy and Burythorpe, Settrington, Duggleby and Wharram le Street on the Wolds. The Hovingham villa found in 1745 with a bath house and two separate pavements has great interest because the Hall nearby was the centre of a very broad estate in later centuries. This extended almost to Malton in 1066. It may be that the villa played the role far earlier. Other villas at Langtoft, Beadlam, Oulston, and Crayke have no obvious links with Malton.

The discovery of Roman villas and other buildings has been largely a matter of chance and there is no reason to suppose that those found are the majority of those that once existed. Suggestive finds include a stone coffin found near Hood, dedicated by Aurelius Serenus to his beloved wife Coscinia Mammiola and to the 'Divine Shades' and another stone coffin found at East Ness, north of Hovingham, made for Valerius Vindicianus, his wife Titia and two children of this prominent Roman family.

Traditions of mosaic finds come from several other sites, including Breckonbrough farm, west of Newton on Rawcliffe, the east farm at Cawthorne, and at Burton east of Pickering, at Cornbrough and at Blansby park foot, near a quarry where Dr Kirk believed he had found Roman mason's tools. Tiles, mosaic fragments or other evidence of buildings come from Cold Kirkby, Potter Brompton, Huttons Ambo, Duggleby, Newton Dale, Amotherby, Settrington, Old Malton and elsewhere. All await detailed investigation.

Roman Roads

The best known Roman road is that which takes a north easterly course from Amotherby to Wrelton and Cawthorn, and continues across the moors to Lease Rigg. This road was of little use in later centuries-when it was called Aldgate, the old road, from the Norse, or Wade's Causeway, either from a supposed Duke, or a Deity, and the Norman French 'Caucie' meaning a raised way. Some of the moorland stretches, much robbed of surface stones are partly visible today, and its course can be seen near Riseborough. At Great Barugh in Pickering Vale, this was still "the causeway to York" in 1650. The road below the Cawthorn camps was described in 1823 as "twelve feet broad, paved with flint pebbles, in great perfection". The original source and destination of the road are an unsolved problem. The road points to coastal Goldsbrough rather than Whitby, and from Amotherby, may point to Stamford Bridge rather than York.

Another raised causeway in the low ground between Sherburn and Wykeham is visible as a raised ridge. The Burgh Head or Stoney Causeway passed from Seamer towards Scarborough rock .A few other Roman roads have been excavated in very short stretches, and others revealed during imparking at Newbrough and Sledmere, or in road repairs near Malton and Norton. When the main drain was put down Castlegate at Malton, it went through a well paved Roman road for much of its length. Another road at Newbrough was found ten yards out of the line of the present road. Most of the remaining Roman roads in the Ryedale area were probably either below or close to modern roads. Unconfirmed nineteenth century reports of Roman road discoveries include those at Ness, Bulmer, Harome, and Crayke, while some short stretches have been more recently found below Stillington and elsewhere.

Roman roads have been inferred from the names, destinations, directness and long distance purpose of some later routes, and by the irrelevance of many of these to the townships through which they pass. Stars of roads focus on the main towns and forts and the longer distance roads in part include those. More recently air photography has revealed linear and other features not previously known. A number of "roads" are distinguished from others in twelfth and thirteenth century records by being described as 'streets', from the Latin word meaning paving. A few other names, like 'herepad', meaning army path, the 'Welham Trod' and some long distance Balks may carry similar implications of a raised way. Such things are suggestive rather than conclusive. Taken together the street roads do form a through- road system of sorts but our understanding of it is woefully incomplete. Nothing has yet been found in Ryedale of rest stations or post houses along the major roads, and only one stone, known in the 18th century and now lost, has been thought to be a milestone.

Names in a Landscape

Roman and other early sites can be suggested by the names applied by later people to stones at Harum and Beadlam or to several places called Stainton. Several castle names in the landscape may derive from Latin 'castra' and refer to features no longer obvious. Unexplained castle farms appear at Bilsdale, Swinton, Ryton, Newsham and in Castle Hill at Sutton. Many well placed 'brough' or 'borough' names come from the old English burh meaning fort. There is a line of borough features on either side of the Roman road known as Wade's Causeway including Riseborough, Flamborough, Beauborough, Coldbrough and Scorbrough.

Other borough names are not scattered at random over the landscape. Three riggs above Dalby have Sutherbrough, Stonebrough and Haverbrough. Among the villas were Burton House at Oulstone and Roughborough. Many promising sites await study including Cornbrough, Brambrough at Stittenham, Burtoft at Ampleforth, Coldbrough at Snainton, Cambrough at Hutton Bushell, Burton Riggs at Pickering and Brough Hill at Settrington. Emmeldburghs may be the fourteenth century name for the Roman Cawthorn camps which by the nineteenth century had become Burrowse's camps.

There are other places called 'wike', a name sometimes derived from Latin 'vicus'. This occurs at Wykeham north of the Beadlam Roman villa and at the village of Wykeham near Scarborough, where a Roman road changes course near St Helen's spring. There is also a lost Wykeham in lower Ryedale and another north east of the Malton fort. 'Cold harbours' have been suspected of having a function in relation to Roman Roads. They occur at Upsall and Hawnby, one north of Pickering, another at a road junction south of Helmsley and one east of Kirkby Moorside is marked by the unusual early enclosure called Ravenswyke.

Religion

The Romans showed a tolerant approach to local deities, sometimes merging Roman gods with their native equivalents. Malton had an inscription to 'Mars Riga' and those at York include dedications to Hercules, Serapis, Britannia, Fortune, Jupiter and Mercury, to the mother goddesses and to the 'genius of the place'. A fourth century shrine has been found at West Heslerton apparently set in an elaborate landscape.

The city of York had a Christian Bishop by 314 and the Emperor Constantine, attributed a victory in 321 to Christian intervention. His mother Helen was traditionally supposed to be the discoverer of the

Table 1. Street Roads in the 12th and 13th centuries

The Street	West Rounton-Thirsk-Raskelf moor-Easingwold-Stamford Bridge-Thorpe le Street-South Cave-Brough
Hambleton Street	Whorlton-Daletown moor-Cold Kirkby moor
High Street	Scawton moor-Oswaldkirk-Stonegrave
The Street	Hovingham-Barton le Street-Broughton-Malton
Malton Street or Braygate Street	Brafferton- Raskelf moor-Newbrough-Yearsley moor - Coneysthorpe-Hildenley-Malton
Wade's Causeway	Hildenley-Amotherby-Habton - Newsham-Risebrough-Wrelton-Cawthorne-Lease Rigg
Mook Street or Royal Street	Norton-Burythorpe moor-Westow moor-Scrayingham- -Buttercrambe
The Street or Humber street	Burythorpe moor-Leavening wold-South Newbold-Brough
The Street	Norton-Rillington- Sherburn - Potter Brompton- Folkton
High street	Norton-Wintringham wold-Helperthorpe
The Street	Norton-Wharram le Street
High street or Garrowby street	Stamford Bridge-Fridaythorpe-Bridlington
The Beverley Street	Saxton,-Foxholes-Langtoft-Driffield
The Street	Duggleby-Sledmere-Cowlam

cross on which Christ was crucified. Christianity was allowed to become a recognised religion. Helen was canonised and is locally remembered in well and church dedications to St Helen at Wykeham, Amotherby, Sherburn, Sheriff Hutton and in a cluster near York. Continuity cannot be proved and it is likely that the Christian beliefs were only held by a minority.

The Later Roman and Dark Ages

The long peace of the third century ended in 296 with internal dissensions, in the period when the Emperor Constantius and his son Constantine were at York. York probably became the command centre for the 'Dux Britanniarum' in a revised organisation of northern defences. The Malton fort was rebuilt. A Roman coin hoard of the period was found in 1912 at Shunner Howe near Blue Wath, high on Blackamore. The fourth century brought heightened military activity throughout the district.

The withdrawal of Legions to Europe to defend against new tribes attacking from the east or to support the claims of rival Emperors, ultimately weakened the British Province, itself raided by Picts from the north and Anglo Saxons from the sea. Signal stations were built later along the coast, including those at Scarborough and Filey, to warn of attack, and may have been combined with the posting of a new rapid reaction cavalry force to Malton, and some restoration of the fort. Anglo-Saxon mercenaries were taken into the army. They were deployed along Roman roads. Their cremation urns have been found at Heworth near York and Broughton near Malton. A fifth century Anglian comb, an enamelled silver breast pin, a sword and a somewhat later brooch come form the Malton fort area.

The imperial control of Britain ceased about 410 after the departure of the last Legion. It is presumed that either local military rule continued or native administration was restored. We know little of this misty age of legendary rulers, of Arthur, Vortigern and Ambrosius. Gildas, the nearest chronicler to the time, wrote of this as a period of flourishing vices, when the island was flooded with an abundance of goods that no previous age had known. Yet the forts emptied and the towns shrank. York has some legends about armies of spearmen, but the Malton fort and town vanished below ground. Probably the Parisi area retained some unity as Deira, a British name for what appears to be the same district.

The Anglo-Saxon Expansion

Stories were told of an Anglian called Soemil, who separated out a kingdom called Deira, in east Yorkshire and another called Ida who was said to have made a landing at Flamborough. Early settlements made at Fyling, along the Cleveland coast and further north in Bernicia, now Northumberland, show that there were isolated landings but early inland settlements near the Roman roads in east Yorkshire, such as those around Sancton and Newbald, may have been the source from which generations of Anglians moved outwards.

They settled the Wold valley and left extensive pagan cemeteries at Garton, Driffield and elsewhere. Grave goods have come from pagan burials as far afield as Acklam, Cottam, Wharram and Towthorpe in the valleys of the Wolds, and across the Derwent basin at Wykeham. The settlement became dense and permanent enough to leave two hundred graves at Heslerton at the foot of the Wolds.

A king called Aella ruled Deira about 569-599 and his successor Aethelric 599-604. There were battles, remembered in Welsh songs, but they were fought further north, when the Pennine kings of Rheged resisted the Bernicians with great loss of life at Catterick. There are no such stories for Deira. Perhaps the mid sixth century plague, the rising water levels and other unknown disasters among the British population cleared the way for fresh migrations. One people seems to have replaced or moved out among the other, but the direct evidence of conquest is slight.

It was the Anglian King Aethelfrith of Bernicia, not the men of Deira, who campaigned widely and gained broad lands to settle that had belonged to the Brigantes. He also took over Deira about 604 and probably ruled it through an under-king. A great expansion of Anglo Saxon power followed. It may be significant that isolated burials showing some wealth, occur further afield, on the Malton street, on the Hambleton Street, on boundaries, and in older burial mounds, both as cremations and inhumations. Sixth century brooches come from Bulmer and Kingthorpe, while a young woman buried above Hawnby at Sunny Bank had gold and silver hair pins, a stone spindle whorl and a bronze bowl.

The old Welsh Laws portrayed a society of scattered settlements organised within townships, grouped in districts to support visiting kings and their officers. Local farmsteads were separately allocated for different purposes, to house the king, his official, a church or some specialist. This was not very different to the Anglian hundreds that replaced them, with a Kingthorpe or Coneysthorpe here, a Tollerton for a tax collector there, and a Wrelton referring to a gallows. Whether by conquest, purchase or marriage, the ancient estates were acquired until almost all bore English names. Both Kings Edwin and Oswy seem to have had British consorts, and estates may have come with them.

Around the Beadlam, Roughborough and Musley Banks villas, later township boundaries follow anomalies quite different from elsewhere. This raises the possibility that the villas continued working as farmsteads with their old territories into later times. The more recent field pattern at Hutton Bushell seems very regularly planned and tightly aligned on a Roman road, perhaps a hint of other continuity. Burton Riggs kept its own small suite of cultivated lands in Aldfield. The villa land at Hovingham remained a major estate centre. The Malton fort did not apparently retain any significance in later times and yet the Anglian village of Malton was placed, strangely enough at the far eastern tip of the land to be cultivated, not centrally as was more usual.

Place-names ending with 'ingaham', 'ing', 'ham' and 'ington', mark Anglo-Saxon homesteads, which gave their name to townships. Many occupied the Rye, Derwent and Wold valley sides, with settlements where the springs break out. Exceptions occur at the lowland river crossings of Yedingham and Newsham, and even at the high moor fringe site called Lastingham. Other names ending in 'burn', 'lea' and 'feld', recall the landscape into which they expanded. The most frequent township names end in 'tun', the same element as in township, the basic unit of settlement and cultivation.

The overwhelming dominance of such place names suggests a general occupation of the available lordships by Anglian people. It also implies a large scale use of the available arable and pasture. This conclusion is reinforced by the considerable English element in field and landscape names. The survival of British personal names like Cedd and Chad does however suggest some merger of people. River names derived from the Welsh like the Leven above Thornton Dale, the Dove, the Derwent and the Esk, or hill names like 'Penn' at Gillamoor hint at their co-existence, but the rarity of the element 'Wahl' as in Waltun near Kirkby Moorside, Walles near Ebberston and perhaps Walsgrave near Scarborough, implies an over whelming Anglian dominance.

Anglian Kingdoms

The early Anglian kingdom of Deira stretched from the river Humber northwards. There is no evidence for the northern boundary towards the Tees, before it was merged with the more northern principality of Bernicia, which ran at least from the Tees to well beyond the river Tyne. The two became Northumbria. Since both names are earlier than the Anglians, it may be that Deira marks the old area of the Parisi and did not include all Blackamore. Like their predecessors, the Anglian Kings appear to have travelled between a number of royal villas or halls, the location of most of which is very uncertain.

Edwin the son of Aelle of Deira returned to kill Aethelfrith in battle in 616 and became King of all Northumbria in his place. He made a new marriage with the Princess Aethelburgh of Kent. She brought with her a Christian priest from Augustine's mission to Canterbury called Paulinus. He persuaded Edwin to accept baptism in 627. At a royal villa on the Derwent, King Edwin was saved by the thegn Lilla from assassination. Lilla might plausibly be associated with Lilling near York, and he was apparently buried in Lilla Howe, at a junction of boundaries near the source of the river Derwent, high in Blackamore.

Several places have with some plausibility claimed to be the site of the royal villa on the Derwent east of York -namely Kexby, Aldby near Buttercrambe, Malton, and Yedingham but evidence is lacking. A few other royal villas are known. One was at Goodmanham in the East Riding, where the grove was a seat of Anglian pagan religion. There was another at Crayke which carries a Welsh name and could have a similar association. A third royal villa was at Little Driffield, where there was an unusual church site, a fair with unusual customs and a nearby 'spel howe'. This refers to a meeting place for speech at a burial mound in the open air.

Speech howes or crosses occur in the shire at such other places of undoubted early significance as Ripon, Guisborough, Knaresborough, Burstwick and Boroughbridge. This adds much interest to the Spelhowes at Marton-Moxby in the Vale of York, at Flotmanby, at Brandsby in the Howardian Hills and most particularly to the Spelcross near Wombleton, which are presumed to be meeting places of early local government. Tradition claimed that the isolated Kirkdale church was first built at the stone cross which stands in curious isolation two hundred yards east of the famous quarry.

The Christian Church

King Edwin accepted the Christian priest Paulinus as the price of an arranged marriage with a royal bride. The priest led the king and his court to a formal conversion in 627, when the monarch and members of his court were baptised. Paulinus missioned in several parts of Northumbria and Lindsey making what appear to be mass baptisms in Yorkshire rivers. It is a moot point whether those being baptised were Anglians or British. Choice may not have been a major factor. Between Easingwold and Stillington, a Paulinus cross stood in isolation six centuries later. The traditions of Paulinus baptisms at Malton and Snainton do not seem reliable, but those for churches backing on to the river Swale may have a better claim.

King Edwin built the first York church amid Roman ruins and a few years later began its replacement by a larger stone church. The Pope sent Paulinus a 'pallium', signifying his investiture as a bishop but this arrived too late. Edwin was killed by a British king Caedwalla at Hatfield in 633. Paulinus and Edwin's Queen returned south, leaving only the deacon James behind them. The kingdom of Northumbria briefly broke up, but the kings Osric of Deira and Eanfrith of Bernicia who renounced Christianity, were killed within the year. The Christian king Oswald recovered the Northumbrian Kingdom in battle against Caedwalla and reigned over the re-united Deira and Bernicia for eight years .He and his successors employed under-kings to administer Deira.

Anglian Monasteries

The movement to found both monasteries and churches was begun by King Oswald who brought men like Aidan from Iona, where he had been exiled with the monks of St Columba. Lindisfarne became a monastery. He died after a short reign in 642. Traditions of an unfinished monastery at Oswaldkirk in Ryedale are unconfirmed, and the church dedication could be to the later Archbishop Oswald, but the site remains potentially significant .A rare dedication to St Columba was given to the church at Topcliffe in the vale of York.

King Oswy, brother of Oswald, succeeded to the throne and enjoyed a long reign in which he gave six estates for monasteries in Deira, including one at Streoneshalch, the later Prestby near Whitby in 657. Here the Abbess Hilda of the Deiran royal house, who had heard Paulinus preach, trained a cadre of bishops who would mission much of

England. The monastery became the burial ground of the royal house with a dependant house of nuns at Hackness. An under-king of Deira, Oethelwald, son of Oswald, asked Cedd Bishop of the East Saxons to found another monastery, where he might frequently hear the word, pray and be buried. The Bishop ritually sanctified the site, west of Lastingham, finding sufficient supplies to break his fast.

The southern Church mission, inspired from Rome and Canterbury and the northern mission enlightened by the traditions of Iona, resolved their differences at the famous Synod held at the Streoneshalch monastery in 664. Oswy's son Alhfrith was at the Synod. He was probably the under-king of Deira, but tradition claims that he fought his father at Oswy's Dykes above Ebberston, and when wounded took refuge further down hill in Ilfrid's cave. When Cedd came north for the Synod, he visited Lastingham but both he and thirty monks died in a plague. Chad went there to build a stone monastery, where Ovin a noble came to labour and which Bede visited in 735. A remnant of the huge stone cross remains.

Other monasteries were formed at Coxwold and Stonegrave. King Ecgfrith in c685. gave Crayke to the saintly Cuthbert and a monastery was built there. Pope Gregory, patron of Augustine's mission to Canterbury was the subject of a biography by a Whitby monk. The early church at Kirkdale is dedicated to St Gregory. Within it are two elegant tomb stones, once said to bear the name king Oethelwald and the tassels of a pallium respectively. They are high status monuments and the plague that wasted Lastingham's inmates, might account for a movement of the shrine. Recent excavations tend to confirm the view that an important church was at Kirkdale. Fragments of great crosses have been found at Stonegrave, Lastingham and Hackness.

Parishes for People

The early history of parish churches is never clear. There is little evidence to go on. A parish was the district that supported a church, by rendering payments of tithes in return for spiritual services. Some of the oldest parishes seem to represent the great estate of a single lord at the time when tithes were first given. Some churches even stand in manor house or hall precincts. Other parishes seem more likely to originate as the districts of missioning monasteries. The church of Whitby is sited near a major settlement, but St Gregory's, Kirkdale and St Hilda's, Ellerburn occupy remote valley sites, with minimum agricultural possibilities. Whatever their origin, their status dwindled for Ellerburn became a chapel within Pickering parish and Kirkdale in 1145 was described as the church of Welburn.

Pope Gregory had advised the conversion of pagan holy places to Christian use and this could account for the site of the unusually isolated church at Westow, meaning Wife's Stowe. Places called 'Stowe' have frequently proved to be of some early religious significance. Kirkby Moorside church is near a large burial mound and an eighth century Anglian coin was found in the churchyard. Hovingham has a stone altar frontal of the period showing Christian scenes. The parishes of Terrington, Hovingham and Westow could have churches sited at older pagan sites, because their names may indicate holy places.

Several wells and churches have dedications to early saints, even though the church itself may not be as ancient. It seems unlikely that later Vikings or Norsemen would favour St Felix who gave name to Felixkirk, a Burgundian who accompanied Paulinus, or to the Anglian St Botolph at Bossall or to St John of Beverley at Salton. St Hilda of Whitby was the dedication of several more churches while St Cuthbert was remembered at Crayke, Hackness and probably in the Cudbrightgate above Pickering. The great soke manors at Pickering, Whitby, Stokesley and Wintringham had churches dedicated to St. Peter, but so were those at Scrayingham and Langtoft. Holy Well dedications were rare on the waterless Wolds, and those around Blackamore were mostly to St Mary but St Wilfrid's spring is at Cawton above Gilling, St John's well at Moxby and St Ced and Chad wells survive in Lastingham village. The early character of many of the dedications is remarkable.

From Anglian Northumbria to Danish Yorkshire.

Viking raiders landed and looted the Northumbrian monastery at Lindisfarne in 793. Thereafter, for year after year, they ravaged the English and other European coasts for easy plunder. Defence against such sudden concentrations of force proved impossible to organise. After 850, raiding parties of Vikings camped through the winter. They obtained horses and became mobile, moving easily around the whole country. From 865 'a micel here', a great army, moved easily around the island. Halfdan king of the Danes and Ubbi, leader of the Frisians led them into York in 866 and again in 867 causing great destruction.

Halfdan carved a Danish kingdom from the broader Anglian kingdom of Northumbria, settling his army in Deira in 876, while most of Bernicia beyond the Tees remained English. The kingdom of York held by the Danes stretched from the river Humber to the river Tees, and lasted till 954. A succession of kings left their names, their coins and little else, by which to know them. Closer links were forged between York and the Viking kingdom of Dublin after 910. Both towns were important centres of seafaring trade. Ragnall and Sigtryggr ruled as kings of York and Dublin, until the southern English briefly resumed control. Thereafter, short Viking reigns were interspersed with periods of English rule for another thirty years.

From Kingdom to Earldom

The southern King Athelstan expelled the Dublin Vikings and received the submission of the north in 927, after the battle of Brunanburh. He destroyed the Danish fortifications at York and distributed the booty that was found within. A coin hoard found at Bossall may date from this time. The lead chest contained silver rings, fragments of spurs and hundreds of silver coins, including some traded from middle Asia. Olaf of Dublin restored rule by Norsemen but the southern King Edmund took York again. After the last Viking King Eric Bloodaxe was killed on Stainmore in 954, King Eadred finally brought Yorkshire under the permanent control of the southern English kingdom.

After a political settlement, the English King Eadgar appointed outsiders as Earls, who were subject to his influence. He confirmed lighter taxes and great legal autonomy to the Yorkshiremen in 962. The King kept the taxes, the succession dues from major thanes, privileged royal courts, a mint for issuing coinage and other interests in York, and the right to appoint both Earl and Archbishop, but he had only a modest royal estate in Yorkshire. The old royal estates of the Anglian kingdom of Deira probably went to the Earl to support his household force, which may have been kept at Earlsburgh just north of York. An Anglian dynasty ruled as distinct Earls of Northumberland, now a long way from the Humber and beyond the Tees in old Bernicia. The land of St. Cuthbert, the holy man's folk, in Durham, retained a separate identity largely untouched by Danes or Norsemen. Yorkshire had become part of England.

York with several thousand people was the only sizeable town. Here were the seats of the Earl, the Archbishop and a ruling elite that included Danes and Norsemen. The river port could receive the sea going vessels of the day, assisted up river by a water surge called the

Ouse bore. The town was a centre of craft industries and merchant traders. York enjoyed a measure of self government under a Hold or high reeve and had its own lawmen. The wider shire took its name from the town. Many of the leading figures in York also held country estates. Danes had probably replaced Anglians as lords in many places after 876 when the chronicler says that they 'shared out the land of the Northumbrians and they started to plough and to support themselves'. A separate Norwegian settlement was made in the 10th century from Ireland. This further altered the composition of the ruling groups in Yorkshire, and added village names like Northmanby and the Irish sounding Duggleby.

Three Ridings made up the Shire. Older districts called hundreds were grouped into at least twenty eight wapentakes, for military and taxation purposes. The name may derive from the brandishing of weapons by free men to show approval at their gatherings. North east Yorkshire held the wapentakes of Langbaurgh, Dic (later Pickering Lythe), Maneshou (later Ryedale), Bolesford (later Bulmer), Gerlestre (later Birdforth), Allerton, Buckrose and Dickering.

Most of the wapentakes were named from their rural meeting places at some hill, dyke, burial mound, ford, tree or cross. Allerton kept its older name as a small shire. Other older and smaller units, probably Anglian hundreds, survived in the east and west divisions of Pickering Lythe and Langbaurgh or were remembered in Coxwoldshire, Whitby Strand, Haverfordlythe and Holdelythe, these last the southern parts of Pickering Vale and Ryedale. Hundreds called Scard, Acklam and Toreshou were spoken of in Buckrose wapentake and others called Huntou, Turbar and Burton in Dickering wapentake in the north Wolds in 1066. The language, customs, landscape and coinage of the people showed much of Scandinavian culture mingled with many underlying Anglian traditions that survived.

The Great City of Yorvik

Scandinavian York was developed south and west of the ruined Roman fort towards the rivers Ouse and Foss and in the area of the Roman town on the west bank of the Ouse. By 1066 seven administrative districts within the city, included one under the control of the Archbishop, and there were several churches serving small city parishes, containing together more than sixteen hundred properties. The townsmen had extensive pasture rights in eleven neighbouring townships.

Some of the most exciting archaeology ever undertaken has revealed that York was already a centre of manufacture, often in rather squalid working conditions, behind houses within unchanging boundaries. Here were craftsmen working in metals, jet, glass, amber, deer horn, wood and bone. They wove cloths, tanned leather, cobbled shoes, processed fish and minted a silver coinage. The Danish merchants brought back silk, furs and skins, ivory, rare stones and Rhine pottery.

Lords of a Countryside

Within their country estates, the new lords established some new townships and renamed others, but many places including those of administrative centres kept their older names. Several clusters of place names, ending with 'by' or 'thorp', do occur in some areas, often preceded by Danish personal names. Elsewhere a single settlement with such a name seems to be squeezed between townships with older Anglian names and could have been divided from them. The balance of Scandinavian and Anglian varies between districts. Pickering Lythe wapentake has twenty six townships ending in 'tun', five 'bys' and three 'thorps'. Old Ryedale had thirty 'tuns', eleven 'bys' and six 'thorps' a similar balance, but there were more Scandinavian names in Cleveland. Much of the surviving language of the higher pastures speaks of their gills, slacks and sets. The lower land is chiefly 'ings' and 'carrs', given its names from the Danish and Norse tongues.

Some of the estates of the greater families were closely related to the old 'shires' and to the early 'parishes', and in some cases were identical with them. They centred on a lord's great hall and farmstead, which the Normans would call 'manors'. They often had the outlying lord's or demesne farms called 'berewicks', away from the main holding. Much of the remainder of these holdings consisted of the over-lordship of free men within what were known as 'soke' estates. The soke holdings could be near or far from the hall, but outside the Wolds, were still compact enough to form identifiable blocks.

The sokemen were relatively free men who held their estates in return for fixed money payments, attendance at courts and probably allegiance and military service. The larger 'sokes' in 1066 belonged to the King, the church, the Earl and to the families of the greater thegns, some of which had provided previous Earls. The local soke manors

23

Table 2. Some Scandinavian Language found in the Landscape

Enclosures	toft, garth.
Water	holme (meadow), wath (ford), beck (stream), fitts (lush grass) keld (spring)
Valleys	gill (steep), slack (shallow), wham (small) dale,
Hills	knoll, knott (round), ness (headland), sett (high pasture)
Cultivation	ovenham (intakes), broates (clearings) thwaite (clearing)
Woods	lund (grove), skogr (wood) skew,
Roads	gang, gate,
People	Aislaby (Aslakr), Amotherby (Aymundr) Barthorpe (Bark), Blansby (Blanda), Brandsby (Brandr), Brawby (Bragi), Bugthorpe (Buggi), Coneysthorpe (Conungr or king), Duggleby (Dufgall), Farmanby (Farman), Firby (Frisians), Fornthorpe (Forni), Ganthorpe (Galm), Helperthorpe (Hjalp), Hildathorpe (Hildigr), Holtby (Holti), Kettlethorpe (Ketill), Menethorpe (Mening) Mowthorpe (Muli), Normanby (Northman), Raisthorpe (Hreidar) Roxby (Rauthr), Slingsby (Slyngr), Stearsby (Styr), Thirkleby, (Thorgils), Thornthorpe, (Thorgrim), Towthorpe, (Tove) Weaverthorpe, Wiganthorpe (Vikingr)

described at that time had between four and forty-four outlying estates connected with them. These were rated for taxation at between seventeen and one hundred and twenty nine carucates.

Some of the sokes appear much reduced by the granting away of clusters of estates to other people. This converted sokeland into new independent lordships called manors, with important legal rights. The process would continue in the 12th and 13th centuries. The estates could be subdivided among heirs. They could be partitioned, sold or carried to other families in marriage.

A mixture of great, medium and small lordships was apparently the result by 1066. The few available sources of information probably conceal forgotten early sokes and wider overlordship. A hierarchy of great and small lordships dominated late Viking society. Thegns with more than six lordships paid the King an inheritance tax of eight pounds, while those with less paid only two pounds.

Early Farming

Arable farming was managed in named places called 'vills' or townships. The township was the tract of land off which a community lived, but only the enclosures of the homesteads, arable fields and meadows were always fully appropriated within boundaries. Pasturing still sometimes extended over part or whole of the broader 'parishes', which represented earlier estates. Most townships eventually appropriated all the types of land necessary, within a well defined boundary, but very late intercommoning survived at Fyling, Spaunton and elsewhere. Some high townships around Ryedale once even shared distant low meadows. Woodlands shared by several townships were still familiar in the 14th century. The bounded townships as measured in much later centuries varied enormously in size, from 350 acres at Wath and 670 acres at East Ness to the large townships of Sledmere 7040 acres, Wintringham 5340 acres and Settrington 4986 acres. The great majority fell somewhere in between.

The cultivated land of a community was assessed for paying taxation in 'carucates' and 'bovates'. 'Carruca' was Latin for plough. 'Bovate' was later rendered as the more homely oxgang. Eight oxgangs made a carucate just as eight oxen might make an ideal heavy plough team. When the assessments were first made, they must have formed a real judgment of ploughing done. Over time the ploughing changed, but the assessment in carucates and oxgangs usually stayed the same. An oxgang indicated a farmer's share of the total township holding and hence his share in any tax to be paid. His share of the field land carried with it the farmstead or house, and also meadow, wood and common pasture rights beyond the fields, in tracts that were often shared by several townships.

The moorland dales including Bilsdale and the Esk valley were thinly settled with cultivations at Urra, Westerdale, Danby, Hankton and Egton. Single dales farmsteads seem initially rare and those dales

Table 3. Some Soke Estate Centres & Their Lords in North East Yorkshire in 1066

Earls	Principal Halls & Values listed.
Earl Siward	Whitby-£112;Loftus -£48;Acklam – £48
Earl Morcar	Pickering-£88; Easingwold-£32; Bridlington-£32;Burton Agnes- £24
Earl Edwin	Northallerton-£80
Earl Tostig	Falsgrave-£56.
Waltheof	Howsham-£4
Archbishop	
Aldred	Weaverthorpe -£14
Thegns	
Ormr	Kirkby Moorside-£12; Hovingham-£12; Bagby-£8; Langton-£12
Kofsi	Coxwold-£6
Ligulfr	Bulmer-£5
Bjornulfr	Topcliffe-£4
Gospatric	Seamer-£2;Hutton Rudby.£24
Havarthr	Stokesley-£24
Thorbrandr	Buckton-£4
Karli	Hunmanby-£12

bearing the names of the Scandinavians Bila, Brandr, and Trutr at Bilsdale, Bransdale and Troutsdale seem to suggest that entire dales may once have formed private pastures.

People in Their Places

The townships or named places listed in the Domesday Book as existing before the Normans came are not dramatically different to the townships of later ages, and most carry the same names. Each place might include a 'thegn' or a 'sokeman', 'villeins' and 'bordars'. Despite

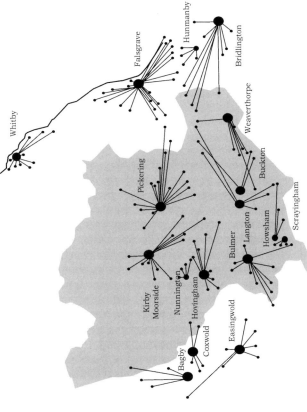

The Great Estate Centres
of Late Viking Times

● The Soke Manors

· Remaining outlying estates

Modern Ryedale

Whitby

Falsgrave

Hunmanby

Bridlington

Weaverthorpe

Pickering

Buckton

Scrayingham

Kirby
Moorside

Langton

Bulmer

Nunnington

Howsham

Hovingham

Bagby

Coxwold

Easingwold

important differences, these statuses have many similarities with later manor lords, yeomen, husbandmen or farmers and cottagers respectively.

Over seventy thegns, whether of Norse, Danish or English descent, are named in 1066 in north east Yorkshire. Most were of modest estate, but there were also middling and very great landlords. It is possible that in several cases more than one person carried the same name. For example, Ughtred of Cleveland may have been distinct from Ughtred of Ryedale. If he was not, he was indeed a great proprietor, but then he certainly was in either case. There may be more than one thegn named Ormr. It remains very clear that large lordships or overlordships took up a very high proportion of the whole. One of the main elements of feudalism already existed. A higher aristocracy was not a Norman invention.

Table 4. The Greater North East Yorkshire Estate-Lordships in 1066

Over 150 carucates
Earl Morcar; Ormr;
100-149 carucates
Earl Siward; Earl Edwin; Earl Tosti; Archbishop of York;
Gospatric; Ughtred; Ligulfr;
50-99 carucates
Gamal; Havarthr; Knutr;
25-49 carucates
Waltheof; Northman; Svein; Arnketil; Thorbrandr;
Thorketil; Ulfketil; Bjornulfr; Kofsi; Asketil; Bishop of
Durham
15- 24 carucates
Madalgrim; Thor; Karli; Ulfr; Eadmund; Merleswein

Only two places in north east Yorkshire have any record of the numbers of people before 1066. Both of these were great soke estates. Northallerton had 66 villeins with 35 ploughs working 44 carucates of land. Within the 85 carucates of its sokelands were 116 sokemen. Falsgrave near the coast had 108 sokemen with 46 ploughs working 84 carucates of land. These records suggest average farm holdings of six oxgangs. More realistically, there may have been some combination of full eight oxgang holdings and other carucates that had been sub-divided.

Since many townships were only rated at one, two or three carucates, with eight oxgangs to the carucate, it is likely that single farms and modest hamlets were well represented among the places which later became populous villages. Various estimates can be attempted, for the population of farming households in the entire area depending on the assumptions made.

A Christian Church

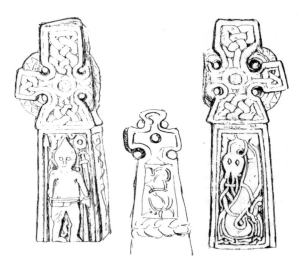

Carved Stone Crosses from Middleton Church

The Anglo Saxon monasteries of Lastingham, Crayke, Coxwold, Stonegrave and elsewhere were swept away by the Danish 'army of the pagans' or were repossessed by the heirs of their founders. Yet the Danish and Norse Kings and their English successors who nominated the Archbishops, found it convenient to restore the authority of the Christian church. Large estates were given for the support of the Archbishopric. The King backed Archbishop Oswald when he tried to limit alehouses to one a parish, and to restrain 'drinking to pegs' (competitive drinking). King Athelstan visited the major northern

29

Table 5. 1086. Churches Recorded on the Estates of Earls and Thegns in North East Yorkshire

Morcar	Easingwold, Pickering, Foston
Siward	Acklam, Malton,
Tosti	Hackness (& Scarborough rock chapel)
Waltheof	Barton le Street, Crambe, Slingsby (priest).
Merleswein	Stonegrave
Gospatric	Brafferton, Hutton Rudby
Ligulfr	Bulmer, Kildale, Sutton (priest)
Ughtred	Seaton, Guisborough, Helmsley
Ormr	Kirkby Moorside, Hovingham, Kirkby Knowle (priest)
Gamel	Brompton, (Edstone), Marderby (priest)
Thorketil	Huntington, Bossall
Northman	Little Ayton, Marton, Kirkleatham
Havarthr	Stokesley
Bjornulfr	Topcliffe
Thorbrandr	Kirkby Misperton
Bishop of Durham	Crayke
Sumarlithi	Crambe
Asketil	Old Byland
Karli	Seamer
Knutr	Brandsby
'St Hilda'	Hackness – (two churches).

minsters of Ripon and Beverley, making gifts out of old royal dues from the county. He also restored the York minster canons, with a grant of the oats from Trent to Scotland, which had once been reserved for the royal hounds.

Some wealthy rural lords were buried under carved stone crosses where a churchyard is later known, at Crambe, Helmsley, Hovingham, Nunnington, Kirkby Misperton, Levisham, Lastingham, Middleton, Pickering, Sinnington, Ellerburn, Westow, Sherburn, Old Malton and Old Byland. The crosses commonly show a hunting scene, a warrior, a bound dragon or some story from Norse myth, yet they are Christian crosses. Some believe that the crosses were already in the graveyards of churches at those places. This may prove to be the case, or they could just be cemeteries. The Northumbrian system of large parishes based on a few minster churches had seen some subdivision, but many parishes were still huge and some churches were ruinous. Only the ancient minsters at York, Beverley, Ripon and Durham had small communities of canons to serve them. Kirkdale and Stonegrave are spoken of as minsters, but this may merely be some memory from a distant past. No complete record of existing churches has survived. Only a few were recorded by the Normans in their Domesday book. On the other hand, a church was being viewed as part of the accepted requirements of a thane, and most of the major thegns listed in 1066 did have a church somewhere on their estates.

Christian and Pagan Belief.

None can say how deeply Christian beliefs and practices had penetrated Anglian society, and it is at least possible that most Scandinavian people were little influenced. Centuries later, a Christian veneer barely concealed the older calendar of celebration for Easter, May Day, Midsummer and Yule. Easter was appropriated as the occasion for a Christian festival and Midsummer Day was re- dedicated to St John the Baptist. The pagan customs of many of these older feasts remained unchanged.

The days of the week, Tuesday, Wednesday, Thursday and Friday are still named from the Anglian and Norse Gods. Several prominent hills remain dedicated to the God Odin or Woden, from whom the old Anglian Kings claimed descent. A Norseman would also hear the stories of Woden, who was said to have hung on a tree for nine days and nights. Among the holy places dedicated to Woden were Roseberry in theVale of York, Roseberry at Kilburn and 'Othenesburg', now known as Roseberry Topping, a hill of dramatic appearance in Cleveland.

Yorkshire folklore has much that finds a happy home in Anglian or Norse paganism. 'Old Scrat' haunted 'Scratch alley'. As the Devil, he was used in legend to explain the inexplicable Devil's Causeway, a Roman road in north-west Yorkshire, and the impressive Devil's Leap at Roulston Scarr. He was credited with the erection of Freebrough Hill, the scooping out of the Devil's Punchbowl, better known as the Hole of Horcum, and the throwing of the great stone at Rudston. The Norse horned god had the look of the Devil about him.

'Hobs' and 'boggles' were everywhere, and linger in a great many field names, while 'fairies' were credited with moving churches from the original sites that were chosen at Levisham, Middleton and Kirkdale.

Holy springs abounded. Some of these may well have existed long before and been re--dedicated to some Christian saint. Dragons haunted Handale, Loftus, Sexhow and Rudby in Cleveland and Caulklass, Loschy Hill and Slingsby in Ryedale, according to local legends. Archbishop Wulfstan in c1002-1023 urged his priests to cast out every heathen practice, sacrifice, divination, witchcraft, or idols and sanctuaries around stones, trees or wells. He portrayed his church as struggling against old ideas and behaviours.

A Better Priesthood

Archbishop Wulfstan tried to reform the clergy, over whom he had little control. Most churches were rectories, valuable properties where the church tithes and other dues belonged to the rector, probably selected by the thegn who founded the church or his descendants. Wulfstan's clergy were told to find twelve men to swear that they would obey the priests' law, and attend the summons of bishops and archdeacons. He urged them not to buy each other's churches, and he sought compensation from laymen who violated sanctuaries, or who wounded and drove out priests, who insulted altars or placed wrong things in a church.

The Archbishop wanted Sunday to be observed. He threatened to fine priests who were disrespectful of a church. He chastened others who performed services in the wrong order. Those who said the mass at unconsecrated buildings and altars, without wine or more than three times a day were condemned. Clergy were fined if they forgot to ring the hours or gave out a wrong festival or fast date. He encouraged them to baptise new born children within nine days, and not to refuse baptism or confession. Those priests were punished who failed to shave, who left one woman for another, who assisted wrong doers, became drunk or became 'ale minstrels'. This sounds like a programme for reform. The things not to be done sound like things that have been done.

Some modest revival of the church is presumed for the later Scandinavian period. Archbishop Aldulf in 1002 made a York shrine for the earlier Archbishop Oswald, but no holy well carried the name of a Norse saint and only one church, St Olav's near Earlsbrough, outside York. A few new churches are attributed to the late 10th century, including the first built at Wharram Percy but perhaps also those at some of the places called Kirkby. The Archbishopric benefited by gifts from

Scandinavian Sundial at Kirkdale

Gamel and Ulfr son of Thorald which included the Salton estate in Ryedale and Ulf's horn.

Masonry with alternating long and short blocks of stone and a few other early architectural fragments, survive at Hovingham and Wharram le Street. The Lastingham churchyard was back in use for burials, leaving 10th century cross fragments and the curious grave covers called hogbacks. Fragments of carving at Oswaldkirk have been credited to the 11th century. West towers with twin bell openings and mid wall shafts occur at Appleton le Street, Hovingham, Middleton, Wharram, Terrington and Bulmer but some could be later building in the old style. There are 11th century sundials to be seen at Edstone and at Old Byland with an inscription mentioning the 'house-carl' Sumarledan. At Kirkdale a famous inscription tells us that in the time of Earl Tosti, the broken and fallen church was bought by Orm son of Gamel, and rebuilt.

The Earldom and the Danes

The renewal of Danish attacks on southern England after 975 led to the payment of regular tribute called Danegeld in 991. King Ethelred bought a peace, but the ravaging and invasions did not cease. Yorkshire with a Danish leadership unwilling to fight other Danes was less troubled. Sweyn, king of Denmark came up the Humber in 1013 and accepted the submission of the northern Earl Uhtred, before driving out

King Ethelred and subjugating southern England. His son, King Canute invaded the north in 1016, and ruled for twenty years as King of both English and Danes. During his reign, he defeated Norway, and visited both Rome and Scotland. He chose another Dane called Siward as his Yorkshire Earl from c.1033. Earl Siward conquered the northern parts of old Northumbria and later led armies to Cumbria and into Scotland where he defeated Macbeth. He was buried in 1055 at the Church dedicated to St Olaf, that he had built just north of the walled boundary of York.

Siward's son Waltheof was too young to be made Earl. An alternative candidate, Gospatric of Bamborough in Northumberland, a descendant of Earl Uhtred, was rejected by the King Edward. He chose instead Tostig, son of Earl Godwin of Wessex and brother to Earl Harold and the Queen. The Yorkshire thegn Copsig of Coxwold was made his deputy. Tostig negotiated a peace to stop Scots raids but when he journeyed with Archbishop Aldred to Rome in 1061, the Scots again wasted Northumberland.

Earl Tostig had Gospatric's supporters Gamel son of Orm and Ulf son of Dolfin, killed at York in 1063. The next year Gospatric himself was killed at the command of Queen Eadgith. Tostig tried to increase taxation and to divert court incomes, upsetting the ancient assurances given to Yorkshire. This raised opposition in the county. When the men of Northumberland revolted in 1065 and marched to York, the Yorkshiremen joined them. The thegns and the men of York destroyed Tostig's Danish housecarls, a strong force of over 200 dependants, near the Humber, and marched south to ravage his estate in Northamptonshire. Earl Tostig's rule had brought a breakdown of the southern royal authority in the north. The rebels outlawed Tostig and invited Morcar, brother of the powerful Earl Edwin of Mercia to be their Earl. Tostig's attempt to overthrow northern independence was over.

1066 and All That

King Edward the Confessor died in January 1066. Tostig's brother Harold became king. Tostig had gone to Flanders where he gathered a fleet of sixty ships. He entered the Humber to raid Lindsey in Lincolnshire but was driven out by Edwin and Morcar. He escaped with only twelve ships to Scotland. Harold Hardrada King of Norway accepted the exiled Tostig and Copsig as allies and with three hundred vessels sailed up the rivers Humber and Ouse

They disembarked unopposed at Riccall on the river Ouse, ten miles from the city of York. King Harold immediately moved north, but Earls Edwin and Morcar prematurely, on the 20th of September, engaged the Norwegians in battle at Fulford and lost, perhaps lacking support in the shire. Many were drowned in the Ouse. The men of York made a settlement and the Norwegian king withdrew to Stamford Bridge, a centre for routes from all directions.

King Harold reached Tadcaster on September 24th, and marched rapidly through York the next day, to attack the invaders at Stamford Bridge away from their ships. His army won a convincing victory. He killed Hardrada and Tostig and reduced the Norwegians to twenty four ship loads. King Harold marched south to meet the Norman cavalry and archers who had landed unopposed at Pevensey on the 29th. He was defeated and killed at Hastings on October 14th, only nineteen days after the victory at Stamford Bridge. Archbishop Aldred of York crowned William the Norman as King, at Westminster in December.

Edwin and Morcar surrendered, but Merleswain, the younger Gospatric and some thegns escaped to Scotland. At first the new king tried to rule through the old leadership. After King William levied taxes to pay his mercenaries in 1067 and 1068, the north rose again, led by Merleswain, Edwin and Morcar. The King came to York with his army and the rebel leaders fled back to Scotland. The men of York submitted and William built a castle within the walls of the city. Now he replaced the northern leadership by Norman military officers, leaving five hundred men in York castle under William Malet and Richard FitzRichard. He sent Robert de Comines and a similar force beyond the river Tees to Durham in the Winter of 1069. They looted and they were slaughtered by the locals. A general rising ensued. FitzRichard was killed outside York. The Yorkshire thegns and the men of York besieged the castle.

King William the Norman quickly moved north once again. He cleared and ravaged the city. He stayed eight days and built a second castle. A force went north through Northallerton and beyond to the Tees in 1070 to avenge Comines. Legends claimed that the King and six others were separated from the main body, when they were returning from Teesmouth, perhaps from a camp at West Coatham, riding in snow down the west side of Blackamore. They said that 'Billy Norman kept hissen warm wi swearin'.

The Rebellions and the Harrying of the North

The Norman King had achieved control of the north, but only for such time as his army was present. During the Autumn of 1069, King Sveinn of Denmark entered the Humber with a strong fleet. Merleswain, Gospatric, Waltheof son of Siward and many thegns joined the Danes at York. The Normans fired houses near the castle, but the flames spread and York burned. The Danes and their allies stormed the castles killing many Normans but they spared sheriff William Malet and Gilbert de Ghent for ransom. During December 1069, William marched north again, although delayed for weeks at the river Aire. Once at York he made a deal which took the Danes back to their ships. The castles were secured and a detachment sent to watch the Danes.

The King dramatically changed his policy. Instead of seeking to defeat the northerners in battle, he destroyed the sources of their power in the estates that sustained them. For the first time, the Normans attacked the peasantry, their settlements, crops and livestock in Yorkshire, through the winter, in what has become known as 'the harrying of the north'. There was famine. This was perpetuated wherever seed corn was lost. Some settlements were deserted. The Scots under Malcolm also raided into Cleveland. Some locals may have been taken prisoner or even sold themselves into servitude. Many Scots households gained English servants. When King Sweyn returned to Lindsey in the spring of 1070, the strong local support for him was no longer there. William drove him out.

Trouble haunted the wasted lands for years. This was a military occupation. The Yorkshire Earldom was suppressed, but the Earldom of Northumbria north of the Tees was allowed to survive a little longer under Gospatric. The bishop of Durham was given extra endowments. Norman sheriffs appointed by the King ruled in place of the Earls in Yorkshire. Thomas of Bayeaux was brought in as Archbishop of York to re-organise the church. Earl Gospatric visited York to welcome the new Norman Bishop Walcher for Durham but the king replaced Gospatric in Northumberland with Waltheof son of Siward, who had married a Norman bride.

Waltheof's power was real enough. He sent a force into Yorkshire to kill the sons of the thegn Carl while they were feasting at Settrington. This was an act of revenge for Carl having killed his grandfather Earl Aldred, continuing an earlier family feud which had erupted at intervals since 1038. They only spared the good Cnut, and Sumarled who was absent. Waltheof himself joined a revolt in 1075, when rebels again welcomed a Danish fleet which damaged York. He was beheaded that year.

Malcolm Canmore brought the Scots into the north of England again in 1088, perhaps as far as the Howardian hills. The Norman Robert de Mowbray was made Earl in Northumberland and 'New Castle' was built to buttress the border. As late as 1085 the threat of another Danish invasion, led King William to order devastation of the Yorkshire coast. Although the attack did not materialise, the devastation may have done.

The New Landowners.

The King took all the old estates and redistributed many to his principal supporters as 'tenants in chief'. The royal demesne was enlarged and administered by the King's sheriff. The French community soon held one hundred and forty five houses in York. Ancient estates were amalgamated to support powerful castles in the Pennines and in Holderness. A new aristocracy of Norman, Breton and Flemish landowners took over estates, mostly as absentees, in the first generation. The county was too shattered to support many Normans although some received great lordships in other shires. The Normans had adopted the French tongue and much of their laws back in Normandy. They found Yorkshire speech hard to understand and they needed intermediaries.

By 1086, the Count of Mortain, half brother to the King had a considerable estate in north east Yorkshire. This had previously belonged to the thegns Sveinn, Ughtred, Waltheof and Ligulfr. His main interests were in Cornwall so he sub- let most of his Yorkshire lands to the Normans Nigel Fossard and Richard Surdeval. Berenger de Tosni received much land that had belonged to Thorbrandr and Gamel.

Robert Malet gained some estates of Leysingr, Eadmund and Asketil. Ralph Paynel received the modest estate of Merleswain, while Hugh son of Baldric had mixed estates including some of Kofsi, Arnketil, Thorr, Ormr and others. Some of these men quickly settled their own sub tenants in parts of their lands. William de Percy was given Bjornulfr's Topcliffe, Northman's lands in Cleveland, Karli's Seamer and St Hilda's land at Hackness. Percy also took out a tenancy of the Whitby estate from Earl Hugh of Avranches, a sign of early commitment to the shire.

A Concentrated Recovery

Over half the townships were still wholly or partially waste in 1086 when the Domesday Book was completed. This records the slow progress of recovery, as much as the strength of the devastation. Oxen may have been as rare as people to work the land. Early recovery was concentrated in a few places within any single lord's estates. Decisions had to be taken and choices made. It was not a matter of the better land being revived first.

Each new owner examined his particular estate and decided what to do with it. The Domesday survey revealed the results. Sometimes the

---

Table 6. Active Demesne Farms and Their Lords in 1086 (within the area of modern Ryedale)

King William	Pickering, Wrelton, Malton
Archbishop	Salton
Richard Surdeval	Barton le Street
Robert of Mortain	Nunnington, Barton le Willows, Howsham, Kirkham
Nigel Fossard	Bulmer, Sheriff Hutton area, Farlington,
Berenger de Tosni	Sinnington, Leidthorpe, Buckton, Settrington, Duggleby, Menethorpe, Hinderskelfe
Abbot of St Mary's, York	Kirkby Misperton, Spaunton, Dalby
Robert Malet	Byland
Hugh	Foston
Ralph Mortimer	Wintringham
Ralph Paynel	Stonegrave
Hugh Baldric	Kirkby Moorside, Hovingham, Laysthorpe, Gilling, Buttercrambe, Langton, Norton, North Grimston, Coxwold area
Hugh Baldric's men	Hovingham soke
Wulfbert	Sand Hutton
Walo	Scrayingham
Geoffrey	Langton or Sherburn area
Odo, crossbowman	Bugthorpe, Skirpenbeck
Ulfketil	Birdsall

old hall was abandoned as the administrative centre for a great soke overlordship, and a new one formed some distance away. Richmond in north west Yorkshire with an early castle at a new site, replaced Gilling. Amidst the Wolds, the old soke centre of Buckton, which shared a name with Buckrose wapentake, may have given way to Settrington soon after this time, although the Buckton settlement survived in the hands of major tenants.

The results seem curious but they make sense. The King had fifteen empty settlements at least in Pickering Lythe, but he had an active demesne plough, and seven villeins with two ploughs in a fully active township at Wrelton. That is as many farmsteads as there would be centuries later in the village. People would be removed from some townships to get others going again, adding to the sharp contrast between many places with no evident activity and others thriving a decade or more after the harrying. The high Wolds were almost totally emptied of villeins. Substantial recovery could take several forms. In some places, the demesne farm was active, in others a villein community and sometimes both. A few places including Coxwold, Skirpenbeck, Pickering, Wintringham, Bulmer, Slingsby and Settrington seem packed with villein farmers. Other settlements showed dramatic increases of value -including Coxwold, Scrayingham, Buckton and Seamer. Old soke estates showed collossal falls in value. Pickering's value fell from £88 to £1.0s4d. Most of the recovering estates were breaking even, or at worst had quite modest falls in value.

The Normans in Control.

Norman authority was consolidated by the castle, the knight and the church. There was a period of martial law, during which time the sheriff Hugh Baldric travelled with a substantial armed force. There were brigands in Blackamore. Nor were the borders secure. King William Rufus faced war with the Scots. He added Cumberland to his realm in 1092. He built Carlisle castle and settled people there. A number of surviving pre-Conquest thanes were initially quartered in Cleveland estates, but they seem to have been moved elsewhere. A new Jewish community was settled at York. Soon, there were the first baronial rebellions. Robert de Mowbray rebelled in Northumberland in 1095 and was replaced.

The ruling groups in Normandy had for some time sponsored a revival of the influence of the Christian church. Much of this spirit was

Table 7. Active Villein Farms in 1086
(within the area of modern Ryedale)

King William	Pickering 20, Pickering soke 10, Wrelton 7, Malton 8, Crambe 5, Harton 4
Archbishop	Salton 4
Richard Surdeval	Barton le Street 8
Robert of Mortain	Nunnington 4, Slingsby 18, Helmsley 6, Crambe 5, Barton le Willows 11, Warthill 2, Howsham 8, Kirkham 12
Nigel Fossard	Bulmer 25, Sheriff Hutton area 5, Farlington 5, Cornbrough 1, Lilling area 3
Earl Alan	Foston 12
Abbot of York	Kirkby Misperton 13, Lastingham 1, Spaunton 9, Dalby 6
Berenger de Tosny	Leidtorp 15, Sinnington 8, Huttons Ambo 16, Buckton 12, Menethorpe 9, Settrington 16, Duggleby 5
Robert Malet	Byland 7
Ralph Mortimer	Wintringham 18
Ralph Paynel	Stonegrave area 7
Hugh Baldric	Coxwold area 54, Cawton 3, Kirkby Moorside 10, Kirkby Moorside area 36, Hovingham 10, Hovingham area 43, Laysthorpe 2, Gilling 3, Brandsby-Stearsby 11, Buttercrambe area 5, Langton/Sherburn areas 43, Norton 12, North Grimston 6, Scrayingham 15
Wulfbert	Sand Hutton 11
Walo	Scrayingham 10, Scrayingham soke 19
Odo	Bugthorpe 3, Scradiztorp 4, Skirpenbeck 27
Two men	Leavening 5

now applied to Yorkshire. Perhaps it was the Norman church that was the greatest new influence brought to bear on local society. A new York Minster was built and given a full staff of canons. Church courts were separated from civil courts and given important powers. The Pope in 1074 had forbidden clergy to cohabit with women and the new Norman Archbishops sought to enforce his will. Pope Urban in 1108 offered remission of punishment for sins here and in purgatory, subject to divine grace, to those who confessed their sins and went in holy war to fight against infidels. William de Percy died on the way to Jerusalem and Gospatric returned with some bone fragments regarded as holy relics.

Revived Monasteries

A three man mission came north from Evesham Abbey in Mercia to York where sheriff Hugh Baldric directed them to Newcastle. They visited old northern shrines and settled at Jarrow. There was a desire to refound Benedictine monasteries in the refugee and robber filled wasteland. Reinfrid, a soldier turned religious, prevailed on William de Percy to allow him, as a hermit, to use the old monastery ruins at Prestby, on the east cliff next to Whitby. Other men gathered about him seeking to adopt a monastic way of life, including the ambitious and well connected Stephen of York. Despite the new lord William de Percy's patronage, they were disturbed by officials, probably after they had brought the fields of Prestby back into use, and by raiders from sea and land. A hermitage was one thing, a monastery was another.

Some of these monks moved to William de Percy's Hackness under his relation Serlo de Percy. The other monks in about 1078 went to Lastingham with Stephen. Both groups built churches. With further trouble at Hackness, Serlo appealed to the King and moved from Percy land onto Crown land, probably constructing yet another church. Reinfrid returned to the hermit life, perhaps at the Westcroft hermitage and was later buried at Hackness.

Stephen's monks began to build a massive church at Lastingham, which they only partly completed. This included an underground crypt and the upper church from an apsidal east end, westwards as far as the crossing. Troubled again, they abandoned the work before 1087. They were offered a more secure site by Earl Alan of Richmond at St Olav's church outside York. They began to build St Mary's abbey in 1088-89, centred on a massive church with staggered apses at the east end.

Another monastery building with an apsidal east end arose when the Hackness monks returned to settle at Prestby near Whitby, under another William de Percy as their first Abbot. The King and the barons gave lands in Whitby Strand, Ryedale and the Vale of York to the York and Whitby Benedictine monasteries. It is just possible that some of the earliest gifts were a return to the church of estates which had once belonged to ancient monasteries.

CHAPTER 2
THE EARLY MIDDLE AGES

The New Men.

King Henry I defeated his elder brother and rival Robert Curthose at the battle of Tinchebrai, thirty five miles east of Avranches in 1106. There was some fighting in Yorkshire. After the victory, he visited York castle and Pickering, making it very likely that a castle had been built there. The king redistributed the land of Robert's supporters, Robert Malet, the Earl of Mortain and Robert de Stuteville, along with some Crown estates to 'the new men' who would hold them as 'tenants in chief' of the crown. One observer said that 'he raised them from dust'. Among the new men were Nigel d'Albini, ancestor of the great Mowbray family, Eustace Fitzjohn, ancestor of the later Vescys, Walter Espec, Robert de Brus and Ansketil de Bulmer, the descendant of an old local Viking family. Walter de Chauncy received the honour of Skirpenbeck and Hugh Bigod was given the honour of Settrington.

The ancient estates were re-arranged in new baronies, sometimes called 'honours', which had lordship over lesser estates as well as their own demesne lands, with the right to hold courts for their tenants and keep the court revenues. This was another move away from the older rural organisation. Although the pattern was not too different from the old soke manors, the sites of administrative centres were sometimes changed. The barons held these great fiefs and other associated privileges in return for providing agreed numbers of knights for the King's feudal army during the fighting season and for other services to the crown, including attendance at wapentake and county courts.

The barons built new castles and halls as their homes and as administrative centres from which to develop their home farms and other income-generating estates. The quick witted Walter Espec at Helmsley castle, and Eustace Fitzjohn who married Ivo de Vescy's daughter at Malton, were among the great men of the day. Both served as royal judges throughout the north. Their knights were settled on the smaller lordships within each barony to perform the knight service. The King himself kept an enlarged Crown estate, including the soke manors of Pickering, Falsgrave, Knaresborough and Easingwold. His marriage to a Scots princess Maud secured the peace with Scotland provisionally, but Walter Espec at Wark, Eustace Fitzjohn at Alnwick and other Yorkshire barons gained major estates near that border.

The Castles

Many castles were built with ditched earth mounds called mottes and ditched courtyards called baileys. Both had timber stockades and the great dry ditches outside them were made steep and kept clear of vegetation. The motte was a high command and fighting platform, a lookout, and in certain circumstances a last ditch defence. The bailey usually held the lord's hall, a family home as well as a centre of management, but there were also kitchens, brewery and bakehouses, stables and some quarters for household servants and retainers. Pickering had a neat motte, said to be forty five feet high, with no room for a hall at its crest. The first bailey was set out against a hill slope on one side, a defile on another, and given a dry moat on the other two sides. The site was well away to the north of the older hall and church, and probably stood alone at the edge of field land. The hillslope was later quarried for stone which made the curtain wall above even more secure.

The castle has been variously credited to King William I, William II or Henry I. Since the latter monarch visited Pickering about 1106 and gave away the site of the older hall, we can infer that a castle existed by that time. However, a second motte sited across the stream on a natural clay hill remains an unsolved puzzle. This has no ditch, but also stands apart from the town amidst field strips. This may have been an earlier venture or built for some temporary need. Crown power in the shire would be centred on the York, Knaresborough and Pickering castles. Neither King nor Baron in north east Yorkshire imposed 'castle guard' duties on local tenants as happened at Richmond and Skipsea, but Pickering sokemen were obliged to maintain the outer timber defences of the bailey.

The sites chosen for castles in the earliest years of the military occupation were often set apart from settlements, but not all occupy naturally defensible sites. There were also variations from the motte and bailey pattern. Helmsley has a massive rectangle of deep ditched earthwork, set in flat land but believed to have held the great hall of Walter Espec, a man of gigantic stature, black hair, brown piercing eyes

The Motte at Pickering Castle

and sonorous voice.

Kirkby Moorside castle remains only as an extensive ditched rectangle of high, sloping ground, of unknown date, distant from the town it overlooks. Neither castle shows signs of a motte. Ivo de Vescy at Malton built a castle on a contracted site above and commanding the old Derwent river crossing of the Romans, well away from the Old Malton church and village site, but it is possible that he used the earthworks of the Roman fort as the bailey.

Nigel d'Albini, a favoured royal official, was allowed to marry the divorced Mowbray countess, and was awarded the rebel Stuteville's family estates before 1129. He had a castle at Thirsk, sited where the market place is today, another castle on the fine hill site at Hood and possibly the castle at Kirkby Moorside. Nigel Fossard became a tenant in chief for many of the rebel Earl of Mortain's scattered estates. They were organised around several castles. One was at Foss in a valley behind the coast near Mulgrave and Lythe. A second was strongly placed on a ditched spur of the west wolds at Mont Ferrant, near Birdsall.

Further afield, Guy de Balliol was at Stokesley castle, the Mennills at Whorlton castle and William de Percy at Maiden's Bower castle between two rivers south of Topcliffe. Robert de Brus was granted a great Cleveland fief and probably built the castles at Yarm, Skelton and

45

Danby, his major tenants adding those at Levington and Kildale. Herbert the Chamberlain built no castle at Weaverthorpe, but he had a chalkstone house immediately east of the church.

Castles are not well recorded, but are often mentioned merely as a 'capital messuage' or chief house. Eustace Fitzjohn was the King's custodian of Knaresborough at one time, and of the coastal lordship of Falsgrave with its large soke at another. He was granted a small new barony at Brompton by Sawdon, created from fragments of several old estates, where slight remnants and legends recall a castle.

Ansketil de Bulmer, son of Ligulfr, and sometime steward to the Fossards, was raised to be King's sheriff of Yorkshire. He was probably the first to have a castle near Hutton church, which became Sheriff Hutton, and where earthworks of the motte remain. Gilling may have had an early motte suggested only by a name and a modest bump in a garden. A motte and bailey at Acklam on the west Wolds may have belonged to William de Scurris. Felixkirk has the mound of another motte belonging to the military order of KnightsTemplar.

A modest barony was created from Gospatric's estate and from soke lands west of Pickering. This was given to the Fleming Turgis Brundos. A neat motte and bailey castle was built a short distance apart from the village of Cropton, and not at the parish church village of Middleton. The motte was set against a steep hill slope and offered a considerable view. The bailey was on the east side, near to open common land. Turgis was also given a border barony at Liddel, by Ranulph le Meschin who had been granted Cumberland after King William II conquered the old core of Gospatric's Strathclyde. The somewhat misty figure of Turgis also held both Scawton and Nunnington in Ryedale, and indeed, for a time Rotherham in south Yorkshire. His heirs were known as Turgis and William of Rosedale, presumably because Cropton Castle overlooked the narrow lower course of the stream from that dale. The east side of Rosedale was also part of the barony.

The Royal Forests.

King Henry I decreed that a huge area, from the walls of York to the coast, should be considered as 'Royal Forest', where venison and 'vert', the major game and the woodland that gave it life, were to be preserved solely for the King. The Forests embraced most of Bulmer, and the whole of Ryedale and Pickering Lythe wapentakes in the North Riding, and nearby districts known as Ouse and Derwent and Haverford

Howe bridge- river Rye-junction of rivers Seven & Rye-river Seven to its source--------

Ralph cross-West Shoner howes-Loose howes-William howes-East Shoner howes----

Wheeldale beck-junction with Mirk Esk-junction with Esk-junction with Lithe beck-fork of Lithebeck-end of Calverleygate-under brow of hill to a Great Stone-Silhowes-Foster Howes-Scograine howes-

Lilla howe-source of river Derwent-junction with Talebeck- along Talebeck-King's Bridge-sike to old foss of Eliscroft---

Greenhead-foss between Suffield moor and Scalby-Thornlaw-Swinstyhaw

Ingaldraksykes-Hardale end-Wolf Pits-Greendyke-Blawyke-high water mark of sea

Middle of the marsh-Thursbridge-water drain of Tevendrait-middle of Filey marsh-Hertford stream-river Derwent

Lythe in the East Riding. The lordships which had already been granted to monasteries, comprised Whitby Strand, and the Spaunton Lordship between the rivers Dove and Seven. These also became royal forests and saw their hart, hind, wild boar and hawk reserved for the monarch. Some woodland rights were left to the abbeys. The monks of St Mary's Abbey as lords of Spaunton were compensated for any loss with a permanent grant of a tithe or tenth of all venison taken, both in flesh and hides.

Officers were appointed to guard the royal forests. Estates at Sproxton near Helmsley, at Kingthorpe, and Levisham near Pickering were among those held by fee-foresters, as 'serjeanties'. These were held rent free, but in return for the tenant's service as a forester. Guy the hunter of Aislaby held half of that township for training a royal hound. New cultivations and timber felling were severely restricted and heavy penalties threatened. The well wooded areas about Pickering were already confined to land overlapping the narrow valley sides of Blackamore, despite the misleading impression of the Domesday Book, with its brief descriptions which merged wood and pasture. During the mid-year month of the deer's fawning season, access to pastures was limited and pig pasture in woodlands was controlled in the 'mast season'. Within Cleveland, there were distinct Egton, Danby, Skelton and Stokesley forests, which belonged to Barons. The Wolds lordships had neither forests nor chases, there being little remaining timber and nothing of the wild life it sustained.

Serious punishments faced hunting offenders, including the removal of body parts, for those taking deer. The lord of Allerston, a man of old Viking descent, was quite exceptionally allowed the privilege of hunting hare and fox in 1189. He would have needed hounds to do so. Roger de Stuteville was licensed to have hounds for taking wolf and hare throughout all Yorkshire and Northumberland. Major barons were allowed some broader exemptions from forest law, where they held large estates within royal forests. They developed their own preserves called 'chases'. Walter Espec within Ryedale Forest gave three deer a year as a tithe to Kirkham Priory, and had his own forester, Ulfketill, living near the Helmsley 'cemetery gate'. The Mowbrays at Kirkby Moorside and Hovingham had similar privileges. Both the Mowbrays and the Stutevilles, who later recovered the Kirkby Moorside estate from them, reserved game in Farndale.

The Knights

The new barons and their knights resettled the landscape with freeholders, villeins and cottagers during the century after the Norman 'harrying of the north'. Most were involved in farming, and can be thought of as farmers, although that was not the word then used. The most important group, sustaining most of the rest, were the 'bondmen', sometimes called 'serfs' or 'villeins'. They were settled as 'unfree men', to work their land in return for payments in kind, and for labouring works on the lord's estate. Most of the known manors began functioning again at some level of activity.

The few Normans, Bretons and Flemings formed a new ruling class of manor lords, joined by a few old Anglo- Scandinavian families who had weathered the storm. These included the Gowers, descended from Guer of Stittenham, the Greystoke heirs of Forne son of Ligulfr and the heirs of Ughtred of Allerston, son of Gospatric. New sub-tenancies were soon made. Turgis granted Cawthorn to Ralph de Neville. The Aguillons settled at Kirkby Grindalythe and the Scurris at Acklam. There were many more such families. Often they would take their name from the place where they settled. Others gave their names to the settlement. Place Newton and Wharram Percy recall long vanished manorial families.

Other 'free men' were given estates in return for services that were neither military nor agricultural. Roger Mowbray, son of Nigel d'Albini settled freeholds near Thirsk on his butler, usher, cook, baker and musicians, as well as granting fees to members of the knightly class. Although small baronies or 'honours' were formed within Pickering Lythe, at Cropton, Seamer and Brompton, and a few other men held estates by knight service, most of the tenants in the district in 1158 were still sokemen or free 'men of the wapentake'. They formed the juries of twelve called together by the sheriff.

Some rose in society and others fell. Reginald Buscel married into the Norman Percy family and was granted manorial rights, in old crown land at Ebberston and Hutton, which became Hutton Bushel. Stewards could do well. Peter de Ros, a steward of William of Albemarle, married Walter Espec's sister, and his heirs inherited that barony. Robert de Wyville a steward of Roger de Mowbray, and Richard de Wyville an Espec steward, tenanted the important Slingsby and Sledmere fiefs. The Wyvilles became significant enough to found a monastery.

Several Espec knights tenanted lands around Helmsley and in the Wold country. These men mostly had halls rather than castles but you can never be quite sure. The 12th century timber hall among substantial earthworks at Hutton Coleswain, named from a man who held his estate in return for duties defending the York castle gate, was later replaced by a stone building. Only excavation can reveal what is within the earthworks at Bossall, Hovingham or Wath and other places with reputed castles.

The Church Organised

The Normans thoroughly re-organised the local church, into the broad archdeaconries of Cleveland, East Riding, Richmond and York. Within them, the smaller deaneries, of Cleveland, Ryedale, Bulmer and Dickering extended over north east Yorkshire, initially based on the residences of hereditary deans. The early Archbishops reinforced their organisation for the support of the great minster church of York, setting aside many estates to support the canons and other officials who made up the enlarged staff of the cathedral.

Canons held estates called 'prebends' at Langtoft, Ampleforth, Bugthorpe with Stockton, Husthwaite, Osbaldwick, Salton, Stillington,

Strensall, Fridaythorpe and Warthill. Several of the estates were carved from the ancient church properties near York. The Minster Treasurer was given Alne, Skelton, Tollerton and Wigginton north of York. An Archbishop granted Salton, and Brawby near the river Rye, to the Prior of Hexham who had a prebendal seat at York Minster. As a result, Salton gained a substantial Norman church .

The new royal Castle at Pickering made the old Hall at the head of Hallgarth redundant, so King Henry I gave it, with the church in the neighbouring enclosure to Archbishop Gerard. This gift was made with the other churches of the royal manors of Pocklington, Driffield, Kilham, Aldbrough and Snaith. Gerard transferred the church to the Dean of York who gained the old hall of Earl Morcar, a separate rectory manor and courts functioning through the vast Pickering parish.

Herbert the Chamberlain of Winchester had a grant of Londesborough in the East Riding together with the manor and soke of Weaverthorpe. He built a hall of chalk stone around a timber framework. Tony Brewster excavated the fifty seven foot by twenty one foot building, with its five foot thick walls. A little to the west of his hall, Herbert built the fine new church at Weaverthorpe in another stone, brought from some distance. This towers above the Wold Valley, a powerful statement of Norman clerical power.

Many parish churches were rebuilt in stone, with other churches and chapels new built as the countryside filled with people. Almost every village had a chapel in the Middle Ages. Walter Espec's uncle William the Noble probably founded the chapel of St Hilda, high in Bilsdale, before 1122. The Vescy's Malton castle had a twelfth century chapel. The village of Butterwick had a chapel within Foxholes parish by 1140.

The parish of Pickering retained the ancient extent that it had before the Normans came until 1233 when Allerston and Ebberston, and Ellerburn, Farmanby and Wilton were hived off into two new parishes. There had been talk of new chapels as early as 1128. The distant places called Kingthorpe and Goathland had chapels, but remained in the old parish, a long moorland walk for a burial or a baptism in any age.

The Rectors who held the church received the regular tithe incomes. This was a tenth of any increase of crops or stock within the entire parish. Tithe was one of the most successful taxes ever devised. It required no effort but collection, while giving the recipient a considerable share of the efforts of everyone else. Not only that, payment was compulsory, enforced by spiritual sanctions and the law of the land. The major parish churches also held a carucate of land, known as the 'glebe'. As a result of early endowments, Kirkby Misperton became a two carucate church, making it an attractive living for the rest of its history. The list of its rectors reads quite differently from those of other churches.

New building must have been stimulated either by the new landowners or the tithe owners, although who actually paid is rarely clear. Norman masonry fragments with zig zag, nail head, mask and other early decorations survive in churches that have been much altered since. Clearly, a great building effort produced simple nave and chancel structures, often with side aisles added before the end of the century. Some large, early churches such as Pickering were given apsidal east ends but so was the smaller building at Felixkirk. A few like Bossall had a plan like a cross. The investment in buildings was considerable with elaborate carving of decorative details at doors, windows and chancel arches. North Grimston gained a font, richly carved with a portrayal of the Last Supper.

Priests to Cure Souls.

The names of many parish priests, chaplains and clerks are recorded, witnessing charters before 1150, including Hugh the priest of Pickering, Nigel priest of Malton and Ingelram priest of Welburn. Great men had their own chaplains and clerks and could offer their rectories to friends or relations. When William Hay and Robert Chambord gave Slingsby church to Whitby abbey, they reserved the tenure of their clerk Sampson. This sounds like a shared patronage, perhaps two estate lords combining to form a parish church, but we cannot prove that it was a new church at that date. At the same time, efforts were made by senior churchmen to encourage the clergy to live by higher standards and without wives.

Others chose different routes to what they saw as religious goals. The Christian impulse has commonly been expressed in a variety of ways and in these unsettled times, a scatter of hermits bulk large in the record. They were the first known residents at the more remote places. Reinfrid was at Whitby and Hackness, and is linked in tradition with the caves at Wrench Green. Edmund was at Farndale, Osmund at Goathland, Robert d'Alneto the famous hermit at Hood, Sedman at St. Leonards near Egton, the Saintly Godric in Eskdale and others at Saltburn, Dunsley, Sandsend and Mulgrave. William de Bossal built an oratory deep in the marshes, at St Francis Isle, in the parish of Ganton. Some hermit settlements developed into complete monasteries.

Monasteries, New and Old

There were already other monasteries, Holy Trinity Priory at York and Selby Abbey; but the Benedictine abbeys at York and Whitby for a time had a near monopoly on local giving. The monastery at York known as St Mary's Abbey kept the Manor of Spaunton near their old monastery site at Lastingham, but rented out the estates around it to laymen. These made attractive tenancies, free of the usual obligations of knight service. Abbot Geoffrey before 1115 granted eight oxgangs at Hutton le Hole to Gospatric son of Waltheof. He was to keep no woodland mares, nor a sheepfold for more than fifty sheep, though the proviso was later relaxed.

Abbot Savary, a decade later leased Normanby, apart from a small church farm holding, to Robert Frazer, for six marks rent each year. The stock in the manor was to revert to the monastery when the lease fell in. New Ryedale manors came to St Mary's, in grants from Turgis Brundos at Sproxton and Nunnington, and from Ivo de Vescy at Gilling. The Chauncy family gave much at Thixendale and the Bigods gave property at Scampston. These properties were leased to laymen for monies paid regularly into the rent roll, yet the settlements show the influence of the monastery to this day.

The accidents of history caused other distant houses to benefit in these early days, even Rouen and Evesham. Arnulf de Hesdin gave Appleton le Street church to St Alban's abbey to pay for their kitchen expenses. William de Percy gave interests at Felixkirk to the military order of Knights Hospitaller. When new kinds of monasteries appeared locally, they gained at the expense of the established houses. There was a remarkable flood of giving. The barons gave broad estates to the new monasteries, which were often of their own foundation, and where relations so minded, could participate in one of the main movements of the age. There were empty lands to give. Their knights supported their foundations with further gifts.

Why so many grants were made is rarely obvious, but a real religious spirit can hardly be denied, as well as such motives as conscience, display, fashion, the search for worldy or other-worldly advantage, and a mere wish for memorial. Twenty first century sceptics speak of the gifts as a sort of insurance policy and there was that. Most benefactors wanted the prayers of monks to help them in their passage through purgatory towards an expected after-life. At the same time, the monastic houses offered an alternative ideal, a glimpse of a world different from the mundane pre-occupations of knight, cleric or serf.

Augustinian Canons

Archbishop Thurstan, a man who wore a hairshirt, worked with the King and the barons to promote the Augustinian canons. They had a practical appeal. They could serve as priests in churches while living communally and following a rule. William the Treasurer of York and his brother Herbert son of Herbert gave Weaverthorpe church to distant Nostell Priory, to support their guesthouse. Walter de Gant, lord of Hunmanby gave most of the Bridlington estate to found an Augustinian Priory there. His man, Adelard the Hunter gave Ganton church. Robert de Brus gave most of Guisborough to form that Priory around 1119-24 adding many of the churches throughout his great Cleveland estates.

Walter Espec on the advice of his Uncle William, a canon at Nostel Priory, founded Kirkham Priory around 1121-22. The endowment included seven churches, among them Kirkby Grindalythe church in the Wold valley and the church and three houses in Helmsley, with the tithes of a parish that included most of Bilsdale. Roger de Mowbray founded a monastery at Hood, which was settled by a party of canons from Bridlington Priory. They moved again in 1145 to a new site and founded Newbrough Priory. Mowbray endowed them with the churches at Hood, Kirkby Moorside, Kirkdale, Hovingham and Thirsk.

Peter de Cordanville gave Sherburn church to Guisborough Priory. Many other grants flowed to the Augustinians as well as churches, but the churches were an important beginning. The gift of a rectory gave the readiest means to maintain an early monastery. Sometimes only the right to appoint the priest was retained or in the longer run some modest pension but some rectories were major earners in monastic balance sheets till the end of their days.

The Cistercian Monks

The Cistercian Order was welcomed at Rievaulx near Helmsley by Walter Espec in 1131. Their arrival was part of a missionary movement, with representatives of the Order, negotiating for sites on equal terms with the founding baron. These austere monks sought a detachment

Table 9. Churches given to Monasteries and Minster Officials

Dean of York	-Pickering
Dean and Chapter of York	Weaverthorpe (transferred from Nostel Priory)
Chancellor of York	-Acklam (after purchase by the Archbishop)
Prebendaries of York Minster	-Ampleforth-Langtoft-Salton
St Mary's Abbey.York	-Kirkby Misperton-Normanby-Lastingham-Dalby-Kirkby Underdale-North Grimston-Foxholes-Foston-Gilling
Whitby Abbey	-Skirpenbeck-Hutton Bushell-Seamer-Hackness-Slingsby
Bridlington Priory	-Ganton-Willerby
Kirkham Priory	-Birdsall-Burythorpe-N Grimston-Westow-Kirkby Grindalythe-Sledmere-Garton-Crambe-Huttons Ambo-Helmsley
Guisborough Priory	-West Heslerton-Sherburn
Malton Priory	-Langton-Norton-Wintringham-Brompton-Old Malton
Byland Abbey	-Rillington
St Albans Abbey	-Thorpe Basset-Appleton le Street to St Albans
Nostel Priory	-Wharram le Street
Newbrough Priory	-Coxwold-Hovingham-Kirkby Moorside-Kirkdale
Hexham Priory	-Salton -Edstone
Little Marish Priory	-Yedingham-Sinnington
Haltemprice Priory	-Wharram Percy
Marton Priory	-Sheriff Hutton (a transfer from St Mary's, York)
Holy Trinity Priory York	-Barton le Street -Crambe
Thornton Abbey	-Acklam

Laymen retained Scrayingham, Bossall and Levisham churches.

from worldly affairs, quite different from the Benedictines and Augustinians. They were well experienced in what they did. Their monasteries were built in remote places. The Order accepted lands but refused manors, churches, tithes, mills and farms within villages. Where settled sites were given, as at Hoveton and Welburn near Kirkby Moorside, they cleared them, buying out freeholders and allowing the villeins to move away. Even the granges or detached farms which sustained the monastery, were kept apart from the settlements of ordinary people, and worked by lay brothers under monastic supervision. The Pope gave the Order freedom from paying parish church tithes in 1160.

The Cistercian way of life was simpler, less worldly, and more ascetic than that of the Benedictines or Augustinians. This was an ideal which readily appealed to some of the younger brethren of the older monasteries. They showed signs of having settled down in comfortable ways. A breakaway group of a dozen from St Mary's Abbey, in search of a stricter rule, won the sympathy of the Archbishop, but experienced years of difficulty before becoming established. After winning other powerful support, they established Fountains Abbey. Kirkham Priory was nearly split in two, soon after the Cistercians arrived, with talk of some of the brothers founding a separate house at Linton. Nothing came of it. There may also have been trouble at Whitby Abbey.

Refugee monks of another order, driven from the Scots border, were first settled by Roger Mowbray near his castle at Hood. They were led to adopt the Cistercian rule. After several more moves, they diverted lowland streams and settled on newly drained land called Byland, to build another great monastery. All was not sweetness and light. Monasteries disputed with laymen and each other over broad spheres of influence and local boundaries. Heirs sometimes sought to recover what ancestors had given away. One contemporary said that Byland monks were not beyond moving boundary marks and sending hungry rats into their neighbour's corn. One Byland abbot refused the gift of Kirkby Moorside church but another accepted an interest in the church at Rillington.

The Battle of the Standard

King David of Scotland took up arms on behalf of the Empress Matilda, daughter of King Henry I, and a rival for King Stephen's throne. He attacked southward in 1138. The younger Brus, some Percys,

Eustace Fitzjohn and Bertram de Bulmer joined him, but the bulk of the northern Barony remained loyal to the new King Stephen. They were rallied by Archbishop Thurstan, and with Bernard de Balliol leading royal troops and Peveril's men from Derbyshire, they assembled at Thirsk and marched to Cowton Moor, north of Northallerton.

The elder Brus appealed to the Scots King for a settlement, reminding him of help given to him in earlier campaigns. Bishop Ralph of Orkney addressed the Norman barony, reminding them of their conquests in France, England, Apulia, Jerusalem and Antioch. He poured scorn on their opponents claiming that the Scots army was more fitted for rioting than battle. A wagon with a mast carrying a crucifix and a silver pyx, and banners of the old Yorkshire Minster churches was taken to the battle field as a 'standard'. The Scots rushed forward with frightening howls but William of Aumale, Walter Espec and others of the northern barony led their Norman knights and bowmen to victory against them. A force subsequently marched on Malton to besiege the garrison in Eustace Fitzjohn's castle.

William of Aumale

William of Aumale was lord of Holderness with a great castle and a port at Skipsea. He was given custody of many Crown lands and was named Earl of York, after the battle of the Standard. The continuing struggle between King Stephen and the Empress Matilda allowed the Earl to dominate much of Yorkshire. He built a castle on Crown land within the bounds of the old soke manor of Falsgrave, at the readily defensible Scarborough rock around 1134-1138.

The Earl seized Bridlington Priory in 1143 and destroyed Gilbert de Gant's Hunmanby castle. He acquired control of many baronies by Crown grants of wardships, including the Fossard and Brus fiefs. He cleared farmsteads in Whitby Strand and the Egton district to make hunting chases. He reduced Mont Ferrant castle after the younger Fossard had seduced his sister. The Cistercian Order opposed him when William sought the Archbishopric of York for a relation. Abbot Ailred of Rievaulx appealed to Rome, and a Cistercian, Henry Murdac was elected Archbishop instead. Aumale excluded Murdac from York and the Archbishop was obliged to operate from Ripon and Beverley.

The royal dynastic squabbles ended after the death of King Stephen's son. The heir to the Empress made an arrangement with the King. Subsequently he was able to succeed to the throne as King Henry

II. After doing so, he obliged the indignant Aumale to give up Scarborough castle and control of the royal demesne in Yorkshire. King Henry rebuilt the Scarborough castle in stone, as a new focal point for Crown power in the north, spending nearly £600 on the works between 1158 and 1165. The 'great ditch' was dug two years later, probably the Damyet gutter to drain land west of the castle, for the founding of a borough. The years 1168-1169 saw the building of a great castle tower, the first high-rise royal keep in the county with multiple rooms, private fireplaces and gravity garderobes. Crown power was re-established.

The Recovery of Farming

The farming landscape held common fields on the lower limestone, on the chalk hill slopes and in cultivated islands on the Tabular hills These were probably very ancient. Other islands of cultivation stood out amidst broad wastes in the lowland townships of inner Ryedale and the vale of York, while in lower Galtres, broad fingers of cultivation pointed towards York, separated by infertile mires. The dryer wold valleys showed quite a different picture. Here was a different system. The fields sprawled across the valley bottoms, the infields near the settlements intensively cultivated, the higher outfields less frequently worked, but in active periods extending the ploughland to cover all the land, with no great areas of permanent moor or waste.

The Norman Conquest briefly broke the continuity of ploughing in many places, but the old clearances of the better land were easily restored to use. The Normans did make changes which carried long-term consequences when they chose some estates for particular tasks. Sometimes estate centres were moved. Falsgrave would lose its role to Scarborough. A manor, newly selected for demesne cultivation, to supply a lord's needs at his hall or castle, would long remain so. There are few distinctions that make the local histories of townships differ more, in any age, than that between the estate village and the community with freeholders.

When lords gave entire townships to monasteries, whether to site abbeys and priories or to become monastic granges, an older kind of community gave way to a new one, with new methods of farming, where production for local subsistence could give way to supplying the needs of the monastery. There were some other significant changes of use. Blansby near Pickering had ploughlands with evidence of activity back to Roman times. The King's foresters added a sizeable tract of adjoining common to make it into a huge deer park, where the animals could breed in safety.

Common Field Townships

In conventional townships of the 12th century, a settlement of bondsmen or villeins worked two or three large adjoining fields, each subdivided into a dozen or so furlongs or flatts. These were blocks of five to ten yard wide strips, usually going in the same direction. They were cultivated in common but cropped by the owner or tenant of each strip. Often their riggs and furrows survive with a slight S shape, where the ox teams of four, six or eight oxen yoked together for ploughing, veered to turn on the headland. A group of strips formed a flatt or furlong, A group of flatts or furlongs made a field. Together the strips formed the villein's share of the field land, the main component of his oxgangs, of which eight made a carucate.

The furlong names, expressed in the old languages of Anglians and Scandinavians, usually told of the character of the strips or the previous nature of the terrain. Flatts were once a compact group of strips in single ownership but more often the strips of the bondsmen lay mingled. They could be at a regular position in each furlong. Two oxgangs was a frequent holding for a villein; eight or ten in demesne for a manor lord. In some places, fifty sheep were allowed to pasture for each carucate, but this varied with the township. A carucate of new land was allowed to be taken in from the waste for a new minor religious settlement in early 12th century Goathland. New intaking of land beyond the ancient fields did occur before 1200 at the moor fringes, from Snainton to Coxwold and Yearsley. Arable intakes from five to fifty acres were made during King John's reign. Broadly speaking, it appears that the fields in many townships now reached the limits that they would long retain.

Villages

Whether most of the villages were created or laid out in the 12th century is debatable. Villages could have been formed in the larger townships long before. There is little evidence that the movement from scattered farms to compact villages was mainly in this period, although the growth from one to the other in some cases may then occur. Signs of abandoned farmsteads do occur within areas of mediaeval common fields but they can belong to far earlier times. Some thirteenth century 'toft' and 'thorpe' names, suggesting outlying houses at Kirkby Misperton and Aymotherby, later vanish into the fields. Villages at Hutton and Sinnington are not adjacent to their fields, and older detached inclosures may mark earlier settlement sites. Outlying farmsteads for arable cultivation certainly became unusual in common field townships, although common in the dales, where they adjoined their own ring-fenced arable land. It is likely that a variety of developments occured.

Whether the villages were old or new, some may well have been laid out anew by the Normans. Many had one or two rows of more or less regular house plots called tofts, sited along a road or stream or arranged around a green, with their crofts or backyards stretching behind to a back lane, a ditch or a headland. The lord's manor house was commonly at one end of the village street. Some seem like ribbon development but others have a hint of planning with regular tofts of roughly equal size. At Kirkby Misperton, early documents show St Mary's Abbey owning two house plots near to the door of the house of the Malton canons, and receiving another toft next to the courtyard of the parson of the church. An Abbot's close in later records, may mark the same site.

Villages containing more than one manor were far less regular. Their house rows ribboned outwards from a scatter of manor sites, spread over quite wide 'village' areas, as at Brompton, Snainton, Slingsby and Thornton Dale. Separate roads pointed in different directions, each with its own settlement. The presence or absence of small streams was a major influence. At Thornton Dale, some of the parts have different names, Roxby, Farmanby, Liedthorpe and Thornton and there are outliers in the valley above at Dalby and Kettlethorpe.

In another situation, nearer the moors, large greens equipped with ponds for watering stock characterised the dry limestone villages at Levisham, Newton and Fadmoor. In the different circumstances of the Wold valley, even now, villages show earthworks well beyond today's houses, reaching towards the township boundaries. This seems often to reflect a tendency to build a new house a bit further over, rather than on the same site. Chalk houses had to be frequently rebuilt. When it came to moving the walling stone, the arrangement had much to recommend it.

People in Villages

Villagers appear in the records by name, before the end of the twelfth century, but usually it is only priests and freeholders who are named, as witnesses to charters and not the villeins or cottagers. At Helmsley, we hear of Goduin, Drew son of Thockeman, Master William, Robert the chaplain and Robert dean of Helmsley before 1183. A little later, the clerk Thierry has a son John and a daughter Albreda. Hugh Herre is Albreda's husband. Robert son of Henry son of Tokeman, Everard the herberger, Hugh son of Ernulph, Basilia Basset and Benedict of York appear with Sigerith daughter of Robert of Nunnington as owners or tenants of house plots. William son of Robert the miller paid a rent of three shillings to William son of Walter the clerk of Helmsley.

The picture is similar elsewhere. In the villages of Pickering Lythe, inidividual sokemen are mentioned by 1158 at settlements that were probably empty at the time of the Domesday survey of 1087. We have a mixture of Norse and French names. They include Gamel and his brother Gospatric of Roxby, Engenald of Wilton and Torfin of Allerston. One man, Asketin son of Thorald of Pickering gave Rievaulx Abbey a toft near Pickering castle. Other Pickering men were Reginald and Richard son of Liveve.

Ryedale seems to have someone at most settlements by this time. Unspac of Hovingham, Gernagotus of Cawton, Robert of Fadmoor and Siward of Rook Barugh suggest a remakable recovery. They would need many others to work the fields of those townships. There are some soke men with lands in more than one place. The taking up of vacant tenancies in one place by survivors at another might well happen in a period of recovery. Soon after mid century, the family of Ansketil de Ryedale had lands from Wombleton to Habton, while one sister was a nun in Watton Priory .

New 'Towns'.

A new kind of community called a 'borough' was created by several members of the Norman barony. Unlike other settlements, boroughs were not dependant on arable or stock farming, although a few cows and pigs might roam their streets. The burgesses made their livelihood by other means, in the crafts, trades and services. They enjoyed trading advantages within the borough market. Land was set out for borough sites near castles at New Thirsk, New Malton, Skelton, Yarm, and Scarborough, but separate from the monastery at Whitby.

Other boroughs were grafted onto older settlements at Northallerton, Stokesley, Pickering and Helmsley, never far from the castles, which gave them their initial stimulus. Among the most successful borough towns were the coastal and river ports. Yarm, like York, could be reached by ships on several tides and saw the early export of lead and wool. Whitby was an estuary borough on the river Esk, down below the Norman monastery at Prestby and the old settlement of Whitby high on the east cliff.

Such boroughs started small with a dozen or so burgage men, and were founded surprisingly early in the 12th century, probably replacing older hundredal markets. Burgage was granted at Whitby in the time of King Henry I while Thirsk borough existed by the 1130's. William of Aumale may have started the Scarborough Old Borough on the high spur above the sands, west of his castle. His successor King Henry II issued a charter setting burgage rents at 4d and 6d a year, depending on whether the houses were gable or sideways on to the road. A payment to the King of £20 for the liberties granted to Scarborough began in 1163. The second New Borough at Scarborough existed by 1175. Its streets were aligned in a quite different direction to the first town. Scarborough enjoyed eminent early success, supplying fish along the river system to the inland marches of the shire and exporting the wool of Blackamore and Yorkswold.

The Ryedale Boroughs

The borough of New Malton was founded north west of Malton castle before 1150, either by the King or Eustace Fitzjohn, who returned from Scotland and was restored at Malton in his later years. The borough site was quite separate from Old Malton village and church. A generous area of sloping land, apparently athwart old Roman roads west of the castle was given curving boundary banks and ditches, which were eventually walled on all sides except for the abutments on the river Derwent and the castle.

The borough boundary did not initially include the low street of Castlegate which led to the Derwent river crossing below the castle, or the extra-mural suburb called Newbiggin. Within the boundary of Malton, freemen from several country manors took up 'burgage' plots at modest fixed rents, a penny or twopence a year according to the number of doors in the house. The lord gave them a limited freedom to run their own affairs and more privileges could be bought at later dates. They had their own chapel in the large market place and another developed beneath the castle.

The smaller Helmsley borough was not laid out till around 1191 by Robert de Ros who had inherited the lordship by marriage with Espec's sister Adeline. Boroughgate marks a narrow street of small toft plots east of the castle. Tradition claimed that Helmsley market moved from the churchyard, where Boroughgate and Bondgate meet to the generously laid out market square, but there is no hint as to when this might have happened. The burgesses paid eleven pounds for customs which were described, presumably rather loosely, as based on those of York.

The borough at Pickering crept quietly into being, initially concentrated in the small tofts of another Boroughgate, between the castle demesne and the village, before the time of King John. It could have begun when Robert de Brus of Annandale briefly held the manor and socage at farm from the King in 1163. A line of descendants of that family were prominent in the town for centuries. The thirty three men of Pickering made payments into the king's courts in 1169. Thirty three freemen were still spoken of in 1301, when they were separately listed, in addition to sixty two bondmen.

Hospitals

Another poorly recorded movement established small hospitals, either on through-roads or at the approaches to boroughs. With the chapels attached to them, they were served by brothers and sisters in holy orders. At this time a hospital seems to have been concerned with care rather than cure. Some later hospitals did approximate to almshouses and others were particularly earmarked for those with conditions thought of as leprosy. Most hospitals gave the travelling poor, temporary relief and over night accomodation. The foundation dates of hospitals are rarely known and even their existence is sometimes only suggested by the chance survival of a name; a Spital Bridge, a Spital Close, or the Spital Inn at Barton le Willows. Unexplained Spital closes occur at Gilling, Ganthorpe, Mowthorpe, Terrington and Hovingham.

Gerbert de Place gave land at Newton to the St. Leonard's hospital at York. So too did Norman and Osbert Bushell at Ellerburn. By 1148,

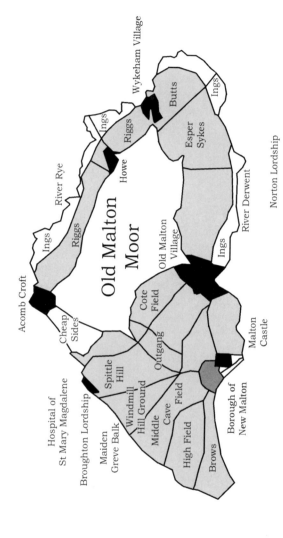

Acomb Croft

River Rye

Ings

Riggs

Cheap
Sides

Hospital of
St Mary Magdalene

Broughton Lordship

Maiden
Greve Balk

Spittle
Hill

Windmill
Hill Ground

Middle
Cave
Field

High Field

Brows

Borough of
New Malton

Malton
Castle

Outgang

Cote
Field

Old Malton
Village

Old Malton
Moor

Howe

Riggs

Ings

Wykeham Village

Butts

Esper
Sykes

Ings

Ings

River Derwent

Norton Lordship

Early enclosures of Settlements
Common Fields
Walled Borough of New Malton

The Plantation of the Borough of New Malton in the Fields of Old Malton in the 12th Century

this great Hospital, which was run on a very large scale, had land at many places including Cawthorne on Wade's causeway, but the choice of sites may not be significant. Hospitals at Pickering and Goathland were convenient for that route. The earliest hospital outside York was formed at Goathland in around 1119 when a band of brothers was allowed to remain in Pickering Forest, as long as they provided a refuge for travellers. Orm's leper hospital just outside the borough of Whitby at 'Spital' bridge and beside an early river Esk crossing, was dedicated to St Michael, who 'rowed the boat ashore'.

The boroughs of Northallerton, Yarm, Thirsk, Pickering, Scarborough, Whitby, Malton and York had one or more hospitals on their approach roads. One was sited on the Derwent island between Malton and Norton. Others hospitals were at Upsall, Hutton Low Cross, Stainton, Bagby, Osgodby, Pockley, and Crayke meadows. The Fulk's bridge below Snainton attracted a settlement of Knights Templar, who provided alms for travellers on specific days of the week. Knights Hospitallers secured the Manor of Stainton Dale, with an obligation to provide a travellers' hospital there. Together with the hostelries at monastery gates, the hospitals witness to a concern for the problems of the travelling poor. Taken together, they may have provided a circuit of places to call at, for an overnight stay.

Milling Corn

Many specialised crafts were concentrated at York, or in the new castles, monasteries and boroughs, but corn mills and river fisheries were rural. The water mills mentioned in the 1086 Domesday Book were too few and too distant to deal with the crops produced. There had probably been others. In some cases the site rather than the mill itself was mentioned. With the recovery of agriculture, manor lords and monasteries invested in more mills for grinding grain, anxious to have the incomes generated, and equally keen not to pay the mill charges of others. Hand mills called 'querns' were restricted, and tenants were obliged to use the manorial mills. They paid 'multure' to the miller at rates varying between an eleventh and a twentieth of the corn ground.

Even such small places as Fryton, Foulbridge, and Sproxton eventually gained their own corn mills, as did quite small manors and monastery granges wherever there were suitable streams. Fast flowing rivers had several mills along their course. Wintringham had two water mills on the lower course of a stream near the distant river Derwent.

Yet, even a diminutive stream with a good flow, could when dammed, drive a mill sufficient to grind the corn of a modest manor. The millpond served as a useful fishery. Much of the Wold valley and some areas of low lying Galtres and the Marishes lacked good streams, so that watermills were rare, but early windmills appeared from the late twelfth century.

The water mill was a major investment in the mediaeval manor, and charges on mills for rents and debts were as good a guarantee as you could get. St Mary's Abbey made a life lease of the Kirkby Misperton mill to two clerks before 1145. The agreement provided that timber would be supplied from Spaunton Forest if the mill burnt down. The rent was forty six shillings a year. Keldholme Priory received Little Edstone mill from Hugh del Tuit. A rent charged on the Sinnington mill paid for oil for the St. Mary altar in Little Marish priory. The Cistercian Abbey of Rievaulx leased its Fryton mill to Newbrough Priory but the Cistercian Abbey of Meaux later had several mills at Wharram le Street.

King Henry II restricted the dyeing of cloth to York, Beverley, Thirsk, Malton, Scarborough and other demesne boroughs, where weaving was early established, but late in the twelfth century, a few water powered fulling mills were introduced on countryside streams for shrinking, thickening and felting the cloth.

Rare Industry for Nature's Products

Some industrial tasks were undertaken where the raw materials were found. Iron stone was extracted from outcrops along the Blackamore valleys. The industry began in the Iron Age and continued till the nineteenth century. The Wold people needed iron but lacked it and it was probably brought from Blackamore.

A few stone quarries are known to be ancient, the largest probably continued from Roman times at Malton, Amotherby, Hildenley, and perhaps Pickering. New quarries were opened in valley sides near building sites, for monasteries, castles and churches. The Pickering castle quarry strengthened the north and west defences of the castle.

The Rievaulx quarries were given a diverted water course to move the stone to the monastery building site. The lord of Hutton Bardolf gave Kirkham Priory the ancient quarry at Hildenley with access by the customary way, for the monk's carts. Malton Priory was conveniently near Roman quarries and Roman ruins, which were also robbed to provide stone for several East Riding churches. A line of limestone and freestone breaks out along the west edge of the Wolds, but the chalk country lacked the best building stone for major structures. The hearthstones known as 'bakestones' were dug up near Helmsley and Spaunton.

Offshore sea fishing from the port boroughs soon exceeded the casual fishing from most of the coastal villages, where single fishermen had appeared at early dates but Flamborough, Filey and Bridlington developed on a comparable scale. Fish from Filey were already taken inland for sale at Stamford Bridge. The Ouse, Derwent and other river fisheries were important manorial perquisites. Several stretches passed to monasteries. They were eventually supplemented by breeding ponds and storage stews for fresh fish. The Abbeys of Byland and Rievaulx had fish weirs in the Tees, where the salmon ran.

Sea salt was essential for preserving meat and fish. Saltings for boiling and evaporating brine on the banks of the River Tees at Coatham and Normanby were perhaps older than the Normans, but continued for centuries. Old salt roads called saltergates ran inland towards Pickering Vale and Ryedale. Many monasteries secured a salting of their own.

Monastic Farming

The flow of land grants to monasteries continued for some time, including some major acquisitions. Amfrey de Chauncy gave St Mary's Abbey four carucates at Thixendale and properties in Skirpenbeck to Byland Abbey, Whitby Abbey and the York Hospital. Most were leased to laymen. Roger de Mowbray gave Newburgh Priory a large estate in Hovingham. Reginald de Brompton gave low meadows, field acres, new wold intakes and pasture for eight hundred sheep at Potter Brompton to Bridlington Priory. A monastic house might build up an estate from a series of gifts and purchases, sometimes quite deliberately. As their resources grew, the monks attracted mortgages and properties sometimes passed into their hands when people were hard up, or in the phrase of the time, 'in their great necessity'.

The monastic estates were organised to yield income in a variety of ways. When Peter de Cordanville gave Sherburn church with its carucate of eight oxgangs to distant Guisborough Priory, this posed management choices. Augustinian rectories were sometimes granted away to yield a rent, as an alternative to appropriating the valuable tithe crops and young animals. Distant properties of all kinds were commonly put out to rent. The Benedictines rented out local manors and other freeholds to laymen, often giving early tenancies to families of Anglo-Scandinavian descent. Some Whitby Abbey tenants were obliged to send men to work at the home farms of the monastery during busy seasons, as part of the tenancy agreement.

Whitby Abbey pioneered early cattle farms called 'vaccaries' at the edge of the moors, probably employing abbey servants. The Cistercian monasteries built up networks of estates outside the local manorial system, based on granges worked by lay brothers. These formed another class of hard labouring brothers compensated with better food and a secure life. Rievaulx Abbey at its peak had one hundred and forty monks and four hundred lay brothers. The Cistercians maintained their unworldly detachment by siting their granges away from villages. Rievaulx Abbey soon held a great swathe of properties, stretching from Teesmouth to the coast near Filey, including much of western Ryedale, the Marishes, Bilsdale and great tracts of moorland. This was an economy of its own.

Other monasteries copied the outlying grange system and the institution of lay brothers but also had granges, farms, rectories and manors within villages. Bertram de Bulmer gave a grange at Sutton on the southern fringe of its common fields on the Howardian hill slopes in Galtres Forest to St Leonards Hospital in 1136. Byland Abbey and Newbrough Priory had many granges in the Hambleton Hills and York Vale. Bridlington Priory had farms in and around the Wolds, while Kirkham Priory sited on the river Derwent was represented in both terrains. Monastic vaccaries, granges and sheep cotes re-established the isolated farmstead, often on new sites and frequently for specialised stock rather than arable farming.

The Sheep Grange

There were monastery farms where the emphasis was on arable crops, cattle or even iron working or other industry, but the sheep grange characterised much of north and east Yorkshire. Early grants came in three forms. A donor might give the right to pasture a fixed number of sheep, up to two or three hundred in a township. Alternatively he could allocate pastures, bounded and separated off from a township. Thirdly, he might grant the entire township. The gift of a right to put so many animals on a common could lead to running sheep with the local animals, or to moving flocks between several townships. The Wolds near Bridlington certainly saw monastery flocks moved from place to place. The northern junction of fields and commons in the Ryedale and Pickering Vale townships of the limestone country, saw a line of granges founded where generous grants had been made of Blackamore pasture.

Rievaulx Abbey received the two townships of Griff and Stilton close to the mother house at an early date. The entire township given to a monastery and managed as a grange did occur at Hoveton and Welburn on the lower limestone slope, at Skiplam grange with its outlying Ewe, Wether and Lund cotes on higher slopes, and in the dales where shepherds at outlying cotes, watched the flocks on the sheep pastures above the Rievaulx and Kirkham granges in Bilsdale.

Hoveton is only remembered in the name Howekeld, west of Kirkby Moorside. The township was already settled when it was given to Rievaulx abbey. They cleared it completely and settled new boundaries, where previously three townships had shared the low commons. Free holders were bought out in 1154 and the villeins were allowed to move away. Sunnive was offered six marks and a cow. The Whitby hospital was given six shillings for a freehold and some old clothing. Three other ladies were given six marks and cows for their properties. Peter de Hoveton took twenty marks and a horse, and his wife had two cows, ten sheep and ten lambs as compensation for their five oxgangs.

When King Henry II gave the vast lowland area called the Marishes to Rievaulx in 1158, from Allerston beck to Kirkby Misperton, Peter de Surdeval added Theokmarish and the King separately donated Kilverdmarish. The old Scandinavian farmsteads stood on islands of cultivation. The freeholders of the townships nearby surrendered their common rights. Then began the development of a new style of farming. The old manors were converted into new granges. The lay brothers built houses and sheepfolds and tilled the land. They dug the new friar's dyke, an early drainage improvement. Kekmarish Grange grew to include three hundred acres of arable and another three hundred acres of pasture. Drainage improvements were almost a Cistercian speciality. Byland lay brothers drained the final site of their monastery and made access to WoodKeld spring at Daletown for their Murton Grange. Rievaulx lay brothers moved water courses at the monastery and diverted streams to their Sproxton Grange.

Women in Nunneries

St Gilbert of Sempringham founded a new monastic order in Lincolnshire offering a religious life for women as well as men. This proved popular in Yorkshire in the later years of the twelfth century. When Eustace Fitzjohn returned to his Malton castle from exile in Scotland, he endowed the Gilbertine Order with his redundant halls and the churches at Old Malton and Wintringham. Legends speak of plans for a local women's house being abandoned. Malton church was adapted to serve a new Priory built to hold thirty five canons and thirty lay brothers. The Priory was given an Old Malton manor, its demesne, the church and the church land, a river fishery, fishponds, a tangarth, a corn mill, and moor sheepfolds within the township.

The monastery received many more gifts of manors, rectories, lands and pastures. Extensive granges were established in the Wolds, the Howardian hills and across the valley in the townships from Sinnington to Levisham and Goathland. The saint wrote his last letter at Malton in 1189, urging his canons to abide by their rule. A double monastery was also founded at Marton in Galtres Forest but the arrangement proved unsatisfactory and the nuns were soon moved to Moxby, not very far away. Other Gilbertine houses at York St Andrews, at Watton and at Ellerton gained local interests. Watton Priory developed a large holding at Birdsall.

The Cistercians were strongly opposed to houses of religious women being linked with the Order, until the early 13th century. Small Benedictine nunneries were founded in Yorkshire, mostly in the period 1150-1160. A remarkable movement produced houses with a Prioress and twelve nuns at Wykeham, Little Marish, Moxby, Rosedale, Keldholme, Arden, Basedale and elsewhere. Several later adopted the Cistercian rule and moved to more isolated sites.

Wiliam de Rosedale a descendant of Turgis Brundos founded Rosedale Priory, and his successors of the Stuteville family, confirmed their holding of the whole of Rosedale east side, Bagthwaite towards Hartoft, and the bark of wood cut for tanning at Cropton. Roger de Clere and his wife gave all of Little Marish to establish a Priory, a small township south of Ebberston on the north side of the river Derwent opposite Yedingham, the name by which it was eventually known. He added Sinnington church and several other properties. Peter de Hutton founded Arden Priory high above the west side of Bilsdale, and Robert de Stuteville gave a tract east of Kirkby Moorside, to establish the nuns of Dove, later known as Keldholme Priory. The estates of the nunneries were more modest, but were locally endowed by the manorial families who provided many of their inmates.

The monastery buildings were arranged into inner and outer precincts. There was some provision for lodging visitors and pilgrims, even poor travellers, to whom alms might be given. The church was usually on the north side of a regular cloister square, with a dormitory on the east side, and an access way into the church to go to the night offices. The lower side of the cloister held the refectory and kitchens that served it, and the west side held either the lay brothers quarters or in a small house the Prioress's lodging. Outside this area was usually an outer courtyard which held stores, barns and housing for cattle, pigs, oxen and sometimes doves, with granaries, and buildings for the brewing and baking done on the site. Industrial buildings could include a mill.

Outstanding Monks

In a sceptical age, the early aspirations, and the continuing dedication, of those bound by monastic rules of poverty, chastity and obedience, in a highly disciplined religious society are hard to imagine. The continuous, almost monotonous round of praise and prayer, of religious contemplation and study, apart from the ordinary world, attracted men and women from the better off levels of society. The ideal was remarkable, both for what it offered and what it lost. Some of the ablest people of the day seem to have been among its exemplars.

Ailred became Abbot of Rievaulx in 1147 and died in 1166. He was a Northumbrian of old English descent raised at the court of Scotland. He wrote several books and he wrote of his monks that 'Our food is scanty, our garments rough, our drink is from the stream and our sleep is often upon our books. Under old tired limbs there is but a hard mat. When sleep is sweetest, we must rise at a bell's bidding. Self will has no scope. There is no moment for idleness or dissipation. Everywhere peace, everywhere serenity, and marvellous freedom from the tumult of the world. To put all in brief, no perfection expressed in the words of the gospel or of the apostles or in the writings of the fathers, or in the sayings of the monks of old is wanting to our order and our way of life.'

Robert the scribe, a canon of Bridlington Priory wrote a treatise on music. The canon William of Newbrough, who spent most of his life in

70

that house, wrote down the good stories of his day, along with dreams, visions, portents and comments on the effect of the stars on human affairs. Gilbert of Sempringham began as a Lincolnshire parish priest. When approaching death and losing bodily strength, he told his Malton canons of the bitter and tedious nature of life, but admonished them for the welfare of their souls, to repress vice, exalt justice, and to observe the institutions and traditions of their order the more strictly, since they were free of the occupations of the lay brothers.

Small Trade

Soke manors, parish churchyards, borough market places, and the great city of York were the main venues for early trade. Specialised crafts were concentrated in York providing luxuries for which lords, the clergy and the inmates of monasteries were the main consumers. Tithe payments provided parish churches or the monasteries who secured them with surpluses, some of which could be stored, but much of which had to be resold. The young St Godric trudged from place to place, with staff in hand and pack on back, selling small wares at farms before he tackled the boroughs and the market booths. Many monasteries secured toll exemptions at ports and local markets. The city also had its financiers. Knights went into debt to its Jewish community. Richard Malebisse owing much to Aaron of Lincoln was prominent in the massacre of Jews by debtors at York in 1190.

Some commerce could bypass markets and fairs. The early vintners, imported wine by ship over the great distance from Gascony, and appeared in the entourages of abbots and barons. Wool was the principal commodity convertible into other forms of wealth. The baron William de Stuteville in the half year ending Michaelmas 1203 raised vast sums from stock sales, with sheep selling at a shilling or so. Wool trading by contract linked local collectors at York, Beverley and Scarborough with Flemish merchants. A shipman might take out wool and return with wine.

Much of the annual woolclip was eventually stored, two hundred and forty fleeces to the sack, in great monastic and baronial woolhouses, ready for sampling by travelling buyers from Flanders or Italy. The Byland Abbey woolhouse is recalled in the name of Thorpe le Willows, and impressive stonework marks the site of the great Rievaulx woolhouse at Laskill in Bilsdale. Iron travelled in small quantities from dale sites to early local smiths. Lead for church roofs came from

Richmondshire through York. Sea fish was widely distributed. Some three thousand herring were annually sent from Whitby via Thornton Dale to St Leonard's Hospital at York.

The Young King's Rebellion

Henry the son of King Henry II was associated with his father in ruling the kingdom from 1170. They called him 'the young King'. He may have controlled crown lands in Pickering Vale, for he made a sizeable grant from the estate to Wykeham Priory. The heir to the throne is usually a problem. Allied with disatisfied barons and with William the Lion, King of Scotland, he rebelled in 1172-73. Some Pickering and Scalby sokemen were fined for involvement and Pickering castle was strengthened afterwards. Bernard de Balliol and Robert de Stuteville captured the Scots king at Alnwick, and imprisoned him at Richmond castle. Roger Mowbray of Thirsk joined the rebels, but Geoffrey Bishop of Lincoln, an illegitimate son of the King, fortified Topcliffe castle and attacked Mowbray. Roger was twice defeated by royal forces near Northallerton.

Action seems to have been largely confined to the Vale of York but when it was over, the King added new outer defences called a barbican to Scarborough castle, and had work done at Pickering castle. Peace was made in 1175 when Robert de Stuteville supervised Crown castle building at Scarborough and Edinburgh. Archbishop Roger of York was given custody of Scarborough castle. He was the builder of a York palace, with its own chapel, the new York minster choir and Ripon church. He may have had a hand in the reconstruction of the large Scarborough church. King Richard I gave this church, with its valuable tithes of fish to the Cistercian Order, to finance their chapter meetings at the mother house of Citeaux.

The Life of the Barons

The great baronies, sometimes called 'honours', were firmly established and passed by descent through generations of the elder sons of a few great families. If lines failed, there might be a division among daughter co-heirs and their husbands. Some estates prospered enough for small portions to be separated off for younger sons or to provide marriage endowments for daughters. When a lord died, the estate reverted briefly to the overlord until a 'relief' payment was made. If the heir was under age, the owner of his wardship could enjoy the estate until an enquiry was held to prove that the heir had reached maturity. Custody of the ward could lead to his marriage with your daughter. Wardship and marriage became a property and Kings were always interested in the descent of major fiefs. The rising Stuteville family recovered much of the old estate that their ancestor had forfeited for rebellion, including Kirkby Moorside, which was taken from the Mowbrays and restored by the King's courts.

Much of the political history of the region centred around the barons. It was not just the wealth of their great estates that counted, but the feudal and semi feudal links that went with them. The Percy estates of Topcliffe and Seamer, Robert de Turnham's Mulgrave, Peter de Brus's honour of Skelton, Eustace de Vescy's honour of Malton, Hugh Bigod's honour of Settrington, Robert de Ros's Helmsley, William de Mowbray's Thirsk and Hovingham, and Hugh de Balliol's Stokesley all had substantial demesnes and had associated knight's fees. Only Settrington and Hovingham lacked a great local castle.

Settrington seems to have replaced old Buckton as the focal point of that estate, but it is not obvious what happened and Buckton is lost, appearing only as a junction of roads on an air photograph, and slight earthworks on the ground. Wath near Hovingham had curious unexplained but substantial stone ruins, and there are stories of a castle.

The great men followed the King in European wars. They fought on the Scots and Welsh borders and they rode on Crusades. They travelled between their castles and halls to consume local surpluses, to administer courts and to 'sweeten' their rooms. Their entourages seemed like little courts. Roger de Mowbray had a singer, jongleur, minstrel, fiddler and chaplains as well as the usual household officers.

At the wealthy end of society the English, Norse, Normans, Flemings and Bretons were merging into a single aristocracy. Descendants of Maldred, Ligulfr, Halfdan and others of local lineage from before the Norman conquest still tenanted estates from Hutton le Hole to Habton, from Bulmer and Hinderskelfe to Scarborough. The heirs of a Gospatric had lands in Roxburghshire and Ryedale. The boroughs offered other good opportunities to the younger sons of free men. Lines of Ughtreds and Halfdans would become Scarborough's main property owners.

Marrying Norman had a certain cachet but marrying 'English' could help secure rights to property. Allerston passed by marriage from Torphin's heiress to the rising Hastings family. The French Percy name had such weight that it was taken by some who merely served or married them. Norman surnames were fixed early, mostly taken from continental homelands such as Percy, Eure, Montbrai and many more, but Norse names stuck, at that level, as well.

Soon, Yorkshire places gave new surnames and the habit spread down the ranks. French personal names became dominant much further down the social scale with an occasional hint of Flanders or Brittany among the Roberts, Richards, Williams, Emmas and Matildas. A Scandinavian first name became quite rare. Yet French remained just as infrequent in the landscape, with only the occasional Malpas, Bellifax, Rievaulx, Harriet Hare or Nattie Fonten marking some innovation. The language of war, horses, and the forest spoke more of the Norman, but the hills, dales, woods, carrs, fields and moors kept the rich language of those who worked them.

Monks' Stories

Conversation is the essence of social life and story telling was a major part of pleasure. The written culture of the monks probably played quite a minor part in ordinary local life, but it did decide what was to be remembered. Little William at Newbrough Priory was asked by Abbot Ernald of Rievaulx to write a history. He included the stories that others told him. His childhood had been spent in Deira, near the Gipsey Race and he heard there of the intoxicated rustic who heard the noise of revelling coming from a hillock a few furlongs from his village. He went through a door in the mound, where many were feasting and was offered a cup of drink. He left the drink but fled with the cup, which being of an unknown material, unusual colour and strange form was afterwards given to King Henry I. There were marvels he had seen, such as the skies blazing red three times in the year 1192, and others he hadn't seen from distant counties, where some rose from the grave, men saw demons and some children were green.

A wonderful event occured when a limekiln was made at Malton Priory in 1197 and after the August sunset, was fired from below. A man fell in the seven foot pit nearby and did not re-appear. Asked if he was hurt, he replied 'I am killed' and he was. Two more went in and died as suddenly. A third descending cried, 'I die, I die, pull me out.' He was retrieved but his clothes seemed rent and for days he languished. Next day another man went in to recover the bodies, with no trouble at all, but discovered that all the deceased had bruised left eyes. This was a great mystery.

Others added stories to the local stock of tales. They told of Mowbray captured by Saracens on crusade and ransomed by the Knights Templar. They said that he fought a lion and brought it to Hood castle. A Murton woman blamed her ailments on a cooked frog eaten in a loaf but thought herself cured by St William of York. Whitby monks credited their first Abbot William with miraculously obtaining such holy relics as the head, arms and two thighs of the seventh century Anglian Abbess Hilda.

A story of hunters in the middle years of the twelfth century had them pursuing a wild boar into the Eskdale hermitage,where the hermit died. They fled to refuge in the borough of Scarborough, but the Whitby abbot imposed penalties on them and their successors, which are still carried out in 'penny hedge' rituals to this day. Stories buried in later legend may even contain some fragment of truth. The name Rosamund's Tower attaches to a fourteenth century stone tower at Pickering Castle. The 'Fair Rosamund' was mistress to King Henry II in the twelfth century, but a tower could have formed part of the timber outworks that survived until 1322.

No Stranger King

King John stayed overnight at William de Stuteville's Cottingham castle in 1201. He visited his own castles at Pickering and Scarborough, and then crossed Blackamore with the royal hounds to call at Gilly Park Castle, otherwise known as St Julian's, where he issued a charter to the nuns of Keldholme Priory. This monarch travelled much around his kingdom. He held courts, demanded subsidies from the Cistercians, fined boroughs that offered an inadequate welcome, and returned more than once, to hunt boar in the Forest of Pickering. At other times, his sheriff ruled the county amidst strong and unruly barons. William de Stuteville bought the office of Sheriff of Yorkshire, and a licence to make a new castle at Buttercrambe in the first year of the reign. Danby Castle had long been in Crown hands, recovered from William of Aumale and valued for its hunting, so the Brus's had moved to Skelton Castle. Peter de Brus bought the return of Danby from King John. Castle stonework found at Castleton may belong to the period.

Old timber works at many castles were replaced by stone curtain walls in the contemporary military style, built around new halls, often when a castle changed hands. Most gained a stone chapel. Robert de Ros had married the Espec heiress of Helmsley. He added a strong keep to the castle and chartered a small borough. Robert deTurnham had quelled a revolt in Cyprus and was rewarded with the barony and the hand of the Fossard heiress. The couple had probably built the new castle at St Julian's Park, south of Egton, beside the old Roman road called Wade's causeway, and away from the old Mulgrave motte. They also founded Grosmont Priory. The Stuteville family recovered the right to their old Kirkby Moorside fief and they also replaced the heirs of Turgis Brundos at Cropton. Both castles gained stone curtain walls, although at uncertain dates. The King's Pickering Castle, in 1203, held a garrison of two serjeants and twenty two footmen under Brian the Usher, who served as the constable with sixty shillings a year for his maintenance.

The King against his Barons

Some Yorkshire barons had no continental lands and they showed little interest in King John's French campaigns. William de Mowbray, Peter de Brus, Richard de Percy and Eustace de Vescy, the heir to Malton, refused to join an overseas expedition to Poitou or pay a war tax in 1214. They were joined by Robert de Ros, the lord of Helmsley and Wark castles; Nicholas de Stuteville the lord of Cropton and Liddel castles and Henry de Neville, the lord of Sheriff Hutton in Galtres. These barons were prominent among the 'northerners' who played a vital part in forcing an agreement on the King during 1215. This was called the Magna Carta and came to be seen as a basic statement of English liberties. Vescy, Mowbray, Ros and Percy were on the council of twenty five barons set up under the Charter. All had castles around Blackamore.

The King's revenge was swift. Over the two previous years, he had spent heavily, fortifying Scarborough and Pickering castles. During 1212, Scarborough castle took delivery of six hundred and ten sides of bacon, fourteen tuns of wine and ten lasts of herring. His loyal supporter Peter de Mauley, had been awarded the Turnham heiress of Mulgrave and her estate with its castles in 1214. Now, demolition was ordered for Vescy's Malton castle. Great seige machines were built at Knaresborough. Geoffrey de Neville was given charge of Scarborough with a garrison of ten knights, sixty serjeants and ten crossbowmen. The King led a whirlwind campaign through the Winter of 1215-1216, forcing all the castles of his opponents into surrender except Helmsley. The town of Thirsk submitted when John threatened to burn the houses.

The Chamberlain Geoffrey de la Hoge surrendered Skelton castle. A resurgence of rebellion in the New Year was ended by the King's death.

The Knightly Class

The class from which the knights were drawn enjoyed a growing significance as the incomes from their demesne farms began to approximate to those of earlier barons. Widows had the right to a dower third of their husband's estate, and the failure of baronial male lines offered some knights a chance of social promotion. The younger sons from the Norman families of Fossard, Lutterell, Paynell and Surdeval gained new Ryedale estates. Sir Nicholas Mallory had property in the East Riding as well as at Terrington, and its neighbour Mowthorpe. Sir John de Stonegrave held Stonegrave, Nunnington and the New Hay in Ryedale, from John Paynel for two and thee quarter knights fees. Richard de Grey settled at Barton le street and Roger de Stapelton at Wath, where his branch of that family long held the stone house. Nicholas de Hastings gave his young son Henry a 'capital messuage' at Hungate in Thornton Dale, with lands at Roxby. These men in their turn could sublet estates to others, building those feudal hierarchies of obligation, which in the end became too complicated and were done away with.

Stewards could do well in any age. Thomas the son of Geoffrey de Etton whose relation Ivo de Etton was constable of Tickhill castle, founded the important Gilling family. Drew de Harum served as a steward to the second Robert de Ros, lord of Helmsley in 1210, but William de Harum held office as coroner of the county in 1251. Richard de Wyville, another Helmsley steward, made Slingsby his main seat and he was able to fortify the house in 1216. He granted the mill to his nephew Laurence and a freehold to his sister's husband. Some ended their days in monastic retirement. Nicholas de Habton had a manor mortgaged to Deodonatus Medicus and Amiot the Jew of Pontefract, but he fought for the barons in 1217, before retiring as a monk to Meaux Abbey.

Disafforestation

Old forest customs were made into a code of law under the Assize of the Forest in 1184. From now on, oaths promising good behaviour were to be sworn by all over the age of twelve who lived in a royal forest. Inquests were to be held for any dead deer. Officers called regarders and agisters were appointed to guard the venison and the woods, and to control pasturing wherever the deer might go. The taking in of fresh land was to be more tightly controlled. Customary rights to timber were to be exercised under the supervision of foresters. Ownership of large dogs was restricted or the claws of their forefeet had to be struck off. The better off bought exemption from this clause by paying fines, which were equivalent to early dog licences. This would become a trend, whereby controls to defend the deer and the wood, steadily gave way to the licencing of exemptions to raise money.

King John needed money to pay mercenaries to fight his wars, and he readily sold privileges for cash. He sold off most of the royal forests in north east Yorkshire. Ryedale wapentake was disafforested although some timber management customs remained. Whitby Strand and Spaunton forests were returned in 1203 to the monasteries who supervised them. The forest between the rivers Dove and Seven passed to the Abbots of St Mary's York, and would be administered from their manor of Spaunton. A small Forest of Farndale was retained by the Crown, with a forester living at Dowthwaite. The Forests of Danby and Egton were returned to Barons.

The remaining royal forests were Galtres Forest, reduced in size, Pickering Forest and the small Forest of Farndale. The King's deer and boar were sometimes hunted by the monarch and those he favoured, but were more frequently culled to supply the King's larder. An early Galtres hunting lodge was built near Easingwold and a 'hunt house' was erected on Goathland moor. A number of 'thwaites' or clearings had already been created in Galtres Forest as 'laundes' or preserves for the deer to pasture in safety, and large enclosures called 'hays' were made from Scalby and Dalby commons in Pickering Forest.

Blansby Hay was converted into a stone walled deer park. Alan Wastehose went there to take deer with seven grooms and twenty seven greyhounds in 1203. The King's fool was sent to hunt in Pickering Forest in 1225 and occasionally the King hunted there himself. Orders came from King Henry III for deliveries of twenty to fifty deer and ten to thirty wild boar at a time. The Steward of Galtres was probably called on more often, for the king was frequently at York. One year two hundred does had to be delivered to the City for Christmas. This was the same season that the king's wardrober, Peter 'Chasepork' was buying scarlet cloth at the city, for stranger knights coming to the feasting. Another year there was an order to supply a hundred hinds and a hundred boars. There was occasional poaching but the fee foresters appointed under-foresters and the royal forest organisation became more elaborate.

The picture is less clear in the disafforested districts, but knights bought licences for new private parks at Riseborough, Scawton, Gilling and elsewhere, while the old baronial parks continued at Helmsley, Kirkby Moorside and Hovingham. Kirkham Priory had some rights of chase about Helmsley. Even within Pickering Forest, the leading men were allowed parks at Cropton, Sinnington, Seamer and Troutsdale. Abbot Robert of St Mary's, York enclosed a wooded hill to make Normanby park in 1204. These parks enclosed the deer within double banks and ditches. The space between was filled with brushwood to keep the deer in and the poachers out. Probably the parks were stocked with the hardy but manageable fallow deer, kept primarily for supplying lordly larders. The Minster canons gained Strensall park and the Bishop of Durham had a large park at Crayke with a one hundred and fifty foot, one-way, deer leap.

Many other manor lords bought rights of free warren which allowed them to monopolise the hunting of lesser game within their demesnes, but these never encompassed the deer. The Dean of York Minster secured the right to hunt hare, fox, badger and wildcat in Galtres Forest. A rich Scarborough burgess called Ughtred, whose ancestors had hunted the district before the Normans came, bought similar rights in Pickering Forest. Elena de Percy at Seamer and Peter de Mauley at Julian Park gained like privileges. The Master of the Order of Knights Templar was allowed to take a stag in the company of forester Nicholas de Hastings as he passed through Blackamore in 1259. Archbishops, Bishops, Earls and Barons were allowed to kill one or two deer when journeying through a royal forest, but they were obliged to summon the forester with a blast on a horn. Aeries of falcons, merlins and sparrow hawks were maintained for the Norman sport by the lords of Cropton and Levisham.

Wood in the Forest

Royal grants led to the movement of heavy timber over long distances for major building projects. Richard Malebisse was allowed two hundred and fifty oaks in Galtres Forest to rebuild Wheldrake Castle. Pickering Forest timber was despatched in 1227 as far as York, Scarborough and Topcliffe. Many woods were not Crown demesne but belonged to manor lords. These valuable assets were fenced in at early dates. The manor lords at Levisham licenced the burning of wood into charcoal, for use in local iron smelting and for sale. Some other woods were used in common by the men of a township, indeed some were still common to several townships.

The customary rights of the local inhabitants were written down as forest organisation became more elaborate. The right to wood for a particular purpose was called a 'bote'. Pickering men could have green and dead wood for 'housebote', dry wood for 'firebote' and 'haybote', this last used for fencing. They also had rights of pasture, and could take their pigs to the woods to grub up the feed of the woodland floor, free of payment, at an appropriate time, known as the 'mast season'. Within disafforested Ryedale, Helmsley burgesses enjoyed 'husbote and haybote' meaning timber for houses and fences.

Easingwold and Huby men saw their claims to timber in Galtres forest disputed, as the woodland was reduced. They settled for a total of thirty oaks a year. They had common pasture for oxen, cows, horses and hogs except in the fence month, and paid pannage dues for their pigs, but had no pasture within Galtres forest for sheep or goats. When heavy timber was supplied, whether from private or common woodlands, this was now only at the view of the foresters, who tended to become wood-mongers. Forest officers in outlying areas were allowed to require local inhabitants to provide their food and fodder for their horses, a practise that was wide open to abuse.

The Church-Expansive and Expensive

Each parish church in the Diocese was part of a 'Latin Christendom' unified by Councils and supervised by a hierarchy reaching to the Pope in Rome. There were difficulties. King John's conflict with Rome led Pope Innocent to excommunicate the monarch in 1209, and to place the kingdom under 'interdict'. Church services were restricted while the monarch took over the monasteries, and diverted their revenues to meet his own commitments. When the Abbot of Whitby died, the Crown profitably administered the Abbey estates without an abbot for three years. The Papal appointment of Italian clergy to take the revenues of English livings was a recurring abuse, with low paid substitutes left to do the local work. The Pope in 1213 appointed his nephew to a wealthy York prebend and a foreigner was appointed to Lastingham church in 1232. The system was attacked in 1232 by

The Norman Crypt at Lastingham Church

Sir Robert de Thwenge of Kilton Castle.

The growing prosperity of rich laymen and churchmen paid directly or indirectly for the new Universities, for the Crusades against other religions and to secure the Holy Land, for the rebuilding of monasteries, and the enlarging of parish churches. Many Yorkshire parishes, perhaps with typical populations of around three hundred people, rebuilt their churches and erected small chapels in outlying villages. Often, a north aisle was added to an existing church, then a south aisle, and perhaps an enlarged chancel, with side chapels and even transepts, by which time the small Norman structure had been lost in a much altered whole. Some were rebuilt altogether, but small gradual alterations seem to be typical of many.

There were other disputes settled in the courts between the regular church and the monasteries, who were often undertaking rebuilding programmes in these years. The Cistercian order claimed exemption from tithes by papal and royal grants, but tithes had been previously paid on the lands they acquired. Byland Abbey agreed to substitute a payment of twenty shillings a year to Hawnby church, instead of rendering the ancient tithes for Murton township. There were settlements in 1220, substituting fixed payments called 'moduses' payable from Rievaulx Abbey to the Dean of York, instead of the tithes on the Marishes. Kirkham Priory and Willian de Roos quarrelled concerning tithes of the chase at Helmsley.

Great churchmen sometimes had a local impact. The York Minster Treasurer fostered the church of St Giles, which was rebuilt at Skelton in the Vale of York, unusually, all in one style. It was known as 'Little St Peters' and tradition claims that it was built with stone left over from Archbishop Walter Grey's new transepts at York Minster. This same Archbishop bought the Acklam church estate from Thornton Abbey and endowed it on the Chancellor of the Minster in 1223. Acklam became the country seat of a series of very wealthy church administrators. Through out his diocese Archbishop Grey pressed parishioners to supply proper vestments, plate, books, candles and banners for processions, holy water stoups and images of the patron saint of the parish church.

The Church in Daily Life

Many Barons including Vescy, Stuteville and Brus, like their ancestors before them, made the long crusade to the Holy Land in 1241. These great men had their own private chapels and chaplains. Educated churchmen, known as clerks, contributed much to local administration, including the written records. Helmsley and Malton already had schools run by men in holy orders. Stone chapels had been built in the castles at Pickering, Helmsley and Malton by mid century and were endowed with income to support a chaplain, and for candles permanently burning. Even the mighty sought the help of the faithful at death, with bequests to priests to pray for departed souls and money for distribution to the poor at the funeral, in the hope of securing their more valuable prayers. At the monasteries, their names on the prayer roll ensured a place in a petition that was almost continuous.

The great occasions of public and private life were sanctified by the parish priests. The rituals, ceremonies and advices of the Christian church, as they had evolved over centuries, were brought to bear on some of the life and death problems of the people, but we only find the better-off bulking large in the record. Walter Hayrun was married to a Hastings daughter at Allerston church door, after much family negotiation, before going within for a mass. A woman was 'churched' at Beadlam chapel in 1288. A baptism was recorded at Sheriff Hutton church and another at Mulgrave Castle. The infant Peter de Mauley 'born about the hour of cock crowing', on a March morning in 1279, was baptised a few days later by the Grosmont Prior, with two godfathers and a godmother. A neighbour knight came visiting at the 'purification' of the mother on the third day.

Saints Alive and Devils not Dead

The mediation of saints was thought important in prayer, transfering the virtue of the one to reinforce the petition of the other. Archbishop Wickwane insisted on church dedications, and in 1287 several churches including Bulmer were re-dedicated. The saint's day decided the annual parish church festival. On the eve, day and morrow of the feast the ploughs were stilled, as they were again on the twelve days of Christmas and at the main moveable feasts related to Easter.

Bishops still preached against pagan practices but the ancient Celtic interest in springs and wells remained, and some springs were sanctified at unknown dates by dedication to the saints. Probably there were the well dressings, better known in other shires. The Christian Church never denied the existence of devils. The persistence centuries later of the local customs of gathering twigs of the rowan tree on St. Helen's day and placing them on buildings to protect against evil spirits, or marking witch posts at cruck house thresholds with St Andrew's cross, suggests that the struggle between Christian and older thinking was not over.

Holy wells and springs without dedication occur at Easthorpe or Hildenley and in the 'halikelds' at Hovingham, Brompton, Wharram and Huby. Wells dedicated to St Mary or Our Lady are known at Newton by Wintringham, Cropton castle, Malton and Pockley and might reflect the rising interest in the Virgin Mary in the later Middle Ages. Other saints were invoked at the wells and streams of St Anne at Hinderskelfe, St Mary Magdalene at Spaunton, St John at Moxby and Harpham, and St Robert at Levisham. Far older dedications seem likely to belong to far older times. St Martin at Staxton, St Helen at Reighton, Sherburn and Wykeham, St Ched and St Chad at Lastingham, St Wilfrid at Cawton and St Julian at Nafferton, were popular waters, remembered locally for many centuries more. It is significant that many wells and springs across the shire carry dedications of an earlier origin than the Normans, while the many crosses only carried secular names, like William's Cross, Lilla Cross and Mauley Cross.

Table 10. A Calendar of Saints Days Celebrated in Ryedale	
January	14. St. Felix. 21. St. Agnes
February	2. Purification of the Blessed Virgin Mary (Candlemas). 5. St. Agatha 14. St.Valentine
March	2. St. Cedd. 12. St Gregory. 20. St.Cuthbert. 25. Annunciation of the Blessed Virgin Mary
April	23.St. George
May	3. Invention of Holy Cross. 15. St. Helen
June	17. St. Botolph. 24. Nativity of St John the Baptist. 29.St. Peter and St. Paul
July	4 Translation of St. Martin
August	5. St. Oswald. 15. Assumption of the Blessed Virgin Mary
September	1. St. Giles. 14.Exaltation of Holy Cross. 29.St. Michael
October	31.All Saints
November	2. All Souls. 6. St.Leonard 11. St. Martin. 25. St. Catherine
December	24. St Thomas. 28. Holy Innocents' Day

The Many Ways of the Religious Spirit

The virtues of help for the poor, for the sick and for prisoners were preached, as well as warnings against the seven deadly sins. Hospitals served travelling people and the sick. They enjoyed much support.

84

Table 11. The Value of Some Churches, estimated for Pope Nicholas to Tax in 1291

£106.13.4	Scarborough
£100	Langtoft
£66.13.4.	Bridlington, Sheriff Hutton
£60	Nafferton, Helmsley
£53.6.8	Kirkby Grindalythe, Seamer, Salton, Brompton, Middleton
£46.13.4.	Appleton
£40	Settrington, Ampleforth, Bossall, Crambe, Hovingham
£36.13.4.	Sheriff Hutton, Kirkby Misperton
£33.6.8.	Scrayingham, Hackness, Stonegrave
£30	Terrington
£26.13.4	Wharram Percy, Foxholes
£23.6.8	Wintringham, Kirkdale
£21.6.8.	Rillington, Malton, Kirkby Underdale
£20	Brandsby, Barton
£16.13.4.	Lastingham, Kirkby Moorside
£16.0.0.	Shirburn, Gilling
£13.6.8.	Heslerton, Langton, Skirpenbeck, Birdsall, Bulmer, Slingsby, Normanby Oswaldkirk, Thornton
£12.0.0.	Thorpe Basset
£10.13.4.	Westow
£10.	Ganton, Dalby, Wykeham
£8	Cowlam, Burythorpe, Norton, Sinnington
£6.13.4	Yedingham, Edstone
£5	Levisham, Scawton
£4.13.4.	Nunnington

Kirkham Priory founded a new hospital at Pockley in 1261. Town brewers and bakers sent alms of bread and ale to hospital lepers. The Hospital of St Nicholas on the street lane approach from Wade's Causeway to Pickering, became the wealthiest body in the town before the end of the century.

The poor of the bigger borough towns were missioned by new brotherhoods of Friars, Franciscan, Dominican and Carmelite, each

85

order with its own nuance of poverty, learned preaching or asceticism. Refugee friars gained brief rural settlement at Hatterboard outside Scarborough, at Kildale and at Farndale, but the movement was basicly urban. The Dominican friars of Scarborough visited Pickering to preach the crusade in 1291. The semi-monastic military order of Knights Templar was formed to sustain pilgrimage to the holy land. The knights enjoyed considerable local support. They acquired manors at Foulbridge, Allerston, Westerdale, Cold Kirkby and Lockton, along with a scattering of rents elsewhere and they made annual local collections.

The roles of hermit, anchorite and recluse continued to attract those who sought a solitary way of religious life or who tried to draw attention to their manifest piety in the hope of patronage. An Oxford student, Richard Rolle returned home to Thornton Dale and persuaded his sister to give him two dresses and a hood, which he wore to look like a hermit. He went to Pickering church and sat in the constable John Dalton's seat, to gain attention. Next day he put on a surplice, sang mass and preached with sufficient verve to bring tears to the eyes. Dalton dined him, reclothed him and gave him house room in which to live as a solitary. Richard urged the household to love virtue and reject wordly vanities. The devil came to him, as he saw it, in the form of a woman with temptations. Richard reduced some troublesome demons, by prayer, to a heap of black ashes, which contained hoofprints - or so they said.

A Knight Templar

Among the Common Fields

The tracts of common field were regularly cultivated according to such typical and customary crop rotations, as oats, beans and then the 'fallow', a season of rest for the soil. After fallowing came the renewed annual sewing of winter and summer seeds. The few large fields, or sometimes just two sides, of a township's arable land held the field shares called oxgangs. These were held as strips in the furlongs that made up the fields. This could mean that a man with an oxgang held a dozen or so acres in strips sited at a score or more of different places, around the fields. At Alne in the vale of York, the separate strips eventually numbered over two thousand, making for an incredible geography, but one that each cultivator knew intimately.

The pasturing of fallow ground, the folding of sheep and the spreading of the muck-heap were the main means of restoring fertility to the fields. Folds and heaps were important assets. Some monasteries were given land for large sheepfolds in which to collect manure. William son of Ulf gave twelve perches at a Kirkby Misperton sheepfold to St Mary's abbey. Torfin and Allan de Allerston added a sheepfold near Moor Howe beyond the fields, to a pasture for five hundred sheep given to Rievaulx Abbey as well as an acre of meadow to supply litter for the fold, because the donors were to have half of the 'faldage' and half the muck.

Until some accepted limits of the field were reached, or were demarcated by 'acredikes', there could be some expansion of the cuiltivated area, at the expense of common carr or moor. The oxgangs grew larger in acreage if new furlongs, sometimes called 'riddings', were cleared at the fringe of the common fields. About 1185, Keldholme Priory was given the right to break up moorland at Ingleby, on the far side of Blackamore. A later Cloughton document specified that if any more land was broken up in the moor, the tenant would receive the share of one oxgang.

Some other land newly taken in was not included within the oxgangs. The low grounds of Galtres saw modest intaking amid the extensive carrs. New thwaites appeared in the dales, Thackthwaite in Bransdale, Hogthwaite and Duvansthwaite at Farndale and Stainthwaite at Levisham. Occasionally some fringe land near the fields, often called 'ofnames', was cleared, measured in acres and apparently managed separately from the field oxgangs. Sometimes valuable new meadows were created, as marshes dried out or were drained. Abbot Roundell of

St Mary's Abbey inclosed eighty acres as meadow in Normanby marshes about 1209. It was reckoned to be worth a shilling an acre at each mowing.

Table 12. The Language of the Fields	
Strips	riggs, ends, butts, acres, brecks, dales, hills, keavels, lands, breds, wandales, narrow lands, broad lands, hunger hills
Added land	aynhams, ornhams, ofnams, onnams, inhams, innings
Clearings	thwaite, ridding, assart, intake, foredales, broates, royd, rum, stocking
The Languages of the Closes	
Structures	bield, bower, byre, cot, fold, fehus, gannock, helm, lathe, hulls, hus, mistal, teafall, shippon, skali

Demesne Farms

Some of the largest farms were at the great demesne manors .The Stuteville's had five hundred and twenty arable acres at Kirkby Moorside. Roger de Mowbray's Hovingham demesne was one hundred and eighty seven arable acres and fifty acres of meadow. At Barton le street, twenty four of the seventy six oxgangs, belonged to Lord Grey while thirty villeins and nine cottagers held the rest. The Pickering demesne embraced one hundred and ninety four acres, worth eight pence the acre, thirty meadow acres valued at one shilling and sixpence an acre, ten acres kept for the bailiff's horses, thirty acres in Constable Ings worth a shilling an acre, and seven acres of meadow in the Frith at sixpence an acre. Meadow valuations per acre everywhere exceeded those of the arable.

Many townships had officers known as reeves or 'graves' in charge of the farming, and where meadow was extensive, employed 'haywards'. Their first task was to protect the lord's interests. Lady Joan de Stuteville and others like her kept a manorial dovecote full of pigeons fattening on their tenants' corn, as well as on their own. The manor lords could call on their villeins and cottagers to do customary work on the demesne land, particularly in the busy seasons, sewing, ploughing, harrowing, reaping or carrying corn, as well as making small renders in kind, although paid labour was becoming more significant. Eighty seven of the Pickering oxgangs were held in 'ancient bondage' by villeins and the works, arising from them, including the repair of the milldam, were reckoned to be worth a considerable sum.

A Barton le Street freeholder was bound to supply a load of rushes to his lord. The lords of Sproxton had the annual right to two hundred and eighty eggs and twenty eight Easter hens, probably most useful in supporting a village feast or for Easter egg rolling down hills. Ampleforth tenants handed over Christmas pigs and strikes of nuts at Martinmas. These places already sound like the typical 'estate village' dominated by the big house, but not everywhere was like that.

Dales Farming

A different farming system expanded into the moorland dales where common fields were either the modest islands of cultivation at Danby, Egton, Westerdale and Urrah, or there were no common fields at all. The twelfth century monastery stock farms called 'vaccaries' had led the way. One at Goathland held twenty cows and a bull. A new freehold cattle farm with some thirty acres was taken in at Allantofts near Goathland late in the 13th century. Aisled buildings found at Spaunton moor and Dundale, amidst the Levisham moors, may have provided winter housing for stock.

Other new clearings, sometimes called 'thwaites', but with a wide variety of other names, housed the single mixed farmsteads which now spread along the valleys. There was no village. Each farmstead stood within its own modest arable, meadow and pasture closes, reaching from the valley stream a small way up to the steeper daleside. The common sheepwalks above were shared, subject to the oversight of the manor court. Eskdale and its feeder dales, Farndale and Bransdale, Bickley and Crosscliffe, part of Rosedale and other valleys not in the hands of monasteries, slowly filled with farmsteads along the daleside paths. Hartoft dale was still being colonised in this way by men from neighbour villages and dales late in the thirteenth century.

Sometimes, the dale holdings were assessed in traditional oxgangs to calculate their renders and taxes, and subjected to similar obligations. Ninety bondmen in Farndale were bound to do a day or two's ploughing, some harrowing, three or four boon days in Autumn, and to cut and cart hay and grain or move millstones for the new lords of the Wake family. Even where large bounded pastures had been given to monasteries, and settled with valley granges and higher sheepcotes, this kind of scattered settlement would eventually replace them, most extensively in Bilsdale. Baron Hugh Bigod's sheepfolds and Keldholme Priory's houses on Kirkby Moorside moors could equally develop into isolated farmsteads.

Monastic Empires Growing

The monasteries continued to acquire estates well into the thirteenth century, often in a more deliberate way by purchase. Watton Priory gained a holding in Birdsall from William de Harum. Malton Priory gained a property of manorial scale from Alan de Knapton, and a Kingthorpe farmstead from Thomas son of Torbrand. Rievaulx Abbey received Raisdale from William Mowbray. Anketin de Heslerton gave Yedingham to Litte Marish Priory and Ellerton Priory gained a Habton estate, to support a chantry at the altar of St Laurence in the monastery. Rosedale Priory acquired the Middleton mansion from Eustace de Vescy, but without the church or the freeholders. It has been known ever since as the Nuns' Garth. These were not minor acqusitions. There was also some rationalisation. Nostel priory being far away transferred Weaverthorpe church back to the manor lord Reginald son of Peter, who gave it to the Dean of York. St Mary's Abbey at York returned Sheriff Hutton church to Emma des Humes, so that she could endow it on Marton Priory. The abbey retained a modest pension payment.

Other monastic orders followed the Cistercians in adopting the grange system, or variations on it, with well capitalised farmsteads, including a chapel, distant from the mother house. They were worked by lay brothers or abbey servants, and seasonal hired labour, under skilled supervision, sometimes with cattle specialisation or even an industrial emphasis.

Wool remained the oil of monastic economies. Malton wool sales in 1251 brought a high proportion of what was needed to run that house. Rievaulx in 1275 sold sixty sacks of wool, each of 240 fleeces, implying 14.000 sheep. Some new properties were acquired for development as granges. Alan Malecake granted a Lockton property to the Rosedale nunnery. The toft, and croft with pasture rights for two hundred sheep, eight oxen and other stock at Lockton and Kettlethorpe made a sizeable farmstead, with a good moor stint. There was a separate acre in

Ketelcroft and wood in Staindale. This is the last we ever hear of Kettlethorpe which was mentioned in the Domesday book, but vanished into the monastery grange.

Ralph Bolebek transferred fifty two arable acres at Dundale in Levisham, near the crest of the Braygate and Limpseygate roads, along with pasture for a thousand wethers and one hundred and twenty other stock, to Malton Priory in 1230. Surviving earth banks, footings of buildings and ponds witness their use of this valuable moor edge grange, which Hugh Bigod bought back into lay ownership twenty five years later. Robert and William Bolebek gave Rosedale Priory a Newton on Rawcliff grange with pasture for three hundred sheep. The grange site was at the far fringe of the common fields of Newton. Byland Abbey like Rievaulx had entire townships managed as granges, including over four hundred acres at Angram and near seven hundred acres of Wildon. Monasteries throughout the century settled boundary disputes with each other.

Where a monastery held a manor or a rectory, the involvement could be just as significant, but more closely linked with the ordinary management of fields and pastures. Monastic owner ship of moveable goods was remarkable in many townships, sometimes exceeding that of the manor lord. At Allerston in 1301, of the £5.12s.3d paid in tax, the lord paid £2.5s.0d, the monasteries £1.18s.11d, and the rest of the township paid £1.6s.8d. Malton Priory in 1308 had considerable flocks including one hundred and sixty ewes and two hundred sheep at Ryton, along the road from the monastery, five hundred more at Brompton where they held the rectory, two hundred at Kirkby Misperton and six hundred pasturing in Middleton parish. All were subject to tithes. On the other hand, the Priory had twenty seven arable oxgangs at Rillington and worked thirty two oxgangs of Thoraldby from their grange in Mowthorpe. They kept eleven ploughs at Wintringham, seven at Mowthorpe and eight more at Swinton. Mowthorp sometimes employed thirty six men.

Quarrels with laymen were not unknown. Agnes de Vescy's officers were high handed with Malton Priory cattle, impounding some till they died. A large number of lay brothers and abbey servants from Rievaulx did substantial damage to William de Sproxton's crops in 1300.

Table 13 Some Significant Monastic Manors, Farms and Granges

Bridlington Priory	Acklam, Crome, Cloughton
Byland Abbey	Airyholme, Angram, Wildon, Murton, Boltby, Balk, Old Byland, Wethercotes, Tilehouse, Rillington, Deepdale
Ellerton Priory	Barugh
Guisborough Priory	Sinnington, Sherburn
Keldholme Priory	Rook Barugh
Kirkham Priory	Helmsley, Sproxton, Bilsdale, Sledmere, Westow, Whitwell, Duggleby, Mowthorpe, Leavening, Barthorpe, Sledmere, Thixendale, Kirkby Grindalythe, Crambe
Malton Priory	Mowthorpe, Wintringham, Ebberston, Amotherby, Lockton, Swinton, Levisham, Newton, Knapton, Rillington, Linton, Hutton, Marton, Hoggecote, Broughton, Sutton, Welham, Ebberston, Goathland, Aislaby, Slingsby, Edstone, Ryton, Sinnington
Marton Priory	Sherif Hutton, Cornborough Fosse house
MeauxAbbey	Wharram grange, Birdsall, Octon grange
Moxby priory	Ampleforth, Foulrice
Newbrough Priory	Fryton, Hovingham, Wombleton, Scawton cote, Hood grange, Wath grange, Kirkby Moorside
Rievaulx Abbey	Griff, Stilton, Hesketh, Sproxton, Loftmarish, Marishes, Raisdale, Welburn, Skiplam, Sonley, Lundcote, Newton, Newlathes, Laskill, Blakemoor, Billsdale, Urra
Rosedale Priory	Newton, Cropton, Lockton, Middleton
Whitby abbey	Goathland
Wykeham Priory	Snainton;Ebberston
Yedingham Priory	Snainton, Allerston, Ebberston, Wilton, Sinnington
York, St Mary	Spaunton, Normanby, Kirkby Misperton, Foston

On the Road

The fields, carrs and moors of the farming landscape, were penetrated by through roads called 'king's highways', which enjoyed some legal protection and linked the market towns. A few other long distance routes across many townships were thought of as 'great ways' and if there was a hint of paving, they added the word 'street'. Some of these roads followed ancient prehistoric and Roman routes. Many of the riggs running up to the high moors carried riggways, a little in lee of the windy tops, on these ancient tracks. The word 'stie' was used for many rising roads. Where side roads dropped towards the valleys, the sheep made their multiple tracks down the hillsides, some to fords, called 'waths' and to the rare bridges that replaced or supplemented them. The fast flowing river Esk had seven mediaeval bridges. The dales were circuited by minor tracks, which joined the new farmsteads together, in a spherical circuit of neighbourhood. Many roads over commons were not limited - indeed you often made your own road, but burial mounds and crosses could help settle a way.

In the lower grounds, the few bridges across the sluggish river Derwent at Seamer, Foulbridge, Norton-Malton, Kirkham and Buttercrambe channelled much traffic. Foulbridge was jointly maintained by Yedingham Priory and the Knights Templar. The Norton-Malton bridge included an island hospital. A late bridge replaced a ferry at Yedingham.The Rye was spanned near Rievaulx, by bridges at Newsham, and Howe below Pickering, and at Helmsley, where there was a bridge chapel. Minor bridges were mentioned as more numerous documents appeared - the Hanging bridge at Scawton, the Shaken bridge and Laskill bridge in Bilsdale, Crossow bridge at Salton and the Basset bridge at Settrington. Blawath on the high moors, Grundstone wath at Cropton and Farwath near Lockton remained as well known fords.

The more parochial roads of the common field townships formed a rough star of routes, at least during the fallow season. Once the crops were sewn, these gave way to balks and headlands offering tracks which turned sharply around ploughed furlongs. An ancient map might show a different pattern of roads in summer and winter. These common ways passed from the villages through the fields to such assets as the ings or meadows, the woods, and the water mill. Most of these roads had names and they were usually called 'gates' as were most other roads. Thornton Dale had at least eight gate - roads while Pickering had thirty three, one named from the wolfpit to which it led. Spaunton township had

Linegate, Davygate, Haygate and Stepingate. Malton, Pickering and Thornton Dale had broad 'outgangs' serving as drove ways to their commons.

Great Ways

Great ways, the 'magna vias' that are mentioned in the old charters, seem to mean great distances rather than great traffic. Among them were the road linking Helmsley, Pickering and Scarborough through numerous villages, on the one hand, and the Beverley road or Whitegate running south through Foxholes, on the other. The 'magna via' east of Hartoft dale passed through no villages at all but joined another road on a moor rigg at a junction once marked by a cross. The 'magna via' through Skirpenbeck was described as the road to Scarborough and the 'magna via' through Huttons Ambo led to York. The Scrayingham smith had his workshop in the 'kings street'. Some of these routes are today's roads but some have become mere moorland footpaths.

Aids to travellers were few, but more than sixty crosses in and around Blackamore marked junctions and routes, one cross sometimes visible from another. Not all the crosses have an obvious purpose. One on the low road between Allerston and Ebberston stands on a boundary. The Jinglebee and William crosses on the Lang Gate across their moors between Hackness and Lockton seem to mark junctions of no great significance. Remains of crosses occur less frequently outside the moors but do include those at Westow, a cross south of Norton, Whinny cross on Yearsley moor, and the so called stone chair near Settrington. Tradition claims that lights were hung at Huntington church tower, to guide the traveller through Galtres, and that horns blown at Stainton Dale in Pickering Forest, drew attention to a travellers' hospital.

A Little Traffic

Manorial road tolls taken from through traffic were not often recorded. Perhaps there was rarely enough traffic to make them worth collecting, but Roger de Thirkelby at Helperthorpe tolled a penny for each horse, ox, cow or ten sheep passing through. Cheminage, otherwise called 'gatelaw', was a road toll levied in Pickering Forest by the foresters, who used lads to collect pledges. Monasteries with goods to move from distant granges to the mother house and to market, bought

Table 14 Boundary marks of the Barony of Middleton.1334

Alda on the Costa – (old course of the stream.)
Standing Stone above the Spital Myre – (possible boundary, milestone or cross near the Hospital of St Nicholas, on Street lane, and the low wet mires.)
Meredike – (ditch of wet area.)
Saintoft croft – (isolated house and close at north edge of Pickering Fields.)
old Wolfpitgate – (road to wolf pits.)
the gray stone in eller land – (ellers for alder trees)
the 'boret thorn above flat maryng'
Lofthouse – Rowantree - Standing stone in Wheeldale moss
Blawath – (blue ford.)
Shunner howes (burial mounds), William howe, Shunner howe,
Ralph's Cross
the Seven River by Bruindesdyke
Ditch of Sinngton park – (deer park.)
Crest of Riseborough hill, near Thornton Park
Risedike and up Costa to Alda

charters to avoid such levies. Malton Priory claimed a grant of exemption for their carts, wagons, and horses with packs on their backs in Pickering Forest. They sent wood from Goathland to pack fish at Scarborough.

John Ingram allowed the Cistercians to make a road south of East Heslerton and they secured a right of way through Habton moor between two of their pastures, where a road survives to this day. St Mary's Abbey obtained toll freedom to move from a ford at Appleton le Moors southwards through Sinnington township, towards their other estates. Richard de la River in 1279 allowed Byland Abbey free passage through Brandsby wood.

Pickering and Galtres Forests saw some of the heaviest traffic in timber, brushwood, turves, heather and bracken. The Lady Isabella de Vescy had much under wood delivered to her Malton castle from Pickering Forest, and received thirty one full oaks when she lived at Scarborough. Kirkham Priory received a grant of turves for fuel from Traneberrymoss near the river Foss in Galtres, and brought wood along the great road from Howsham. Twenty four cartloads were moved annually from Fryton near Slingsby to the island hospital between Malton and Norton.

Hexham Priory tenants at Salton were obliged to carry the Prior's provisions whenever he was in Yorkshire, and they carted timber when required to his house, to the guest hall and to the mill. St Mary's Abbey tenants at Gilling had to find a cart each Autumn to carry grain for the Parson, as well as taking their grain to his barn. Specialist carters were few and far between, mentioned in 1301 at Coneysthorpe, Appleton, and Swinton, perhaps because they were near to the Hildenley quarry, and at Byland Abbey, Farlington, Bulmer, Whitwell, Ampleforth and Malton. Geoffrey Balloc of Pickering had a four wheeled cart.

The Fisherman's Coast

At the opening of the 13th century, the value of 'merchants goods' at such inland boroughs as York, Northallerton, Yarm and Malton exceeded those at Scarborough, and dwarfed those of Whitby and Coatham. It would not always be so. Wool and lead were the most valuable early commodities that were traded, but the coast increasingly supplied the inland area with fish. The small ships of the day could penetrate deep inland along the rivers to the towns and other small landings in the Vale of York.

Scarborough gained a new charter from the King in 1253, giving the burgesses the right to build a high and low water harbour, and soon constructed both a pier and a quay. The highly successful borough bought many extra liberties from the Crown, including a forty five day fair which meant virtually continuous fish trading through the busiest season. Buyers and fishermen were attracted from far afield. The burgesses negotiated a new agreement with the Cistercian Order, who held the parish church, to lighten the burden of fish tithes. The King enjoyed a modest yet regular levy on all fish caught. Other huge shipments of fish went to York when kings were at the city. The King ordered a delivery of five hundred congers and ten thousand haddocks in 1252.

Whitby had a more restricted hinterland. The burgesses also lost some liberties when an Abbot bribed King John's court into a verdict favorable to the monastery rather than the borough. Town-gown conflict at Whitby arising from the verdict continued for centuries. Nonetheless, Whitby and Scarborough fish regularly reached Foss Bridge at York. Yedingham Priory received a thousand fish as the annual rent of their house at the port. Byland Abbey annually received a thousand haddocks from Cleveland.

Other secure inlets of the north east Yorkshire coast benefited, as rising east coast floodwaters, eroded the older Holderness havens of the East Riding. Peter de Mauley, lord of Mulgrave had built the third castle of that estate in the valley south of coastal Lythe, where he secured a Wednesday market, and a long St Oswalds Fair. This may have accompanied the founding of Sandsend, soon a community of more than fifty three tofts without any farm land. Redcar and the salt port of Coatham secured fairs and markets, and there were boats at Skinningrove.

Village Markets and Fairs

A few markets at the old head manors of the sokes were ancient, and without known charters. Probably they were old hundredal markets, as at Easingwold and Bridlington, and became associated with the boroughs that replaced them at Stokesley, Northallerton, Whitby and Pickering. Any grant of borough rights always implied a market. Agnes de Percy's fairs at the great crossing of Roman roads at Stamford Bridge seem to be at least as ancient. In the late thirteenth century many manor lords bought charters from the Crown for weekly 'markets' with annual 'fairs', usually at villages with a parish church. Sunday and churchyard trading often lingered while a few market crosses have survived.

These market charters regularised existing trade, and gave the legal right to take tolls between agreed hours and within acknowledged boundaries. Charters were granted on condition that existing markets were not damaged. Scarborough went to court to close Sherburn, Brompton and Filey markets, but at least one was active later. Clement of Settrington Green attended Sherburn Market about 1278. Manor courts could appoint officers to check the quantity, quality and sometimes the price of goods offered. After 1269 bakers and brewers offending against the assize of bread and ale were liable to be ducked in stinking water.

Byland Abbey took the trouble to secure exemption from tolls in Helmsley, Pickering and Scarborough markets. Malton Priory had a similar grant from William de Vescy at Malton. Pickering burgesses were accused of taking tolls from all traders between the river Seven at Sinnington and the Skitterick beck at Ruston, and between the river Derwent and Loosehowe on the moors. These were the bounds of the old hundred of Pickering. The Duchy of Lancaster recovered the tolls

**Table 15. Some Chartered Village Markets
and Fairs in North East Yorkshire**

Ryedale	Barton leStreet (1246) Hovingham (1252) Kirkby Moorside (1254) Stonegrave (1257)
Bulmer	Buttercrambe (1200, 1343. 1353) Stamford (1243) Newton on Ouse (1282) Tollerton (1291) Terrington (1302) Sheriff Hutton (1378)
Birdforth	Easingwold (1221) Birdforth (1253) Kilvington (1257) Thirsk (1291) Coxwold (1304)
Langbaurgh	Guisborough (1219) (1263) Great Ayton (1253) Lythe (1254) Skelton (1281) Kildale (1254) Egton (1269) Whorlton (1269, 1337) Coatham (1257) (1292) Eston (1281)
Pickering Lythe	Brompton (1253) Thornton (1254, 1281, 1303) Sinnington (1263) (1303), Seamer (1382)
Buckrose	Heslerton (1252, 1303) Scampston (1253) Sledmere (1303)
Dickering	Bridlington (c1200) Hunmanby (by 1231) Filey (by 1221, 1240) Kilham (1227,1334) Burton Agnes (1257) Thwing (1292) Carnaby (1299) Lowthorpe (1304) Wansford (1304)

from the burgesses soon after, and let them separately to John son of Adam Brus and his partners. Elsewhere, the yield from market tolls seems modest. Kirkby Moorside market yielded £2.6.8. in 1281-2, and the Sherburn tolls were £2 in 1287.

The markets served people in limited areas but fairs had a wider draw for buyers and sellers. The fairs usually ran for at least three days, the vigil, the day and the morrow of the feast of a patron saint. Egton being remote, secured an eight day St Hilda fair. The Lord of Easingwold and Pickering bought extra fairs in 1291. Great fairs at York, Beverley, Ripon and Boston had a far wider reach. When a

Thornton Dale man found a deer snared in his yard in 1311, he took the skin to sell at York and with the proceeds bought some fur for his coat. The forty five day fish fair at Scarborough, continuing from the Feast of the Assumption of the Virgin Mary until Michaelmas had as wide an appeal for monastic and foreign buyers and should probably be thought of as a great international fair. Taken together, the fairs spread throughout the year, provided a regional calendar by which town craftsmen and pedlars could reach local buyers.

Countryside Industry

Early rural industry was largely confined to corn milling and to those crafts whose raw materials were extracted in the countryside. Some castles and monasteries might sustain a small group of specialised craftsmen. Most of them had bakehouses and breweries. Some industrial activities noxious to the deer were restrained in the early years within the Royal Forests, but monasteries seem to have secured exemptions for the tanning of leather. Keldholme Priory was given the bark of the trees in Bransdale, surely implying the existence of the tannery that was later at the monastery site. Skins were steeped for long periods in pits of oak bark. Other tanneries eventually grew up a few miles apart, throughout the district, with the exception of the Wolds.

Evidence of mediaeval potteries has been found at Staxton, Grimston, Brandsby, Thirlby, Potter Brompton, Ruswarp and Scarborough. They are also mentioned in documents or hinted at by the Pottergates of Pickering, Helmsley and Gilling. Many carpenters and a few turners were active where the woodland was plentiful. Turf was cut locally as a fuel wherever it was available and there were acknowledged areas for cutting including the turf moor above Allerston. Building stone was still rarely used. Most buildings were of timber with infill walls of wattle and mud. Millstones and gravestones were worked up near Cloughton on the coast. Old Roman quarries persisted in use and those at Hildenley, Pickering and Malton may fall in this class. The Wolds used chalkstone and was short of timber. Bakestones were found at two or three places in the moorlands.

Spicers were at Harome, York and Whitby, and are to be thought of as akin to later grocers. 'Cummin' rents occur and Geoffrey de Etton in 1219 leased Gilling mill to Simon son of William for the annual rent of one pound of pepper. The salters at Oswaldkirk, Helmsley and Pickering are presumed to have brought the product from the Tees, along the salt roads through Keldholme and Saltergate, or later from the saltpits on Scarborough sands. Common ovens were built for some manors while cooks and bakers appear in the towns and a few villages. The Weaverthorpe oven was worth three shillings a year but the Helmsley oven was worth forty shillings.

The corn mills belonged to the manors so they proliferated whereever manors were subdivided, or where sokeland was converted to manors, and at monastic granges. Payments made in the thirteenth century from the townships of Middleton Parish in place of works on the Pickering mill dams, suggest that new mills had been made within the sokeland on the river Costa. Millstones were made from the rock at Cropton moor. A water corn mill required substantial investment but provided a steady source of income, giving a good return. Robert de Ros had a Howsham mill worth sixty shillings comparable with seventy eight shillings and eightpence from Robert de Everingham's Sherburn mills, fiftysix shillings and eightpence from Robert de Chauncy's mill at Skirpenbeck, and twelve pounds a year from the two Helmsley mills.

The newer windmills were built in the low flat lands where the river flow was sluggish, as well as in the waterless Wold uplands. An early windmill was sited at the Knight Templar's manor of Foulbridge on the river Derwent, deep in Pickering Vale. Sheriff Hutton had both windmill and water mill by 1282. The Prebendary at Stillington in Galtres had two watermills and a windmill a few years later. The excavation of a 14th century mill at Rillington revealed the pit and block which supported the central upright timber of a post windmill. Village fulling mills were sited on streams at Allerston, Ebberston, Harome, Farndale, Lastingham and Thornton Dale.

The number of village blacksmiths suggests that ironstone was extracted on some scale. Many undated cinder hills marked the valleys of Blackamore, until they were removed to make modern roads. Iron working was recorded from time to time in many moorland dales, including those at Hackness, Rosedale, Levisham, Bilsdale, Wheeldale and Glaisdale. The Bolebek family had iron workings in Levisham wood by 1209. Eustace de Vescy had an early iron working, in the same period, at Bagthwaite in lower Rosedale. Small bloomeries were near the iron outcrops. St Mary's Abbey contracted with John the smith in 1339, for him to locate, work up and supply sixteen stone of iron weekly at Spaunton manor, using wood supplied under the forester's supervision. Barbed arrow rents also suggest iron was readily available at Farndale and north of the river Esk at Stanghou, Mooresome and

Skelton, while an early nailmaker was active at Danby. Charcoal burners in woodland lodges at Glaisdale, Levisham and Riccall made a product essential for bringing the hearth temperatures up to a level sufficient for working the iron. Newbrough Priory received six hundred skeps of charcoal annually from Brandsby in the Howardian hills.

Prosperous Boroughs

Each borough grew in its own way. The old and new boroughs at Scarborough saw tofts divided for newcomers, but Malton borough had sufficient space within its walls to grow by inward encroachment. Whitby moved away from the old village on the east cliff down to the waterside, onto river muds at Grapelane and Sandgate, and across the river Esk, to absorb the old Flora estate into Flowergate and to make a new riverside settlement at Baxtergate. Pickering borough stretched south of the castle towards the church, but the burgages overlapped into the market place. The small borough at Helmsley gained a generous market square.

Successful boroughs were centres for craftsmen but none approached the scale of York. By 1300 the typical Yorkshire borough housed a dyer, a fuller, weavers and a tailor in the clothing trades, a skinner, a tanner and shoe makers working leather and other burgesses working metals or supplying foodstuffs. Scarborough was the greatest success. Its burgesses bought extra liberties from the Crown, including control of the nearby Crown manor of Falsgrave and exemption from Pickering forest law in 1253. They could pay an annual rent to the Crown of £76. Pickering burgesses paid a total of fifteen shillings and eightpence to the Earls of Lancaster, with another three pounds for the tolls and market.

The wealthiest people at Pickering in 1301 were the Brothers and Sisters of the Hospital of St Nicholas, with Adam Brus, William Malecake and two ladies who possibly came from the same families. These people were more of the village than the borough. Brus was a knight who served as a castle official. Members of his family were called 'de Pickering' when they were away from the town. On occasions they were royal tax and customs collectors, and one appears as an effigy in the church. Malecake's ancestor had helped supervise the building of Scarborough castle. William served as bailiff of Pickering Lythe and the family had country manors. Other locals like the despenser, the chamberlain, two stock keepers and the woodward seem to have filled castle and manor offices. Within the borough, five people including Andrew the dyer were accused of making cloth of an improper width in 1275. The tailor was quite well off in 1301 and the townsmen included a fuller, baker, cooper, fisherman, butcher, shoemaker, skinner, potter, salter and weaver.

Unlike Pickering, New Malton was quite separate from the village at Old Malton, itself a sizeable community, including the monastery with the mother church. The Castle was also quite separate, home at different times to the long successions of Vescys, William, Agnes, John and William, who still claimed the brewer's fines, and tolls of the Saturday market and an eight day fair. By 1301, the castle was the home of Lady Isabella de Vescy de Kildare. At least three other town families were wealthy, the Locktons, the Slingsbys and the mercer. The first and probably the second had country manors. During 1275, Adam of the Bridge had sold twenty sacks of wool which found their way overseas. There were prosperous masons, working the stone quarries at each end of the town. The St.Michael Chapel in the market place had a nearby house for the chaplain. There was a fishgarth in the river. The borough held a 'medicus' or physician, and a wiseman. Among the craftsmen were the walker or fuller, dyer, miller, windmiller, brewer, chapman, gardener and carpenter. York vintners sold their wine at Malton.

Helmsley borough was on a smaller scale with only thirteen burgesses enjoying the market and tolls. A lorimer made metal parts for harnesses and there were the dyer, tanner, cooper and cook. The borough may not have looked so different from the village, for close by were the homes of seven freemen and twenty cottagers, in a community served in 1285 by two mills and an oven. A few other well sited market villages without any borough privileges expanded their crafts to comparable scale, including Ebberston where there was a skinner, tanner, weaver and dyer but Sheriff Hutton and Kirkby Moorside as yet showed little sign of industrial significance, outside their castles.

Castles in Use

Mediaeval Kings toured the country, staying at their own castles, in their baron's halls, at monasteries or friaries, and at the Archbishop's palaces or at the Bishop of Durham's castle at Crayke. Purveyors had to range ahead to ensure supplies. Wine shipments sent ahead of the Norman King in 1252 went to Kirkham Priory, Pickering castle, Scarborough castle and Whitby Abbey. Malton castle was visited by

King Richard I and later by King Edward II and King Edward III. Any castle could lose significance when the lord's residence or administration moved away. Danby castle still functioned in 1242 but later dropped out of use.

Other castles saw modest developments, occasionally military, but more often for better living. Fortified outer courtyards called barbicans were built outside the old castle gates at Pickering, Helmsley and Scarborough. They gave their approaches a stronger defence in depth against such weapons as the 'trebuchet', claimed to have a range of three hundred yards. Malton castle gained a new gateway but its character is unknown. The many timber buildings within castle walls have left few remains, but surviving stone work hints at such improvements as extra chambers, good wells, wall venting toilets called 'garderobes', and fireplaces set before wall chimneys to secure an updraft. Castles rarely feature in documents and the life within them is not easily glimpsed. Joan Stuteville of Kirkby Moorside, who married Hugh Bigod after the death of her first husband Hugh Wake, and secured the market, had a lady riding side saddle on her seal and is credited with inventing the habit. Edmund of Lancaster's old nurse Sophy was quartered in her retirement at Pickering Castle.

Some castles saw military action in 1261 when Simon de Montfort led the baronial opposition against King Henry III. Significant barons, with the custody of local castles including Hugh Bigod, Baldwin Wake and John de Vescy, actively campaigned elsewhere in the country in these struggles. John de Eyville of Thornton on the Hill fortified Hood Castle with crenellated stone walls in 1264. He set fire to Raskelf and campaigned widely that year to Richmond, Scarborough and Whorlton in Cleveland. Forty seven rebels including an 'arblaster' held Scarborough Castle against the forces of the King. Montfort's men were defeated at the battle of Evesham the next year. A great new estate was created for the king's son, Edmund Crouchback, in 1267, which later came to be called the Duchy of Lancaster. He was given the honour of Pickering, and the lordships of Scalby, Easingwold and Huby. Crown power now relied upon Scarborough and York castles. Three years later, Mowbray, Bruce and Vescy were on crusade with Prince Edward in Palestine.

King's Law and Barons' Law

Fragments of the parchment rolls of the King's Assize courts survive from King John's reign. They speak of the tragedies in the everyday life of the small communities. After the death of Ralph at Normanby, Roger and Luke from Marton, the next village, fled away. Adam Burkigill was outlawed for the death of Hugh at Wrelton. Ralph de Bolebeck erected forges at Rumbald's wood in Levisham, an offence in a royal forest. In the time of King Henry III Phillip de Fauconberge built the dam at the stream below Appleton le Moors, to the nuisance of his neighbours.

Baronial courts existed by royal grant and King Edward I ordered searching enquiries into their legal rights and abuses of power, in the period 1274-1281. Jurors heard many accusations, but their validity is unknown. Some said that Roger de Wrelton had appropriated a chase for foxes and hares at Cropton, that an Ebberston man had built a house with a courtyard, narrowing the kings highway, and that a Brompton chaplain had a false measure for wine. The Scarborough constable had seized corn at Ganton for the castle and had it threshed. Coroners and bailiffs were charged with taking bribes and with extortion. Even sheriffs were said to free prisoners charged with serious crimes, in exchange for money. They said that Geoffrey de Neville of Sheriff Hutton had raised large sums, for forest offences that were denied. During the enquiries, major barons and lesser lords from Hinderskelfe to Hawnby presented evidence for their rights of warren and their amendment of the Assize of Bread and Ale.

Forest Law was separate, with its own hierarchy of courts and some summary justice. On the ninth of May 1282, a shepherd told Pickering foresters of two robbers in the Dale at Bickley. They ran there, to find John of Coxwold, who had stolen horses, oxen, cows, sheep and goats. He refused to surrender and shot an arrow towards them. They pursued him, wounded him and caused his companion to behead him. They sent only the head to Pickering caste 'according to the custom of Blachoumoor'.

Many lords ran other lesser manor courts and enjoyed the fines from any breach of the local customs that they enforced. The Kirkby Moorside tenants of the Stutevilles and Wakes were taxed annually at Michaelmas, gave 'merchet' for their daughters, paid 'gersumes' and gave the Lord every tenth pig. The Buttercrambe bond tenants owed barley malt at Christmas.

Table 16. Gallows in North East Yorkshire, in 1275.

Buckrose	Thomas de Chauncy (Skirpenbeck), Baldwin Wake (Buttercrambe) Reginald FitzPeter (Weaverthorpe) Robert de Ros (Howsham) Baldwin Wake (Scrayingham) Roger Bigod (Settrington) William Wyville (Sledmere)
Bulmer	Abbot of St Mary's, Dean and Chapter of St.Peter's, Abbot of Byland, John de Bulmer (Bulmer) Baldwin Wake (Buttercrambe) Ranulph de Neville (Sheriff Hutton, Sutton on forest & Raskelf) Earl of Lancaster (Easingwold)
Dickering	John de Graystock & Roger de Somervill (Burton Agnes) Archbishop of Rouen (Kilham)
Langbaurgh	Walter de Fauconberg (Skelton) Sir Marmaduke de Thweng, Peter de Mauley (Lythe) Nicholas de Meinil (Whorlton) Hugh de Eure (Stokesley) William de Percy (Kildale) Richard Malebis (Little Ayton) William de Roseles (Aislaby)John de Bulmer (Wilton)
Pickering Lythe	Earl of Lancaster, Roger Bigod (Levisham) Alan Buscell (Hutton) Scarborough Borough, John de Bulmer (Thornton Risebrough) William de Vescy (Brompton)
Ryedale	Abbot of St Mary's York, Abbot of Byland, Robert deRos (Helmsley) William de Vescy (Malton) William de Wyville (Slingsby) Baldwin Wake (Kirkby Moorside)
Birdforth	Richard de Malebise (Hawnby) Roger de Mowbray (Thirsk) Abbot of Byland (Sutton) Thomas de Colville (Coxwold)

Wealthy Men

Table 17 The Ryedale Wealthy of 1297-1301

Allerston	Sir Nicholas & Emmelina de Hastings
Appleton le Street	Sir Robert de Bolton
Birdsall	Sir Peter de Mauley
Buttercrambe	Walter de Langton
Gilling	Sir Ivo de Etton
Helmsley	Sir William de Ros
Hovingh m	Sir William de Hambleton
Howsham	Lady Isabella de Ros (& Langton)
Kirkby Moorside	Lady Joan de Stuteville
New Malton	Lady Isabella de Vescy
Settrington	Sir Roger Bigod
Sherburn	Ralph de Fritheby
Sledmere	one of the Wyvills
Slingsby	Thomas & William de Wyvill
Stonegrave	Sir Walter de Teye
Wath	Sir Miles de Stapleton
Weaverthorpe	John son of Reginald

The rich are always with us and they stand out. The lords and the monasteries had built up great wealth, power,and patronage. Most of them held courts, several with the power to hang people for a range of offences. The taxation records of 1297-1301 show these wealthy elites. At Kirkby Moorside in 1301, when a tax was levied on moveable goods, the baron paid £2.2s.6d. out of the township total of £4.7s.0d. The levies were mostly on the stock and produce of farming and the crafts, since the Lords' luxuries and monks' spiritual goods were exempt.

Leaving aside the Earl of Lancaster, who had assets in many counties, the Baron William de Roos of Helmsley was the wealthiest local man. The Lady Isabella de Vescy at Malton castle and Lady Joan Wake at Kirkby Moorside and Cropton castles were in the same class. Some barons and knights with local estates had their main estate elsewhere, and so bulk less large in the record. Lady Ida De Neville at Sheriff Hutton and Sir Ralph Greystoke at Hinderskelfe were among them.

A few of these people left enduring monuments. Sir Walter de Teye can be seen in effigy at Nunnington church, holding his heart and praying, as does a Wyville knight at Slingsby, and Bolton ladies at Appleton le Street. They were not exempt from everyday problems in their lives. John Graystock married Isabel in 1297. After a separation, she sued him for alimony so he offered to resume habitation. Another Graystock wife departed for Ripon with another man

.

More Ordinary People

Some people were paid wages, sometimes in cash as well as in kind. The only coin minted til the late 13th century was the silver penny, of which two hundred and forty weighed a pound. They were sometimes cut in halves and quarters but from 1279-80, the half penny and the quarter penny were introduced. A chief forester might be paid a penny halfpenny a day but Roger Mowbray in 1297 gave his Hovingham forester, a quarter of wheat every ten weeks, an esquire's livery robe or twenty shillings at Christmas and allowed him to make what he could from all the trees blown down with their branches and the bark. Castle chaplains were paid between £2 and £3 a year but could dine in hall. The Pickering warrener in 1322 had the usual penny halfpenny a day. At the time, a young oxen could value at three shillings; a sheep a shilling; a bullock or a cow five shillings. A quarter of wheat might bring three shillings and a quarter of oats two shillings. Excavations at Allerston manor, among the footings of a good hall with green glazed tiles, found the bones of oxen, pig and sheep, shells of oysters, cockles and whelks and the antlers of red and roe deer.

Village people do appear in the tax lists, thirty of them at Hovingham with Wath, twenty at Stonegrave, twenty three at Nunnington and nine at Buttwerwick but only five at Fadmoor and twelve at Nawton with Beadlam, casting the doubt whether the majority, let alone the poor, ever made it into the lists for taxation. Our impressions are constrained by the records that survive.

When better evidence appears, all it not as it seems. The village of Sproxton had thirteen taxpayers in 1301, with William de Sproxton and the lady of Sproxton paying much more than the others; four or five middling payers and the rest paying little enough. Yet an inquiry made in 1298 showed Robert of Sproxton the deceased lord, possessed of a substantial demesne, a watermill, a turbary and a bakehouse. Fourteen free tenants held field land. There was a parker, an oak burner, a tinkeler and a miller. There were fourteen cottages with tofts and seven more tofts laying waste. Were this not enough, St Mary's Abbey had another capital house there, with field land and a fifty acre wood tenanted from Rievaulx Abbey, and yet another four cottages. We have forty two buildings in a very large village, which after several outbreaks of plague still had seventy three taxpayers in 1377, and yet only eight farmsteads in the 19th century.

Then there are the real surprises, the villages that are far larger then ever expected in 1301, because they have since become deserted and forgotten. The site of Ryton village today is a green field without a building and a ploughed field alongside it. The green field reveals a modest ditched square, the line of a road with a few stone footings poking through the ground, some fishpond earthworks, a few more recent tumbles and some made up footpaths. Here was once a major village, bigger than most in the 14th century. Roger de Wrelton, probably also known as Roger de Percehay was the main man, paying over ten shillings in the tax, as a fifteenth of his moveable goods. The whole place paid about seventy one shillings. The Prior of Malton paid just under eight shillings. Thirty four other tax payers rendered sums from threepence to seven shillings and sixpence. There was a cook, a cooper, a shepherd, cowkeepers, a smith, a baker, a studhird even a wardrober and Thomas the harper. There were people called Courcy and Daiville and some from France, Aragon, Muscoates and Bilsdale. Could 'Robert of the Hope' be at a public house?

Within the villages, there were the inevitable layers. Brandsby with Stearsby had the manorial family - Thomas and Alice de la River who together paid thirteen shillings and three pence. Six other people paid sums over three shillings, nine paid sums over two shillings, three paid over the shilling and ten paid merely a few pence. The lower taxpayers just don't appear at several other villages.

Although the middling payers, who were often the villein farmers, were tied to a place by the obligations of their tenure, there are signs of movement. Pickering in 1301 had people from Burniston, Edstone, Wrelton, Middleton and Barugh within its own district, from Ganton, Egton, Brotton and Barnby from not too faraway and wanderers from Lincolnshire and Poitou. Nicknames were common and perhaps very temporary, such as Alan 'Potfulofale', Alan 'par le Roy' and Leticia 'Petit'. Names were not always fixed and some were known from a place within the village where they lived. We hear of the spring, the end house, Trane lane, Wollergate, and Howe at Pickering.

The Public House

The scattered 'gildhuses' mentioned in twelfth century and thirteenth century charters are perhaps early enough to refer to old pre-conquest institutions, but that hasn't been proved. The name was attached to cliffs and dales at well spaced sites in Falsgrave, Wykeham, Blansby above Pickering, Welburn and Bilsdale, and slightly later at Byland, Acklam, Knapton and Hunmanby. Chroniclers say that 'gildhus' means a feasthouse and there may be some link with the parish.

Stanard the vintner probably imported wine. He was at Scarborough by 1175 and gave his name to Stanardgate. Within a century there was a tavern at that town, in Burghwellgate near the cook, the mill and the borough spring. Wine reached the barons castles. Peter FitzHerbert as castellan of Pickering was required to soak boar's heads in wine. Among those selling wine at Malton in 1219 were men from York, and Robert the nephew of the steward of Settrington. Churches accepted an obligation to provide hospitality for wayfarers, and both monastery gatehouses and roadside hospitals served some of the functions of the inn. In 1239 Yedingham priory agreed to receive Guisborough canons with litter, candles and fuel on certain occasions at Sinnington.

Alehousekeeprs were regulated under the Assize of Bread and Ale from 1202. Not long afterwards, Richard the Sledmere carter was found dead in his bed, suffocated by immoderate drinking. The Assize was revised on a sliding scale in1267 when country brewers were selling three or four gallons of ale for a penny. Offenders against the Assize could be ducked in water. The amendment of the Assize and the right to take fines of brewers was commonly but not always linked to markets and three weekly courts. These who had the amendment by royal grant were early licensing authorities. They included several monasteries, the Knights Templar and the Knights Hospitaller, the Dean and Chapter of York, the Earl of Lancaster and lords Wyvill, Bolton, Hastings, Bulmer, Vescy, Roos, Wake, and John de Eston at Thornton. Elsewhere the privilege belonged to the Lords Mowbray, Malbys, Sherburn and the Prior of Kirkham.

Manors needed a brewery. When thirty Kirkby Moorside bondmen did their twenty day-works, they expected the customary food and drink to be provided as of right. The burgesses of Malton in the late thirteenth century had a grant of the amendment from the baron. They could sell ale in their own houses but common brewers paid a fine. A Geoffrey the Brewer is mentioned at the town in 1301 and he may have been the first common brewer. Hostelries are rare but do occur at Hawnby, Rillington and Newsham.

CHAPTER 3
THE LATE MIDDLE AGES

A different world was emerging as the 13th century ended. Kings Edward I and II sought to control Scotland. The result was forty years of border instability, from 1296 to 1346, with sustained periods of war and raiding. The cross border Norman aristocracy was split. The catastrophe of the Battle of Bannockburn forced the transition to a military system, where wardens of the border marches drawn from such families as Percy, Neville and Dacres, provided what were almost private armies, subsidised by the Crown. For for a long time Crown authority was weakened. Rivalries between the dynasties who claimed the English throne, would feed on the rivalries between the new giants of the north, during the 'Wars of the Roses'. The Yorkist victories at Towton 1461 and Hexham 1464 raised the Nevilles high, but the Percies were back soon afterwards and it fell to Richard Duke of Gloucester, as the king's brother to restore royal power, by temporarily replacing the Nevilles and appeasing the Percies. The Anglo-French conflicts, called the 'Hundred Years War', from 1337 to 1453 only achieved the loss of assets in north west Europe.

There was some shift of significance among the different groups that made up society. After the death of Thomas of Lancaster, the lesser northern barons, while still influential locally, were drawn into the networks of influence and patronage of the great regional families. The new parliaments were made into an occasional advisory conference, linking regional elites with the centre, but with no particular power. They made no laws, and little stir, until King Henry IV allowed parliamentary petitions. The native merchants, including some in Yorkshire, prospered as home manufacture and export of cloth replaced export of wool, but it was Hull and southern ports rather than York and the Yorkshire coast ports that had the main gain. The rise of London as the merchant hub and giant consumer of the nation's supplies and people, began and made Newcastle, source of its coal, into the principal port of the north. The Crown turned to the merchants for financial support with heavier customs and loans. In the countryside, the move from personal services to a wage economy, from demesne farming to leases, created new groups of middling men in towns and villages, but by the end of the 14th century, pestilences had reduced population so dramatically that it was a smaller world in Yorkshire, with less arable and more pasture.

Thomas, Earl of Lancaster

Thomas of Lancaster, a grandson of King Henry III, succeeded to his father's Earldom in 1296. After his marriage to Alice Lacy, his English estates were second only to those of the monarch. He served with his uncle King Edward 1 in several campaigns in Scotland and visited Pickering occasionally. Three men beat and wounded his wife's esquire in Pickering church. When the Earl's cousin came to the throne as King Edward II, Thomas led the baronial opposition to the unpopular royal favourite Piers Gaveston, who had been several times banished, but always returned. Henry de Percy and other barons pursued Piers and the King northwards through York vale to Newcastle in 1312. The couple took ship for Scarborough, where the King left Gaveston secure in the castle, but he ran short of supplies and was obliged to parley with the barons at the Franciscan Friarage. Promises of safe conduct were broken and Gaveston was executed in June.

John Dalton of Kirkby Misperton was the Pickering castellan. He had taken Pickering Vale men to Newcastle and led three hundred men, clad in green, at the seige of Scarborough Castle. About 1314, the Earl spent £341 building a new two storey, limestone-tiled hall in the Pickering castle bailey. His young wife resided there for a year, her expenses being £285.13s.4d. Dalton later marched his local force to Lancaster and to Tickhill, against the King, but they were never allowed to array against the Scots. The King had his vengeance at the Battle of Boroughbridge where Thomas was captured, along with John Dalton. Thomas was executed but Dalton offered a hundred marks and gained release. The Earl was later thought of as a popular hero, almost a saint, optimistically seen as a defender of liberties, because he opposed an unpopular king. His hat was worn to cure headaches. At Pickering, his officers were the subject of much complaint. They said that Thomas brought many with him, who came only with their bows and arrows in their hands, but ended up with rich manors and rolling acres. Even the Constable of the castle was accused of extortion. A later Bailiff was charged by a villein with taking nine shillings for a dog licence, from a man with no dog.

The Scots Disaster .

A major disaster turned the course of northern history. King Edward I sought to control Scotland. He ruled from York for a time and personally led his armies northwards. William Wallace raised the level of Scots resistance in 1297 and was attacked at Alnwick by William de Vescy. Thereafter, the Scots repeatedly raided the northern counties. Robert Bruce was crowned King of Scotland in 1306. Edward II succeeded his father the next year. His army was defeated at Bannockburn in 1314, after which the Scots raiders were free to sweep deep into Yorkshire. Their ways were reminiscent of earlier Danish and Norman harryings. They attacked the population, destroyed crops, moved fast and carried off farm stock. The Scots under James Douglas, swept through Osmotherley to the outskirts of York in 1318, and there was talk of burnings at Northallerton and Scarborough. Randolph was near York in 1320, and an inexperienced force of laymen, raised against him by the Archbishop, was slaughtered at Myton on Swale.

Robert Bruce rode through Yarm and down the west side of Blackamore in 1322, nearly capturing King Edward II at Byland Abbey. Easingwold saw slaughter. Marton Priory was devastated. The nuns were driven from Rosedale, while Kingthorpe manor, Moxby Priory and Rievaulx abbey were damaged. Tradition claims that Helmsley church was twice burnt by the Scots, and fire damaged columns were pointed out a hundred and fifty years ago. Bruce occupied Malton castle and sent raiders over the Wolds towards Beverley. The Scots would accept bribes to leave single settlements or whole districts unharmed, and a two hundred marks ransom was negotiated for Pickering Vale to escape further ravishment. When the Scots had gone, many parishes had their tax burden dramatically cut in recognition of their inability to pay. Throughout north east Yorkshire the reductions were so marked that a major disaster must be presumed. Rievaulx and Byland Abbeys both asked for tax relief. The Whitby Abbey levy was reduced from £109 to £50. A later Scots forray resulted in David Bruce being chased from York by Queen Phillipa and beaten at Nevilles Cross in 1346. Sir Ralph Hastings of Farmanby was killed at the battle.

Pickering Castle Defences and Privacy

Pickering castle saw major improvement after the worst of the

Curtain Walls and Towers at Pickering Castle

Scots raids. The King dispossessed the Earl of Lancaster's heirs, but his new keeper Thomas Ughtred repaired the roofs of the old hall and the woolhouse in 1322, and built an expensive privy near the new hall for £4.4s.4d. The inventory of the hall building was still modest, a table of boards and trestles, some forms, brazen pots, a tripod and some vats. The King stayed hunting for three weeks, during which time he gave the Pickering poor three pence, donated a coat to a Rievaulx monk and tipped John Ibbotson for following him a whole day hunting a stag. He paid a five pounds bill for net ropes at Lockton, and then rode off to visit Whorlton castle, where two women singing songs about Simon de Montfort were treated more generously than the Pickering poor. He spent another night at Laskill woolhouse.

Orders were issued that Pickering castle was to be strengthened, with a barbican before the main gate and an outer gate across a drawbridge. A new curtain wall replaced the old timber walling, but the new wall included several towers of stone, linked by a raised wall walk, but entered from the bailey. The towers held private rooms with separate fireplaces. There were privies set in the walls to vent outwards to the ditch. Here was privacy and comfort indeed. New weaponry was also installed including a 'springald' with a hundred bolts, and eight crossbows with a thousand bolts. Soon afterwards the castle was restored to the Lancaster heir.

114

Castles Old and New

Malton Castle had also been given a new gateway but no detail is known. With the death of the last baron Vescy, and the end of the widow's dower right, that castle reverted to the Crown. The King quartered Joan Comyn and her household there, and when the merchant Gilbert de Ayton was eventually declared heir to the Vescys at Malton, though not at Alnwick castle, in 1318, the castellan briefly refused him entry. When Gilbert died, he was at his house at Wintringham. The widowed Isabella de Vescy lived at Hood Castle in 1319. The decline of Malton castle may already have begun, when a generation later, the Malton estate was divided between three co-heiresses and their husbands. Helmsley Castle kept its importance as the main residence of the powerful Ros family, but Pickering Castle came to house royal constables in new half-timbered lodgings. King Edward III visited both castles in 1334 but such royal visits were becoming infrequent.

New castles of several kinds were being built for rising men, for Geoffrey Scrope in Upsall Park, for Sir Ralph Bulmer, sometime Sheriff of Yorkshire, at Wilton in Cleveland in 1331, for Sir John de Heslerton at Wilton in Pickering Lythe in 1336 and for Sir Ralph Hastings who bought a Slingsby manor from William de Wyville, and in 1345 obtained a licence to fortify it. He was sheriff of Yorkshire for two sessions. Sir Thomas de Etton's high castle keep or tower house at Gilling was perhaps the most impressive of all, with walls between eight and fifteen feet thick. Above a pointed barrel roof was an upper hall, thought to be 48 feet by 28 feet. He had a licence to empark Gilling woods in 1374. A castle at Hinderskelfe was built for the Greystokes. Ralph Neville in 1335 emparked Sheriff Hutton woods and made a deer leap near his old castle, soon to be replaced on a massive scale.

Estate and castle officers were contracted for their posts. Robert son of Ralph de Greystoke charged his estate at Hinderskelfe and Ganthorpe with twenty marks a year, two robes, one with fur and one with linen, and a saddle, proper for a knight, yearly, by a deed to Sir Thomas de Bolton, probably his steward, in 1323. He gave another 'livery' to Hugh of the Dispensary, employed as his forester, payable in corn, clothes and wood. William of Overton, the constable of Helmsley Castle, received three pence a day and a robe worth twenty shillings a year. The park keeper had a penny halfpenny a day and a ten shillings robe.

Many other manor houses and granges were given moats especially in the lowlands, from Cornbrough to Snainton and from Harum to Lilling. The defence they offered was slight, better protection against local trouble makers than a Scots' army They could double as a fishpond. Elsewhere, simple towers called 'peels' were built, which seem to be offering a limited bolthole security at Bilsdale, at Yedmandale, and for the de la River family at Yearsley. Other castle sites remain mysterious, at Bossall, Low Hutton, Howsham and elsewhere, with little more than a legend to rouse our curiosity.

Prayers for the Mighty

The parish churches were closely linked with their rich and powerful patrons. Wealthy men and women in their approach to an expected after-life maintained the distinctions enjoyed in this life. As death approached, the clerk was there to write the will and to remind the ailing of forgotten tithes, of the need for prayer and of local obligations to the church. Charity was often greatest from those who lacked heirs. The chancels and their associated chapels show most signs of rebuilding and the rich were often buried in them. Others still looked to the monasteries. Alice the widow of Walter Percehay, lord of Ryton, in a plague year, wanted burial in the Old Malton Priory, against the corpse of her husband. She made a generous provision for that house, and for a burial feast, and left clothes to her daughter the Prioress of Yedingham. Kirkham Priory remained the burial place of some the wealthiest families for another century.

The memorial brasses, the carved grave slabs, and the stone effigies left by the wealthy in the churches have suffered badly over time. Where they survive they do reflect the social divisions of the day. A lady in elegant drapery is portrayed in a well carved effigy at Appleton le Street. Sir John Bordesden of about 1329 displays a fine surcoat at Amotherby and a Wyville knight who was said to have fought with a dragon, reclines under his canopy at Slingsby. Many floor monuments have worn away but the higher the status, the nearer the altar seems to have been the rule.

Wealthy men, in their wills, endowed priests to say masses for their souls after death, to assist their passage through purgatory. Many settled for prayers for a year, or for a few years on the anniversary day. Some went much further, giving houses and lands of great value, for accomodation and to provide the revenues that would sustain a chantry priest. He might be given an extra altar to seek the intercession of a particular saint, or even a new chantry chapel built onto the church. Three chantry chapels project from the south side of the great church of Scarborough. Pickering has lost one but retains another, where a school was later held and the priest had a room above.

Table 18 Some Early Local Chantries		
Appleton le Street	1339 & 1381	Thomas de Bolton.
Ayton	1334 & 1384	William de Ayton
Brompton	1326-31	John Moryn
Gillamoor	1183-92	William de Stuteville
Helmsley	1371	Robert & Emma de Flaynburgh
Kirkby Misperton	1317	Alexander de Barugh
Malton Castle	c1251	Agnes and John de Vescy
Malton St Michael		
Old Malton	1383	William de Ayton
Pickering castle	1227	
Pickering	1337	William de Brus
Pickering	1395	The Burgesses
Pockley	1338	William de Ros
Scarborough	1296	The Burgesses
	1390	Agnes Burn
	1380	Robert de Rillington
	1380	Robert Galoun
	1397	The Burgesses
Sheriff Hutton	1350	Ralph de Neville
Seamer castle	1328	Henry de Percy
Seamer	1314 & 1351	
Thornton Riseborough chapel. early 13C. Alan de Wilton		
Wykeham	1319-21	John de Wykeham

The founder of a chantry gained a continuous petition of prayer, for the health and destination of his own and other named souls. Sir John de Heslerton in 1333 established what was virtually a college for six chantry priests at Lowthorpe. These priests were often better educated and better rewarded than the ordinary vicars and their chaplains. They appear as something of an elite. At Northallerton, the chantry priests ran a reading and song school and chantry schools may have existed elsewhere. A tradition that Robert de Pickering, a member of the Brus family who became Dean of York, may have founded the Pickering Grammar School is unproven but his family maintained a chantry there and he did establish a school at York.

The Church and Churchmen

Most parish churches had aisled naves sufficiently large to house their parish populations, and insisted on attendance at major festivals, from the more distant villages and dales within the parish. Village chapels had become numerous, indeed normal, as were other chapels at castles, hospitals and monastery granges. The naves of churches and chapels probably served a multitude of secular as well as religious uses. The borough of Malton had two chapels and Malton castle another but tithes went to the older parish church at Old Malton.

The tithes formed the most important church revenues and became chargeable on almost everything, including fruit trees, fish, seeds, eggs, bees, honey and pigs. Archbishops intervened at very different dates over a long period, to settle definite shares of the parish church incomes between the rectors, who were by now usually monasteries, and the vicars who, as substitutes, did the local work. The tithes of the major corn crops, and tithes of wool and lamb were the main prizes at stake. Each church saw a distinctive settlement arrived at. The local priest gained a secure living with a definite income, but commonly the distant monastery received a large part of the local dues, while providing little that was obvious in return. Sometimes a fixed pension was awarded instead, and this could eventually drop in value. Monasteries also leased their rectories to others for a fixed sum, leaving collection of the tithes to the tenant.

Some men in holy orders, particularly the rectors, were wealthy. Thirty four oaks granted from the forest of Pickering to the Dean of York suggests that as rector, he had his substantial house rebuilt, at the head of Hallgarth in Pickering, where the tithe barn was its neighbour for centuries. Robert de Place, the Brompton rector of 1344, was wealthy enough to want a marble stone worth forty shillings over his grave, near the great altar in the church. He owned silver ware, a coverlet, matching wall hangings, two horses and some law books. Others appear to have enjoyed the life. The Middleton rector was said to keep four gazehounds and hunt at will. A Normanby rector was a harehunter, and a Levisham parson hunted with a crossbow. He was known as Roger the Bell. Most vicars and chaplains were much poorer, small farmers as well as priests, thoroughly immersed in day to day life. The priest of Lastingham had six oxen and two cows. The Ebberston vicar was charged with removing a green oak from the wood. The vicar of Kirkby Moorside took the pilgrim road to St James of Compostella in Spain.

The house of Master William Melton at Acklam was quite exceptional, housing a high dignitary of the church. His hall had a counter with carpet on four chairs, four forms and ten cushions, some covered with carpet work and some with arras. The parlour had a feather bed, bolster and white cloth blankets, the one coverlet decorated with red flowers and the other with a crowned letter M. There were several chambers, one at the stair head holding bedding, including old coverings with imagery on them. The great churchman's own chambers had a counter, red swans on the coverlet, a painted cloth over the bed, black buckram curtains, a long board, trestles and a form.

Problems for the Clergy

Vicars were thought of as having 'the cure of souls' and dealt with the whole gamut of human problems. The church seemed to reward the faithful, and its pronouncements formed part of the framework of thinking. The lower clergy offered codes of belief and behaviour, and through the confessional could bring sinners to book. They could offer penance and absolution. Thomas Holycross of Pickering was moved to go on pilgrimage for a year. Robert Manning raised at Malton Priory had translated Bishop Grosseteste's treatise on 'The Seven Deadly Sins', as well as writing a history, versifying old chronicles into the native tongue. The seven sins were 'sloth, lechery, envy, covetousness, gluttony, pride and wrath'. With such a list, the sinners were never in short supply.

Those of great status were not exempt. Archbishop Melton ordered Sir Geoffrey de Upsall to maintain his wife in 1323, and required Sir Peter Mauley to do penance for his adulteries with Alice de Eyville and with Sarah of London. Peter was required to fast periodically for seven years and to visit five shrines. The Beverley chantry priest, John of Wintringham, had to promise to avoid suspect places and co-habitation with any ladies, after some forward behaviour with two of them.

Desperate criminals could find temporary sanctuary in churches. A Malton killer escaped arrest and reached St Mary's Castlegate, York. A guilty man from Sherburn found a haven in Old Malton Priory. Such men were given a limited period to reach a port for embarkation, such as ten days to reach Newcastle from Kirkby Moorside, or Berwick from Salton.

The church framed life in patterns of regularity. Saints days formed part of the calendar of the church year and of other social life. The Pickering forest courts and rent days were on St Andrew's, St William's and St Cecilia's days. Pope Urban had decreed the Feast of Corpus Christi, when, on the Thursday after Trinity Sunday, a street procession could raise aloft the consecrated host. King Edward at Pickering in 1334 gave money to feed a hundred poor people on the feast day. There were annual rush bearings to clear out the church building, 'rogation' perambulations of the crops in the fields and there were visitations. Archbishop Corbridge moved around his diocese calling at some parish churches and monasteries, and his officials reported back from others. Archbishop Melton called his diocese to prayer against the marauding Scots and to more prayer for fine weather, in the face of the heavy rains of 1319.

There were baptisms, marryings, churchings of women and funerals. William Latimer was born at Scampston during the reign of King Edward III. The locals remembered his baptism in St Andrew's Church, Rillington, when Sir William Place and Walter Percehay lifted him from the font. Roger Bigod had a daughter born that year and in the same week, Thomas Lockton's brother was made a canon of Malton Priory. John Austin of Scampston saw his brother go off to be a canon at Kirkham and a Rillington man entered the house of Friars Minor at York. Clearly the church offered a career for some. From the noble families, men rose high in the monasteries. St Mary's York had Abbots called Alan of Nesse and John of Gilling. Byland and Kirkham had heads of house drawn from the Helmsley family. Prioresses of Rosedale bore the names Kirkby, Pickering and Ros.

Monastic Obedience and Chastity

Many monasteries and nunneries were now experiencing problems of morality and discipline. Lapses from the rule of poverty, chastity and obedience recurred over several decades. Recruits came from the better off section of society and the habits of home died hard. Entry to a nunnery offered women from well known families the main alternative to arranged marriage. Archbishops struggled to maintain standards. At their visitations, the nuns were urged to attend services, to refuse gifts, to lock cloister doors and to avoid boarders, secular girls, useless servants, fancy girdles and puppies.

From 1306 the Friars Minor visited nunneries to hear confessions. The worst cases were sent to other houses to do penance. Keldholme Priory was rent by disorder and rebellion, under a succession of Prioresses, over two decades. Small cliques of nuns involved Kirkby Moorside laymen in their squabbles. Mary de Holm was incontinent with a chaplain in 1318. At Arden Priory, the nun Joan Punchardon became a mother, in the decade when Agnes de Thormondby at Basedale yielded to persuasion three times, and Clarice de Speton had an affair with Geoffrey de Eston. The Molesby nuns were locked in at night.

Punishment could be severe. After a lapse of some years, when she chose to live with a married man in London, instead of continuing on her pilgrimage, Maud of Terrington was obliged to kneel at the Keldholme Priory gates begging for admission, and once inside was to do penance, for all her life. She was to be last into the choir, and when not in the choir was to be kept in solitude. Maud was not to go outside the precinct or speak to lay folk. There would be no letters. She was not to wear the black Benedictine veil and was never to wear a shift next to her skin. On Wednesdays she was confined to bread and vegetables and on Fridays to bread and water. On those days, she went barefoot around the cloister in the presence of the convent, and had two beatings from the Prioress, as against one beating on more normal days. She was excluded from chapter meetings, and instead was to lie prone at the choir entry, to be spurned by their feet, if they wished.

The monasteries show similar problems for men, in this period, which were not necessarily typical of the remainder of the long history of the houses. The Archbishop told Whitby monks to be silent in the cloister and not to wander the country with bows and arrows. Dogs were to be chased out of the inner precincts. Newbrough canons were urged not to go drinking after Compline. At Kirkham Priory the canons were urged to look after the sick properly, and to avoid spending time warming themselves and drinking in the infirmary. He asked that they keep buffoons out of the refectory.

A seemly equality in sharing the necessities of life was continually challenged by the tendency to treat clothes and other things as private property, despite the commitments each monk entered into. The monks at Kirkham were not to receive private gifts and their carrels were to be searched annually. The Benedictine Order saw the same problems, but settled for new rules in 1336, which embodied a slightly more moderate discipline. Private property was still restricted but more meat eating was allowed.

There were particularly troublesome lay brothers at Arden and Rosedale. Marton Priory in 1314 held the canon Alan de Shirburn who confessed to relationships with three women at Bootham and Stillington. He was ordered not to speak to any women without permission and even then was to be overheard. Another canon Stephen of Langtoft was given the same punishments for his activities with two women of Marton and Huby. A lay brother Roger de Scampston had been even busier with ladies at Brandsby, Farlington, Marton, Menersley and Stillington. His punishment was much more severe than that imposed on the canons.

Monastic Poverty and Management

Many monasteries saw a slide into deficit finance. Over ambitious building programmes, an indulgent way of life and sheer bad management could raise regular expenditures too high. An excess of spending over income in any one year could also arise easily, from a fall in income after harvest failure, or animal contagion, from the Scots raids, or from such local disasters as the collapse of the Whitby Abbey nave or the Guisborough church roof fire. The forward selling of crops, asset sales, and grants of favorable leases offered tempting, temporary solutions but reduced long term viability. Appeals could do something. A Pope allowed Malton Priory to grant forty days relaxation of penance, to those who visited Old Malton Priory church at the four feasts or their octaves, extended by a later pontiff to a year and a day. Measures of local retrenchment were often adopted, and occasionally licenced begging through the diocese. Archbishop Melton told the Whitby Abbey monks to moderate their eating, drinking and servants. Recruitment was stopped, and the granting of pensions and long leases inhibited.

Malton Priory had debts of near £252 by 1255. Kirkham Priory was deeper in debt by 1314 when moderation was urged. Seven years later the amount borrowed reached nearly £844 and there were twenty two other regular commitments called corrodies and some pensions burdening the house. Rents had been lost from properties towards Scotland. Thirty years later the debts had not eased. This was not necessarily a disaster, provided that the loans were serviced.

Kirkham Priory

Most monastic houses introduced annual accountancy audits, departmental accounts, and regular supervision of officers and their expenditure. Outsiders were given oversight of the smaller nunnery economies. A Newbrough canon guarded the temporalities of Arden Priory from 1302. Generous retirement packages were sometimes necessary to secure improved management. Abbot Thomas de Malton left Whitby Abbey in 1322 with a Whitby chamber, an Eskdale manor and its profits, the provisions of three monks for him and a companion, clothes, wood, turves, wax, three servants, transport and food for his guests. A retired Prior of Newbrough enjoyed the manor of Hood.

People At Play

Robert Manning in his *Handling Sin* of 1303 spoke of the people's pleasures, of carols, wrestling, of Summer games in the churchyard, interludes, singing, piping, idle plays and japes, 'making fool countenance', jugglers and deeds of strength. Dancing bears were portrayed in the stained glass of York Minster and many minstrels in the great church at Beverley. There were fifty two Sundays, a great many holy days, and the slack seasons of the year. This was a young society and much that was done would today be thought of as children's games.

Mediaeval illustrations show people playing 'hoodman blind', 'leap frog', 'hot cockles' and 'barley break' where couples catch each other. A vast litany of throwing games used anything from stones to sheep bones.

Backgammon was played at Pickering castle in King John's time. King Edward visiting the town paid a man who had worn his helmet at jousts at Woodcock, Newmarket and Burstwick. Hare coursing was probably already a sport in Pickering Forest, attracting such enthusiasts as the Rector of Normanby, Lady Maud Bruce, William de la More the Malton merchant and Nicholas the Tailor, who are all named as hare catchers. Harpers and pipers were present in a few villages. A group of men from Dunnington had a commitment to dance in York minster in procession on the Thursday in the week of Pentecost. Peter de Mauley, the Dukes of Lancaster, the Bigods, the Hastings, Lady Wake and Robert of Scarborough sent their minstrels to the 1306 feast when the Prince Edward was knighted. Lord Ros had harpers who visited Whitby Abbey.

The Alehouses

The major manor lords, and the monasteries claimed the Amendment of the Assize of Bread and Ale. This made them licensing authorities and gave them fines of brewers who offended, if they made ale of insufficient quantity, quality or price. It was customary to display a bush outside the house to notify the manorial ale tasters that a brew was ready for their inspection. Most villages seem to have had one or more houses where ale was regularly made and sold at any one time, but it is not clear how fixed they were in particular houses. At Allerston with three separate manors, each had an alehouse. Pickering had alehouses licenced by the Earls of Lancaster and others by the Dean of York. Running the alehouse was part time women's work, and in the towns and market villages at fair times, many would put their wives to brewing.

At Pickering in 1334, when demand was inflated for the Duchy of Lancaster forest courts, the brewers were mostly women, married to husbands of some substance. Brewing for sale was not an activity of the poor. These women were connected with castle officials, traders or the church, in almost every case. Among them were the chamberlain and the despenser, the tailor and the dyer, a merchant and Isabella of the

124

hospital. Taverns sold wine but were confined to the larger towns. Scarborough and later Malton had a tavern in the town.

Forest Offenders

Forest offences were numerous, and despite the apparent rigour of forest law, poaching may well have been seen by many as a pastime, if not a right. Barons and knights from within the forest were out and about hunting animals, William Latimer at Saint Hilda's Cragg and in his own Sinnington park taking deer, Lady Blanche Wake of Cropton with her men on the commons and Sir Ralph Hastings at Crosscliff above Ebberston. Sir John Moryn's cousin took a hind to the great man's house, presumably at Brompton. More ordinary mortals included a party from Farndale, others from Rosedale and the Westerdale chaplain.

Parties from nearby areas seem to have taken a particular delight in raids into Pickering Forest. The Meynells came from Whorlton Castle, the young Peter de Mauley from Julian Park castle with his park-keeper, the Percys with their hounds from Kildale castle. Four men took a hart to William Wyville's house at Slingsby. On one occasion, while the King was at Pickering, a rebellious group took forty three harts and fixed nine of their heads on moor stakes, in an act of defiance. Wild deer were getting scarce but deer parks still functioned like farms. Edward II had fifty bucks and twelve hinds in one delivery from Pickering for his Christmas table. Spaunton forest seldom saw the hart and hind any more.

Pickering forest officers were still exercised about other forest offences, but also much involved in raising income. They collected pannage payments for pigs taken to the woods, some £1.17s.4d. in 1322. The under foresters made cattle drives, to find all the strays in the Forest. They chased Ebberston and Yedingham priory cattle out of Stockland pasture and required payment for their return. Owners of cattle, sheep and oxen were fined a penny a foot for escapes, but forfeited them on a third offence. Heather, bracken, wood, birds, nuts and iron from the seashore were taken and sold. Payments in 1322 included twelve shillings for thirty six cartloads of old brushwood. A man took a whole timber house frame from Foulbridge out of the forest and moved timber to Shirburn to build a house.

The Derwent river had managed fisheries with fishermen paying for licences at Howe, Foulbridge, Yedingham and Scampston. Some High moor agistments were now let for pasture at the Hole of Horcum, at Allantofts near Goathland and in some tracts north of Scarborough. The forest of Whitby had earlier seen half wild brood mares and fillies running free on the open commons and Bridlington Priory raised horses on Scalby moors. Now Blansby Park was sometimes used for cattle and for horses. Thirty brood mares and two fine black stallions, managed by a groom, ran alongside fallow deer and pasturing cattle. The cart horses were kept out while the King's mares were there. The Black Prince ordered his Farndale keeper of the wood to deliver a single oak, suitable for shingles, for roofing Gillamoor chapel.

Farm and Society

Agriculture was the bedrock for almost everything else, but changes were taking place. The farming expansion of the thirteenth century had ended with harvest failures, livestock epidemics, some famine years, damaging Scots raids, pestilence, and perhaps even soil exhaustion. They did not all happen at once and waste tofts without tenants could appear at one village, while another showed signs of expansion. New markets were founded at Terrington, Coxwold and Sinnington in the early 14th century and new inclosures were sewn with oats in dales above Cropton. Elsewhere there were some small signs of shrinkage. The low lying Templar manor of Foulbridge, where two hundred and thirty four acres had been sewn with corn and maslin, went down to pasture.

Water levels may have been rising in the lowlands. Byland Abbey raised banks to protect pastures at Rillington in 1342. The tidal rivers Hull and Humber rose four foot higher than usual in 1356 and again ten years later. Derwent-side meadows were flooding in 1360 and again a decade later at Knapton. Flooding on the north side of Pickering Vale in 1379 was blamed on the Old Malton milldam and when the Abbot wouldn't act, two hundred armed men rode off to wreck it.

Villein services were slowly being replaced by money dues. Some villeins' works for the lord at Pickering had already been commuted by 1313. Slingsby bondmen paid rents for their house and two oxgangs, but two shillings paid at mowing time replaced old services. Small obligations to the Church and to foresters lingered longer. Tenants of Whitby Abbey annually did four days mowing, four days haymaking and two days hoeing. Salton men were obliged to move the Hexham

Medieval Fields North of Middleton

Prior's timber for repairing his houses and for the mill. Gilling tenants customarily sent a man and oxen to carry the parson's grain.

Walter Percehay was lord of Ryton and Hildenley. He made his will in 1334, leaving his soul to the lord of heaven, and his body to be buried at the old Malton Priory church. The black cloth draped round his body would bear the shields of his arms and those of his ancestors .Ten pounds went in alms for the day of his burial, and another forty silver shillings would be given among the poor. He bound his executors, on peril of their souls, that no poor man go without his penny or his pennyworth of bread. Walter's demesne farm animals were divided between his wife Agnes and his elder son William. Four other sons were given forty shillings each and divided his arms and armour between them. The several daughters, including nuns at Watton and Yedingham had lesser sums. Sisters and nephews were remembered. At Ryton he had twenty four oxen and twenty four cows but at Hildenley he had eighteen more oxen. From the two manors came a hundred and ten quarters of oats, sixty quarters of rye and twenty quarters of wheat. Agriculture was still the basis of society.

The Black Death

The plague struck the nation in 1348, locally recorded at many places including Skelton, Barton le Street, Kirkby Moorside, West Lutton and at Cropton, where the annual value of the mill dropped from £4.13s. 4d. to thirty shillings. No group of people was exempt. Many clergy died that year and sometimes their successors as well. Henry Lord Percy died. Richard Rolle died. Sir Ivo de Etton of Gilling made a new will, fearing his male heirs might fail, and so settled the estate on his daughter in law's family.

Archbishop Zouch on July 28th, 1348 called for prayers for the removal of the mortality and the infection in the air. Special arrangements to make confessions followed on February 4th, 1349, and on April 28th, papal indulgences were offered. On June 20th, the consecration of extra chapel cemeteries was promised for burials in Cleveland. At Harum by 1353 most of the tenants were dead through the great mortality. The chroniclers agreed on the suddeness of the attack and the helplessness of the people against it. The disease returned in 1361-62, when Lord John Wake died. Archbishop Thoresby called for prayer then and again in 1368-69 and again thereafter.

The numbers that died have been estimated as between a third and a half of the people. The incomes of estate owners shrank and new tenants were hard to find, but inevitably, the loss for some was a gain to others. Good land eventually found new men to farm it, and it was marginal land that first went out of cultivation. As estate incomes fell, many changes followed, sooner or later. John of Gaunt's officers in 1374 merged the incomes of the once wealthy Saint Nicholas hospital with those of his Castle Chantry, while requiring the hospital to be maintained.

With a scarcity of workers, wages rose and probably real incomes too. A Statute of Labourers passed in 1350 sought to control wages and prices, by putting them under the control of justices. Wages were running at two pence, three pence and threepence halfpenny a day. The new Commissions of Labourers and the Peace launched the 'justice of the peace' system which would evolve into a kind of local government. There were cases brought against labourers for withdrawing their services for greater reward. Clothes were subject to the 1363 statute, decreeing who was to wear what, confining workers to blanket, russet wool cloth and linen girdles. It was felt to be outrageous, that some wore clothing not appropriate to their estate and degree. John Gower complained of small folk demanding to be better fed than their masters and decking themselves in fine attire.

Table 19 Some Township Taxpayers in 1377

Kirkby Moorside with Farndale, Bransdale and Gillamoor 511

Pickering 435	New Malton 354
Helmsley & Carlton 282	Bilsdale, Welburn, Newton grange and other places of the abbot of Rievaulx 248
Ebberston 181	Old Malton, Howe & Wykeham 180
Nunnington 156	Brandsby & Stearsby 153
Ampleforth & Laysthorpe 141	Slingsby 123
Hovingham 128	Terrington 126

Thornton Dale, Ellerburn& Calfscot 124

Crambe & Barton 123	Harton & Claxton 114
Langtoft 100	Sheriff Hutton 110
Appleton le moors 100	Gilling & Grimston 105
Buttercrambe & Aldby 99	Spaunton & Lastingham 88
Harome 86	Lockton 87
Sproxton 73	Bilsdale & Urra 79
Allerston & Loftmarish 77	Farmanby 78
Salton 71	Sinnington, Marton & Edstone 77
Whitwell 70	Middleton 69
Farlington & West Lilling 73	Cawton 63
Pockley 69	Goathland 62
Nawton & Beadlam 66	Bulmer 63
Hinderskelfe & Ganthorpe 63	Normanby 62
Kirkby Misperton 64	Huttons Ambo 60
Rosedale 66	Stonegrave & Riccall 67
Foxholes 57	Cotom 50
Oswaldkirk 53	Scawton 54
Kingthorpe 56	Wrelton 53
Swinton & Broughton 55	Barton le Street 57
Aislaby 47	Hutton & Dowthwaite 54
Habtons Ambo 40	Wombleton 46
Newton 40	Scackleton 40
Welburn 45	Barton le Willows 45
Cornbrough 40	Ryton 40
Aymotherby 49	Foston 42
Stittenham 48	Edstone 48
Coneysthorpe 42	Flaxton 42

Barughs Ambo 39	Fryton 35
South Holme 33	Thornton le clay 38
Bossall and Barnby 33	Sand Hutton 37
Coulton 32	Levisham 37
East Lilling 31	Appleton & Easthorp 47
Wilton 30	Butterwick 21
Muscoates 23	Potter Brompton 22
East Newton 22	Dalby 20
Wiganthorpe 12	Settrington 92
Birdsall 70	Langton 58
Westow 54	Thixendale 51
Weaverthorpe 57	Acklam & Leavening 40
Kirkham 39	Scrayingham 33
Rillington 35	Howsham 31
Helperthorp 32	Burythorpe 23
Mennythorpe 25	Sutton & Wellom 27
Kennythorpe 15	Mowthorp 15

Farming Lords and Demesne Tenants

Lordly involvement in arable farming was sometimes reduced and the demesne arable and improved pastures were leased to tenants. They gained new opportunities with increased security of tenure and fixed rents, instead of the old obligations to work the lord's land or perform other services. Monasteries also leased lands to tenants on a growing scale, while lay brothers gave way to paid abbey servants, to work the demesne land that remained. Rievaulx abbey once had hundreds of them but only three lay brothers remained in 1380. Tenant farmers came to dominate Bilsdale and many other lands once worked directly.

This was not universal. Many demesne farms supplied the market as well as the hall. John de Lockton at Hutton on Derwent and a prominent man in the borough of Malton, sold thirty nine quarters of barley at the town in 1388, leaving ten quarters more, three quarters of peas and three quarters of corn. A further fourteen acres were sewn. He worked eighteen oxgangs of land and meadow, and his estate held three dovecotes, a forge on the common, water and fulling mills, and a common bakehouse. His barn in March held ten quarters of corn, eight of rye, ten of barley and twenty of oats. There were thirty acres sewn with corn, eight to be sewn with barley, twenty two acres of peas to pull and one hundred and twenty three acres of failed rye. He had seven grown horses, more young horses, seventeen oxen and many cattle and sheep. His hall held a dossal, a banquer and six cushions, a little board and trestles and two fixed tables. His four poster bed was draped with red worsted.

Wool Growers.Wool Merchants and Cloth Manufacturers

The demand for sheep's wool stayed strong. The wool trade entered new channels, a change with many strands, producing new growers, new traders and new manufacturers. Among the sheepmen, the monasteries and the great barons gave way quite slowly to new middling rearers. Malton Priory had run five hundred sheep on Ebberston's Kirk Moor from the grange at Malton Cotes. By 1366, Thomas Westhorpe of Brompton, probably a descendant from old sokemen, was running flocks of more than two thousand five hundred sheep from this and other old granges. Yet, Whitby monastery accounts thirty years later still record caring for lambs, the purchase of barrels of pitch, tar, grease and rennet and the washing and shearing of sheep. The Duke of Lancaster - John of Gaunt still had a Pickering stock keeper in 1393, with flocks of 2639 sheep, who bought in 545 more.

Merchants from the Yorkshire region began to replace the Flemish and Italian buyers who had exported much of the clip to the industrial heartlands of European cloth manufacture. William Tyrwhit of Beverley bought sacks in Ryedale, at Foxholes and Weaverthorpe in 1361. William More of Malton one year contracted to take £35 worth of Whitby Abbey wool. Bartholomew de Scalby traded on some scale and Thomas Helm of Malton handled vast quantities of wool for Malton Priory. Roger of Hovingham gathered wool from Bilsdale to Malton in 1361. Other wool traders included men from Scarborough, William de Kirkham of Pickering, William de Towthorpe, Nicholas de Lockton and William de Knapton of Malton, William Potter of Shirburn and both Richard at the Gate and John Dobson of Cropton. Sacks were gathered from Weaverthorpe to Grimstone and Eddelthorpe in the Wolds and from Ganton all the way across Ryedale.

A native cloth manufacturing industry spread outside the boroughs into the villages. York was still dominant in dying cloths, but the craft was practised at Whitby, Malton, Pickering, Helmsley, Scarborough and Northallerton. Fulling mills proved a good investment on the strong streams at Lastingham, Thornton Dale, Harome, Farndale, Allerston, Ebberston, Sherburn and elsewhere. Cloth production at the boroughs was supplemented by weavers at such villages as Appleton, Hovingham and Buttercrambe. Towards the end of the century, weavers were producing died cloth, plunket and blue at Sand Hutton, Thirlby, Coxwold and Kilburn. William Pape of Helmsley wove two cloths, dyed blue, annually for ten years, then plunket cloths for another ten years. Six other weavers were making cloths there including Henry Brabener, perhaps one of those of alien descent, encouraged to settle by the Crown in order to foster the craft.

York as the Craft and Shopping Centre

The great places of Yorkshire remained York with 7248 adults registered to pay the poll tax in 1377, Beverley with 2663 and Hull with Hull bank with 2324. York may have had 15,000 people. During the plague centuries, the city absorbed many migrants from the countryside, with Ryedale strongly evidenced in its freemen's rolls. The city was outstanding in the shire, the focus of a vast diocese and of northern civil government. A concentration of small crafts made York the industrial centre of the county, with such specialities as eleven goldsmiths, twelve pinmakers and manufacturers of rivets, armour plate and locks. Ninety two crafts joined in the 1415 mystery plays on Corpus Christi day, drawn from the metal, clothing, food, hide and horn, marine, building and joinery trades. York pewterers complained of tinkers repairing with lead. Hornpot lane turned out combs. There were several spicers and saucers.

At the city shops in 1446 you could buy eyelets, kid gloves or an inkhorn, London girdles and Doncaster knives, small 'New year's gifts', 'truelove knots', jet hearts, green ginger and sugar. Chapmen carried these things to fairs throughout the shire. York merchants made bequests to county roads and bridges at Stamford, at Thornton by Helperby and elsewhere in Galtres. Even the rising called the Peasants Revolt of 1380 was only evidenced at Scarborough, and at York where Robert de Harum, a mercer of rustic origin, was a leader in the attack on Bootham bar.

The Ryedale Towns

The largest places in north east Yorkshire were the boroughs of Scarborough with 1393, Whitby with 641, Pickering 435, Northallerton 373, New Malton 354 and Helmsley with 282 adult tax payers in 1377.

132

Table 20. The Yorkshire towns in 1377. Number of adult taxpayers		
York 7248		
Beverley 2663	Hull 2324	
Scarborough 1393	Pontefract 1085	
Doncaster 800	Tickhill 680	Whitby 641
Selby 586	Sheffield 585	Kirkby Moorside 511
Ripon 483	Wakefield 482	Hedon 482
Hornsea 435	Howden 420	Pickering 435
Allerton 372	Richmond 370	New Malton 354
Bridlington 379	Kilham 363	Driffield 348
Pocklington 351	Patrington 372	Preston 371

Towns were different, their borough areas compact with small house yards, but the figures are a little deceptive. Pickering included some country areas whereas Old Malton, a large village was not included with New Malton. Kirkby Moorside with 511 seemed as big as many boroughs but the figure included populous Farndale and Bransdale. The village had nonetheless come a long way, without the advantages of borough status.

The ports were tightly packed in limited space. The trade that would one day underwrite them was making its appearance. A ship lost off Whitby in 1384, was bringing coals from Newcastle, and in 1395 coal was imported for the abbey. More significant at the time, Scarborough and Whitby welcomed the vast herring shoals that appeared off the Yorkshire coast in 1393, an early sign of the shift of herring from the Baltic into the North Sea. The fishermen of distant ports and foreign nations came to fish these offshore waters.

The inland towns changed less, but merchants and some craftsmen could do very well. Malton had already recorded a distinctive brewery. A Malton mercer could pay as much tax as some manor lords. There were weavers and a dyer, a goldsmith and a spicer. The town gained a wine tavern and saw the small and unexplained development outside the walls called Stowbigging, later Newbiggin. There were fish garths in the river and by 1392 there was a school house in Spitelmangate. The dyer and the merchant William de la Moor lived as neighbours in Appletongate. John de Lockton owned several Malton houses including those tenanted by the barber, and the dyer's daughter.

133

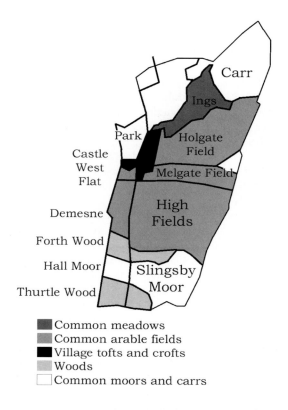

- ▨ Common meadows
- ▨ Common arable fields
- ■ Village tofts and crofts
- ▨ Woods
- ☐ Common moors and carrs

The Ancient Landscape of Slingsby Before Inclosure

At the smaller borough of Helmsley, the keeper of the castle and three other men became a small middle class, tenanting much of the old demesne estate. A place was made for Agnes the anchorite. The Boy Bishop Nicholas, elected from the minster choristers to travel raising charitable donations, called at Malton in 1396 where he spent fourpence on sausages and rode on to Helmsley where Lady Ros gave him a coin called a noble. All the towns were small by later standards but at the time they seemed large. Their skylines were low, with one storey houses, the churches the more prominent above them. Communities which became un-imaginably larger, in later centuries, were modest then.

More Comfortable Styles of Living

Great men sought more comfort and privacy, but also greater display. Kings visited the county less and crown castles were no longer the focus of attention that they had been. The power in the region passed to the Earls and Barons, and to the maintained men who wore their livery. Pickering castle was repaired while it was in the hands of the Duke of Lancaster, John of Gaunt, who had large stables in the outer bailey. It is likely that his constable Sir David de Rawcliff and his wife Margery now permanently occupied the stone Hall built at Keld Head, at 'Old Walls close', rather than the steward's lodgings in the castle. At Scarborough castle, the bridge fell down in 1361 and for a while you couldn't get in.

Private chambers were the great requirement in the living quarters of castles and manors although common halls were retained. The upper room inserted in the rafters of Harum Hall, reconstructed at the Ryedale Folk museum, shows this very well. The second Kirkby Moorside Castle could belong to this time. Even the last monastery, founded at Mount Grace in forgotten Bordelby in 1396-97 by Thomas Holland, Lord Wake and lord of Kirkby Moorside, displayed the concern for comfort and privacy. Sixteen brothers were given two storey houses and gardens, only dining in the refectory on Sundays and feastdays.

The new baronial castles at West Ayton and Gilling had strong rectangular towers, with separate kitchen, hall and chamber floors, sited amidst a miscellany of manorial buildings. Another alternative was to erect the towers at the four corners of a regular walled courtyard, with buildings ranged against each wall between the towers. This allowed numerous private rooms and spacious kitchens, a chapel and other specialised rooms. The castle at Hinderskelfe may have been of this type. Danby Forest gained a new courtyard castle, on the smallest scale, near its second park, built for a Neville Lord Latimer.

The new markets were opened at the rich men's gates, at Seamer in 1376 for Henry de Percy, created Earl of Northumberland and in the new market square of 1377 in Sheriff Hutton village for Sir John de Neville, whose son Ralph would become Earl of Westmoreland twenty years later. These wealthy households comprising both a family and many retainers were heavy spenders on food, coloured cloths, jewellery, horses and furs. Much was consumed and little was kept. Even the rich had few substantial possessions. Dyed cloths and furs displayed social distinction so that those with low incomes were forbidden to wear scarlet and allowed no fur beyond lambskins. This kind of legislation linking dress materials to social station was often repeated. In a world of sharp social differences Thomas Lord Ros thoughtfully left £20 for poor tenants in his will as well as £5 for five chaplains to sing for five years for his soul in Helmsley church.

The greatest castle was built for John Neville in 1382, on a different site from the old motte and bailey, within the village street of Sheriff Hutton. This eventually included three courtyards with seven towers. There were numerous fireplaces and garderobes. Neville was Warden of the East March and builder of Raby Castle. Ralph Neville Earl of Westmoreland left his son Richard the two tapestries in red, green and white in the great room of Sheriff Hutton Castle, twelve plates, a shield with an ewer of silver and an arras bed. Other castles then in use have since fallen to ruin at Seamer, Roxby, Harum and many other places.

Men of Substance

The surviving wills of well off people show what was valued enough to be separately bequeathed. They ignore such ordinary things as drinking horns, leather alepots, willow baskets and earthenware. Archaeology discovers these and in recent years, responsible metal detector enthusiasts have added to our knowledge of the small metal objects of the middle ages, more numerous than was thought, including many tiny strap ends and numbers of small pilgrims' 'ampullas' made of lead to hold holy water. Monasteries offered small insurances known as corrodies. For a sum paid, you received guaranteed accomodation and food. A Yedingham corrodian had seven loaves and portions of flesh, fish, ale and cheese weekly in 1379.

Wills stand out among the scant and largely formal local records of these times and yet they have their formalities too. There was usually a religious preamble. A will of 1408 laid responsibilities on the executors at Habton *as they should wish to answer before the supreme judge'*. Sir John Bigod of Settrington sought burial in the choir of the church before the image of St Mary. He left his best carthorse to the church as was the family custom, along with a cloak of ruby velvet and much candle wax for burning. Six men would bear torches and four marks would be given among the poor on his funeral day. Quarters of wheat were to be sent to monasteries. John Marshall of Helmsley in 1407 had a bay horse called Byward, with saddle and bridle, which went to pay his mortuary, the burial gift to the church. Sir William Wyville, the Slingsby knight, gave his saddle horse and armour.

Many other bequests were more often in kind than in cash. They tell of what was valued and this was changing. Some had acquired a Flanders chest, a fine laver, a nut cup or silver spoons. A few had aspired to arras work or even cloth of gold, to a chafing dish to keep food warm at table, or a puff for spraying rose water. Many more had andirons, spits, iron bases below and iron chimneys above their hearths. Cressets were made for lighting. Men left rings, often signet rings. There were tapestries and painted cloths to hang on walls. The advent of serious furniture brought more permanent beds, tables, forms for sitting on, the occasional chair and chests.

The rich could rejoice in the possession of a fine bed of arras, a chest of spruce and a gold chain of authority. Locks and keys made for rooms and chests hint at the growing concern with smaller possessions from gloves to new pewter vessels, from russet clothing to valued leather dublets. The notion of the heirloom, linking personal property with lineage, was strongly expressed. Henry Eure of Old Malton inherited two silver salts for life, as heirlooms to pass on to his daughter. The things thought valuable enough to be separately bequeathed, were different for the less than wealthy. Agnes Lockton of Huttons Ambo left her scarlet gown and a hood to daughter Mary in 1381. Robert Percehay had the big mattress and the servant Alice a blanket. A Harum man left a 'womble' to his apprentice. A Helperby husbandman in 1456 made bequests of a chair, a pair of querns, a sickle and four oxen. The Northallerton blacksmith willed six brass pots, pewter, his own brewing vessells and a pair of bellows.

There were a few books in English now. Richard Rolle had attempted a translation of the bible and Robert Mannynge a Malton man who became a Gilbertine monk, had written a history for the lewd. More remarkable was John Percehay of Swinton, who had several books in 1392, including the 'Brut' and a 'Life of Lazarus'. Mary Ros of Helmsley had a Greek primer that was formerly her father's. Sir Thomas Ughtred in 1398 had an ivory coffer bound with brass holding the written romance called the 'Brut'. Several of the Roos family at Helmsley had books, including legends of the saints, histories, religious works and a copy of Mandeville. Elizabeth de la River widow of Thomas, at Brandsby had a primer and a 'boke of rules'. Robert Thornton of Newton about 1440 made his own compilation of history, romance, religion and medicine, including fragments of the life of

Alexander the Great, tales of Richard Rolle, charms for toothache and an account by a woman who had visions of purgatory.

Manor Courts

The manor courts continued to regulate many aspects of local life. The court jury, sitting with the lord's steward, established local bye laws and received the presentments of defaulters. They might appoint a reeve, assessors for deciding the level of fines, a constable and other officers to make the system work. Villages of any size had wooden stocks since 1405, in which to place the unruly, but small fines were the main means of securing conformity. The court fines covered the expenses of the court and could return a gain. The manor courts registered the transfer of properties by accepted rules of descent, enforcing the tenant's obligations to his lord, including the upkeep of buildings. They punished trespasses against the lord and settled cases of debt or the detention of goods.

Offenders were brought to book for hedge breaking, cattle straying into the corn field, unlicensed pulling of heather, the taking of turf on the common or failure to join such common works as cleaning dykes, maintaining the pound or repairing the lord's milldam. Pickering Hallmote court dealt with an Eastgate man who took a wagon and six oxen into growing barley and wheat. There was the man who took another's scythe. The issued a judgment on six wives who brewed, but didn't send for the aletaster to test the quality of their ale, before they sold it. In this young society, there were many cases of assault. John Flesh-hewer drew blood, insulted and wounded Richard Whitwood of Wrelton in 1423. Thomas Rawson of Foxholes appeared before another court, because his dog had bitten twenty Bridlington Priory sheep.

National legislation added new responsibilities to manor courts but removed the more serious crimes to the justices of the peace, the assizes and higher courts. These included the worst assaults, woundings and murder, a more common charge than in later centuries. The courts often set serious charges aside. During the hundred years war, it was common to pardon murderers to fill the army. The settlement of claims for small debts was a manor court task which survived most others. Debts appear at this time to play a major part in many ordinary lives.

Tenants and Landowners

Villeins changed into 'husbandmen', as most labour services were replaced by rents. Salton in the middle of Ryedale was worked by twenty husbandmen, each with a house and two oxgangs, and ten 'grassmen', who merely had their cottage and the right to pasture on the common. The break up of lordly demesne by sales and leasing went further. The absentee Dukes of Lancaster leased out their Pickering demesne arable very early, but they still kept the woolhouse and the great flocks of sheep in 1434. There were choices to make and large arable home farms continued elsewhere. The Old Malton manor lord still kept sixteen oxen, two waines and two ploughs.

Lord Roos at Helmsley in 1421 held sixteen demesne oxgangs and a twenty acre meadow, as well as two parks. He received the rents of two mills, the few burgages, a common oven and thirty cottages. Richard Marshall, valet and keeper of the gates of Helmsley castle, was paid two pence a day throughout his life. Widow Roos soon afterwards let much of the demesne land to three substantial tenants called Percehay, Overton and Salton. Percehay's house backed onto the Castle. Large scale farmers like these men were of no small account, whether tenants or yeomen freeholders. They often formed a dominant group of four or five main men, who took the decisions in a township, including those governing the farming year.

There were sometimes clashes between landlord and tenant. John and Margaret Bulmer held a large part of Leavening. They went to the courts, when Prior Richard of Kirkham, a monk and eighty armed men drove their oxen and cows and scattered their crops. Grimston had been leased by Gregory Burton's brother to the Prior of Malton for thirty years before 1468. When the lease expired, he claimed that the monks had pulled down the hall, the barn, the corn store, the haybarn and the stable. They had dug pits over six acres, and sold 'arsilia' and marl worth £10.

Mutton and Beef

With a reduced population, some of the demand for arable crops had eased. The market stayed hungry for mutton and beef, and the wool and hides that came with them. Everywhere, meadows were carefully managed to provide hay as winter feed for stock. They deteriorated if the grips were not opened by May to scour the ditches and dry the soil.

Good pasture for stock was at a premium. Cattle were moved, in season, to eat off the better pastures in the dales and on the fringes of the low commons. A cow of the Prioress of Rosedale could be found which had wandered over the moor top into Danby manor. Her flock of ewes pastured Cropton low common, perhaps still managed from the Rosedale sheepcote north of Breckonbrough.

Within a sizeable estate, pastures could be allocated for rearing and fattening. Good pastures were more frequently let to others as what were called 'agistments', or more briefly 'geists'. The Hole of Horcum became an agistment, let annually for pasturing animals from elsewhere and remained so for centuries, before any farmsteads were planted there. The dale bottom at Fryup combined a demesne herd of cattle and agistments rented out to others. The Steward of the Lady Maud de Cambridge in 1432 moved cattle between her Danby and Sinnington estates. The Danby herd comprised two hundred and thirty four beasts and some were sold into Scarborough and Holderness.

A landowner could easily turn the entire common fields of a township over to pasture, in a township with few freeholds, and where the church tithes were the only other property. This was easier still if he held those tithes. The possibilities were greater in the Wolds than elsewhere. On the chalk Wolds of the East Riding, the infield-outfield system had combined continuous ploughing of the infield, with occasional working of arable in patches of the outfield, so that neither permanent pastures nor permanent commons were present on any scale. Rigg and furrow reached everywhere even though much of it was only intermittently cropped. A total conversion to pasture to raise sheep for wool was attractive and village desertion could result as the plowmen were replaced by the shepherd, and the riggs and furrows congealed beneath the grass.

Around the fringes of Blackamore, the Hambletons and the Howardian hills, extensive permanent commons stretched beyond the fields. If some villages shrank, complete desertions were rare and usually had other causes. East Lilling in York Vale was emptied before 1485, probably for parkland, although this could double as pasture. Stittenham saw a similar change soon afterwards. The Sheriff Hutton gentry were involved in farming as well as holding office. Thomas Witham of Cornburgh, who mentioned his stock keeper in his will, sold twenty head of cattle and two hundred sheep to the receiver of Sheriff Hutton, which were driven to Middleham.

The further colonisation of the dales by new farmsteads was quite a different response. The dates are as yet largely unknown but the result is not in doubt. The dales of Blackamore became populous, as Bilsdale and Rosedale gained farmsteads on a scale already known in Farndale, Bransdale and Hartoft. The arable areas were modest. The valleys gave good pasture for cattle and the moors for sheep. Perhaps one was built in Rosedale in 1492 when the Prioress had two pair of forks, two ribs and wall plates with an 'aft-tree' for a building.

Prospering Burgesses

The houses and workshops of small craftsmen filled the boroughs, but there were a few gentry and merchant mansions among them. The prominent families could include the lord's steward or castle constable, a rising merchant or two, rentier landlords, sons of neighbouring manor lords and tradesmen who had profited from their work. Small landlords could do well in the boroughs. A burgage plot held at a fourpence or fivepence rent in the twelfth century, still paid that figure centuries later, so that either subtenanting or the sub-division of plots allowed landlords a useful gain.

The Helmsley castle constable was proprietor of four town houses and fifteen cottages. The Lockton family of Huttons Ambo had a rent roll of twenty eight houses, in New Malton, including those occupied by the spicer, the barber and the dyer. The Pickering burgages were in two groups, eighteen outside the castle barbican in Boroughgate, probably the bulk of the original borough, backing onto Wollergate one side and the slope towards the beck on the other side. Another sixty three burgages were elsewhere, chiefly in the market places sloping down to Stanbrig and on Smiddy Hill or Hungate Green. The larger mansions of the Hastings and Pickering families stood among them. The Dean of York's tenants held the village area called Hallgarth and Kirkham. William Brus held a property called the manor of Eastgate Hall.

Other open space was taken up in the boroughs, as need arose, the new plots making new payments into the rent roll, rather bigger than those of earlier date. Whitby built houses on the bridge that crossed the river Esk. Scarborough built new lines of houses in the streets around its Friarage, and on and around its waterside quay. Pickering erected new shops around the churchyard, and so formed the north side of the road now called Birdgate. These shops, with the houses above, never had a garden between them and washing would hang amid the graves. Some larger encroachments ate into the greens called Smiddy Hill and Potter

Hill. The Duchy of Lancaster court rolls recorded new rents for small encroachments made for a limepit near the North Mill, a parcel near a shop and an eight yards by six yards waste near the churchyard. A new forge on Potter Hill was rented by a smith in 1403, a toft in 'Wollergate' and another plot sixteen *ells* by three and a half *ells* on the south side of the market place.

The boroughs must be imagined from the few things known. The Malton merchant Thomas Brown in 1441 made bequests to Helmsley, Oswaldkirk, Kirkham and Scawton bridges. His fellow townsmen formed a new Guild of St John the Baptist in 1444 to repair the borough roads, the causeway and the Norton-Malton Bridge, which was endowed with rents from thirty houses. The old hospital Chapel on Derwent Island was joined by a hermitage house at Malton bridge end.

Helmsley the smallest of the boroughs, had a dyer John Pennyman, a draper, a mercer, a coverlet weaver, tanners and a glover in the small burgage plots against the water course. Rye Bridge had its own Chapel of Our Lady. Pickering had two stone bridges now. There was a dunghill in Willowgate and the road south was called Malton outgang. Roger Hastings removed cart loads of stone from the St. Ellen quarry, below the walls of the castle, to take to Roxby Castle. The town had a hatmaker and sixteen folk made poor ale including John Walker of Burghgate. A religious guild of the virgin Mary met in the church porch.

More is known about Malton because, at some time, the customs and liberties of the burgesses were written down .It was claimed that these were granted at the first foundation of the borough, but they clearly contain later concessions. The burgesses' free court had two bailiffs and two under bailiffs, a burgess clerk and twelve sworn burgesses forming a jury. The court met twice a year about Michaelmas and on the morrow of Saint Hilary. They levied fourpence fines but for serious offence had a free prison, a pillory and a thew or rack. Burgesses paid the lord's farm, which was derived from a fixed rent, called *gaffelage*, at Michaelmas. The word comes from the gable end of the house but the payment was actually fixed at one penny for a door, and twopence if there were two doors. In a custom that helped larger proprietors, only one rent was paid if separate tenements were merged together in a courtyard.

The burgesses could sell their town properties, bequeath them or give them away, without paying the relief or inheritance tax to any lord as was usual elsewhere. They had the use of the quarries for building stone at each end of the town. The burgesses were free of the lords tolls, except for a daily toll on butchers, probably those who came in from the countryside and a toll on the herring sellers from the coast who paid 'skategeld' in Lent. The borough had four entry roads passing through the gates in their stone walls. They could pasture beasts on the approach roads, and on the aftermath in the fields, except for those parts which were the lord's demesne, as well as in the moor and the large outgang leading to the moor.

The Borough of Malton had gone a long way towards removing control by the lord but other boroughs had gone much further. Not only had the Malton men to pay the town farm, they were also obliged to grind corn at the lord's mill. They were obliged to pay him one sixteenth of the corn ground when a quarter of wheat sold at fourpence, and amounts fixed on a sliding scale for other times. This payment was called 'multure'. They chose their own page, to keep an eye on the two millers.

Ale sellers in the borough paid a fine unless they were tenants of the knight's fee or of the priory. The burgess men chose their own ale taster. He was to ensure that good ale was available at a penny a gallon. If the ale was of poor quality, he had to ensure that it was sold at a lower price. Measures used in the borough were set to the king's standard and checked from time to time. They included the bushell, the gallon, the pottle and the quart for volume and the yard wand for length. Both bakers and butchers were sworn men. Some demarcation agreements had been established, probably after local disputes. No baker of white bread was to bake brown bread for sale. No grocer or supplier of fish was cut his own fish. Shoe makers and tanners were excluded from each other's craft.

A Colourful Religion

The Roman Catholic church still provided a context for local living, although pagan survivals were a widespread undercurrent. A belief in supernatural powers, which could act for or against men and women, was common to both traditions. Robert Thornton at West Newton had an autobiography of the mystic Margery Kempe, and himself transcribed writings into the so called 'Thornton Royales' but this was not a literate society at the local level. Things said, seen or heard were of more daily import than what was written but couldn't be read.

Outside nature, bright colours were rare. Painted walls and cloths, highly coloured vestments, burning candles and stain glass were to be found in the church. Laymen often bequeathed their best gowns to make vestments. Sir Richard Pickering at Oswaldkirk left the best of his green robes without fur to make a vestment for the altar in 1441. The painted images of the saints on church walls brought them to life as only illustrations could.

The wall paintings surviving at Pickering church offered some of the stories of popular religious belief in the 15th century. This was not just bible religion, but showed the Christian heroes, saints and martyrs of church tradition. Here was Saint George fighting the dragon, Saint Catherine enduring the wheel, Saint Edmund the King pierced by many arrows and Saint Thomas of Canterbury being assassinated. A huge lucky Saint Christopher was visible from the church door. The ascent from hell is represented by little figures emerging from a dragon's mouth, each strangely bearing a quaint modesty patch. The Christ story, and the 'Life of Catherine' are shown in picture series like a children's comic. The portrayal of Herod's feast places the story in a context of fifteenth century buildings, furniture, clothes and the fittings of a high table. This even approaches the techniques of the moving picture in a later age by showing within a single picture, episodes from four different occasions. John the Baptist watches Salome in the one part and she carries his head on a plate in another. Fragments of other wall paintings have been found at Lastingham, Kirkby Moorside, Wintringham, Ellerburn and Middleton, picturing bishops, dragons and the holy doom or Judgment Day.

The people loved a procession and the Scarborough burgesses were required to walk in a regular order, some in scarlet and others in robes of violet, and bearing candles on Corpus Christi Day. Rituals encouraged awe and there were some to participate in, like 'creeping to the cross'. Annual rush bearings became lively processions, on St John the Baptist day, to muck out the church at Barton le street. Whitby Abbey on feast days saw the monks enjoy figs, walnuts and oysters, and visits from groups of harpers and minstrels.

It was a common practice for a hired man to ride a deceased knight's horse, wearing his armour at a funeral procession. Elizabeth Vavasour of Thornton Hill gave a candlestick, chalice and paten to stand on her sepulchre. William Overton gave Helmsley church a silver chalice and paten, cruets, ciborium, a chasuble of cloth of gold, and an alb with his coat of arms for the high altar. Most left money for wax candles, going out in 'a blaze of glory'.

Churches were rebuilt where there was wealth, at the prospering borough of Thirsk and at Coxwold, with a new parsonage later called Shandy Hall. The Kirkby Moorside church was given some elaboration, after the Nevilles built their new castle, as was the church next to the Percy castle or mansion at Seamer. A new church tower rose near Lord Hasting's Slingsby castle about 1463. St Michael church at New Malton was given a tower, indeed there was a movement for towers, raised at Gilling, Lastingham, Kirkby Misperton and elsewhere.

Not so much was given nowadays to the monasteries, urged by King Henry V towards more abstinence and piety and less worldly involvement. It was the town friars, the parish churches and the religious guilds which benefited from many bequests. A few manor lords established oratories in their manor houses. Others sought prayers called obituaries, something short of a chantry. In 1454, Sir Robert Constable willed seven marks for an honest priest to sing for him, in Bossall Kirk, for one year after his death.

Religious gilds were formed at many parish churches perhaps even all of them, and at some chapels. Little is known of their activities but they kept lights burning, supported a priest, and a feast, and secured members a good funeral. There was something in common with the mutual aid and insurance of the friendly societies of another day and age. If they were selective, they may also have been divisive, but they brought a little colour to life. Goathland had a guild of St Christopher and Helmsley a guild of Our Lady of Pity. The York Corpus Christi guild formed in 1408 was in a class of its own, with members across the shire. The Lady Mary was probably the commonest dedication and few churches lacked a St Mary altar. Guilds of Our Lady were formed at Wintringham, Middleton and at Pickering, where the guild owned three quarters of a burgage house. There were guilds of St Crux at Sheriff Hutton, St John the Baptist at New Malton and St Catherine at Langtoft.

Saints and their shrines remained powerful talismen. King Henry visited the St John of Beverley shrine and the new shrine of St John of Bridlington in 1421, and King Henry VI was at St Cuthberts Durham in 1448. The church of Scarborough with all its fish tithes, was transferred from supporting the Cistercian Order to maintaining Bridlington Priory and its new shrine. An Ampleforth girl contracted marriage to a York advocate before the tomb of St William of York. An Arncliffe man left 6s.8d. for another man to go on his behalf to the shrine of St Thomas of Canterbury. Pilgrimage may have been widespread, not only to the burial places of the Saints but to other known ports of call, such as

145

Newborough Priory, the Scarborough churchyard, where they said that miracles had occurred, and to St Botolph's chapel at Hackness. The hospital at Flixton lacked regular endowment and relied on annual gatherings. The ampulas, being found widely by metal detectorists, witness to some reliance on holy waters. No local well blessings are remembered, but in 2003 a bush near the Nattie Fonten spring is still draped with pieces of rag left by latter day believers.

The priest was expected to explain the creed, the ten commandments, the seven deadly sins, the sacraments, 'the lord's prayer' and the 'hail mary'. He had to preach the faith, administer the powers of absolution and offer illustrations of virtue and vice. He would make known the seven corporeal acts of mercy -feeding the hungry, entertaining the stranger, clothing the naked, visiting prisoners, ministering to the sick and burying the dead. Here was an ideal that went beyond the mundane and must have seemed an amazing challenge to some who heard it.

Another World; A Different Story

Tales told around the table at Byland Abbey speak of another world of ghosts and appearances. They may be rooted in strong ale, corn cockle, magic mushrooms, vivid imaginations or real experience. That is for the reader to assess. A Rievaulx labourer shared a horse back with a peck of beans. When the horse stumbled and damaged its shin bone, he carried the beans himself. Seeing a rearing horse before him, he bade it in the name of Christ to do him no harm. The horse changed into a revolving haycock, with a light in the middle. After further appeals to the deity, the haycock became a man. The labourer and the spirit spoke together and the wraith carried the beans to the beck. The labourer had masses sung and the ghost absolved.

Other stories told of the Ampleforth tailor returning at night from Gilling assailed by a raven, which he fought, till it turned int_ a peat stack, and again into the likeness of a dog with a chain on its neck. The tailor invoked the Trinity, the Blood of Christ and his five wounds to persuade the spirit to converse. This he did, explaining how he had been excommunicated. The tailor went to great trouble to get him absolution and to have masses celebrated. He ritually arranged to meet the ghost again, who appeared as a she-goat, which turned into a man.

There was Robert of Boltby who was dead but wouldn't stay buried, until a priest was brought to conjure, confess and absolve him. A

Cruck Beams are Exposed at Wrelton in 1964

deceased Rector of Kirkby who had been buried at Byland took night walks. On one of these, he damaged his concubine's eye. The Abbot and Convent dug him up and threw him into Gormire lake. The stories in most cases seem to rely on departed spirits who need conjuring up, confession, prayers said and absolution given, before they can finally depart in peace. They also tell of bad consciences about family quarrels, stolen corn and stolen spoons, stolen slices of a master's meat, false promises, the burial of an un-baptised child, and the rector's concubine, all in all, the small deceptions of day to day life.

A Building or Two

The timber framed structures of jointed oak that survive in York, and in a few rare examples at Scarborough, cannot be found in Ryedale, except in some small fragments buried within a later building. The more typical cruck buildings were numerous and some can be seen, but usually with much later stone cladding forming walls between the great oak forks. A giant cruck house of the Wyvilles remained in that state at Slingsby until a decade or so ago, and even now gives a powerful impression of the scale that a great building in that tradition could achieve.

Stone houses were still rare, perhaps usually confined to church and castle, but sometimes extending to a manor house, a wool house or a monastic grange. By no means all monastery buildings were of stone, outside those around the cloister square.

Good timbers and good stone were re-used, and conversions from one purpose to another are a major strand in local history. An old chapel was converted into a hall at Sinnington in 1432. Richard Wright of that village made a floor, a screen and three new doors. William Carter received five pence a day for making holes in the old stone walls, to insert braces to support the new chambers. He filled up the old windows of the ground floor and plastered them inside over clay. The craftsmen burnt lime, made mortar, and fetched twenty four loads each of wood and stone. The oak screen survived into the early 20th century, dividing the ground floor in two, with a central doorway and a moulded head. The roof had Neville bosses. The upper chamber was probably confined to the northern half of the building, similar to that in the reconstructed hall in the Ryedale Folk Museum. Traditions claimed that the Earl of Salisbury's bailiff lived here at some time. With other buildings which stood nearby, this was a home of Lord Latimer in the early 16th century.

The vicar at Wharram Percy was allowed a house against the church in 1440. The Middleton Rectory mansion was built in 1494 and a fragment may survive in an outbuilding. There were two hearths and a well. Bryan Sandford the Pickering steward felled twenty great oaks at Malton Close near Goathland for Basedale Priory suggesting major rebuilding. Single oaks often went to Whitby, along with ash trees for the coopers. Parts of Pickering Castle were in a state of some decay, but the Countess's hall still stood within the inner ward. One of the best buildings ever built in the district, the slate covered hall, twenty three yards by thirteen yards, adjoining the chapel, was in reasonable repair. Forty yards away was a house called the constable's lodging. This was probably half timbered and on the plan of a hall with two cross wings. The hall was ten yards by seven yards with two cross chambers, buttery, pantry, cellar and kitchen, covered in limestone slate. Two old 'houses of office' for wood and other things had chambers over them, but were decaying in 1538.

Sir David de Rawcliffe and his Wife.

Dynastic Change and Rebellion

Henry Bolingbroke, Earl of Lancaster was denied his inheritance by King Richard II. He landed with a small force at Spurn near Humber mouth in 1399 and marched to his Pickering castle. He was welcomed by Sir David de Rawcliffe, his loyal constable, who can still be seen in a fine effigy, along with his wife, at the parish church. Supporters rallied including Lord Greystoke of Hinderskelfe, and Nevilles from Sheriff Hutton and Kirkby Moorside. Crucially, the Earl of Northumberland and the Earl of Westmoreland joined him on the journey south. He secured the throne as King Henry IV.

Stability was brief. Henry Percy, Earl of Northumberland unsuccessfully rose against the new King in 1402. Three years later, Archbishop Scrope of York criticised the King's taxation of clergy and was joined in rebellion, at camps on Shipton moor in Galtres, by Sir Ralph Hastings of Slingsby, John Percy of Kildale castle, Sir John Colville of Dale, Richard Polan of Sherburn, Prior Geoffrey of Malton and many others. The Earl of Westmoreland parleyed on the King's behalf and agreed to support Scrope's claims, but arrested him, after his supporters had dispersed.

Scrope, Colville and Mowbray were executed, the latter's head spiked for all to see on York city wall. Robert Percehay of Ryton lost his

149

forest offices and estates. Rumour claimed that the monarch's remorse for executing an Archbishop was contributory to his own early demise. Renewed rebellion by Henry Percy ended in his death at the Battle of Bramham Moor, beyond Tadcaster, fighting against the King's Sheriff, Sir Thomas Rokeby in 1408. As late as 1410, Sir Ralph Hastings, after supporting the Welsh Prince Owen Glendower, had his head placed on the Helmsley pillory, as a warning to the like minded.

Foreign and Other Wars

The wars of great men dominate the chronicles of the time. The nobility and the knightly class provided the leaders, some virtually professional military captains, who led their men at arms to fight the French in many battles. Sir William Ayton, heir to the Malton lordship, served in the campaigns of the Black Prince. Sir William Bulmer and Sir William Eure fought alongside Henry V at Agincourt in 1415. Sir Thomas Ughtred of Kexby had a tapestry bearing images of French magnates, probably wartime loot. The Earl of Salisbury was in France in 1431-32 and 1436-37. Despite great victories, all the possessions in France were eventually lost, with the exception of Calais. Open war with Scotland filled eleven years of the second half of the century but fragile truces and permanent insecurity, dominated border life in between the open conflicts. The Earl of Warwick, lord of Middleham and Sheriff Hutton in 1461-4 probably saved the north from another Scots devastation and Richard Duke of Gloucester later effectively organised the north against the Scots.

The politics of the time were dominated by a few earls and barons, but a small number of the manor lords, those with a clear annual income of £40 or more, were eligible for knighthood. Some paid fines rather than accept the responsibilities that went with it. An even smaller group of families, with several manors, worth more than £100 a year, included the Bigods of Settrington, Bulmers of Wilton & Bulmer, de la Rivers of Brandsby, Eures of Old Malton, Gowers of Stittenham, Hastings of Roxby and Percehays of Ryton. Sir Edward Hastings of Roxby Castle near Thornton Dale was four times sheriff of the county. The heads of these families were commonly 'retained', or given annuities, to bind their loyalties to the noblemen.

The prolonged dynastic struggles for power in the latter half of the century, known as the 'Wars of the Roses', saw the dynasties of York and Lancaster compete for the throne. This was not Yorkshire against

Lancashire. The Honour of Pickering was Lancastrian rather than Yorkist. Faction feuds between Yorkist Neville and Lancastrian Percy or Clifford families, added much fuel to the fire. Many found favour and employment with the contending leaders, who wielded considerable patronage, though some gained little enough from it. It was the way of the time. A Helmsley brass removed from Rievaulx Abbey recalls Thomas de Roos executed in 1464 after the Hexham fight.

The feud between the Nevilles and the Percys flared up in the fifties and ran for decades. There was a confrontation at Heworth between the Earl of Salisbury, riding home to Sheriff Hutton with his family, and Sir Richard Percy and his brother in 1453. The next year there was a fight between some Nevilles and the Percy brothers at Stamford Bridge. The Duke of York allied himself with the Neville, Earls of Salisbury and Warwick soon afterwards and the family feud became mixed with the dynastic struggle. The Earl of Salisbury gained the Stewardship of Pickering in1456, marking a period of Neville dominance, but he was killed at the battle of Wakefield in 1459.

A modern memorial marks the site of the worst of the bloody northern massacres, the Yorkist victory at Towton near Tadcaster on 29th March 1461 which gave Edward IV the throne. The Earl of Westmoreland and Lords Greystock, Dacre, Roos and many of their men were among the dead. Old verses claimed that the defeated Richard II was brought a prisoner to Pickering Castle, before going to Pontefract and his death. Towton gave the Nevilles even greater dominance. The Earl of Warwick and others were given the Percy estates and held them until the pendulum swung again. Thomas Gower of Stittenham was given the riding forestership in Galtres forest.

The Castles of the Greater Men

The widowed Lady Joan Beaufort lived at Sheriff Hutton Castle from 1425 when her husband Ralph, Earl of Westmoreland, died. Her son Richard Earl of Salisbury succeeded to Middleham and Sheriff Hutton in 1440. The Neville family retainers and officers included a cluster drawn from the manorial families, in easy reach of Sheriff Hutton, the Pickerings of Oswaldkirk, Withams of Cornbrough, Gowers of Stittenham, Ashtons of Fryton, Constables of Barnby by Bossall, and the Leptons of Terrington. Salisbury even 'retained' Lord Ralph Greystoke of Hinderskelfe in 1448 though with an obligation to fight against Scotland, not in France. His brother George Neville was Lord

Latimer, but he lost his reason, and Salisbury had custody of his estates. Sir Richard Neville, Salisbury's son and heir was in 1449 made Earl of Warwick.

The powerful Neville Earls of Salisbury and Warwick, enjoyed Sheriff Hutton as one of several castles. These included Middleham where they kept great state but they were frequently at Hutton. King Edward IV stayed there in 1466. The next year, there were high life marriages in the castle chapel in the presence of the Earl. Salisbury relied on Thomas Witham, of nearby Cornbrough as steward of Sheriff Hutton and of Danby. He became Chancellor of the Exchequer to Henry VI, Edward IV and Richard III. He added a north chapel to Sheriff Hutton church and in 1481 founded a chantry at the altar of Holy Trinity and St Nicholas in the chapel, requiring prayers to be said for the king.

Lord William Hastings refortified his Slingsby castle a year or two after Towton. He was a supporter of the Duke of York and of his son King Edward IV. He commanded three thousand men at the Battle of Barnet and was made Master of the Mint in 1461. Among other offices, he held the title of Grand Chamberlain of the Royal Household. William was made Baron Hastings and given Ashby de la Zouch where he built a castle. The York city council made gifts of wine, the next year, to this rising man. He was Lieutenant of Calais in 1471 but he also held important local offices, as Steward of the Honour of Pickering and chief northern Steward of the Duchy of Lancaster.

Lord Hastings was licenced to build the new castle with walls and turrets of stone and lime, and to empark land at Slingsby, in 1463, where some older fortification already existed. He probably altered the parish church, as well, although this stood within a few feet of a large private chapel within the castle precinct. He made an unusually compact park, set in a narrow belt of demesne land, running north and south of the Castle, which included the stone quarry. The castle site is now occupied by a 17th century building but it retains the round corner towers, which are locally unusual, in the long curtain wall at the rear, within a substantial ditch which may be of this time.

After the death of the Earl of Warwick in 1471, King Edward gave Sheriff Hutton Castle and extensive Yorkshire estates to his brother Richard Duke of Gloucester, adding Scarborough and the nearby Northstead manor two years later. Richard had been brought up in Warwick's household between the age of twelve and sixteen. He married Anne Neville, Warwick's daughter and employed Gower, Witham, Lepton and Constable. The Duke was nominally deputy to

Henry Percy, Earl of Northumberland as Lieutenant of the North, but for more than a decade, he was the King's principal agent in the north. He was often at Sheriff Hutton. Ralph Lord Greystoke was on his council there. The duke brought benefits to York and to Scarborough, where he based his fleet and developed the Northstead estate by inclosures. He used Sheriff Hutton castle as a prison, most notably for Elizabeth of York.

His reign as King Richard III was brief, from 1483 to 1485. He was welcomed at York in July 1483 and invested his son the young Edward as Prince of Wales. The Prince died at Middleham in early April the next year. Southern rebellions interrupted his celebrations at York and Henry Tudor emerged as a contender for the throne. In 1484, Richard toured the north and established a Council of the North. Lord Hastings would not ally with Richard Duke of Gloucester. After the death of King Edward but before the Coronation of Richard III he was taken, charged with treason and beheaded. He was buried at St George's Chapel, Windsor, where his son endowed a chantry in 1499, giving the Manor of Farmanby, now lost within Thornton Dale. Sir Ralph Ashton of Fryton next to Slingsby was Knight Marshall of England under Edward IV and did officiate at King Richard's coronation. Sir Edward Hastings later backed the pretender Lambert Simnel.

The retainers and household servants of the great men added an uneasy element to local life. Lord Hastings had more than ninety retainers, fifty nine of them esquires. Edward Mauleverer of Dale near Helmsley agreed with his tenants, that he would store weapons, that they would bear, when he called upon them to do so. Such arrangements could easily overlap into local tyrrany, bullying, rule by force and private war. Sir John Bigod from Settrington and a hundred with him were said to walk up and down Malton market place, uttering words of menace. Marmaduke Westhorpe from Ganton outside Pickering Forest was placed high on the list of those who did most harm within it. Thomas Lord Dacre carried off young Elizabeth Greystock in the night for a wedding, but she may have been willing.

Sir Ralph Eure, Roger Cholmley, John Buckton and two hundred Duchy of Lancaster free men with them, were accused in 1499 of riding around Roxby Castle, one St Stephen's Day, blowing horns and threatening to burn the house down, with its owner Sir Roger Hastings inside, if he wouldn't come out and fight them. Roger was accused of riding through market towns with his household servants, carrying bows and arrows in their hands. Lady Hastings riding through Brompton with six servants was once tipped from her horse by servants of Sir Ralph Eure. Such disorders were well recorded but were not necessarily typical of day to day life. There was a system for maintaining law and order and many were brought to court. Possibly most country squires lived quieter lives, of which we know virtually nothing. Fame normally clings to folly, while useful people remain anonymous.

CHAPTER 4
THE TUDORS. 1485 - 1603

When Henry Tudor replaced Richard III on the throne of England in 1485, the change of dynasty brought only temporary relief from the internal strife and external wars, which had brought little gain. The risings connected with Lambert Simnel and Perkin Warbeck echoed the past, each impersonating Yorkists to make claims for the throne. The marriage alliance when Princess Margaret married the Scots king James IV, gave the Stuarts, another dynasty, their later claim to the English throne, but the border peace with Scotland ended in the Battle of Flodden in 1513.

The nobility remained a dominant force in the north and there is little sign that laws against keeping retainers, or the use of Star Chamber courts, had any great effect in controlling these over-mighty subjects. The gentry enjoyed a rising significance. Some knights and esquires, together with the lawyers drawn from their ranks, played a growing role as justices and as members of the new King's Council in the North. They were led by selected nobles and high churchmen appointed as Lords President. The loss of the records of the Council have left a serious gap in the Yorkshire story. It remained for the royal reaction of King Henry VIII to the astonishing risings called the Pilgrimage of Grace and of Queen Elizabeth to the Rising of the Northern Earls, to temper the old aristocracy and open the way for new Yorkshire leaders.

John Wycliff had long since criticised the practices and many of the beliefs of the Catholic church. The vigorous criticism made in Germany by Martin Luther in 1517 would find echoes in England, eventually bringing the replacement of a Catholic by a Protestant church. The Tudor monarchs relied on the merchant class, who were acruing great wealth, notably in London. The expansion of merchant trading revived the maritime life of the nation. In the country at large, the modest population of the late 15th century gave way to steady expansion in the number of people, and they may have doubled by the time of the first Stuart King.

The Kings and the Northern Nobility

The northern nobility were influential and powerful. Continuous trouble on the Scots border gave them great military responsibilities, ostensibly in the service of the Crown, as wardens of the marches or as captains of the fortress at Berwick. Their retainers went northwards with them. Lord Thomas Darcy in charge at Berwick in 1500 held courts at Sheriff Hutton, where Master Eure counted ten score deer, and then rode on to Kirkby Moorside, where he said that there appeared before them 'the fairest company of men that ever I saw at one court in my life'. A later Eure thought that the best hope for the frontier was to staff it with Yorkshiremen.

No nobleman was greater than Henry Earl of Northumberland, sometimes called 'the magnificent' from his love of display. He met Henry VIIth's thirteen year old daughter Margaret Tudor at York in 1503, on her way to marry the Scots King James Stewart IV. The Princess travelled with musicians, trumpeters and a retinue of two hundred. She was lodged at Newbrough Priory for a night and rode on to a Northallerton welcome from the Carmelite Friars. At the entrance to a town, the Princess moved from her palfrey to a litter born between two fair coursers, to give a more regal impression. When widowed and remarried as the Countess of Angus, she spent another night at the Priory infirmary. She rode pillion behind Sir Thomas Parr but entered York side saddle to greet the Lord Mayor with 'luffying countenance and laughtering chere'.

The Percy Earls of Northumberland had several homes in Yorkshire and another in London. Lord Henry Percy courted the lady-in-waiting Ann Boleyn, but she waited for another. York grocer John Blage delivered spices to the great Percy house at Topcliffe. The Dowager Countess Katherine would live in the great house behind Seamer church. Thomas Manners, who married the last of the Roos line to acquire Helmsley, was made Earl of Rutland in 1525, and his heirs used that castle, though not as their principal seat .The Earl of Cumberland sold his estates at Malton to Lord Eure, a rising man of the borders.

The Earl of Westmoreland was often at Kirkby Moorside Castle and at the park, edging Manor vale. He also tenanted the King's Blansby Park at Pickering, where he was Master of the Game. Elizabeth Graystock, the heiress to Hinderskelfe Castle married Lord William Dacre of Gilsland, while John Neville, Lord Latimer of Snape used Danby Castle and park. He wrote letters in 1538 from the Sinnington Hall, which the traveller Leland decribed as 'Lord Latimer's fair manor place.' He had married Katherine daughter of Sir Thomas Parr, but he died in 1543. Tradition claims that Katherine trod the broad green at Sinnington. She was later to marry Henry VIII as his sixth wife.

The Sheriff Hutton Court and Council

Sheriff Hutton Castle

King Henry VIII sent his young illegitimate son Henry Fitzroy, to live at Sheriff Hutton from 1525 to 1530. He was the son of Elizabeth Blount, a lady in waiting to Queen Catherine of Aragon. The boy was made Duke of Richmond. A King's Council in the North Parts was formed about him and an elaborate northern court, with a staff of more than two hundred. A vast sum was spent preparing the castle building. The prince wintered at Pontefract castle and summered at Sheriff Hutton castle. He recovered at Sheriff Hutton from the sweating sickness that he caught at Pontefract. His household was run by the able Thomas Magnus, and great classical scholars provided his education. The poet John Skelton wrote a little ballet to the boy, who sent dutiful letters to his father. Skelton set his 'Crowne of Laurell' at Sheriff Hutton, with three part music, eulogising the Countess of Surrey as the friend of the muses.

Henry Fitzroy had six personal staff, including an almoner and a physician. Sons of peers kept him company, and the tutor complained that they encouraged the boy in horseplay, hunting and hawking rather than study. The castle was packed with servants managing the pantry, cellar, buttry and ewery, scullery and saucery, acatory, wardrobe, poticary and spicery. Others ran the poultry house, bakehouse and brewhouse. There was a barber, porters, carters, launderers and a stable full of horses and their attendants. Leland about 1540 found a base court with houses of office before entering the castle. He thought that the next court had three towers and the third either five or six. The stately stairway up to the hall was very magnificent. So was the hall itself, and indeed all the rest of the house. He said, 'I saw no house in the north so like a princely lodging.'

The Knightly Class

The knightly families had fewer mansions than earls and barons, but great local significance and were often connected with them by marriage. Lady Anne Conyers, of Skelton castle in Cleveland, left her sister in law Lady Bigod of Settrington her black velvet bonnet. The knights themselves were not numerous, but their class included the esquires and others who shared their coats of arms. Some built houses on new isolated sites, squire Strangewayes at South House, Ugglebarnby and Sir John Bulmer a tower house south of Lastingham church, where slight earthworks remain. Others might add a porter's gatehouse to their forecourt. Sir John bought servant's liveries from a Pickering draper and borrowed money off Atkinson of Hartoft to invest in the site of Rosedale Priory, after that nunnery was dissolved.

Table 21. The Esquires and Gentlemen in Pickering Lythe. 1517

Esquires

Ralph Brompton	John Wyville	Ralph Westhorpe
Ralph Buckton	Thomas Boynton	John Barton
Roger Lascelles	John St. Quintin	Walter Percehay

Gentlemen

Robert Bielby	Robert Selowe	Roger Middlewood
William Boynton	Ralph Burton	Richard Ripley
George Hall	Richard Dutton	Thomas Marshall
Bryan Egglesfield	William Wivell	Thomas Elrington
Stephen Geres		

Sir Roger Cholmley 'a black proper stout man' bought the Hastings family manors at Kingthorpe and Roxby. He was made keeper of the King's Wardrobe at Sheriff Hutton, and he was Bailiff of Pickering. Roger's son Sir Richard Cholmeley first wed Lady Conyers, and secondly Lady Katherine Clifford, widow of Lord Scrope. His daughters married very well, by the notions of the time. Margaret's second husband was Henry, Fifth Earl of Westmoreland. These were considerable alliances. Chains were worn round the neck to symbolise the authority of such men. Sir William Bulmer left three gold chains to his three sons. Sir Richard Chomeley, heir to the old Hastings castle at Roxby near Thornton Dale left his brother valuable plate and his best chain. He also had wool worth £100 in stock at Calais and at home two barrels of horseshoes and thirty sheepskins.

Soldiers of the Scots Border

The old ballads praised these martial lords as heroes, leading their tenantry to war. The Earl of Northumberland took three hundred and eighty men to fight the Scots at Flodden in 1513. Both Roger and Richard Cholmley were knighted at that massacre. The verses tell of Lords Lumley, Latimer and Coniers, of 'the aged knight' Lord Scrope of Upsall, and many a gentleman from Ryedale, at Flodden with 'billmen bold from Blackamore'. Sir William Bulmer was in the van, on the seventh of September, with two hundred horsed archers.

'At Flodden Field as men do say, no better captain was their seen. He led the force of the bishoprick, when Thomas Ruthall bore the sway, The Scottish lads were stout and true, but the English bowmen won the day.'

Lord William Eure, trained in arms by Bulmer, became Lord Warden of the Scots Marches and was in many an expedition into Scotland.

'Lord Eure was as brave a man as ever stood in his degree
The king has sent him a broad letter
All for his courage and loyalty:'

Sir Richard Cholmeley known from his dark skin as 'the great black knight of the north', took a hundred men to the battle of Musselbery Field in 1544.He always kept fifty or sixty men about him at Roxby Castle, and he would visit London with thirty or forty men at arms. Sir Edmund Mauleverer raised a force to fight the Scots, in Queen

159

Mary's time, which was said to have crippled him financially. Others like Robert Meynell at Ravensthorp, and Sir Nicholas Fairfax of Gilling, could raise twenty or so archers and billmen. Even Rievaulx Abbey sent fourteen archers and two billmen. Kirkham Priory raised eight archers and four billmen for the musters in 1508. The Rievaulx granges at Welburn and West Ness were still populous enough to provide another useful force.

The Horsleys from Skirpenbeck who settled at Cropton Castle and Beck House Grange were descended from the yeoman archer who sailed north to kill the coastal pirate Robin Barton. This was celebrated in another ballad in which the King was credited with the remark:

'Horsley right, I'll make thee knight,
In Yorkshire shall thy dwelling be.'

From Ploughland to Pasture

The traveller Leland rode through the low moor pastures of Galtres, into the rising corn and pasture ground of the Howardian hills between Crambeck and Malton. He journeyed on into the champagne ground, fruitful of grass and corn, but now largely unwooded, of the vale sides from Malton to Seamer, and back from Scarborough to Pickering. The landscape that he described in 1538 was much as it had been for a long time .Yet enclosures and the conversion of ploughland to pasture had begun.

The change was probably far more obvious in the chalk wolds. The settlement at Wharram Percy had been collapsing for some time but it was reported that another one hundred and twenty four acres had gone to pasture, with four ploughs and four houses lost between 1487 and 1517. These thirty years saw arable farming losses of sixty acres and two ploughs at Harum, sixty acres and one plough at Helmsley, forty acres down at Farlington, one hundred & twenty acres, five houses at South Holme and one hundred & four acres, four ploughs, two houses and three cottages at Stittenham. This was a major step towards the disappearance of Stittenham as a village community. Twenty people were ejected at South Holme in Ryedale as a large part of the field land was put down to to pasture by William Fairfax, the Chief Justice of the

Table 22. Men from Ryedale Communities Mustered Before Sir Ralph Eure and Sir Nicholas Fairfax. 1539-40.

New Malton 166	Pickering 154	Helmsley 110
Farndale 83	Kirkby Moorside 71	
Old Malton 66	Hovingham 63	Slingsby 61
Thornton 56	Wintringham 31	
Allerston 41	Settrington 31	Kirkham and Westow 37
Farmanby 36	Gilling 38	Welburn grange 31
Leavening 32	Birdsall 35	Cawton 31
Nunnington 31	Ampleforth 28	
Pockley 21	Gillamoor and Fadmoor 26	
Salton 24	Knapton 22	
Goathland 20	Marton 20	Rosedaleside 21
Oswaldkirk 21	Kirkby Misperton 20	
Appleton & Easthorpe 20		
Rievaulx and Griff 22	Barton 20	
Rillington 20	Langton 22	Weaverthorpe 19
Aymotherby 20	Thornton 19	
Scackelthorp 18	Scampston 21	Thorp Basset 18
Swinton & Broughton 18		
Cropton Hartoft & Cawthorn 18		
Norton 18	North Grimston 18	Barthorpe 15
Collom 14	Nawton & Beadlam 17	
Scawton 16	Colton 14	West Ness 15
Kirkby Grindalythe 16		
Sinnington 15	Wilton 15	Lockton 15
Habton 15	Wrelton 14	Sproxton 13
Kirkby Underdale 14		
East Heslerton 20	West Heslerton 19	Duggleby 15
Wharrom le Street 15		
Stonegrave 15	West & East Lutton 14	
Howsham 14	Butterwick 12	Wombleton 12
Ryton 14	Thirkleby 11	
Bargh and Bargh 10	Yedingham 11	
Scrayingham 10	Towthorpe 10	Aislaby 10
Keneythorpe & Thornthorpe 10		
Burythorpe 10	Menethorpe 12	Newton 9
Kingthorpe 9	Helperthorpe 9	
Thixendale and Raisthorpe 9		
Edlethorpe 7	Holme 6	Acclom 6
Hildenley ?	Fryton grange 2	

Court of Common Pleas. Records of musters give some indication of the scale of the local communities.

When manor court rolls survive they show something of every day life. At a Pickering hallmoot court, in the reign of King Henry VIII, they elected three reeves, two constables, two inspectors for bread and two more for ale, with two surveyors of wares and two surveyors of water. Heirs came to court to make payments for inheriting their fathers' oxgangs, but sometimes the oxgangs were divided between several sons. They were then described in acres. The description became quite detailed, with the name of the field that each strip lay in and what other strips were on each side of it. The strip system was revealed as in a map. A half acre in the East Field had the Dean of Windsor's land on the east and Thomas Pennock's on the west.

The court acted like a land registry, recording sales by deed, inside or outside the court, provided that an entry fine was paid to the court. A copy of the court roll became virtually a title deed; good evidence of ownership. Another court called a 'tourn' dealt with certain offences in the wider Honour of Pickering. At a single court it was reported thatRoger Loft had taken deer at Sinnington. Flixton township was charged for the state of the 'Scurf' sewer, and highway repairs were needed from several villages along the Scarborough road. Orders were made requiring the Abbot of Rievaulx to clean the Friar Dyke, ordering several townships to clean Costa water and prohibiting unlicenced fishing in the waters of the rivers Rye and Derwent. Pickering was told to appoint a swineherd and so to reduce the number of strays. Henry Armstrong was not to entertain vagabonds. William Hey had forestalled the market, selling goods before the bell rang and Richard Haldore had a dunghill obstructing the king's highway.

To Horse

Yorkshire was becoming a horse country. One proverb said that 'a grunting horse and a groaning wife never fail their master'. Another saying, from some unknown county, claimed that 'if you shook a saddle over the Yorkshireman's grave, he would rise up and steal your horse.' Riding horses were expensive and rare. The Galloway horse was already the tried breed of the north. Jervaulx in the north west of the county was spoken of as the best pasture in England for horses, but Lord Latimer bought a young ambling gelding from Peter Franklin of Glaisdale. John

162

Uvedale at York in 1540, kept a bay horse stallion for 'betterment of breed'.

York was the outstanding town, drawing commodities from a wide area. Transport trades were becoming specialised at York and inns were building new stables along the approach roads. York fairs were proclaimed in 1502 at Malton, Scarborough, Northallerton, Helmsley and Pickering and widely across the rest of the county. By mid century, the city had a regular post service along the route that continued northwards through Easingwold, Thirsk and Northallerton. Heavy goods, including turfs moved into York by water, but coal 'draughts' or carts from County Durham were finding their way into the north of the vale of York. Traffic on horse and foot remained the norm. Thomas Fletcher the Robin Hood's Bay pannierman, and Thomas Kidger of York, followed their trains of packhorse ponies, bringing fish from the coast to the city.

The city of York had many mills but few fields, and it enjoyed ancient rights over neighbouring pastures, intercommoning with some townships, and owning half year rights in others, besides having strays of its own. York cows were proverbially famous, to be given as wide a birth in 'snickel' ways as Cambridge scholars or London apprentices. Critics claimed that the malt merchants of York had consumed the wood for twenty miles round the city for their kilns, and yet malt was dearer in York than anywhere in the north. Wood was so scarce at Bridlington, another place that would develop a substantial malting industry, that forks, speers and 'wyvers' for house building were brought from distant Malton in 1537. You could meet 'Wandering Egyptians' on the roads. Pedlars who set up shop in the porch of a York church were called the 'plague of the age'.

The traveller Leland noticed bridges, as a traveller would. There was Kexby bridge with three fair stone arches, and the other Derwent bridges at Buttercrambe, Ouseham, Kirkham, Malton, Yedingham, Haybridge and Ayton. Pickering had a five arch stone bridge over its beck, a major structure for the age, probably to give passage in river floods. Malton burgess Robert Hansby, whose relation John Hansby was valet to the King, gave money to Howe and Malton bridges in 1520. A Vicar of Acclam made bequests to support the bridges at Stamford, Buttercrambe and Thornthorp ten years later. Similar bequests benefited Scawton, Malton, Thornton, Normanby and Ayton bridges as well as the Pickering 'Midsyke Causey'. Minor bridges were probably more numerous than the available documents suggest. The small bridge at Settrington had a bequest from a local man.

Durham Priory bought raisins, liquorice and sugar from York merchants in 1533, but also leather and ginger at Northallerton. The wholesale and retail roles were not sharply separated. Merchants were few and kept a foothold in other boroughs. York merchant William Rede had a shop at Malton and two houses in Baxtergate at Whitby. York Mayor and merchant Paul Gillour, in 1520 bequeathed his Malton shop to the parish church, provided that he and his family were prayed for yearly. Thomas Rasyn of Malton became a York merchant, and the city merchant John Rasyn left a silver spoon to each of his brother Richard's children at Malton. The brother was given his fox furred gown. William Watson was another early Malton merchant and Laurence Richardson a draper.

Along the coast, Scarborough, Whitby, Redcar and Yarm had only a few merchants but they held many mariners. Ships and boats were already owned in half and quarter shares, to spread the risks incidental to navigation. There were already some specialist merchants called fish mongers. Strong new fishing communities at Robin Hood Bay, Staithes and Runswick sent out cobbles and five men boats, but the Dutch were also off the coast. William son of Roger Strickland of Marske went further afield, to America with Cabot. He was given the task of guarding some strange birds called turkeys on the way back to England. He adopted the bird in his family crest. It can be seen where members of this prominent local family acquired interests, from Boynton to Hutton le Hole.

The Late Mediaeval Church

Sir Francis Bigod of Settrington in 1534 - 5 wrote a treatise, about the diversion of ancient churches to monasteries, in which he criticised monkish averice and sloth. He wanted the monastery incomes to be used to produce a new learned corps of preachers of the Gospel. He actively sought reforms at Whitby and Watton monasteries where he had some influence and employed several clergy in his own parishes. The number of inmates in the monasteries was now very low. Wilfrid Holme of Huntington in his account of the rebellions, criticised monasteries, the worship of saints, superstitions and miracles. A tide of criticism was rising, but chiefly among those who had some contact with the radical ideas that were coming from Europe, where Martin Luther was questioning much that was Catholic in the church.

The everyday record showed little sign of change. A Kirkham canon processed at Westow on 'cross days' to Elle cross, Russel flat nook, Crambom cliff close head, to Whitwell beacon cross, and Fulstie head cross at Crambe saying gospels at each point. Thomas Nawton of Eddlethorpe had a sister Elizabeth, who was a Prioress. She was well remembered in his will. Elizabeth Lutton of Knapton had been veiled at Yedingham when she was fourteen, but after twenty eight years was reported married in 1532.

Prioress Elizabeth Davell of Keldholme Priory settled Sir John Potter with a rent, hay and provender, and common pasture for his horse at Rook Barugh in the summer, provided that he would ride it in the business of the house. He had the two chaplains' chambers to sleep in and sufficient firewood. Richard Dobson and his wife had invested ten pounds in a corrody from the Prioress at Yedingham. This gave them a cottage near the convent church, the annual keep of two cows, a horse, six hens, a cock, an ox in summer, a pig, two calves every third year and the haulage of four loads of turf a year. This would continue into widowhood.

Thomas Greenwood the vicar of Langtoft, made a will giving his soul to God, Our Lady and all the holy company in heaven. His body was to be buried in the choir of St Peter. Every priest attending his funeral would have eightpence, every clerk threepence and every 'unlearned man' a penny. The clerk of Langtoft was given twenty lambs to sell and with the proceeds was to buy a table for the altar. A priest was paid seven marks to sing for his soul. The vicarage farm embraced two oxgangs, sixty sheep and a cow. He had three yards of russet, a gown furred with white and black lamb, a black furred gown, a jacket and doublet, a tawny furred gown and a velvet tippet, a sarcenet tippet and a chamlet jacket. The vicar kept his own horse.

Sir Robert Wildon's velvet hood was given to Kirkby Moorside church to make a 'corporax'. Katherine Tyndale left a small sum in 1537 to maintain a candle to burn in honour of Our Lady at the chapel on Rye Bridge at Helmsley. Robert Kendall at Pickering already had a stall where he sat in the church of St Peter and St Paul in 1531, and he asked to be buried there. He gave monies to the vicar for the high altar and to the Lady Guild to pray for him. Archbishop Melton was convinced that when priests in rural areas didn't have the habit of study, they lapsed into hunting, dice, taverns, wenching and money making. This was the small change of the unchanging church.

Table 23. The Vestments in a Catholic Church 1552. Scrayingham
-suit of green vestments of sarsanet
-vestment of blue saye with a red cross
-two vestments of white bustian with red crosses
-vestment of green silk with a red cross

Sudden Change in the Church

King Henry VIII in 1532 declared himself supreme head of the Church in England, in the face of the Pope's refusal to annul his marriage to Katherine, and to approve a marriage to Ann Boleyn. Archbishop Cranmer of Canterbury declared the marriage to Ann legal in the next year. The Nandykes of Edstone were proud that their ancestor had the keeping of the keys of Ann Boleyn, but a London visit convinced the Abbot of Whitby that the King was ruled by 'one common stued huer Anne Bullan who would have everyone beggared.'

An Act of Supremacy confirmed the King as head of the church. Few protested and Archbishop Lee of York, three years later claimed to know of none advocating papal authority in the York diocese. These were great changes. The surviving churchwardens accounts of the parish churches don't always reflect them. The Sheriff Hutton wardens paid for plumber's solder, had cushions made, bought cloth for a surplice and new bellropes and paid for a mett of wine, as they always had.

A more important change was under way, drawing strength from Protestant thinking in Europe. New lists of religious beliefs were published, and some older ideas dropped, including the giving of indulgences and many saints' days. It was ordered in 1538 that the bible in English was to be put into every parish church. Archbishop Lee ordered daily readings of the gospel and epistle. The bible made available in English opened debate. Thomas Prat of Thirsk could declare that 'God didn't bleed all his blood or he couldn't have risen again', a plain man's scepticism rather than heresy.

A 1547 edict required removal of shrines, candlesticks, effigies and paintings. Poor boxes and 'Erasmus's Paraphrases' were to be placed in every church. The first new prayer book required communion tables rather than altars in 1550. Forty articles of faith were pronounced. A religion of the book was emerging. John Leafe of Kirkby Moorside died in 1555 at the stake in London, denouncing 'transubstantiation'. He could neither read nor write.

The Attack on the small Monasteries

Commissioners were appointed in 1535 to assess the wealth of the churches, and to enquire into the way of life in monasteries. Their stated aim was to seek out moral decay and superstition. Thomas Layton, a commissioner, dutifully wrote of 'great corruption among religious persons' in Yorkshire. There were grounds for occasional suspicion, but the picture was made deliberately negative. Archbishop Lee in 1534 had found Abbot John of St.Mary's, York too familiar with Elizabeth Robinson of Overton. The Commissioners sacked Prior Cockerill of Guisborough who kept great state but who, with five others, was accused of sexual malpractice. He was given the rectory of Lythe to encourage his departure. A Basedale Prioress banished to Rosedale for sins committed was returned as a bad influence.

The recorded 'superstitions' were more eccentric, indicating some gullibility, if they were truly recorded. Basedale Priory claimed milk of the Virgin Mary. The girdle of Saint Salvatoris was lent to lying in women at Newbrough Priory. St Aelred's girdle was at Rievaulx and part of the holy cross with St Stephen's finger at Keldholme Priory. Women went to the image of St Bridgett at Arden Priory to offer for cows that were lost or ill.

An Act of Parliament in 1536 provided for the suppression of monasteries where manifest sin, vicious, carnal and abominable living were daily used. In fact, the state was after their assets. Monasteries with less than £200 a year income were dissolved and their inmates pensioned off. The satirists sang – 'I'll be no more a nun, nun, nun. but I'll be a wife and lead a merry life, and brew good ale by the tun, tun, tun.' Prioress Nandyke of Wykeham returned to her home town of Kirkby Moorside, where she would bequeath two pence to every house at her death. Till the end of their lives, the nuns quietly collected their pensions.

The Pilgrimage of Grace

A Lincolnshire rising was collapsing, just as it spread into the Yorkshire Marshland, to Howdenshire and to the East Riding of

Yorkshire, in October 1536. Neither the real causes nor the character of the rebellions are clear. There had been harvest failures. There was fear of change and widespread discontent. Strange prophecies circulated fortelling change. Many protests were voiced against Crown policies, low born Crown advisors, the conversion of arable to pasture, price rises, taxation, religious changes, monastery dissolutions, threats of church taxes and fears of the abolition of parish churches. Like most northern protests, this was a rebellion against change and perhaps principally against taxation. It came to be known as 'the Pilgrimage of Grace', from a banner showing the five wounds of Christ. Beacons were fired, men mustered and leaders appeared.

The Earl of Northumberland was ill but his relation Sir Thomas Percy of Seamer may have been the significant leader in north east Yorkshire. On October 10th a friar was sent from Beverley to raise Ryedale and Pickering Lythe, and by the 15th it was reported that Malton was up. Sir Thomas Percy attended a Malton muster, where he claimed there were ten thousand people present. Sir Nicholas Fairfax of Gilling went with a goodly number and Cleveland men joined in. Lord Latimer was said to have fled from the commons to his house at Sinnington.

The rebels moved in force towards York and the city allowed them to pass through. They reached Doncaster, where, after long delays, their leaders met the Duke of Norfolk, who had been appointed Lieutenant General of the north. The King had controlled the Duke's slow movement northwards and he was fully in control of what ensued. The rebels were given fair promises, including a general pardon, so they returned home. Then the hangings began. John Priestman of Helmsley and another John Priestman of Bilsdale Hall were exempted from the pardon roll. They anticipated the worst and escaped to Scotland. Their kinsman Henry Priestman of Brandsby was charged with high treason.

A Second Rising

Sir Francis Bigod of Mulgrave and Settrington led a second more localised rising in January 1537. He was opposed to the royal supremacy in the church, and he saw flaws in the King's pardon, with good reason, distrusting the promises made. There were fresh rumours of taxes on weddings and christenings, and talk of a garrison to be placed in Scarborough castle. Cleveland was in a ferment. Men were saying that the Duke of Norfolk would hang his way to Berwick, notwithstanding the King's pardon. Some made plans to capture the Duke. The vicar of Kirkby in Cleveland was asked if the commons would rise again. He was expected to know 'from men's confessions'.

Bilsdale men spoke of recruiting the gentry or their sons, or else they would go 'striking off their heads'. Sir John Bulmer at Lastingham was persuaded to allow the commons to capture him. Sir Francis Bigod met William Hallam and Ralph Fenton of Ganton at Settrington, where plans were made to take Hull and Scarborough. Dickering was raised. Perhaps a thousand were up in Cleveland and a small number were stirred by the yeoman Otterburn about Sheriff Hutton. The Seamer constable was ordered to raise Pickering Lythe. Scarborough was briefly threatened by George Lumley. The rebellion collapsed before significant support was gained. It provided the excuse to cancel pardons for the first rising and to proceed with the dissolution of the greater monasteries.

Order Restored

By February 1537, the rebellions were over. Thomas Howard, Duke of Norfolk ordered Sheriff Hutton Castle restored for his residence. The Duke's instructions were clear. The brewhouse and the stables were to be made up and rooms furnished with bedsteads. Trees were to be felled for charcoal and firewood. The Duke loathed the north, and complained to Thomas Cromwell that the cold northern Winter would kill him. He planned to keep warm. Between three and four hundred load of 'lops and tops' of trees were taken locally for use as fuel and another five or six hundred load near Marton Priory. Sir George Lawson removed fifty four cartloads of earth and scrub from the Castle and spent £200 on repairs. The priest acted as the clerk of works.

Two new stables were made and a slaughter-house. Carpenters fashioned bedsteads, tables, trestles, forms, stools and cupboards. A mill-wright made a horsemill and coopers equipped a brewhouse with vats and tubs. Glaziers mended all the windows including the chapel. Labourers repaired stone walls and a plumber fixed leads and gutters. Two loads of Normandy glass came from York, one load of plank, and six loads of brick and tile. Cornbrough slate came and moss for the stable roof. Twenty four oxen brought huge mill wheels from York. A great copper kettle was delivered, some firdeals for the long dining table, water 'boughes' to carry water from the pond to the brewhouse and forty eight fathom of York rope. Geoffry Fothergill the York locksmith put nine hundred and ten nails in the brewhouse cooler.

The duke took up residence at Sheriff Hutton on April the 17th. 1537. The Council for the Marches attended him there in June. He visited many Yorkshire places, including Topcliffe lodge and Helmsley castle. As the larger monasteries were taken over, he moved the best treasures to Sheriff Hutton, including the jewels hung on St John's shrine at Bridlington. The duke reformed the King's Council in the North and told them to find honest preachers to make people more conformable. He was still extracting confessions from leading rebels in August. They saw him as their scourge.

The Newbrough Prior denied that he had said of the King and Norfolk 'It maketh no matter if one of them were hanged against the other' but he added that 'It was afternoon and he was somewhat alye.' The Prior claimed that when a great company came to persuade him to join the rebels, he ran to a high Priory chamber, cut his hose and pretended that he was lame. Many gentry pleaded that they had been coerced into rebellion, but a movement without leaders was unconvincing.

Lord Darcy, Sir Thomas Percy of Seamer, Sir Robert Aske, George Lumley of Kilton castle, Sir John Bulmer and the learned Sir Francis Bigod were among those executed while Lady Bulmer, a woman of temper, was burnt at Smithfield. Otterburn was hung on Yearsley moor. The Earl of Northumberland surrendered much of his inheritance to the King. Sir Nicholas Fairfax of Gilling was pardoned. The Duke of Norfolk returned south in September.

When King Henry VIII came into Yorkshire in 1541, he received valuable gifts from the gentry and yeomanry, petitioning for forgiveness on their knees. The north had been humbled and was more governable than ever before. His Council in the North was made permanent and would become almost vice-regal, offering a strong counter balance to the northern noblemen. The Bishop of Durham was the first Lord President, and the post was in the gift of the Crown.

The Dissolution of the Larger Monasteries

The larger monasteries in their later days had seemed great gaunt buildings, more blessed with space than inmates. The smaller houses abounded more in servants than monks or nuns. Basedale Priory held eight nuns served by a chaplain, three hinds, two women, two men servants, a boy, a butler cum cook and a brewer cum baker. Marton Priory had sixteen inmates and thirty seven servants. Rosedale Priory

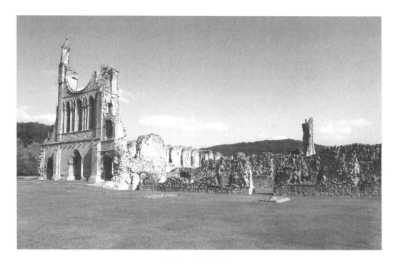

Byland Abbey

held a Prioress and eight nuns employing twelve men and boys. The monks were landlords and by this time their houses were refuges for the few. It is doubtful if the loss of the monasteries was of great local concern, outside a few gentry families.

The houses were surrendered in 1538 and stripped of their moveable assets. There was little resistance. The Prior of Mount Grace was persuaded of the illegality of the Pope's supremacy by the Bishops of Durham and York, but they had some difficulty in convincing his brethren. After three months in prison some proved more tractable. The monks and nuns from the other houses passed easily and quickly into pensioned retirement. Malton Priory pensions ranged from £4 for a monk to £40 a year for the Prior. Several of the canons found new posts as regular clergy. Thomas Norman became the Malton schoolmaster. Late monastic Catholicism seemed to wither away.

The monastery servants departed to find other employment. Some were highly skilled. Prior William of Malton had only lately contracted with Robert Best to serve the monastery as cooper, mending all wood vessels for five years. He was paid with ten quarters of barley malt, the milk of a cow and food while on site. Malton Priory had also employed two brewers, a cook, a cheeser, a fisherman, a maltster, a smith, a carpenter, a farrier and four bakers. Kirkham Priory had used a goldsmith, a plumber and a fuller.

Many granges were already leased to laymen, but the gentry rushed to acquire monastery sites as well as granges, rectories and manors. Some of these had model farm buildings, good residences and great pastures. Rievaulx abbey had twenty seven buildings in two courtyards, including the fulling mill, iron smithy, corn mill, tannery and houses for craftsmen and corrodians, in a well watered site. Byland abbey had kept fifteen hundred ewes at Murton grange and seven hundred at Wethercotes. These were prizes worth having. Almost every township had some monastic property. A vigorous new land market everywhere offered new opportunities.

Table 24. North - East Yorkshire Monasteries. 1536-1538			
Monasteries.	Inmates	Annual Value	New Site Owner
Arden (P)	6	£12.	Sir Arthur Darcy, later Tancred family
Basedale (P)	12	£20	Sir Ralph Bulmer
Bridlington	27	£547	
Byland (A)	25	£238	Sir William Pickering
Grosmont (P)	7	£12	Sir Richard Cholmley
Guisborough (P)	25	£628	Sir Thomas Leigh then Thos. Chaloner
Handale (P)	10	£14	Sir Ambrose Beckwith
Keldholme (P)	6	£29	Earl of Westmoreland
Kirkham (P)	17	£269	Sir Henry Knyvett
Malton (P)	9	£198	Archbishop Holgate
Marton (P)	16	£151	Archbishop of York
Molesby (P)	10	£26	
Mount Grace (P)	27	£323	Sir James Strangewayes
Mount. St. John		£102	
Newburgh (P)	18	£367	Dr,Anthony Belasyse
Rievaulx (A)	24	£278	Earl of Rutland
Rosedale (P)	9	£38	Earl of Westmoreland
Whitby (A)	22	£437	Sir Richard Cholmeley
Yedingham (P)	10	£22	Archbishop Holgate, then John Spencer
Wykeham (P)	13	£26	Mr. Hutchinson
St. Mary's York (A)	51	£1550	

Sir Nicholas Fairfax offered for Byland, Newburgh or Whitby but only received some Byland stone. Anthony Belasyse, chaplain to King

Henry VIII, acquired the Newbrough Priory estate and his son Sir William Belasyse made his home there. Ralph Bade of Helmsley moved into the Marishes grange at Lund. Bilsdale already had forty named farms instead of the handful of old monastic granges and cotes but the Rievaulx grange at Welburn would expand into a village under the ownership of laymen. Roger Marshall bought Malton Priory's Aislaby grange with its seven oxgangs and pasture for three hundred sheep in Cropton and waited for the lease of his gentleman tenant, Ambrose Beckwith, to expire.

Table 25. The Property of Malton Priory at the Dissolution

-Site of the Priory and demesne lands;
-Granges at Sutton, Broughton, Welham, Linton, Mowthorpe, Wintringham (Carr cote), Little Edstone, Sinnington (Friar's Hill)
-Lands at Ryton (Bromehill)
-Rents in New Malton in Castlegate, Old Malton Gate, Greengate, Appleton Gate, Yorkhousegate, Marketstead, Newbiggingate and Spitleman lane.
-rents of cottages in Old Malton (including Lassel house)
-mills at Swinton, half Norton, Wintringham
-rents and farms in Wykeham (including Howe house), Swinton, Amotherby, Appleton, Slingsby, Hovingham, Hutton on Derwent, Thornton & Farmanby, Norton, Sutton, Welham, Rillington, Kingthorpe Thorpe Bassett, West Heslerton, Burdale, Raisthorpe, Burythorp, Kennythorpe, Grimston, Wintringham, Colton, Knapton, Cawton, Southolme, Shirburn, Duggleby, Mowthorpe, Collome, Sledmere, Snainton, Brompton, Newton, Ebberston, Cayton, Ruston, Malton cotes, Sawdon, Lockton, Newton on Rawcliff, Kirkby Grindalyth, Sinnington, Marton, Aislaby, Kirkby Misperton, Pickering and Scarborough
-Rectory Tithes of Old Malton, Norton, Brompton (with mansion), Wintringham (and the manor called Grange garth) and tithes in Newton, Linton, Knapton and Scampston, and five more distant rectories.
Pension from Wresill church.

The old monastery churches were stripped of their valuable roof lead. The convent buildings served as quarries for good cut stone. The monastic mills were good investments and some showed signs of early conversion to other industries. Kirkham Priory at the dissolution already had four watermills, a fish-house and three fulling mills. There was fulling at Keldholme Priory mill by 1555. Other monastery industries were continued and even developed. The precinct of Rosedale Priory held a mill, a kiln and a bark house thirty three years after the monastery closed.

Rievaulx abbey in 1539 included a barker's house, for the craftsman who collected and chopped tree bark for tanning skins. There was a four bay building, which held a bark vat. When the dormitory of the monastery was cleared centuries later, it was found to hold two feet of finely chopped bark. The Earl of Rutland took over and expanded the Rievaulx Abbey iron workings, while his neighbour Bellassis sought to sell him his Newbrough Priory woodlands, conveniently placed to supply the iron works, for conversion to charcoal. The iron manufacture proved highly profitable. Chapmen bought iron from the Earl's warehouse at York and Rievaulx iron became famous far afield.

Prayers or Education

More of the great institutions of the Roman Catholic world were abolished in the next decade. Chantries, hospitals, free chapels, fraternities, brotherhoods and guilds vanished. Their property was appropriated by the Crown and then leased out or sold. The hermits of Ganthorpe, Wath and Brandsby were no more heard of. The vast Helmsley parish kept a vicar but lost two chantry priests. Most of the small village chapels fell out of use, and long walks to the parish church returned. If there had once been too many clergy, now there could be too few.

A new hospital at distant Hemsworth was endowed by Archbishop Holgate, with much of the estate of the vanished Priory estate at Old Malton. The mediaeval St Mary Magdalane Hospital at Broughton near Malton was kept going as an almshouse but the rest of the hospitals vanished. This ended a system of charitable support for the travelling poor. The Duke of Norfolk had thought that the excess of vagabonds abounding in the north, was partly due to the alms that they received. Gentleman Thomas Constable of New Malton left a will phrased in the old Catholic style but instead of money for prayers he left 23s.4d to the poor of Old and New Malton and 3s.4d to the poor of Birdsall.

Many urban properties had belonged to chantries. The Helmsley chantry of Our Lady had eighteen cottage rents which passed to the Crown. Four other houses were charged with obituary prayers. St James chantry in Malton castle had drawn rents from an old Malton cottage, two barns, one with a dovecote in New Malton, eighteen cottages and the common bakehouse. The St John the Baptist chantry in New Malton had owned an Old Malton farmhouse and a house, twenty two cottages, three shops, a barn and garden with two garths in the town. There were buyers who were keen to acquire such rentals.

Some chantry priests had run schools and a few of these were refounded as grammar schools. The Middleton and Pickering chantry schools were kept going with some part of their endowment. Archbishop Holgate founded a new Grammar School in the Old Malton churchyard in 1547 to teach grammar, the liberal sciences and good manners, along with similar schools at York and Hemsworth. The master was to teach Grammar to the literate and where desirable Latin and Greek. This was a very new educational ideal.

The Elizabethan Nobility and Gentry

The second Earl of Rutland, new owner of the Helmsley estate, was Lord President of the Council of the North from 1561 to 1563. The third Earl, Edward Manners, rebuilt the living quarters at his Helmsley Castle. The rooms were given oak panelling, elaborate fireplaces, mullion windows, and ribbed ceiling plasters on two floors. His brother John Manners was the main man in Ryedale in 1585. Matthew Stewart, Earl of Lennox, married to the King's neice, used both the Settrington mansion and Whorlton Castle. Barrelled red deer cooked by a York baker, along with Tees salmon and sturgeon, went with him on journeys to London. He was spied on at Settrington, round about 1560, and removed to the Tower of London, after he and his wife made overtures for the marriage of their son Lord Darnley to the Queen of the Scots.

The widowed Lady Scrope married Sir Richard Cholmleley of Thornton Dale, but continued to call herself by her former name and title. After his purchase of the Whitby monastery, she was described as the first aristocrat to live at Whitby. The last Lord Latimer, a sad, sick individual, saw his abused wife leave for Wales, while he went to the Tower. His four daughter-heiresses took the divided local estates to their husbands. Edmund Lord Sheffield probably gave Mulgrave old castle its new windows, fireplaces and round towers about 1591 and would serve as a later Lord President. Lord Eure removed everything of value from Ayton castle, lead, timber, fireplaces, glass and furnishings in 1594 to take to Malton, where he built a great new house near the ruined castle.

Henry Neville, Earl of Westmoreland was much criticised for

marrying his former wife's sister, with whom Archbishop Young found him 'strangely in love'. The fifth Earl's widow lived at Kirkby Moorside castle with her son and Uncle Christopher. The Earl addressed letters there to Sir William Cecil in 1560 and Christopher Neville was there until 1569. They claimed that he gave the Kirkby rectory to William Barkley, alias Smith, whose wife Katherine was reputed to be his mistress. Kirkby Moorside castle is little known although one of its towers still overlooks manor vale. Excavation revealed that earlier buildings with cruck timbers standing on stone sills, had given way to the solid stone 15th century castle hall, with big wall fireplaces and a kitchen, separate from other buildings. Fragments of a bay window, leaded lights and a fine moulded fireplace recalled the Elizabethan house but the long gallery and many chambers were not found.

The knights were also great men in the country. They were not numerous. Queen Elizabeth granted her honours sparingly. Prominent among the order were Sir William Bellasis of Newbrough, Sir Ralph Bourchier of Beningbrough, Sir William Fairfax of Gilling, Sir Richard Cholmley of Roxby and Sir Henry Gate of Seamer. Bellasis ranked with Saville and Wentworth among the wealthiest of Yorkshiremen. These men too adapted old castles and old monasteries for greater comfort. Cholmeley sent masons to remove masonry and timber from the Kings hall at Pickering Castle for his own Roxby Castle. Another six score new timber trees were cut from the woods to make his new gallery, sawn and framed in Goathland by housewright George Bernard. Bellasis added a new hall to make a baronial mansion out of Newbrough Priory. Sir William Fairfax built new floors on the old castle at Gilling, where a fine Elizabethan room remains to this day.

The Spacious House Well Furnished.

The Elizabethan great country house had much to offer for a new style of spacious, elegant living and generous reception and hospitality to friends. Gilling Castle had many rooms, including a porter's lodge and a far gatehouse; oxhouse, kiln, and stable, school house, 'pleasaunce', 'paradise' and study. The Italian plaster work, the panelling, the personalised chimney pieces and the coloured, heraldic window glass were built into the house but glass and wainscot were long viewed as moveables. Thomas Saville at Welburn separately bequeathed all the glass in his house. Others put their 'ceiling work' into a will as a separate bequest. Style entered the houses with the adoption of interior

176

Nunnington Hall

decoration. The new lath and plaster ceilings were decorated with modelled ribs and pressed plaques of mock foliage were laid upon the joists.

The Helmsley castle hall held two long tables, a cupboard, four forms and an almstub as its permanent furniture as late as 1636. The Elizabethans installed heavier furniture elsewhere. The Newbrough great chamber had four chairs and twenty two stools, and the great parlour held a drawing table and livery cupboards with carpets and setwork. Kirkby Moorside Rectory had a 'great standing bed' in the great chamber. By 1621, Newbrough Priory had twenty three feather beds in as many rooms. The day was lived in a crowd, but the night began to offer its privacy behind a partition wall, as well as a curtain. Once the heavy furniture was installed, there came a desire to keep it that way. Richard Simpson at Edstone left his son Richard merely the great brass pot and a great spit as heirlooms. John Bonville at Spaunton Hall in 1582, left his tables, forms, bedstead, cupboard, chairs, spits and iron racks in the hall, chamber and kitchen as 'heirlooms' for his daughter and son in law, inisisting that all were to remain in the mansion house.

Furniture was covered with carpet, cushions, tapestries, painted cloths or needlework. Nunnington Hall had stumped leather hangings relegated to a garret. Beds were newly joinered and much woodwork

177

was given richly carved ornamentation. When stuffed breeches were laid aside, upholstery became even more necessary. The wealthy bought tapestry hangings, silver vessels, plate, pewter, brass and fine linen and needed new chests and presses in which to store them. Sir William Pickering at Oswaldkirk in 1575 had 'twenty five best shirts' and a vast array of other clothing. Some genius put drawers into chests. The contents of the parcel were little changed but the wrappings were becoming more elegant. The Countess of Lennox left her eight hundred sheep to the custody of three Settrington people but she wanted her grandson, the King of Scotland, to have her new bed of black velvet, embroidered with flowers of needle work.

A four square formal Tudor garden at Gilling offered shade, beauty and relaxation, while the visiting Lord President enjoyed shooting and bowls. Much pleasure was taken in the gardens near the great house, but also in carefully managed parks. Invitation hunts became more elaborate with driven deer and rustic banqueting. Sheriff Hutton park with its lodges and ten score deer attracted Sir Arthur Ingram, though he had his paradise garden at York. The Earl of Westmoreland hunted Blandsby and Kirkby Moorside parks. The four towers of Hinderskelfe looked out over Lord Dacres park, already four mile in compass with fair young woods. The Cholmeleys made a new park near their Whitby house.

The pleasures that were possible indoors, as well as those of the outdoors were expanding. The long gallery, that featured in so many of the mansions seems primarily to have been a venue for the purpose. Thomas Percy, whose timber house at Topcliffe adjoined two parks, enjoyed his music. His inventory included violins, virginals, cornets and a bandora. The Earl of Rutland bought a thesaurus at York in 1594, while Sir William Fairfax had thirty nine books, half of them in English, including one on hawking.

Gentlemen and Gentlewomen

Space and privacy made personal choice of what was done more possible and personal relationships became different. The proverb claimed that all England was a paradise for women, a prison for servants and a hell for horses. Lady Brook at Kirkby Moorside might or might not have agreed. She was the mother of eleven, but she was remembered as 'a good woman, a very good mother and an exceeding good wife.' There was more individuality in at least some lives and so, more to talk about with others.

The wealthy ladies found new pleasure travelling about to make calls in their new vehicles. Edward Manners, Earl of Rutland left an early coach and a litter to his wife. Hester Pickering at Oswaldkirk received her father's coach and pair in 1547. Lady Hoby took a coach drawn by three horses, out from Hackness to call at Linton, and to visit Lady Eure at Malton in1599.

Margaret Dakins was raised at Linton near Wintringham, in an old isolated monastery grange amidst the Wolds. As a young girl she was sent off to experience the godly tradition of the Countess of Huntington's household. She herself trained genteel girls from other families in her Hackness household, where she lived with her third husband, the Puritan Sir Thomas Posthumous Hoby. She saw *busy-ness* as virtuous. Lady Margaret ran a morning surgery to deal with servants and tenants ailments and she read to her young women. They shared much of her busy days, as she sorted and mended linen, made wax lights, walked abroad, or took company in her garden. There were religious exercises, prayers, services and preachings provided by Puritan chaplains. She most evidently had a private life. She meditated and wrote in her commonplace book. She maintained a regimen of strict personal self examination, backed up by the study of sermons and the bible. She and her husband met and conversed on equal terms.

Table 26. Sir William Fairfax's Food Expenses for the Year at Gilling Castle.

	1579	1580
Wheat	63 quarters 2 bushels	69 quarters
Malt	126 quarters	135 quarters
Oxen, kine and whyes	49	50
Rostinges	-	8
Veales	16	22
Porks	26	20
Muttons	150	229
Connyes and rabbits	397 couple	653 couple
Lings	131	52
Kelinges	101	171
White herrings	4 barrels	3 barrels
Red herrings	4 maze	6 maze
Butter, cheeses, spices etc		
Sum	£338.3s.9d	£450.0s.2d

179

Sir William Fairfax's household books from Gilling castle, for the years between 1571 and 1582, suggest the considerable task of managing a large Elizabethan household. Many rooms meant many servants. Roxby castle and Newbrough both retained between fifty and sixty servants and Gilling castle had thirty or forty. The lord of Roxby claimed that his servants sometimes took all the meat pieces with their daggers from the pot and left him none. The Cholmley household, like many others, lacked the Puritan religiosity of Lady Hoby, but there was the same needlework, spinning, dyeing, preserving of fruit and all manner of wrought work by the 'dames of the needle'. The Elizabethan age saw the shift from the distaff to the spinning wheel. Ann Webster of Flaxton in 1570 bequeathed her daughter –'as much wool as will make a petticoat'. Agnes Darcy, who became wife to Sir William Fairfax, wrought for herself a silk carpet bordered with crimson velvet.

Fashion was 'the fantastical folly of the nation' according to a contemporary. This struck men and women alike. Great attention was given to dress, as more variety of cloth, including linen from Byland, Pilfit and Oswaldkirk, dyed with madder, cochineal, woad and indigo, provided new soft colours. Lighter, finer cloths appeared and were imitated. Bays, says and arras challenged the coarser 'huswife' cloth, among those who could afford them. Matthew Frank the Malton draper soon had wainscot in the parlour, where a chest held his money and writings. He stocked 'new gown cloth', fustian, and 'a dublet cloth of Myllame', besides unmade hose and shirts.

The monuments at Gilling, Coxwold and Langton churches show the richer styles of the day. Sir William Pickering of Oswaldkirk and now Byland Abbey was a very fancy dresser. He was considered a suitor to Queen Elizabeth. He was of 'tall stature, handsome and very successful with women, for he is said to have enjoyed the intimacy of many and great ones'. His wardrobe held a black satin woman's gown with hanging sleeves and several women's waistcoats. The York carrier brought a trunk to Helmsley for John Manners in 1586 containing a gown made with white satin sleeves, as well as a bridle and a pillion cloth. His agent advised that enough cloth remained to make 'an upper body according to fashion'. John Joy wrote the next year to tell Manners of the arrival at London of Sir Francis Drake and the rumours of the infinite treasure he had brought in.

The Love for Horses

A good horse was said to have fifty four properties, sharing two with men, two with badgers, four with lions, nine with oxen, nine with hares, nine with foxes, nine with asses and ten with women. The principal property was the ability to take the rider further and faster than his own feet. The visitor to Yorkshire found 'the pot smaller, the ale stronger and the miles longer'. For the gentry, horses became far more than a riding animal. That scholarly Yorkshireman Roger Ascham thought that 'to ride comely' was a necessity for a courtly gentlemen. For some, this became the main accomplishment and principal distinguishing mark of the 'gentleman' Thomas Tusser advised:

'A stable well planked, with key and a lock,
walls strongly, well lined to bear of a knock,
a rack and a manger, good litter and hay,
sweet chaff and some provender every day.'

James Fox, of Thorpe le Willows near Ampleforth, made a will listing his horses before his clothes, one nagg, a gelding called Grey Fenton and three filley foals. Clergymen aspired to a horse for getting round their parishes. The Prebendary of Langtoft, who was also parson of distant Escrick, south of York, had ten horses worth £14.6s.8d in the stable. The Earl of Huntington, as Lord President of the North, another mobile man, kept thirteen horses at York and seventeen at Sheriff Hutton, along with one new coach. Malton was becoming the place to buy a horse. Mr.Langdale at Sancton deep in the East Riding, the Earl of Westmoreland and the Cholmeleys at Brandsby Hall all had horses bought at Malton, while Christopher Hewerdine of Kirkby Moorside was probably sending horses to Scarborough and Cleveland.

There was a down side, as horses became more numerous. The Council in 1575 was told of robberies by some 'young gentlemen and others riding and travelling abroad as masterless men, not having whereupon to live, but living idly in the Ryedale market towns'. The ease with which people moved around was impressive. Archbishop Grindal took sixteen days to get from London to York on his horse but he had the ague at the time. A couple landing from Brussels in 1597, made an overnight stay at Scarborough, and yet they could reach Ness the next day.

Two gentlemen in company together, both horsed, could mean a race. Sir Henry Cholmeley held races outside Whitby church during service time. He was said to have been ruined by fleet hounds and horses. Galtres Forest had a horse race for a prize bell on which great wagers were laid. The Earl of Westmoreland went to Gatherley Moor for the 'horse running days'. Thomas Meynell once won the gold bell at Gatherley. Races were also run by 1602 at Black Hambleton. Viscount Dunbar took the Hambleton gold bell and another won the silver bowl. Bagby moor, and Studfold above Ampleforth, also saw races for a silver cup. Nunnington had some sort of a race course by 1630.

Elizabethan Yeomen

Elizabethan yeomen were prospering as well as the gentry. 'Better head of the yeomanry than tail of the gentry', they said and the distinction between the one and the other was not always obvious. They too arranged their children's marriages. Yeomen could show a fine sense of property and a distinct appreciation of lineage. Some villages had no yeomen and others had many but it was an acknowledged status everywhere. The yeoman had some freehold property, whatever else he might rent. He could witness documents, make a will, serve as a juror and buy and sell property.

George Cockerell, the Goathland yeoman, bought a manor house and groups of freeholders at Levisham, Lockton and Stainton Dale combined to aquire manorial rights. One of the largest villages was Settrington, with seventy seven houses, of which sixteen were freeholder or yeomen properties. There were also fifteen husbandry farms, fourteen grass farms, twenty eight cottages, a parsonage, a fee farm property, a market house and a chantry house. The Grass farms had insufficient land to make a husbandry, while cottages had no land but merely common of pasture. One of the Frank yeomen at Hutton in the Hole decreed 'that my house and land shall never go out of the name of Franke while there are heirs male living.'

The contemporary Elizabethan historian Harrison was probably speaking of the south of England, when he declared that the great material changes of his age were the new chimneys, the shift from straw pallets, hop harlots and a log pillow to beds with mattresses and the move from wood to pewter on the table. These changes are not always evident in local documents but yeomen and craftsmen do show signs of rising standards of living. Yeoman Robert Jackson of Malton in 1570 had a silver goblet and spoons, beside body armour and a lead scales with weights. Not all were so well off. Bart Warwick, of West Lutton, in 1590 left his wife his white cow and his best kettle. Birdsall labourers merely left their apparel to some named fortunate and the rest to the wife.

Many of the yeomanry accepted both family and communal responsibilities. Mathew Frank, a freeholder draper, had wainscot in his parlour, beef flitches, honey bees and a gold ring. He left £6.13.4. for a dinner for his neighbours and twenty shillings a year to the poor for ever. Richard Simpson, the Great Edstone yeoman, was a man of substantial estate, with twelve of the township's sixty four oxgangs, but he also had North Holme and two hundred wethers in the moorland dale of Hartoft. He left a ewe to each godchild and twelve pennies to each person in the parish. One widower left much to his son in law provided he find him meat, drink, clothes, and other necessaries for the rest of his life, and pay for his funeral. One generation had given way to the next.

To Market, To Market

The market economy was fast expanding as population again increased. Some of the old local mediaeval markets had vanished in the leaner centuries. Now fewer markets had a far wider reach. Corn was going into York from all sides, from places up to thirty and forty miles away and being resold into West Yorkshire where towns like Wakefield, Halifax, and Leeds and the rural valleys behind them were filling with people, including weavers supplied with their raw materials by the new clothiers. York could bed over a thousand visitors and stable even more horses.

Camden thought that Northallerton, on St. Bartholomew's Day, had the greatest fair of kine and oxen that ever he saw. Malton market was frequented for corn, horses, eels, fish and implements of husbandry, while Kirkby Moorside had grown to a market town 'not of the meanest reckoning'. Matthew son of John Coates of Malton, in 1581 had interests in the ship 'Prudence', including hogsheads of salmon. He dealt with London drapers, held a stock of hides and left five pounds to the Malton poor. Bridlington was selected as a staple port for the export of malt, grain and pulses, reflecting and encouraging the Wold barley trade.

The Statute of the Highways passed in 1555, and expanded in 1563, inaugurated the system of parish road maintenance, using obligatory local labour. Much criticised in retrospect, it was a major step forward which was concerned only with the through roads.

Under a Statute of 1563, justices of the peace were required to licence the growing army of middlemen, including cattle drovers, badgers, laders, kidders, carriers and buyers of corn, grain, butter and cheese. Yorkshire was exempted from its provisions. All the same, the buyers called badgers and carrriers called cadgers were becoming more numerous. They broke through the old monopolies of the small, largely urban, merchant class, establishing new channels for trade.

Table 27. Spices Spent in a Whole Year at Gilling Castle. 1580

Pepper	30 lb.	2s a lb	£3
Cloves	1½ lb	11s	16s.6d
Mace	1½ lb	15s	22s.6d
Sugar	8 loaves (10 lb each) 18d		£6
cinammon	2lb		15s
ginger	2½ lb	2s.8d	6s.8d
nutmegs	1lb		8s
currants	54lb	4d	18s
great raisins	32lb	3d	8s
prunes	54lb		9s.8d
almonds	10lb		12s.2d
dates	3lb		2s.6d
liquorice	20lb		5s.10d
aniseeds	20lb		20s
more almonds	4 lb		4s.8d
biscuits & carroways	4 lb		6s.8d
isinglass	1½ lb		5s
saunders	2lb		3s.4d
			sum £17.4s.6d

They showed some signs of prosperity. Thomas Brown a New Malton chapman made a will in 1557, leaving a jacket, a pair of hose, a bonnet and a pair of gloves. William More the Settrington chapman gave twenty poor folks 26s.8d., and wanted four yards of line cloth, bought for a winding sheet, 'when it should please god to take him to his mercy'. More four wheeled wagons were to be seen and dished wheels were adopted to take greater weights. William Lacon the Kirkby Moorside tanner left a wain to his brother. Sir Hugh Cholmley used ox drawn wagons in 1628 to move his furniture from Thornton Dale to Whitby.

The Farming Regions

The farming districts were becoming more distinctive, each slowly adapting to exploit their local advantages. Camden characterised one unchanging terrain. He noted 'that which lyeth east and towards the sea is called Blackamore, a land black and mountainous being with craggs, hills and woods up and down it, rugged and unsightly.' In fact, the moorland dales were becoming quite populous, a small farm country, with stock and dairy farms. The Hole of Horcum was newly broken into parcels by Sir Richard Cholmeley, and farms built upon them. Bee keeping was a side line on the southern fringe of the moors. Men like Robert Frank of Hutton and Robert Gest of Brompton left beehives in their wills.

Rosedale west side already had seven farms and a cottage, each farm with between four and ten closes. Rosedale east side had several demesne closes, including those containing the old monastery, a kiln, a bakehouse, the church and the mill barn, but Haygate was a separate farm. There were sixteen other farms and a cottage. The number was increasing. By 1650, there were thirty five holdings, with acreages varing from fourteen to one hundred and twenty eight acres. Most of the thirty one farms had a barn, and a cowhouse but rarely a stable. Thomas Corney farmed some of the old demesne of Rosedale Priory in 1601. One year, he had twenty stook of rye and twenty stook of oats, with twelve sheaves to every stook. His five kyes pasturing in his closes, had two calves that year, and weekly gave two gallons of milk. He kept nine hog sheep, which at clipping time provided nine small fleece of wool. There was tithe to pay, so much for each stook, more for the calves and a penny for each gallon of milk.

A 1563 Act of Parliament inhibited the conversion of field land to pasture, but much of Cleveland was enclosed for dairy farming, in the late 16th and early 17th centuries. The demand for good grazing exceeded the supply. Lower Ryedale saw some piecemeal changes. Stonegrave and Hovingham low commons were divided in 1575 and the Dove field at Kirkby Moorside was described in 1613 as 'late arable now laid for meadow and pasture'. The township of Salton which in 1577 had twenty tenants at will and little freehold, was inclosed and depopulated about 1583. Thornton Dale's Cow carr and Oxcarr were inclosed in 1612. There were probably more changes of this kind.

Some high Wold townships were emptying and going over to sheep but others were not. Sir Ralph Bouchier enclosed Kirkby Underdale in 1583. John Legard a London haberdasher settled at the Wold foot town of Ganton. He built a new manor house of the local chalk stone with a slate roof and by 1587 had opened a rabbit warren on the higher ground. Many Wold valley townships grew barley in their fields. The sheep pastured on the high wold, were folded overnight in the barley fields. Butterwick kept its infield-out field system unchanged. They said that the inhabitants have 'none other neat's pasture or oxpasture but as they cut off a corner of their fields of their arable lands ends, which is in the measure of their arable lands, and not inclosed. The same tenants have no sheep pasture, or common moors or heaths, but only the common arable fields of Butterwick, as they laye them. The soil was not fruitful of pasture or meadow but good for corn which the tenant utterith to the bare corn towns and they buy all their hay for the most part.'

A Statute of Sewers established commissioners, to inspect drains and banks in the low marshes and common carrs. They were active by 1554 on both sides of the rivers Ouse, Rye and Derwent but they undertook no major works, and confined their activities to putting pressure on others, to maintain existing dykes and water courses.

The merits of oxen and horses for ploughing were debated in the common field townships. The oxen needed a good oxpasture at night. Areas were set aside in many townships. Part of Kirkby Moorside high common was stinted for cattle by the Earl of Westmoreland in1560, and such attempts to limit over-stocking of the better pastures may have been frequent. Slingsby tenants still kept their kine and horses without stint, in a marrish ground called the carr, and on their common high moor, and sheep on the moor without stint.

Small intaking from commons was renewed by landowners on the Tabular hills from Cropton to Thornton Dale, but hedges were fired in opposition. Ebberston men threw down hedges and ditches newly made for cattle management, by the Crown tenants at the high moor dale of Bickley. Inclosure for coppicing of timber brought out the Pickering men, who tore down new fences about the haggs. They were called 'a refractory company nothing can curb but the rigour of the law'.

Timber

Camden found nothing remarkable to be met with 'except rambling brooks and rapid torrents in the valleys, among the mountains of

Blackamore', but the last of the timber was there, both native woodland and coppiced woods. Other travellers reported little visible wood between Scarborough and Pickering. Woodland surveys showed old and new woods in the parks and moor valleys. Moorsmen made butter firkins, skeels or milktubs, kimlings or scalding tubs, binks or benches. A turner of wooden vessels occupied the lonely valley house at Thrushfen high in NewtonDale. Rosedale supplied timber wayneblades to Scarborough.

Woodland conservation had become an early subject of national policy. The 1543 Coppice Act had required that twelve standells were to be left to the acre, when a copse was felled. Coppices, locally called 'haggs', were planted and regularly cropped. Pickering had coppices at Shakerstie, Rarriehowe, Braygate, Greengate, Gundale and Haugh Haggs, north of the Castle, mostly managed for the Cholmeley family. Helmsley in 1638 had three hundred and fifty acres of wood, of less than fifteen years growth.

Great timbers were something else. The large oaks called crucks or forks were still cut for new houses, from Settrington to Bilsdale. On the main limestone belt, Spaunton in 1552 had oaks of a hundred years growth, as well as haggs of forty years. Newton dale had fourteen hundred timber trees, and eighteen hundred more only suitable for fuel. Two hundred oak trees were taken at Hartoft in 1602. The great 1585 Settrington sale took scores of trees over the timber - less north west Wolds. Fifty one trees went to Helperthorpe in the Wold valley. One tree could cost five shillings. Timber felling was a way of raising funds for any beleagured estate, but there was some planting too.

The use of timber as an industrial fuel was banned in 1615. The output of the Newcastle coalfield was doubling every fifteen years, so that seacoal was spreading to coastal places and river ports for baking and brewing. Only gentry houses attracted supplies inland; Sir Henry Cholmley carted coal to Thornton Dale from Scarborough. A coal mine was reported at Cropton in 1585 but the veins were very thin. Turf and peat cut from the high and low moors, remained the local fuel.

A Revolution in Industry

Several new industries were developed in Elizabethan times, often with government encouragement, by the grant of monopolies. Foreign technology was brought in as well as some native invention. Doncaster and Richmond became centres for the stocking knitting, which would expand to Dent and Wensleydale. West Yorkshire was already producing a great part of the nation's woollens and worsteds. Silk manufacture started in England about 1561. Metal working and the manufacture of cutlery was developing at Rotherham and Sheffield. Pins were made at Aberford in the vale of York. Commercial malting on a large scale based on many small kilns emerged at Bridlington, Scarborough and York.

The Earls of Rutland developed the production of cast iron at Rievaulx, making a ton a day, over several months of the year. The foreign expert Lambert Seamer raised the mill dam to work the hammer and bellows. The blast furnace installed about 1576 was one of the first in the north of England. Cast hood plates, and firebacks for the bigger domestic hearths, were made as well as cook pots, pans and bar iron. Production continued until 1651. The nature of the brass furnace called Blenken kiln founded in a sizeable building erected at Keld Head west of Pickering, has yet to be discovered. There are unconfirmed reports of an iron forge in lower Bransdale, and of forges at Hartoft and Ebberston, but their significance isn't known.

Jean Carre of Arras sought permission in 1567 to erect glass works in the Kentish Weald, similar to those of Venice. His son Jean, with Amabie the glassman and other Frenchmen came to moor sites near Scugdale west of Hartoft, and at Hutton le Hole, about 1575, to build glass furnaces. They made drinking vessels, linen smoothers and bowls. The industry probably continued until the state limited the use of timber for fuel in 1615.

A mine for 'Rochester or Fuller's earth' was opened at East Heslerton, and another at Sherburn which was worth £10 a year. Salt was evaporated once again in pans at Scarborough and 'train oil' made from fish blubbers, both industries the subject of local monopoly grants. The appearance of rough stone masons at Pickering, Westow, Topcliffe, Malton and Kirkby, by the 1630s, suggests an increased quarrying of building stone. Grimstone pottery and Potterhouse on Helmsley Moor were active. A late 16th century pottery kiln found at Stearsby, made an orange to grey ware, including strap handled jugs, large cisterns with bung holes, water jugs, pipkins and bowls.

The major new industry of north east Yorkshire was alum extraction and refining, developed with the use of foreign expertise. Quarrying of the rock and treatment of the shale was started near Guisborough and Sandsend, and after many years of teething troubles, managed to adapt existing techniques to local conditions. These and other works in Cleveland became the prime producers in England, employing a great many people. Sir Arthur Ingram played a major role in developing the works about Guisborough from around 1617. From 1625, these and Lord Sheffield's Asholme and Sandsend alum works were functioning successfully, using imported coal from the Whitby west side coal yard, and urine collected in quantity from London and the countryside.

Traditional industries of the countryside remained active. Thirsk became a notable centre of the leather trades, and tanneries were active at Sinnington, Hutton le Hole, Kirkby Mills, Falsgrave and Lastingham in addition to those at the towns. Many leather gloves were made for farm work. Legislation required that leather for shoe soles was to stay in the tanpit for at least a year. Malton and Easingwold now had tallow chandlers. Many monastic corn mills changed hands after being sold to investors by the Crown. Foxholes had a windmill by the nineties. Francis Ellerton built a new common oven on the waste at Smiddy hill, Pickering, which has long gone but still shapes the landscape there. Local weavers still made their webs from Wintringham to Bilsdale, but a fulling mill at Brompton was given up and one at Hungate in Pickering was forgotten by 1619, as that industry became concentrated in west Yorkshire.

High and Low Governance in the North

England briefly returned to a limited Roman Catholicism under Queen Mary, but it was not to be permanent. Queen Elizabeth was proclaimed governor of the Church of England, and Parliament passed Acts of Supremacy and Uniformity, restoring a Protestant church with standardised prayers and services. A High Commission was founded in 1559 to enforce them and was active taking oaths from clergymen and punishing absenteeism.

The Queen's Council in the North became the main channel of northern government, in constant touch with her Secretaries of State and the Privy Council. The council functioned as a court, settling many important local issues, and dealing with difficulties arising from the new religious settlement. The Council moved into 'the King's Manor', developed from part of the St Mary's Abbey buildings, just outside the old York city gate. The Earl of Rutland lived there as Lord President, as did Henry Hastings, Earl of Huntington from 1572 to 1595. The King's Sheriff Hutton castle was repaired for the Lord's President at a cost of

£700 in 1573-1575 after which little more was spent for twenty years. Sir Thomas Gargrave as deputy president gave continuity through several presidencies. Members of the permanent Council included the lawyers William Tankred of Arden, Robert Meynell of Hawnby and Sir John Gibson of Welburn.

The Justices of the Peace, drawn from the gentry, were still the main arm of local government, supervising constables, overseers of the poor, surveyors of highways and other local officers, who implemented parliamentary statutes, royal proclamations and council orders. A busy quorum met in quarterly and petty sessions. Assize Judges came thrice yearly to deal with crimes beyond the local jurisdiction. Administration involved much travelling by justices and by messengers. A man was paid to ride from Pickering to Pontefract to warn the officers there of a coming audit. Messengers travelled frequently between Yorkshire and London.

Table 28. Lord Presidents of the North	
1537	Thomas Howard, Duke of Norfolk
1538	Cuthbert Tunstall, Bishop of Durham
1539	Robert Holgate, Bishop of Llandaff, later Archbishop of York
1556	Francis Talbot, Earl of Shrewsbury
1561	Henry Manners, Earl of Rutland
1564	Thomas Young, Archbishop of York
1572	Henry Hastings, Earl of Huntington
1599	Thomas Cecil, Lord Burleigh
1602	Edmund Sheffield,Earl of Mulgrave
1619	Emanuel, Lord Scrope
1629	Thomas, Viscount Wentworth
1641	Thomas, Viscount Saville

Many new responsibilities came to the justices of the peace, for keeping up 'county' bridges, for applying the Statutes of Highways, the Statute of Artificers of 1563 and the 1597 Poor Law, with its 'houses of correction' and work schemes for the poor. The Statute of Artificers introduced annual 'hirings', open air gatherings where servants, labourers and craftsmen were taken on for the year for most employments. No departures from contracted employment were allowed, and labour was compulsory from five in the morning till seven or eight at night. Those aged between twelve and sixty could be compelled to serve in husbandry, especially at harvest time. Men employed in the crafts were obliged to serve seven year apprenticeships.

Wages were annually set by the justices who would attend the statute hirings. These became public employment exchanges for men and women, where they stood to seek work, wearing some token of their work, a tuft of wool for a shepherd, before the farmers and other employers. They weighed up what they saw, and might offer some extra inducement as part of the bargain, together with a 'godspenny' to bind the agreement. John Harrison of Middleton was brought to court in 1607, for not recording his servant's names and wages. Others appeared for leaving their employment.

Table 29. Wages in Yorkshire 1563

	Wage	Clothing
Bailiff in husbandry.	30s a year	6s
Chief hind or chief shepherd	22s	5s
Servant in husbandry	20s	4s
Woman servant	10s	5s
Children over 16	10s	3s4d
Apprentices in husbandry	6d	& meat drink and cloth

Cartwrights Candlemas to Michaelmas with meat 4d a day,
without meat 7d
Threshing winter corn   6d a quarter   ware corn 4d a quarter
Ditching and hedging   3d for seven yards
Paling and railing   12d for seven yards with pale
Harvest mower   4d a day with meat   9d a day without meat
Reaper, thresher, carter in harvest 3d a day with meat
5d a day without meat
Women and other labour in harvest 1d day with meat
3d a day without meat
Other labourers 1st March to Michaelmas 5d a day without meat
2d a day with meat
Michaelmas to Easter without meat 5d
with meat 1½d

Manor courts continued unchanged in outline, but with new officers elected to oversee the poor and the highways. Some manors lost their significance. Malton Priory had administered its estate, through half a dozen manor courts from Sinnington to Norton, all of which ceased. Where there were no manor courts, the same duties fell upon the parish. Constables felt more pressure from above, as the justices sought to ensure that their wishes prevailed. The old Malton manor court had forty two tenants at will, several freeholders and two tenants at nearby Wykeham. At one session, the foreman and jury dealt with three cases of assault, a great many unringed pigs, fences that were down and horses wandering on the riggs. William Ward had broken into the pound and John Robinson with three other men had rescued their animals from the pindar.

Salton manor court in 1577 covered Salton, Brawby, Great and Little Edstone, appointing constables, byelawmen, ale tasters and water graves. The jury heard that the mill was unditched, that other ditches before the houses were not scoured, gripps not made, pigs not ringed while the common carr and the common moor were overstocked. There were rails down in the ings, geese in South Field, gates not made near Butterwick ford and Robert Lister had made a rescue on the pindar. The miller had ground a stranger's corn, before that of the tenants. The jury decided that the miller should not have more than five chickens at the mill.

The manor courts dealt with those things. They only seem minor matters in retrospect but would be important at the time. They did not deal with the man presented by the churchwardens at Burythorpe as a swearer, a drunkard, a ribald, who was contentious, uncharitable, a common slaunderer of his neighbours, a railer and a sower of discord. He went to a higher court. So did the vicar of Kirkby Grindalythe. When he visited Malton market, he was sought for by some opponents at his 'wosthouse', the alehouse where he made his stay. They found another minister in a chair, so they cast salt in his eyes and made his face black. They roamed the houses with rapiers in hands, breaking windows, and brought people out to drink. When they met the vicar, they gave him three hundred strokes.

The Wings of Extreme Opinion

Mary, Queen of Scots had a claim to the English throne of Queen Elizabeth. She fled to England after her husband, Lord Darnley was killed at Edinburgh in 1568. She was moved from Bolton castle in north west Yorkshire, south to Sheffield, the next Summer, in gentle confinement. She remained a focus for plots, while she was held captive.

192

The Earls of Westmoreland and Northumberland rose against Queen Elizabeth in 1569, hoping to restore Catholicism. The two Earls were summoned to York by the Lord President but declined to appear. Percy went from Topcliffe to Durham, where a mass was said. He returned to Yorkshire at the head of a force. Christopher Neville of Kirkby Moorside had much influence with the young Earl of Westmoreland, and he raised one hundred and fourteen men in and around that town. The Earls found some support in Richmondshire, Allertonshire and Cleveland. Yearsley provided a few men but more came from Thirsk.

When the main force came south, Christopher took his men to secure Hartlepool, probably in the hope of a landing by foreign supporters. The rebel army camped for a week at Clifford moor near Tadcaster. No foreign support materialised. Lord Eure mustered a thousand militia and brought them into York, while Lord Clinton and Sir Edward Carey brought munitions and money. They said that 'Yorkshire never goeth to war but for wages'. The Earls fled when a southern army approached. 'The Rising of the Northern Earls' had failed. Christopher Neville left his hiding place in England for Louvain before 1571.

Soon after the rebellion, the Pope excommunicated the Queen as a heretic and absolved her subjects from their oaths of obedience. The English state responded in 1571 by making any denial of the Queen's supremacy in the Church into an act of treason. Attitudes quickly hardened at both extremes. Most people conformed to the established Church, but a few influential gentry kept the old faith and Catholic practices alive. A plot to release the Scots Queen in exile in 1572 brought charges against the Duke of Norfolk. Sir Thomas Fairfax seized the Duke's property from Hinderskelfe castle.

A more permanent threat came from some of the gentry sons who were being sent to Catholic seminaries in Europe. They returned as missionary priests, from about 1580. Many were imbued with a burning zeal, sufficient to martyrdom. They brought new strength to what had seemed a lost cause. Richard Holtby from Fryton became a prominent Jesuit. The north east Yorkshire coast was the safe route for many arrivals who found hospitality with a few sympathetic gentry families in Blackamore.

The government acted against surviving Romanism with growing severity, imposing the death penalty in 1581, for those teaching the supremacy of the pope. There were fines and imprisonment for those offering the mass. Joseph Lambton, a Malton born priest went to martyrdom by execution. Anyone refusing to attend church could be fined £20 a month. Gentleman Marmaduke Lacey at Ganton was fined into poverty. First he had to mortgage his estate, and then sale became necessary.

It was claimed that Blackamore was a bishopric of papists, with Grosmont abbey as its head, where traitors from beyond the seas were received. Joseph Constable of Kirkby Knowle and Upsall was named as another notorious recusant and receiver of seminaries. Claims that three parts of the peope of Blackamore were papists were excessive, but Katherine Radcliffe, Lady Scrope at Whitby Abbey and John Hodgson at Grosmont Priory received many priests and fugitives. Lord Eure at Malton and the Earls of Rutland at Helmsley were powerful enough to give some protection to Catholics. In the end there were scattered pockets of Roman Catholicism, rather than any general revival.

Within the established church, the mass and the confessional had gone. The more obvious Catholic practices ceased. The clergy were pressed hard into conformity. The Old Malton vicar was even required to revise his way of perambulating the fields at Ascensiontide, in line with the new ways or else lose his office. Among the devout clergy and laity, unrelieved consciences waxed the stronger and a strong sense of sin remained in evidence. There would be a slow growth of other concerns with the character and organisation of the church. The questioning of the role of Pope was an acid that could erode an entire priesthood.

Parish churches became preaching chambers for captive audiences, compelled to attend, in new seats called pews. The hope of a hereafter remained, but death brought you to the divine judgment and mercy, unassisted by the intervention of saints or continuing prayers for the dead. Different conclusions were drawn about those things that might influence the divine judgment, including new conclusions about whether a person's beliefs and actions had any influence.

Some took the view that God had pre-determined an elect group, sure of salvation, the peak of a sort of heavenly caste system. John Fletcher of Hagg house at Bilsdale, in 1588 spoke of the 'elect people of God'. Lady Brooke portrayed on a Kirkby Moorside brass beneath a fashionable head dress was sure that 'though worms destroyed her body yet she should see God in her flesh'. Others thought that belief in what the bible said, or alternatively a life of good works, or good living, might help. Remorse might be a factor in securing divine forgiveness for sins.

A growing literature of opinions replaced church authority, as the English Bible extended the debate to widening circles. John Bonville at Spaunton in 1583 sought a Christian burial 'without any pomp' but he left a quarter of wheat to be baked and distributed among the poor folks of Spaunton. Sir Nicholas Fairfax was more concerned with a tomb according to his degree, of £30 or £40 worth, with pictures on it. Some men in wills spoke of their hopes to appear among the 'blessed', and obtain pardon for their sins. Thomas Saville of Welburn in 1587 wanted his confession declared in open sermon at his Kirkdale burial. He was convinced that 'all my thoughts, words and acts are nothing else but abominable sin and wickedness in the Lord's sight'. A Kirkby Misperton man considered his body was in rebellion, conspiring with the lewd affections of his evil mind.

Others took it all lightly enough. The Puritan Archbishop Grindal condemned lords of misrule, summer lords and ladies, disguised persons, and others at Christmas and Mayday games, with minstrels, morris dancers or rush bearers coming into church at sermon or service time, to dance and play with scoffs, gestures and ribald talk, or walking, talking and other bad behaviours. He stopped the clergy running alehouses. Many described as 'evilly disposed towards religion' in the north, were said to hold May games, morris dancing, plays and bear pits on Sundays and holy days, leaving the churches empty, while people swarmed the streets and alehouses.

Although Puritanism could lead extreme mentalities to identify pleasure with sin, there does seem to be truth in the claim. The games began as the sermon commenced, in many churchyards. This can be interpreted in various ways. It might be thought natural enough, with everyone and their dogs packed into a crowded church, on the one holiday in the week. The many cases brought before the courts, suggest that the public response was to do anything but hear the sermon. Card playing was recorded at Stonegrave and Lastingham during church services, and elsewhere ninepins, shovegroats, loggets and a dozen other games. Since it was the preachings that were new, it seems likely that young people went on doing what they had always done, playing games on Sunday.

Armada Days

Gentry could raise small military forces. Sir Edmund Mauleverer took four Daletown tenants to the Scots border with six of his household and ninety others in 1558. Sir William Fairfax led two hundred with a beating drum. Local men went with Sir Hugh Cholmley to Chester for Ireland in 1567. Harquebusiers and pikemen followed Sir William Fairfax to the Scots frontier in 1571.

Local defence relied on musters from the villages and farms, exercised infrequently, on well known commons under the eye of experienced gentry. Constables kept lists of the men between sixteen and sixty. All men under forty, with land worth £15, or goods worth fifteen marks, were required to have a hawberke, iron breastplate, sword and knife; if more than £20, a habergeon, and if more than that a sword, bow and arrows, or in forest districts, bows and bills. Lines of beacons ran inland from the coast to Ampleforth, Pickering and Osmotherley to give warning of attack.

Catholic Spain sent an Armada towards England in 1588. The trained bands formed under their captains. Three hundred Ryedale and Bulmer men, who were given twelve days training with Fairfax, were not used to guns, and received small issues of powder to get used to the flash and recoil. The beacons were guarded, the church bells silenced for use as alarms and men allowed to carry weapons in the fields. Plans were laid for food stores, stock drives and the burning of corn stacks in the event of a Spanish landing. The fleet attacks on the Armada and the good use of fireships proved decisive, with Yorkshiremen playing many of the commanding roles. The Earl of Cumberland, Lord Thomas Howard, Lord Sheffield of Mulgrave and Sir Martin Frobisher commanded four of the larger ships. Frobisher and Sheffield were knighted on the Ark Royal. An unconfirmed tradition claims that the fire ships sent in to disperse their vessels were piloted by Thomas Ferris of Eskdale. The Spanish fleet in disarray, drifted past Flamborough Head, and around Scotland back to Spain.

The Perils of Hard Lives

The Elizabethan increase of people exceeded any expansion of local employment, so that the numbers grew, who were poor and unemployed. Many who were employed had no luxuries and few necessities. To make a bed was to stuff a poke with straw. A contemporary described Malton in 1624, as three hundred families 'many of them poor'. The Pickering 'poor' swept the market place for dropped corn. Whitby 'where there were many poor in winter' gained a new house of correction in 1636, a wry application of the Puritan philosophy that 'man is the master of his fate'. A similar house was set up to provide work and correction at Pickering.

Epidemics recurred at intervals, sometimes local, sometimes sweeping the country. The plague returned on some scale in 1603, moving relentlessly southwards from Whitby, raging at York and again in 1626, cutting off population growth. Infected goods from London were blamed. The York and Malton 'chirurgions' (an early name for surgeons) could offer little to protect against disease and there was much to encourage it. Isolation was the first response. When the plague was suspected at Ampleforth in 1591, Sir William Fairfax told his steward to keep the gates well locked and supervised. Malton built a lodge in the moor, where spinster Elizabeth Wood went to die. Buttercrambe watched the roads in 1637 and the next year Thornton Dale buried its dead. George Clapham of Nunnington died of the plague visiting London.

Some awareness of the links between sanitation and health seemed evident in the measures taken at York, against epidemics in 1538, and the provisions of 1580 for carrying filth out of the city. There was little sign of any realisation elsewhere. Dunghills stood in streets, near front doors, at Scarborough gates and at the Pickering parish church stile. Andrew Borde had written in 1547, of the dangers of corrupt air, over crowded rooms, street and drain stench, night soils, unclean houses and beds, corrupt dusts, dirty floor rushes, dog sweat and fleas, as well as mutual infection and divine punishment. The ideas were abroad, but the time was not yet. People went for an occasional wash in a stream or river, some drowning as they did so on Saturday nights in the river Derwent at Malton. A Newton woman blamed wedding day head and stomach pains in 1651, on having washed her feet. Others saw a pain in the head as a portent of loss. Lady Hoby prayed for forgiveness for her sins during toothache, and felt a sense of assurance of God's love, when it stopped.

The new herbals were read by the educated few, offering hope against many ailments, often based on experience, but subject to few tests, other than those of personal experience. There was some theory, inluding the doctrine of signatures, which thought plants were signed as specifics for particular diseases. The Fairfax family kept a manuscript with their local collection of remedies. These show the familiar reliance on unusual, and even unpleasant materials shared with the wise men and women. Dried toad was good for nose bleed, fasting spittle stood two nights in a dunghill for deafness, but also plantain juice for toothache.

The first Pharmacopoeia appeared in 1618 beginning the classification of the materials of medicine. 'Strong waters' came about the same time to confuse the issue and patent medicines began with the royal patent grants of 1630. Mary Thompson by 1650 had recipes for cherry water, stomach plasters, plague water, powders to provoke sleep and for headache, cures for chin cough and gripings, some lozenges, green ointment and a worm expelling powder. She made many preserves of fruit, marmalade and even perfumed lozenges and she made her medicines with the same confidence.

There was some reliance on the emerging medical profession but probably confined to the well off. Lady Hoby consulted a York physician, who gave her physic and let blood. Another city physician travelled widely enough to let blood for Mrs Bell at Acclam, and to provide an Osmotherley shoemaker with three purges and three powders, for which he charged two shillings and sixpence. John Manners at Helmsley heard of a 'cunning man' in London and thought of sending for him. Well into the next century, Timothy Portington of Malton went to London, to be cut for the stone. Two York Doctors by 1550 were already sending patients to recover at rural Guisborough, where in the manner of all health resorts, a variety of pleasurable activities were soon provided. Holy wells had been banned but returned in response to the new demand for spa waters. Malton spaw became famous. Even its 'nauseous scum' was reckoned a cure for ulcers.

The more day to day ailments, which spoiled any sense of well being, were well known. Lady Hoby had long heavy colds. Mr Tancred in old age was troubled by the stone. Lord Eure in 1606 had the stone and sciatica, at the same time. John Heslerton at Malton endured the cold palsy for seventeen years. Mrs. Thornton at Newton in the 17th century endured everything. She had spleen after eating lobsters, consumption, small pox, pain in the neck and a long litany of sicknesses and disasters. From her many accidents comes the impression that each new invention took its toll. Given a big hearth, some fell into it, given a coach some fell out of it. Mills were places that injured many children. A boy Cholmeley fell from a second floor window and only narrowly escaped digestion by the pig below.

The Borough of Malton had the only known local medical men in this period outside York. George Browne named himself chirurgeon, they said, when he died in William Sleightolme's house in Malton Market Place in 1594. Five years later, there was Ralph Moyser, chirurgeon, but also John Taylor, an apothecary at the town. Dr Wittie, the publiciser of Scarborough Spa, was attending York, Ryedale and Scarborough patients before 1660.

Education in Strange Matters

The disappearance of chantry priests, and the reduction in the numbers of parish clergy, may have reduced the teaching done, but the new emphasis on reading the English Bible and the Prayer book, gave education in reading a strong new purpose. We know little enough of Elizabethan vicars and clerks teaching the first steps, but when the Holgate Grammar School was founded at Old Malton, it was assumed that applicants would already be able to read. Schools are mentioned incidentally at Norton in 1563, Hovingham in 1570 and a Pickering School taught by John Harding in 1594. The record of basic education is poor, scattered and probably very incomplete. A schoolmaster at Allerston in 1606 received compensation from the justices for losses by fire. Graduate curates were allowed to teach schools in 1604 and schools are known to have existed at Brandsby, Buttercrambe, Boltby and Dalby.

The chantry schools at Pickering and its neighbour Middleton survived as endowed grammar schools for centuries. St.Peters School at York had existed since 1557. Sir Nicholas Fairfax founded a free school at Gilling giving £10 to support a master. Richard Greene, the vicar of Burton Agnes in the far Wolds gave money to support an existing school. Sir John Hart, a Levant and Russia merchant, in 1603 founded the Coxwold Grammar School, free for the classics and mathematics.

What was remarkable was the concentration of higher educational effort in such strange channels. On the one hand, Protestantism did mean renewed thinking about religion and an exaltation of the Bible as a source of authority. On the other, those intellectual movements, which formed the 'Renaissance' and the 'Rebirth of Learning', gave travelled and literate gentry an acquaintance with the serious thought and the fantasies created centuries before, in Greek and Roman society. This seemed well ahead of contemporary thinking on many subjects, from medicine to mathematics and from law to philosophy.

Education became centred partly on biblical accounts of long vanished Middle Eastern peoples, and partly on the cultures of other long vanished Roman and Greek elites. There was exercise for the mind, but there was much that was of doubtful value. The young Baron Saville while in Yorkshire, read widely in Aesop's fables, Virgil, Horace, and the Dialogues of Castilion. Henry Saville became tutor to the Queen in Greek and mathematics. Roger Ascham of Kirkby Wiske was her Latin Secretary. The practical things were mostly learnt in the school of life, enhanced a little for many outside the gentry, by the development of apprenticeships.

The struggle for science, with its reliance on observation and experiment, had been oddly pioneered, both by George Ripley the Bridlington canon experimenting to make the philosophers stone, or great elixir, and Lord Clifford at Barden in his retreat, studying alchemy and astronomy. It had to wait till later days. The new learning and the bible too often made the authority of old writings, the test of truth. Much practical learning, drawn from experience, ended in the commonplace book kept by many gentry, where they jotted down any knowledge that was of interest to them, wherever acquired. William Lawson vicar of Ormsby in Cleveland, despite his classical knowledge, set aside the ancient authorities and after forty eight years of practical gardening, published the first northern books on gardening, orchards and bee keeping in 1612-13.

The printed book, in which others circulated their jottings to you, was a major stimulus to study and to thought. John Leland was travelling, wanting to see all England. Sir Martin Frobisher, who sought the north west passage had victualled ships at Scarborough in 1566. A wider world was being revealed and a movement of minds was afoot. Elsewhere in Yorkshire, John Field at East Ardsley produced the first English astronomical tables, Richard Shenne of Methley catalogued plants and Henry Briggs of Halifax proposed alterations to Napier's system of logarithms. Roger Dodsworth born at Newton Grange in 1585, became one of the great scholars, leaving one hundred and twenty volumes in his own writing, and one hundred and sixty two volumes of manuscripts collected. Together, they form the basis on which much northern history would rest. Lord Burghleigh in his forty seven advices to his son might conclude that 'the whole proceedings of the world are but one continued scene of folly' but others, in quiet corners, were seeing a little more than that.

Town Life

Elizabethan Malton still showed its old variety of crafts, with weavers, tanners, millers, and shoemakers, but now also a wheelwright, a coverlet weaver, a chapman and a pewterer. Appletongate held both a blacksmith and a tanner. Castlegate had burgages now, so that the street must at some stage have been brought within the borough. The water mill was there at the lower end of the street. Castlegate and Yorkersgate already had backyard kilns. Village and borough were less sharply distinguished. William Parkin an Old Malton husbandman rented half a shop in New Malton. Old properties were remembered as once having belonged to Rievaulx Abbey or Keldholme Priory. There was other property of the Settrington Bigods. Ralph Rasyn of the merchant dynasty owned several houses, including a shop at the end of St Michael's church, and a house at Bridge End, which sounds like other old church estates and he had a long lease on Lord Eure's Orchard Close.

Minister William Walker in 1591 recorded a baptism in the 'fount after it was made'. Each baptism was witnessed and the names recorded, showing the fine distinctions of the time. Some men were called 'Maisters', Thomas Suddaby and Thomas Lovell among them. Mary Eure and Ralph Rasyn stood witness for the genteel Ralph Moyser. Captain Westroppe was there for the baptism of gentleman John Heslerton's son and on a November Sunday stood by the font with Mrs Margery Constable, come in from Newsham for Lord Eure's son William to be given his Christian name. Marriages were infrequent, not many in any one year. Visitors came to Malton market from the Wolds, John Morwyn from Wharram Grange and John Dobson from Mowthorpe Grange. James Dunneson, a Frenchman, was buried in 1587. There were tragedies too. Alice Dickson was 'bais begotten', with a 'salt peter man' supposedly the father. Agnes Brabiner was drowned in the river Derwent.

Pickering in 1598 had the layout that it would still have two hundred years later. Field strips hemmed in the crofts and prevented much change. Eastgate and Hallgarth together held twenty two families and Hungate another thirteen. Birdgate and Market Place were spoken of as one and included the later Bridge Street with twenty two households. Boroughgate had another twenty two and Westgate twenty five. A description of 1616 classed them in another way. There were twenty two burgages, far fewer than in mediaeval counts, fifty cottages, ten shops, a smithy, a bakehouse and another eleven houses, but perhaps this was not the whole town. The estates belonged to the Crown, the Cholmley family and the freeholders. The Cholmleys held much house property. Sir Richard was bailiff of the Duchy manor but Sir Henry sold a burgage, twelve houses and thirty two cottages in 1598. William

Thornburgh tenanted the chief house called the Parsonage. The timber lodges at the castle were in ruin.

In the earlier years of the century, Robert Plumpton of Dring houses had passed his house between Market Stead and Hall Garth to Robert Hastings. Richard Wood had erected a new shop in the market, nine feet by eight feet and Robert Metham another on the waste, nine foot by eleven foot. A tenter garth had been laid out in the 15th century by the river for hanging cloth to bleach and dry. Now John Leming, a merchant draper, held the old Metham's shop and the Tenter close. John Cante rented the market tolls and the old borough seems to have little role remaining. John Ripley and Robert Robinson were tanners. Around the town were the glovers' limepit, the anchorage close where the recluse had once walked, the dunghills and the new forge on Potter Hill. The schoolroom was in the south chapel of the parish church. There were signs of religious disagreement. Robert Leming in 1594 closed the book in the parish clerk's face. Thomas Walker was suspected of staying away from church drinking in the alehouse, but also of favouring the Romish power in religion.

CHAPTER 5
THE STUARTS. 1603 - 1714

Queen Elizabeth had used her Parliaments to discuss and promote important legislation, which set up a new national framework, not least for religion. This would last for centuries in such important areas as poor relief, highway maintenance, and employment. Tudor councils had enlisted able men, like Wolsey, More and Elizabeth's secretary of state Sir William Cecil, and used them, to shape the policies that increasingly sought to promote national advantage, rather than mere dynastic claims. The reign of the virgin Queen saw significant state support for new industries, as well as overseas ventures.

The accession of James Stuart of Scotland as King, united the English and Scots crowns, ending the need for a border nobility with military power. Scotland remained a separate significant force but was no longer the governing factor in northern politics. James presided over an England, full of people, though not perhaps by modern standards. The growth in population continued into the reign but was steadied by the return of epidemic diseases. More people meant more poor people, whose needs were only partially met by new employments.

The Stuart Kings faced continued difficulties with religion, as a strong Puritan movement emerged wishing to take church re-organisation further, and a lingering Roman Catholicism remained patchily influential. The Kings were short of money to meet the growing cost of government, in a period of rising prices, and sought new incomes, chiefly by levies on trade. The merchants were becoming a main force, and entering a new aristocracy. Parliament became the more significant, as it established the right to control grants from taxation to the Crown. When the King was obliged to call Parliaments to grant monies, the members edged towards controlling policies, as well as payment. The Stuart notion of the 'divine right of kings' sat ill with any such tendency. There would be civil war.

Great Gentry Houses

James Stewart of Scotland became King of England in 1603. Sir Robert Carey of Leppington had horses posted all the way north, from

203

Howsham Hall

London to Scotland, so that he would be first, to give him the news. James happily knighted clusters of Yorkshiremen, as he rode south to claim his throne, Henry Bellasis, Thomas Fairfax, Henry Cholmley and Thomas Metham of Wigganthorpe at York, William Bamborough of Howsham at Grimstone and many others, who caught him further south. The Earl of Rutland proclaimed the monarch at Nottingham. The Scots border was suddenly less significant.

This was an age for comfort not castles. Sir Arthur Ingram, the London financier who came to Yorkshire as Secretary of the King's Council in the North, abandoned the old Sheriff Hutton castle for a York house. He acquired the old Palace site of the Archbishops at York Minster court for a great town house, with a 'Paradise' of walled gardens, fruit trees and shrubs from London, privet hedges shaped like beasts, a bowling green and tennis grounds. His York house would become the social centre for the shire, and house the early York assemblies. Several of the gentry families already had houses in the city, as well as their main residences in the country.

Nor was this all. Between 1619 and 1624, he built the new brick, Launde House in Sheriff Hutton park, where he kept three hundred deer, and was visited by King James I and the Lord President, feasting them on imported almonds and oysters. The house was given walks, amid walled gardens, with fair ornaments, privets cut into beasts, and court

204

walls set with honey suckle. Enjoying vast incomes, Ingram, is said to have enlarged the hunting lodge within the thousand acre New park, near Huby, and made a second house there for servants.

Howsham Hall was built in 1612 by Sir William Bamborough, with two tiers of great mullion and transom windows, replacing the isolated Bambrough Castle, in the river valley, of which virtually nothing is known. Sir Robert Carey, raised to the barony, is said to have had his castellated mansion near Leppington church, but nothing is known of that either. Henry Burton of Birdsall, later a vigorous critic of Catholicism, was tutor to his two sons. Helmsley castle passed, by the marriage of the 6th Earl of Rutland's only daughter, to the absentee George Villiers, 1st Duke of Buckingham.

Sir Charles Cavendish bought Slingsby castle and replaced it with a great mansion, vast in windows and still with us in ruin. Kirkby Moorside castle still had a great dining chamber, a lodging chamber and long gallery, two more lodging chambers with chimneys, all stone and partly covered with lead, and its own brewhouse, stable, oxhouse and dovecote, but there was no-one except the steward to live there. The estate had passed to absentee landlords. The castle was abandoned and part of the stone was removed for the steward's new house at Welburn in 1605. Sir Hugh Cholmeley did not altogether abandon Roxby castle, though the end was in sight. He moved his family into the Whitby Abbey gatehouse, while his principal house there was being made habitable in 1626.

Great houses were being built everywhere for great families, or so it seemed, in a rash of construction. Fine stone buildings in the new style, showed many gables, large regular windows, numerous tall chimneys over good broad hearths, with fine decorated fireplaces, many pannelled rooms, large and small, for public and private purposes, usually including a servant's hall and a chapel, great upper galleries, and large kitchens, amidst formal gardens and wilder parks.

One of the finest of all the new mansions was built at Malton. Ralph, the third Lord Eure, was made Ambassador to Denmark in 1602. He left a rainhead with a date in the early 1600's, on the lodge of his great new Malton house, perhaps marking its completion. He had acquired all of the subdivided Malton manors, taken action to limit the powers of the borough of Malton, and sold his old double- courtyard house at Ingleby. He wrote to Sir Robert Cecil from Birdsall in 1601 but from Malton in 1606. Lord Eure was appointed Lord President of the Council in Wales, holding this vice -regal office from 1607 to 1617. His

Malton mansion was said to be magnificent and on a scale akin to those of Sir John Saville at Howley, and that other house of Sir Arthur Ingram at Temple Newsam. It had a formal garden but lacked a park, so his son Lord William Eure emparked Easthorpe, not too far away, between 1617 and 1620.

Many other halls across the county saw substantial alteration or reconstruction in the early decades of the 17th century, among them Arden, Bossall, Cawton, Coxwold, East Newton, Newbrough Priory and Nunnington Hall. Thomas Heslerton owner of five Malton burgages had a mansion called York House just inside the wall of that town by 1641. Sir John Gibson transformed the old timber house at Rievaulx Abbey's Welburn Grange about 1603, with great stone additions, including a big bay window, so creating a major mansion. Sir Henry Cholmley built a great house at West Newton, site of another Rievaulx grange. Other new families who became prominent local magistrates in these years may well have done as much, the Sothebys at Birdsall and the Hebblethwaites at Norton among them, but nothing of their houses remains to be seen.

John Legard, a gentleman at Ganton had a good Elizabethan hall where his goods in 1638 were valued at £490. The store room held the new pewter, separately listed, including ten little plates, twenty dishes, two pie plates and probably a full garnish of basins, flagons and pots, including a chamber pot. There were various brass pots and pans and a glass case with glasses and apparently glass plates. There were even 'seven cheaney dishes'. The silver plate included several bowls, spoons, poringers and a distributor for sugar. There were ample sheets and pillow cases, wrought curtains, tapestry coverings for beds and tables. His own chamber held a standing bed, with teaster, curtains and valence worth itself £3.6s.8d. Furniture included a round table, livery cupboard, wainscot chair, three red cloth chairs, three wrought chairs and many stools. His stable held six horses, one worth £20. The farm was stocked with thirty five ewes, two hundred and forty five wethers. Many people owed him sums, amounting to £150.

An Orderly Society

This was an age of deference, to those of high status. The York Lord Mayor on his knees, addressing King Charles at the end of an obsequious discourse, full of unlikely comparisons, said that he was the 'glory and admiration of the known world'. The yeomen freeholders,

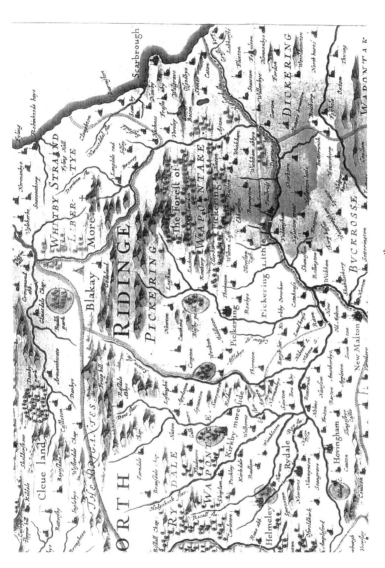

Ryedale in the early 17th Century

merchants and rising craftsmen were no lickspittles, but any challenges to the authority of men of status brought a severe response. A stubborn fellow from Pickering gave Sir Hugh Cholmley unhandsome language, so he crashed his silver topped cane on his head. He was never the same again.

An Oswaldkirk linen weaver was punished for telling a gentleman George Hall – 'Base rogue I am as good as though art'. The justices said this was scandalous and defamatory. A Cold Kirkby man told squire Charles Tankred that he was 'fitter for a swine driver than a JP'. Henry Humble of Kirkby Moorside made contumelious speeches against Sir John Gibson. Freeholders as a class always produce some who speak their mind. Sometimes they went too far. Robert Freeman of Malton said that neither law nor statute would stop him malting. Gentlemen could be brought to account as well. Robert Ringrose of Kirkby Misperton beat the constable and into the stocks he went.

Conversation is the essence of social life. Fragments are hard to find in the record. Friends were known as 'gossips' and some fuelled their stories, by standing under eaves 'to carry tales and make debate'. A common comment about the taciturn was 'He is like a bagpipe, he never talks till his belly is full'. People usually spoke their mind to their equals, and cast aspersions, in time honoured ways. Gossip could descend into defamation and a few cases reached the courts. Favoured terms of abuse were 'whore-monger' for a man and 'whore' for a woman, but we hear of 'damnable wicked queens'. Thomas Brandsby in 1592 remarked that 'this pockie dame had bene twice bathed of the pox at Malton'. Another added, in final condemnation, 'she has a wart on her belly'.

Manor courts dealt with the same matters as of old, but Gilling in 1631 heard of children breaking hedges. Miles Rogers's wife was misusing her neighbours with her tongue, and Thomas Balland, one of three brewers, kept disorder in his house. The justices were much troubled about people on the move, the poor who had no right to settle in other places, but moved to find employment, and the gatherings of travelling sturdy beggars troubling Egton and Normanby in 1609. Ellen Lockwood was charged for harbouring rogues at Kirkby Moorside, two years later.

Thieves took anything of value, a kid of whins at Skewsby, or a pane of glass from Ayton church. Punishment was getting more severe, for offences involving property. Matilda Wilkinson of Thornton Dale took a pair of stockings worth 3d, a tunic and petticoat valued at 4d, and a neckerchief costing 3d. She was whipped at Malton, then moved by the constables to Thornton, to be whipped again on a holiday after evening prayer, from the church stile to her home. A Byland man who took some of the Earl of Rutland's charcoal was set in the stocks and whipped at Helmsley market. A Sheriff Hutton thief was whipped from the Castle to his house. Sir Henry Slingsby had his coach robbed of lining fringe and lace at Newbrough in 1641. Some thieves were branded in the left hand, and a man was hung at Helmsley in 1651 for stealing a horse.

The church kept some authority over moral offences. The more obvious offenders were required to stand in a white shift, with a white wand, in the church, to make public confession. On a well remembered occasion in 1632, two pregnant girls were brought to Danby church, white-sheeted and seated backside forward on two asses. When asked who had brought them to this condition, they declared that the squire's and parson's sons were responsible. This proved to be the case.

Social order was maintained by custom as well as by the law. It was known for the constable to walk a woman, seen as a threat to other women, down a street while they delivered their forceful admonitions. Communities brought people's behaviour into line by setting horns on a door, by 'gaping and putting out the tongue' or by riding the stang, when the youngsters of a village paraded an effigy up and down the street, and shouted jingles, about a man who beat his wife, or some other action that offended village opinion.

Good Cheer

Ales had fled the churchyard and church leaders had set their minds against much that was pleasurable in ordinary lives. The churches had probably been used for wet weather activities of all kinds, but this was no longer the case. The old home customs of men lifting women, and women lifting men, on certain days of the year were frowned on. They led to levity and romping. Old church festivals, now abandoned, moved to the village street. The alehouse was the heir, the natural place for indoor games, and the pavilion for those outdoor, but the games of chance attracted prohibition, as liable to make the poor poorer. The 1635 North Riding alehouse licence banned playing at tables, dice, cards, shove boards and bowls.

The village street was the dry weather playground, for ball games, leaping and running. A rough form of football was widespread, sometimes a bladder kicked in inter-village battles. Dancing was an outdoor activity, in 'here we go round the mullberry bush' style, with a piper, and a kiss at every turn. This earnt much disapproval from some, and brought much delight to others. Thomas Kendall of Marton was a local piper in 1611. Dances for young people called *garries* were held on Midsummer Day at Pickering, and elsewhere, to the accompaniment of a piper. There was reaping and harvest dancing in season. Ralph Theaker a piper and three others ended in the Hovingham stocks in May 1622. All public events were still generally reinforced by a brewing. When John Coates of Aymotherby was buried in 1603, the funeral party had four pennyworth of good ale, with ginger and nutmeg to spice it, two pints of wine, mace and cloves, and two more orders of ale, for the wake.

Ale was a general solace as well as a basic food. There was little else worth drinking. Best ale was a penny a quart, and small ale a halfpenny. Yorkshire in 1552 held 3679 alehouses, 239 inns and 23 taverns. Most villages kept their alehouse. Cropton had three in 1611, Pickering was apparently down to twelve. New Malton had at least nine alehouses and Helmsley had twenty. Those attending Malton to buy fish dined at their 'hoast houses'. Beyond Helmsley, William Jalash brewed, and harboured the lewd and vagrant people, who broke Lord Rutland's hedges, to burn in his fireplace. Thomas Fisher the Helmsley butcher had his alehouse closed in 1625, because he was a convicted Roman Catholic.

Puritans believed in changing the world, and to be fair, changing themselves as well. They unleashed a powerful force. Some thought they could bring 'the kingdom of God' into this world. Neighbours said of the Puritan Sir Thomas Posthumous Hoby that 'he would have an oar in anybody's boat.' These people interfered in the lives of others for what they thought was right, whether the others wanted it or not. The resentment lingers in modern criticism of 'do-gooders'. And so, more was heard of card playing at Kirkby Moorside in the workshops, gamblers playing tables and other unlawful games at Oswaldkirk and Richard Fawcett's Malton alehouse closed, for using play at both tables and cards, in the early years of the century. Tinkers at Nawton were reported, when they sat drinking till drunk, and played cards. Thomas Bellwood, living in the moors, near the source of the river Rye, was brought before the justices, solely because he was a person of lewd behaviour, but he escaped.

There are some signs of the development of better inns. Gentry used them more often, when travelling, sometimes with remarkable effect. Sir Henry Cholmley and his wife 'parted beds, till they lodged in a house with one room, after which they lived kindly enough together'. Predictable results followed. Stables became a necessity, for an alehouse that offered accommodation, and aspired to become an Inn. Richard Otterburn, the Kirkby Moorside gentleman, was charged a large sum for unlicenced brewing for sale in 1610. William Wood built the Black Swan at the town in 1632. Richard Rookes was at the Crown inn Helmsley. That town was well provided with inns. There was the Old Inn at Burrowgate and Susan Simpson's New Inn by 1637 while the Helmsley Castle Gatehouse had been converted into another. A York Vale knight could remark that 'every man loves his Inn better than his home.'

Cash Crops

The demands of the wider world encroached more and more on the subsistence economy, and on production for the local market, as cash crops and the products of industry were sold to distant buyers. Cattle and horses, hams, butter and cheese were among the despatches from north east Yorkshire, but also linen and alum, paying for the luxuries that came back, such as sultanas, spices and spirits. York had more than a hundred people selling tobacco by 1638.

More middlemen appeared, nine corn 'badgers' willing to buy the growing grain in the field at Husthwaite in 1611. Eleven people would exercise the art or trade of a badger at Helmsley. A couple from Gowthorpe bought all the grain in a Terrington barn. An Appleton man bought crops still growing. During 1634 Kirkby Misperton, Normanby and Barugh men respectively, bought sixty, twenty five, and thirty acres of grain still growing in the fields. Sinnington had a resident factor buying up butter and cheese .The Justices complained of a great increase in badgers, ingrossers, and forestallers of corn and grain, as the middlemen bought in advance and in bulk, breaching the old mediaeval rules which had restrained such trade.

The remaining local markets drew on producers further afield. A Wold farmer at Elmswell looked to Malton as well as Beverley. Corn was taken from Hovingham to Thirsk market in 1608. Kirkby Moorside market saw Terrington, Cowton, Northolme and Gillamoor, men buying large numbers of fowl, geese, moorhens, doves and eggs, to sell again elsewhere. The markets were picking up. New butchers shambles were built near old market crosses and bullstakes for 'baiting', a practice reckoned to bring meat into condition.

Malton market was known for wheat, 'meslin' meaning a mixture of crops grown together, fowls and farm implements. Fifty cod fish cost fifty three shillings there in 1613 and you could buy fifty cod's heads, strung on five bands, for 4s10d. Sea fish came from Runswick, Whitby and Filey to the Malton Fish Cross. Henry Best said that Malton was reckoned a better barley market than Beverley in 1641, quickest between nine and ten in the morning, when many badgers who had come from a distance, wanted to buy early and get home before dark. The horse fair was on September 21, and the beast fair on September 29, when horses were galloped north west of the town.

The traffic on the roads changed slowly in character and volume. Lowland roads were little altered, becoming fixed by early enclosures, but the high moors and dales developed a growing network of pannierman's causeways, known as 'trods'. They consisted of cut stone blocks laid edge to edge, for miles to give a sure footing for the trains of pack horses. Many have been removed since, but they survive well around Eskdale, whence they ran into and across Blackamore towards Whitby and Scarborough, and into Rosedale and Bilsdale. Panniermen with packhorses gave name to the 'pannierman's pool' in Maltongate in Thornton Dale, the 'pannierman ing' below Snainton and the 'pannierman close' at Scarborough, where animals were watered or pastured. Butter was sent in fifty-six pound firkins, on packhorses to the coastal ports of Yarm, Whitby and Scarborough, and inland to York, Malton and Boroughbridge.

Quite a different traffic began as English and Scots drovers came down the high Hambleton Street, bringing their animals, pasturing the way, heading for the great cattle fairs of Northallerton, Malton and York, and to the new fortnightly Easingwold cattle markets started in 1638. The Archbishops of York had bought some properties, which had previously belonged to monasteries, to give secure incomes. They included some ancient payments in kind. The Archbishop in 1638 received twelve quarters of wheat, sixteen quarters of oats and twelve capons from Hutton on Derwent. From Whitby came two hundred saltfish, a hundred stockfish and three thousand herrings, half red and half white.

The market towns gained their first 'general store' traders in permanent shops The Helmsley mercer was a grocer and a linen draper too. Malton had a mercer in Wheelgate and a Market place grocer before1659. Squire Cholmley of Brandsby used several markets, buying his saltfish at Malton, clothes, spices, hops and glasses at York, and saddlery at Helmsley, as well as employing the Stillington blacksmith. He bought two horse load of salt from a Whenby villager. One Whitsun he went for a wainrope, plough sock and hatchet to Kirkby Moorside. His Christmas purchases included sugar, sucket dates, ling fish and wine at four shillings a gallon. For New Years Day gifts, he bought gloves and ribbons.

Woollen weavers were scattered around the communities, but the home spinning and weaving of linen cloth developed separately, as a new home industry, in the villages and dales around Blackamore. Much of the raw material was at first locally grown, but more would be imported from the Baltic countries. 'Hemp garth' became the normal local term for a backyard. Hemp and line were watered in springs and streams from Coxwold to Easingwold, Hovingham to Malton and Helmsley to Middleton. There was hemp dressing at Allerston pits by 1602. Around Cleveland and Ryedale, manor courts charged people with fouling waters, as they 'retted' the raw material in water, to separate the fibres.

Spinning and weaving became home industries, a valued second occupation for many. Some mills were converted to fulling mills, where cloth was pounded by hammers, replacing old walk mills. Active fulling mills were at Pickering, Ellerburn, Thornton, Allerston, Kirkby Moorside, Sproxton, Malton, Harome and Lastingham. Thomas Marshall, the Lord Mayor of York, had the cloth mill at Aislaby near Pickering. Small pastures near streams were laid out as bleach garths, or 'tenter' garths, for hanging, drying, stretching and bleaching the cloths. There were linen drapers at Sproxton, Slingsby, Stonegrave and at the market towns in 1610, but it is not clear if these men were acting as clothiers, distributing the raw materials, as well as buying and selling the product. Henry Best from Elmswell near Driffield, recorded how pedlars bought the finest linen cloth for shirts in Cleveland and Blackamore, and brought it to the New Malton drapers, already noted in 1641 for their 'linen and huswife cloth'.

Differences of Opinion

An Authorised Version of the English Bible was published in 1611, but conformity to a settled way of religion was becoming as unsatisfactory for the growing body of Puritans, seeking further reform, as it was for the few Catholics wishing to go back. Strong opinions were held and strong actions followed. Richard Fawkes and others involved in the 'gunpowder plot' sought to blow up Parliament in 1605. John Cowper at a Yedingham church communion, took some consecrated bread and wine and spilt it to the ground, but he had to do penance. The zealous William Boyes, a minister at Goathland, at the other wing of opinion, was required in 1620, to reform 'touching his opinions on matters of religion'.

Others with strong beliefs despaired of reform in the Church of England, and departed to America. Others did nothing so dramatic but struggled within themselves. Alice Wandesford's mother said that the way to heaven was through the gates of hell. The daughter sought to meet her frequent disasters with 'submission to the divine will'. Henry Darley of Buttercrambe was involved in several emigration schemes. The young Thomas Shepard, who knew Ezekiel Rogers the Puritan vicar of Rowley, was forbidden to minister in London. Rowley found him a position as a chaplain at Buttercrambe, where Henry Darley gave him his board, and Darley's two sons found him £20 a year. In his own words, 'I resolved to follow the Lord to so remote and strange a place.' On arrival, he found a 'profane house' with dice and tables played. Very quickly, he effected a great reformation in his host's mansion. The chaplain married Margaret Stuteville of Bossall, and sailed in 1636 to the Massachusetts Bay colony. where he would be the first minister at Harvard. Henry Birdsall migrated to Salem the same year, and several families went from Rowley in the East Riding.

The parish churches were preaching chambers and most were given new Jacobean pulpits, which pushed the parson's head higher than the perimeters of the new pews. Most churches invested in new bells, to summon everyone to attend. The buildings could be an arena for disagreement as well as for faith. Lively disputing was not unknown. Among the laity, church wardens were of growing importance, often drawn from the substantial freeholders and they had opinions too. Vicar Edward Mills worried the elders at Pickering. They said that he gave little attention to preaching or instruction and they wanted a learned and religious pastor in his place. We may not have the whole story, for there are signs that he was just that, but he had to go.

A Puritan squire could appoint clergy to foster his opinions, just as a Catholic squire could protect those who shared his. The private chaplain to a lord, could sustain others in his faith through a neighbourhood. The sixth Earl of Rutland supported a Catholic school at

Helmsley and others of that leaning clustered about the gentry of Gilling, Hovingham and Brandsby. In the less favorable situation around Welburn, there were secret Catholic burials at the Kirkdale churchyard in the night. The Malton minister Francis Proude, and the Slingsby Calvinist, John Phillips preached a different tale, while at Hackness Sir Thomas Posthumous Hoby kept a cadre of radical Puritan clergy. They too sewed seeds which lasted for centuries.

Other churches like Kirkby Moorside faced more mundane difficulties. Their ruined chancels were no longer maintained by the laymen who had bought or leased the tithes, and they began to fall down. Some clergy were merely gentlemen in holy orders, now that the right to appoint them, called the 'advowson' could be purchased by someone of wealth, seeking an occupation for a younger son. Henry Danvers gave the tithes of Kirkdale church to endow a physic garden at Oxford in 1632, a worthy enough object but a sign of how irrelevant the old incomes had become to the church that they once sustained.

King and Country

King Charles I tried to impose a religious settlement on Scotland in 1640. He had sought for years to govern England without Parliamentary grants of taxation, using other less than popular ways to raise money. These included the notorious 'ship money', of which payment was refused by several Yorkshire gentlemen. When a Scots army invaded as far as Ripon, the King had to summon a Parliament, in which the king and his policies were outspokenly resisted. Retreating soldiery were billeted around Helmsley and rioted at Seamer. Sir Henry Cholmeley's trained bands returned to Pickering Lythe.

Some in the Parliament sought to limit the King's power. The King sought to rule without Parliamentary restraint. London was for the Parliament and the King and Queen left the capital in January 1642. The Queen went abroad in February to secure alliances, to raise money by pawning the Crown jewels, and to buy weapons and munitions. In need of a port at which to land them, the King demanded access to Hull, a garrison town with war stores, but was refused by Sir John Hotham and returned to York.

Both the Parliamentary and the Royalist sides contained parties favouring war and others looking for peace. Lady Eure wrote from Malton in May hoping that the Parliament would lay no more taxes, because no one was paying her rents. 'O that swete Parliament would come with the olive branch in its mouth, it would afresh and glad all our hearts here in the north. What will become of us all I know not. I wish you all to take notice of the Women' she wrote. The King called great rallies at Heworth Moor on June 3rd to test support, and he raised his standard at Nottingham on 22nd August 1642. The Civil War opened in September. Many of the actions were spread wide across the country and the local involvement was but a small part of that.

The Earl of Newcastle quickly secured the northern coalfield district for the King, cutting off London's supply of coal. Sir Hugh Cholmley had command of Scarborough and of nearby trained bands in Blackamore, for the Parliament. Early in 1643 he defeated the Earl of Newport's troop at Malton. Sir Matthew Boynton joined him there with two troops of dragoons. He united these men with his own troop of horse, one hundred and thirty footmen and other cavalry. They moved to assault Guisborough, leaving Captain Bushell with a garrison at Malton.

The Stamford, Buttercrambe and Malton bridges were important for access into the East Riding. During February 1643, Queen Henrietta Maria failed to reach Newcastle, and was unable to land at Scarborough. She put into Bridlington, pursued by Parliamentary ships, who fired cannon into the small harbour at Bridlington Quay. She brought mercenaries, £20.000, and a good supply of arms and ammunition. One account speaks of '500 carts, 1000 horses, 3 coaches, 8 troops of horse and 15 companies of foot' passing through Malton on March the 7th. on their way to York.

When the royalists took Stamford bridge, Cholmley retreated to Scarborough but he sent men under Captain Froom, with two troops of dragoons, led by Sir Thomas Norcliffe and Lieutenant Strangeways, to occupy Pickering castle and to destroy Yedingham and Howe bridges. It was too late. They found that the enemy had already occupied Pickering town and castle and placed musketeers at Howe bridge. Captain Froom firing a pistol and beating a drum attacked some royalists at Thornton Dale and took twenty-one prisoners. A month later Sir Hugh Cholmeley changed his allegiance and took Scarborough over to the King, allowing dissenting soldiery to depart. Most of Yorkshire except Hull was in the hands of the Royalists, with some camped near Sheriff Hutton.

The situation changed dramatically, when in 1644, the Parliament bought the support of the Scots, who blockaded Newcastle. Lord Fairfax is said to have taken Bridlington, crossed the Derwent at Potter Brompton and entered Whitby. His main forces invested York. A lieutenant with eighty musketeers yielded Stamford Bridge in April. At

Lord Fairfax

Buttercrambe in May, officers were taken prisoner but the men were allowed to march away home. Sir Hugh Cholmeley with sixty horse from Scarborough raided Buttercrambe again in June. The drawbridge that night was accidentally down and they took Mr Henry Darley from his bed as a prisoner to Scarborough.

The beseiged city of York was given a prospect of relief with the arrival of Prince Rupert's army north of the city. The royalist army was soundly defeated on July 2nd at Marston moor, west of York by the Parliamentary forces led by Oliver Cromwell and Sir Thomas Fairfax. York fell to the Parliament. Sir Robert Belt at Bossall buried his money and valuables and two men were killed in a brief action there. Malton may have seen small actions early in 1644. Sir William Constable, rode through Pickering to take Whitby and Mulgrave in the Summer.

Royalist forces were beseiged at Helmsley castle and at Scarborough, where their privateers still threatened the colliers. Sir Thomas Fairfax in 1644 besieged Helmsley castle with seven hundred foot and three hundred and thirty horse, Sir Jordan Crosland held it for three months but surrendered with two hundred men on the 22nd of November. They marched out with colours flying, drums beating and matches lit. Nine pieces of ordnance, many muskets and pikes, six barrels of powder, money and plate were surrendered. About forty men went to join the garrison holding out at Scarborough. Sir John Meldrum's force took Scarborough town on February 18th 1645 and beseiged the castle. After heavy fighting and a long seige Sir Hugh Cholmley surrendered on 25th July 1645 Sir Matthew Boynton declared Scarborough Castle for the King again in July 1648 but it was stormed after three months on the 15th September 1648.

Gentry who had played prominent parts in the war were required to compound and pay fines for their own estates. Tobias Jenkins of Grimstone paid £350 and George Nendick of Welham £100. Sir Thomas Bellassis and Sir Hugh Cholmeley went into exile in Europe. Tobias Thurscrosse who held most of the Kirkby Moorside rectory but had raised funds for the royalist army, was fined £100.When the time came to fine him again, for more involvements, he only had his clothes and a horse, and was fined on them, but he was allowed to stay at his father's house.

Scarborough was left in a state of collapse. In the wider district, the billeting of soldiery over several years, left a trail of lesser damage. Churches were used as stables. Pickering legend claims that officers were quartered at the house that is now the Bay Horse Inn, and that while soldiery were in the church, both the prayer book and the font were damaged. The Yorkshire Grand Jury would depose in 1660 that 'Yorkshire was the county where was the stage where the foot of the Civil War trod so long and so heavily.'

218

A Confusion of Voices

The monarchy was abolished by Parliament and the King was beheaded in 1649. Alice Thornton of Newton wrote of Charles 'brutally murdered by the hands of blasphemous rebels, his own subjects, the best of Kings.' Others took a different view. Sir John Bouchier of Beningbrough and Henry Darley would be named in lists among those thought of as the 'regicides'. Through out Ryedale, firmly Protestant magistrates and ministers replaced royalists in these years. Luke Robinson of Riseborough Hall, a member of the state council, was especially active. He petitioned on behalf of war -damaged Scarborough in 1646. When he questioned travellers near Malton in 1651, they gave false names and refused to say more. Tom Towler of Upsall & John Mannering of Kilvington proved to be Catholic priests.

Royalist reactions were sometimes lively. On a May night in 1650 four men proclaimed Prince Charles as King of England at Malton market cross. They were hunted throughout the district. Rumour had a Marishes man offering '£500 tomorrow' for a horse, for one of the four men. It was later claimed that the Prince himself moved through Pickering Vale, and had 'potchet eggs' and a bed at an Allerston alehouse. Christopher Holliday, the Malton grocer, reported that Christopher Nendick, Captain Denton, Mr. Mountaine of Westow and a stranger, used a wanded bottle to drink a health to King Charles II, just as the shops were shutting at twilight. One man then proclaimed him King. Swords were drawn, and they came singing from the old cross to John Williamson's tavern. Denton was a renowned sea privateer and Mountaine was the Archbishop's nephew. Robert Geere of Great Barugh was certainly charged with harbouring the traitor Richard Mountaine. They tried to arrest him at Kirkham, but he escaped.

Local government continued well enough in different hands but the clamour of religious opinions gave national and local difficulties. A New Malton mason accused Eizabeth England of being a witch in 1640. In April 1644 Parliament ordered the Maypoles taken down. Meteors caused alarm for twelve miles around Malton in 1650. The eclipse of 1652 'afrighted many folk, leading them to reflect on the Day of Judgment'. Some began to practice the 'priesthood of all believers'. Robert Hickson the Malton 'preacher of the word' lost many of his congregation to a young woman called Jane Holmes in 1652, who said that he was a blind guide. She told Tony Bewedale of Hinderskelf, while in Ganthorpe lane, that he was a sinner with a vile spirit in him, and

George Fox

gave him a drink, that put him in a two hour trance. Lord Eure's priest John Thompson was informed on by a cutler, and had to sit in the Malton stocks.

A Hovingham labourer offered cures for the King's evil and a Snainton man started marrying people in private. A London broadsheet entitled 'Strange news from the North' claimed that three sectaries at Kirkbymoorside had made sacrifices to their God, including a cock, a hen, a dog, a calf and a mother. It may all have been a piece of propaganda, or it may not. Many had their own views on what the divine will was, during a period of intense religious debate.

George Fox appeared in Malton market place in 1651 and travelled on to Pickering, to preach in the church while Luke Robinson was at a meeting next door. He went on to Goathland where he was warmly welcomed by the curate Mr Boyes. Fox won supporters for his 'inward religion'. They became members of the 'Society of Friends'. Some say that they were first called 'Quakers' at Malton. William Dewsbury and

Roger Hebden were among the early Malton converts. Both preached through and beyond Ryedale in his wake.

Roger Hebden a woollen draper and tailor, was deeply affected. He placed his shop in other hands and became an active Quaker missioner. His Fersit House at South Holme was used for meetings of the Society of Friends, from the outset, and it is said that he established the Kirkby Moorside society in 1652. Two years later, he wrote to Fox from York castle prison, where he was incarcerated for thirty to forty weeks, after arrest while preaching at Sheriff Hutton, saying 'Great is the work in the dales above Kirkbymoorside'. He would be jailed again for disturbing the minister at Newport Pagnell, and again for refusing to pay tithes.

The Quakers insisted on a direct relationship between man and his God. They scorned such intermediaries as a church, particularly a state church, or even a priest. It said something that there were substantial freeholders who agreed with them. They suffered for their stand. The Foxholes minister in 1657 demanded tithes of £12.19.4 from Quaker Michael Simpson of Boythorpe. He refused and they took ten horses, twenty three beasts and one hundred and thirty one sheep, later sold at Malton for £91.7s.0d.

Luke Robinson of Thornton Risebrough was a major figure in these years. The elder son of Sir Arthur Robinson of Deighton, he had married the daughter of the York Chancellor Phineas Hodgson, but she died in 1634. Their daughter married Thomas Strangeways of South House, Ugglebarnby, an active officer for the Parliament, and one of four men who seized Catholic vestments belonging to Lord Eure, and burnt them in Malton market place in 1656. Luke was the Member of Parliament for Scarborough in 1645, and Bailiff there on occasions. He was an independant Puritan in the Rump Parliament, and a member of the national Council of State from 1649 to 1659. He was M.P. for the North Riding from 1656-58 and for Malton in 1659.

Luke Robinson dealt with such eccentrics as Ralph Walker, who announced a book in Old Malton church which forbad payment of church tithes. He saw the gypsies apprehended at Normanby, who came from Butterwick, but were lately of Newgate prison. They had passed through several counties telling people's fortunes. With Mr. Percehay of Ryton, Luke Robinson set up the Pickering House of Correction. A busy justice, he had a witchcraft case in 1652 at Scarborough. He told quarter sessions that Kirkby Moorside chancel was in great decay and liable to fall. The churchwardens said that since Robert Otterburne and Tobias Thurscrosse had the rectory with all its incomes, then they ought to repair the chancel. They were duly charged. Tobias wrote to Sir William Ingram saying scandalous and reproachful words against him.

Magistrates conducted marriages from 1653 to 1658. Robert Stafford presided over several at Langtoft. Besides Luke Robinson, the local group of Parliamentarian JPs included Benjamin Norcliffe of Nunnington, Richard Etherington of Ebberston, Christopher Percehay of Ryton, Richard Darley of Buttercrambe and Henry Hall of Lilling. At Kirkby Moorside, Luke duly married John Green aged 31, to Elizabeth Bransdale aged 31, in the open Market Place.

William Luck at Kirkby Moorside was a radical Presbyterian minister, and William Sturdy chosen as parish register, was probably of a similar leaning. Mr. Luck joined with the ministers of Thornton Dale, Edstone and Lastingham in a 'movement for the suppression of vice and the punishment of offenders'. This was probably that time, spoken of by the old wives of later generations, when Ryedale ministers began making 'sygills', small seals or charms, in order to drive out those that were being sold by the women thought of as local witches. It was a time of great controversy. Leonard Conyers, the ejected minister of Lastingham molested Lucke, and assaulted his own successor at Lastingham, Phillip Peckett, even managing for a time to lock him out of the vicarage. Dame Clara Vaughan at Whitwell spoke scandalous words against the Commonwealth.

The Restoration of the Monarchy and the Established Church

Sir Barrington Bouchier of Beningbrough Hall met General Monk and the army between Northallerton and Topcliffe in January 1660 and brought them to York. The period 'between the Kings' was at an end. Charles II was enthroned as the new monarch. The High Commission and the Council of the North had gone and with them northern government. A full Cavalier Parliament was revived and Cromwellian legislation cancelled. A garrison returned to Scarborough castle. Puritan justices were replaced by traditional gentry.

Bishops were restored in the established church and dispossessed clergy re-emerged. A new drive for religious uniformity was expressed in an 'Act for the Uniformity of Public Prayers' requiring use of the restored prayer book, and insisting on oaths of loyalty. The idea of one all embracing Protestant church died. Some radical vicars left the church in 1660, and more were evicted from Goathland, Kirkby Moorside, Malton, Lastingham, Oswaldkirk and Stonegrave. Enoch Sinclair a godly man and good preacher left Slingsby and John Lucock the curate went from Birdsall. When all the clergy were required to swear allegiance to the state church in 1662, some other ministers refused. Hopes of significant church reform ended.

Mr. Denton at Oswaldkirk didn't conform, but he was well connected, and moved to West Newton Grange where he quietly continued Presbyterian meetings. William Lucke the Kirkby Moorside minister went to Bridlington, where he kept a radical flame alive, and established an important Presbyterian tradition. Sir Thomas Norcliffe's widow at Langton, a lady of notable piety, sheltered some ejected ministers, who had been reduced to poverty. Sir John Gibson at Welburn, once again a justice of the peace, told the constables to search for Anabaptists and Quakers. He had started a common place book in 1656, when he was a royalist prisoner at Durham castle. Among the translations of sermons from the Greek and Latin, devotional prayers of his own, and recipes, he had a note saying that 'a Quaker is a church rebel'. Religious dissent went underground, but would wax strong under persecution, while the established church lost some of its most vigorous people.

Men had grown used to expressing opinions and differing opinions remained. Captain John Smith died in a drunken affray with 'roundheads' at Thorpe's Malton Inn during 1661. Sir Thomas Ingram said of the 'giddy commons' a year later that 'they'll stir but to their own destruction'. Cromwellian captains were involved in the rising of 1663 centred on Farnley Woods near Leeds. Captain Strangewayes, now residing at Pickering, Francis Driffield of Easingwold and Thomas Lascelles of Mount Grace were among the suspects.

The rising led to the notorious Conventicle Act of 1664, which banned separate prayer meetings of five or more and promised heavy penalties. This encouraged informers. Compulsory attendance was again attempted in Anglican churches. Dogs were whipped out of Kirkdale church, when their howling became too much. There was some gain, here and there, in the dales. In the face of dissenting competition, the rights of mother churches were relaxed and the outlying Cockan chapel gained burial rights in Bransdale, joined by Farndale soon after, while a wooden chapel was built at Newton on Rawcliffe.

The Quakers did not attend the parish churches. Nor did they go underground. They ignored the state's decrees and continued openly to pursue their 'inward religion', missioning widely and aggressively. Thomas Slinger the Helmsley vicar was challenged by Quakers from

Bilsdale, Ampleforth, Oldstead, Antofts and Helmsley, who tore his surplice and prayer book at a funeral in 1665. The wrath of the law fell upon them.

They stood firmly by their principles. Many members were heavily fined for refusing to pay church tithes. Robert Tindall of Duggleby had a swine worth 7s. taken from him because he wouldn't pay the parish clerk's wages of 1s.8d .Robert Mainforth of Butterwick lost his great iron pot worth 11s. for refusing to pay the clerk 5s.4d. Robert Pearson of Rosedale was in Pickering castle for twenty weeks for refusal to pay tithes. Another Quaker spent almost a year in the prison at Pickering castle and died there. George Fox was imprisoned for a time at Scarborough Castle. These were stubborn men and women.

The 'Friends' held regular meetings in their own houses, drawing members together from wide areas, to 'wait on the Lord'. They organised monthly and quarterly meetings and other 'meetings for sufferings' to give support to each other. They established burial grounds on sites of their own choosing at Lowna, Lealholm, Cockan, Rillington, Farndale, Leavening and perhaps Barton le Street. Malton Friends built a meeting house in Spital Street in 1677, and a Kirkby Moorside meeting house was in use soon after, where friends gathered periodically, while continuing to meet at members' houses. Their reach knew few bounds. John Richardson of Hutton le Hole, a friend of William Penn, would ride four thousand miles in two long visits, to the new lands across the oceans, preaching to American Indians. This society, which stressed the individual, became better organised than those that emphasised the group.

A Catholic King

King James II reigned briefly from 1685 to 1688. A Ryedale widow said that she thought he was a Catholic at heart, and she was right. Nunnington Hall provided his principal local supporters. Sir Richard Graham, later Viscount Preston had inherited Nunnington Hall from an uncle and married Ann Howard daughter of Charles Earl of Carlisle. He had served as Charles II's Ambassador to the court of Louis XIV and became Secretary of State to King James. After the King's flight, he was accused of plotting his return and was imprisoned. They would say of him that he was 'great in the palace but greater in the prison'. His daughter Catherine married William Lord Widdrington, who continued to support the Prince across the water. He was employed in the Queen's household. Both families offered havens for those of their faith, maintaining a Benedictine priest with the help of collections from farmers. The Gilling vicar wrote sadly in his register '1678, baptism, son of Lord Widdrington, as I was told.'

The opposition to any restoration of Catholicism had grown stronger with the passing years. A count made in 1676 had shown that of 8090 adult persons in old Ryedale only 152 were 'popish recusants' and 253 were other kinds of dissenters. This will not have been the whole story but it was very suggestive. Gilling, Hovingham and Malton had some Catholics, and a priest Thomas Thwing was circulating about Kirkdale. At Kirkby Moorside and Lastingham, where Presbyterian ministers had served, there were clusters of Protestant dissenters. Neither could be seen as a great threat but the Catholics always raised fears, far in excess of their numbers. The King was led to offer concessions to Protestant dissenters in order to gain tolerance for Catholic dissenters, but he had to re-impose the laws against Catholics a year later. The country wouldn't have it. He sought to appoint Catholic justices, men like John Crosland of Helmsley, but the gentry were broadly against that.

Charles Rymer the New Malton mercer and Francis Rymer the innkeeper were charged in 1685 with publishing false news tending to stir up rebellion. A yeoman from Holme in Ryedale said he would fight for the Protestant claimant to the throne, the Duke of Monmouth, as long as any blood remained in him. There were trimmers too. Sir Thomas Belassis is said to have dexterously shifted his sails to every change in the wind. From Royalist he became Republican, marrying Cromwell's daughter, turned to a Monarchist at the Restoration, a Revolutionist when James II lost his crown and he was finally a councillor to William III.

Scarborough Castle was seized by the Earl of Danby, as part of the so-called 'Glorious Revolution', bringing Dutch William of Orange to the throne, with his wife Mary, daughter of King James II, in 1689. It was neither glorious nor a revolution but it mattered. This was a compromise that worked. A New Malton linen draper could say 'God damme the King William and Queen Mary' but the succession to the throne had been peacefully secured.

Toleration for Nonconformists

The arrival of a Protestant King and Queen necessitated the 'Toleration Act' of Parliament of 1689. This gave religious freedom to all but Catholics and Unitarians, although dissenters still suffered some political disadvantages. Religious dissent surfaced more widely than might have been expected. Only freeholders had the sort of security that allowed much choice and that wasn't limitless. They could now openly use the quite numerous houses, that were licenced in the years that followed, for dissenting worship, by these emerging denominations, and by Quakers. Each local group became free to follow its own course.

The dissenters were not all of one mind, particularly in their convictions about church organisation. There were the Quakers and at least three other bodies of opinion, which showed signs of becoming separate sects, if not denominations. The Presbyterians wanted an organised church, run by its membership, but without Bishops. The Baptists stressed adult recruitment to the church, by a definite decision and commitment. The Congregationalists were then called Independants. They took the view that wherever a group of people gathered, there was a church and that neither hierarchy nor elaborate organisation was needed. Each nuance had implications for the respective roles of members and ministers.

Religious nonconformity became respectable, and yet toleration, within a few decades, proved erosive of the need to be different. The well organised Quakers survived but outside the market towns the dissenting groups withered away. Parish registers record old dissenters rejoining the church, although family tradition might deliver them again into revived noncomformity, in a more expansive age. Even the Quakers showed signs of becoming a denomination within the wider society, rather than a challenge to it.

Life in the established church seemed a litle quieter as the old fires burned low. If its piety was more conventional than challenging, it proved broad enough to include a majority of those who were concerned. The Church of England exemplifed respectability, and identified most closely with the social hierarchy and the state. From both, came encouragement for a new movement to achieve 'a reformation of manners'. It was argued that piety and virtue were to the pleasure of the Almighty. Justices were charged to deal with offences of profanity. Men from Farndale and Bilsdale were charged with saying such things as 'the devil burn thee'. A Helmsley man from Sour Leys was in fault for 'god damn thee' and 'a pox on thee'. One Welburn man told another 'Thou hath the French pox in thy nose'.

Old Devils

Catholicism had turned older gods into evil spirits. The Protestants and particularly their advance guard, the Puritans, had taken much of the 'magic' out of religion. The prophecy, the rituals, the curses, the relics; the people, days and places endowed with especial holiness, had largely gone from the church. Whatever needs they had met still remained, and older beliefs were not yet extinguished outside the church. Even within it, there was something of magic remaining. The ability to hold conflicting beliefs at the same time is not rare. Canon Atkinson, a nineteenth century historian and clergy man in Danby dale thought that the beliefs and practices of popular paganism only weakened under the impact of the schoolmaster and Methodism in a much later century.

The magic of this seventeenth century continued. The evil spirits remained in the imagination. Tree posts of mountain ash, called 'witch posts', were still marked and erected at the entry, from the threshold into the cruck houses, to ward them off. Fragments of the wood were sought on a particular day, St Helen's Day, by following a different route each year, and placed everywhere as something more than just lucky charms. Four people from Danby claimed to have seen the fairies at their midnight revels in 1650. An Easingwold man was accused of conjuring up the devil. Nathan Warner of Castleton talked to a 'hob' in 1694, the local name for a much talked of society of goblins, of which individual hobs, were reckoned to haunt hearth and home. He restored the faith of another villager, who had lacked the courage to admit to his acquaintance with the hob. The 'dark ages' had not altogether gone.

A cluster of so-called witches were active around Blackamore. Molly Milburn of Danby was whipped in 1663 for bewitching cattle. The magic cubes that she made, included ground bone taken from skulls at the gibbet, mixed with blood, toad heart, worms and graveyard moss. They were carefully inscribed with the acorn of long life, hearts crossed by a key, the lover's knot, and other symbols, which had to be inscribed in the right order, in the right way, at the right time, in an elaborate ritual, seen as essential for their success. She also turned out garters for young lasses, inscribed 'my garter is yours to win', in order to make a shilling or two. Mother Migg of Cropton and Dinah Suggit of Levisham used crystals. Nancy Skaife of Spaunton moor was credited with the ability to prophecy. She would tell fortunes, and she knew the recipe for magic cubes. Hester Mudd of Rosedale could use the evil eye, and 'turn herself into a cat.' Susan Ambler was put in the ducking stool for putting a spell on sheep.

Marriage

The choice of marriage partner was arguably the only important social decision, that many young people ever took. This was much anticipated, not least because marriages were delayed in to late years. Young people threw nuts in fires to see which way they cracked, or sought prophetic dreams, by placing graveyard moss under pillows, to show the partner that fate would give them. The crystal balls of witches were consulted to foretell fate. Their love potions and charms were bought to influence fate.

Old people advised that 'it was better to marry over the midden than over the moor'. There was wisdom in the advice to 'never judge a woman or linen by candlelight'. There might be walks down 'love lanes'. After youthful 'trothplight', the giving of promises at some old oak, lads bound garters round a girl's leg, as she promised to be true. They were removed by the winner of the young men's race following a wedding. Bella Matthew's garter bore a small lock, and a hands off message for the victor. She 'was well favoured in the shape of her legs'according to an observer.

Another old saying claimed that 'he who would the daughter win, must with the mother first begin'. Where there was property, the arranged marriage was normal. Henry Best described the procedure in the Wolds, where parents made the initial approaches. An arranged marriage at Hovingham between William Consett, elder son of a freeholder and Elizabeth Bradley, a widow of West Ness, was thoroughly practical, in providing the essential elements to establish a new household. An agreement bound the woman's mother to give him two cows, two whies, a horse, two oxen and household goods worth a pound, within the month. The boy's father was to give the parlour end of his dwelling house, and half his local land. Even gentry wives were subject to the robust rituals of 'getting the bride to bed'. Aids to passion were offered. A popular aid to conception was an eelskin of live snails worn over night. A seducer told Mary Eure that matrimony was a sovereign remedy, if not the only complete medicine for all feminine infirmities. He was something of an optimist.

If marriage was not that, it was, among other things, an essential partnership for the management of every farm, a great many craft workshops and most estates. Widows and widowers on farms, had to remarry quickly to keep things going. The working relationships were of a kind now rare outside farming, and getting rare within it, but involved a wide range of complementary duties. Writers of the time spelt them out. They either stun a 21st century mind or reduce it to helpless hilarity.

Some gentry relationships had the opportunity to be more variable. An accepted notion of the gentleman was that he was one who could live idly and without manual labour. Alice Thornton blessed with a melancholic husband, and not notably hilarious herself, said 'they were like two buckets in a well. When one was up, the other was down'. Quite otherwise was Elizabeth Charlton of Danby married for the seventh time in 1681, having had 'eleven children by six husbands, three by Lord C. and two others gotten by the way'. She was described as a 'well shaped buxom strumpet' and they said that she was 'one made to temptation'.

The Perils of Childhood

Alice Thornton's account of a gentry childhood, tells something of an age of incredibly high mortality, among the young, at all early ages. The child faced the injurious dealings of evil persons, the neglects and brutishness of nurses, the carelessness of others, 'overlaying', bad food, evil milk and the 'malice of Satan'. She experienced early injury against a hearth stone, ailment from beef not well boiled, and the small pox. She was thrown in flight from the hands of a swinging boy. There was a storm at sea, and a servant who put fire embers under the stair. And from generation to generation, it was much the same.

Her children at Newton grange had poor milk from wet nurses, high falls from ropes strung on beams, ill digested meat and over -strong medicine. There was suffering from rickets, consumption, convulsions, small pox and cough. A daughter played with pins and one was stuck in her throat. A son fell four yards in a hay barn. The mother delivering a child was 'on the rack' for two hours. There was half a year of haemorrhoids and a quarter year, unable to touch the ground because of a lame knee. She had gangrene in a nipple. Astonishingly, she thought she deserved worse for failing in her duty, though she admitted that she was not given to any sinful enormous crimes.

Midwives were licenced from 1660 to 1700. They formed a

medical service well scattered through the district, with Mary Moore at Lockton, Martha Richardson at Kirkby, Kath Burwell at Sheriff Hutton followed by Elizabeth Daice and Ellen Midgeley, Elizabeth Consett at Hovingham and Margaret Conyers at Helmsley, Ann Constable at Skirpenbeck and Elizabeth Bell at Settrington. What difference they made has yet to be discovered. The parish registers show the marked contrast between good years, 1673 and 1685 at Midleton parish and the bad years 1682 and 1683 when there four to five times the number of burials. This didn't change. There were still bad years in 1748 and 1749.

Farming and the Early Inclosures

The process called 'inclosure' could be partial or complete. It could replace large common fields and meadows under communal management by smaller fields under individual management. It could alternatively, replace part or all of a common moor or carr, by individually owned plots, in which no common rights remained. It could be arranged for a manor or a township. Inclosure could be done all at once, or at intervals. Much of the local history of farming in particular townships is governed by the way that inclosure was done.

An estate township could inclose faster than a community of freeholders, for then the agreement of many people was essential. Crown commissioners in Elizabeth's time faced trhe problem at Pickering. They wanted to improve the commons, which they called the waste - a bad start. They suggested that the Queen should have two thirds but would offer the parson a third, from which the copyholders and the poor could be satisfied. Such an arbitrary plan had no chance of getting anywhere with a large body of freeholders.

Much later, in 1676, Pickering's 260 houses still had 2516 cultivated acres, arranged in six fields of scattered strips, some of them in ridges, rising up to a mile long in the sloping land, where their riggs are visible to this day. Nearby Newton had three fields totalling four hundred acres. The two townships shared their unaltered commons. Some of the oxgang land had been put down to pasture but not permanently. Behind this apparently unchanging scene, one slow kind of enclosure was under way. In a multitude of written agreements, the free holders confirmed their exchanges of strips with each other, so that they could consolidate larger blocks. In time these would be enclosed in a peacemeal fashion, bringing closes into the fields. This required manorial consent or a 'custom of enclosures', because pasturing rights, in the aftermath of the field crops, were being lost. But it happened. The tithe owner had objected, at the York assize courts in 1668, but the Pickering men swore to a custom of inclosures, laid down but opened every fallow year. The Court jury went against the judge's advice and found for them. The case was heard again, but again the great man lost and the small men won.

Table 30. The Pickering Fields, Ings and Commons; Acreage in 1676

Fields		Ings	
Little East field	181	East and West	540
Tofts field	85		
Malton Gate field	361		
North or Castle field	369	**Oxpastures**	
Westgate Low field	390	East side	127
Beacon or Swainsea Field	238	West side	75
LittleDale field	150		
Newton three fields	400		

Carrs	
Eastgate	455
Westgate	338

Commons above the town	
Scallaymoor and Howledale	110
Haugh Rigg, West Moor, Keldell moor and the Yates	865
Low moor	310
High moor	1763
Newton dale	148

Pickering arable, meadow and pasture	2516
commons	3929
Newton fields	400
sum	6845

Elsewhere, common fields were being enclosed in a different way. Local agreements were made at Slingsby, Hovingham, Wombleton and Hutton le Hole, among other places. Thomas Worsley and the Marquess of Newcastle, proprietors of the two main Hovingham estates, derived from the ancient manorial and Newbrough Priory properties, made an inclosure in 1661. Hutton le Hole, where ownership was more divided, used six local commissioners to inclose their field land in 1670, while leaving their commons untouched. Thomas Hebblethwaite's will speaks of enclosure at Norton and Sutton, and in 1675 John Hill and other owners enclosed the fields of Farmanby and the west side of Thornton Dale. There was serious discussion about enclosing the fields at Ebberston.

The general trend was towards more pasture, even within the fields. Butter shipments were increasing. Some from Helmsley and Malton even went northwards to Yarm, along with much from the Vale of York and Cleveland. Whitby was becoming famous for cheese. A Scarborough list of 'firkiners' of 1677, included men at Ebberston, Lockton and Cropton. Butter was often the significant cash product on the farm. Thomas Blackbeard of East Ness had thirty six trenchers and eighty four bowls in his milk house in 1694. George Sunley at West Ness in a smaller house, had six skeels, two cans and forty six bowls. Farndale and Bransdale seemed to lack the ox, hay and wain houses prevalent in Bilsdale but they did have about thirty cowhouses and thirty barns on the same number of farms. Most of the Rosedale houses consisted of two parlours, a chamber and a milkhouse. Thomas Frankland at Hartoft in 1692 had a milkhouse, replete with churn, skeels, a can, butter bowls and dishes. Joseph Watson at Rosedale had a milk house, and a water house, perhaps for cooling.

Other Ways of Living

Linen manufacture was expanding into the major home industry, a second occupation in many households .The room on the far side of the threshold could hold young calves, or it could hold a weaver's loom. Stephen Boyes the Goathland miller was typical of many in 1656, with a linen web in his parlour, and nine linen sheets and nine hempen sheets to hand. A Bagby man inYork Vale had both a milk house and a loom house with looms, webs and yarn to the value of £23, as well as a spinning wheel worth £3 in 1694. A new estate fulling mill was built at Helmsley in 1697. Mrs. Palmes, the Malton landowner, appears to have converted her great Hall gatehouse into a linen manufactory. Pulped rags from the linen trade, now supplied paper mills at Ellerburn, Byland and Oldstead.

Whitby and Scarborough were becoming ports of great and growing importance, awakening the lure of the sea and providing well paid new employments. After 1660 shipbuilding became a substantial industry, at both ports. This included the building of many collier brigs, for the rapidly expanding Newcastle and Sunderland coal trade, down the coast to London and Europe. The number of vessels locally owned and manned increased in the growing Baltic trade, as well as coal ships. Fish were still carried inland by lines of ponies. Thomas Taylor the York pannierman of 1675 had a house and stable at Robin Hoods Bay for his ten horses.

The Saltwick alum works was active south east of Whitby, with a new east side yard for imported coal. Other works were at Eskdale, Littlebeck and Stoupe in Whitby Strand and several more in Cleveland. Great containers stood in Whitby streets to collect the urine necessary for the process, while many a farm had a 'lant jar' to collect the fluid. Seaweed was burnt along the coast to make kelp, a source of potash.

The ports became 'nurseries of seamen', a magnet for inland men seeking better wages, and a focus for small investors to buy a profitable share, in a ship or in a voyage. By 1690, inland Lockton and Farndale already had a mariner or two. Coastal exports and imports were far greater than in the early years of the century. The coastways export of butter and corn was buoyant, joining the alum and the knitted woollen stockings from north west Yorkshire. London groceries, Baltic timber, flax and naval stores poured back into Scarborough. Three naval wars were fought with the Dutch and the enemy fleets hovered, threatening the coastal coal convoys.

The Great Houses

The new mansions were very impressive. With the restoration of the monarchy, and the sense of security based on rising wealth, many a squire reconstructed his hall, in stone or in newly fashionable brick. They were still built with arrays of chimneys breaking the skyline above many gable ends. They used imported Baltic deals for floors, and French glass for the many ample windows, which new window taxes made into status symbols. Heavy furniture made from imported woods came into the houses. The cynic remarked that 'the meal is no better, eaten off a mahogany table'.

West Newton Hall had long corridors, wainscotted rooms with large fireplaces, large windows with window seats, extra cupboards and the big kitchen chimney of the times. The great parlour was hung with family portraits. There were scarlet and grey chambers, and a study. A four poster bed had yellow hangings. Each room had a large over mantle with classical orders. Each item of furniture, pewter or brass carried the owner's mark upon it. Outside was a chapel croft, an avenue, a garden and a brick Summer House.

Most of these houses have gone and the survivors are much altered but there were many of them, not all of huge dimensions. Beck House at Cropton was rebuilt in 1668 and Muscoates Hall in 1669. Thomas Worsley built a new house at Hovingham in 1679, to which his son would add gardens. The younger Thomas Worsley returned from the Grand Tour in 1684. Many like him were impressed by the ruins, they had seen, from the classical architecture of Greece and Rome. Their houses would begin to mirror them. Before long, pilasters and pediments, casement windows, classical columns and rusticated gateways would enter the builders' vocabulary for the country house. Pickering parsonage house, where that noted courtier Henry Osborne lived, the largest house in the town, was pulled down and rebuilt with two cellars in 1698 in a more conventional style.

Brick had been known for centuries and was a major industry at mediaeval Beverley. Brick buildings emerged slowly in Ryedale. Easingwold brickmakers would travel out, find a suitable clay, squeeze it in horsemills, clamp it in wood moulds and fire the bricks on the building sites for gentry houses. Bricks were made at Oulston for Newbrough priory mill in 1689, and Huby had a bricklayer in 1692. This started a long, slow change of the landscape. The Galtres lowlands towards York and other areas with no stone, would increasingly adopt brick as their dominant building material.

The greatest of the old country houses gave way to another. The Malton mansion fell to two daughters of Lord Eure. Mary married William Palmes of Naburn and Margaret wed Thomas Danby, the first Mayor of Leeds, about whom his relations said, that 'he was very free from that fashionable vice of being a good fellow.' But the sisters Peg and Moll quarrelled. The great Malton house is said to have been divided between them, stone by stone, and it has certainly disappeared. In place of the old peak of the local social system came a new one. The greatest building of them all was Castle Howard built by Vanbrugh and amended by Hawksmoor for the Earl of Carlisle, between 1683 and 1694, sweeping away Hinderskelfe castle and village in the process.

Table 31. The Number of Hearths in some North East Yorkshire Houses in 1670 –1673

39-Sir Hugh Cholmley (Whitby Abbey)
38-Viscount Fauconberg (Newbrough Priory)
37-William Palmes Esq & Madame Margaret Danby (Old Malton)
32-Sir Francis Boynton (Burton Agnes)
28-Sir Roger Langley (Sheriff Hutton Park)
26-Sir Thomas Gower (Stittenham)
24-Lady Wentworth (Howsham Hall)
23-Sir William Strickland (Boynton); Sir John Napier Bt. (Seamer)
22-Lady Anne Sydenham (Hackness Hall)
21-Lord Fairfax (Gilling castle)
19-William Thornton Esq (East Newton)
18-Sir William Strickland (ConeysthorpeHall); Earl of Carlisle (Henderskelfe Castle)
17-Lady Hebblethwaite (Norton or Welham); Charles Tancred Esq (Arden Hall); John Gibson Esq (Welburn Hall)
16-John Scur Esq (Sutton WC); Hugh Cholmeley Esq (West Newton (or Rievaulx)
15-Sir Watkinson Paylor (Skirpenbeck); Mr Weddle (Strensall); Lady Sara Hotham (Fylingdales)
14-Sir Thomas Norcliffe (Langton Hall); James Danby Esq (Kirkby Knowle); Edward Hutchinson (Wykeham Abbey); Mr. Watson (Helmsley castle)
13-Mr Charles Belasyse (Oulston); Mr Christopher Pearcihay (Ryton); Sir John Legard (Ganton); Mr Wm Barnard (West Heslerton)
12-Reginald Graham Esq (Nunnington); Mr. William Rogers (Westow); Mr Belt (Buttercrambe); Thomas Cholmeley (Brandsby); William Cayley Esq (Brompton)

The Changing Elite

New times brought new men, by marriage or purchase, into the great estates. George Villiers, second Duke of Buckingham, went overseas into exile after the Civil War, and his forfeited estates were assigned to General Fairfax. He returned quietly in 1657 and married Fairfax's daughter Mary. He recovered his estate in 1660. He was made Lord Lieutenant in West Yorkshire and was active in the court circle and as a member of the Cabal government of King Charles II. He was occasionally active in the York social circle, where he met his paramour Lady Shrewsbury. The Duke retired to Helmsley castle in 1687 on the accession of King James II and lived there for eight years. He died at Kirkby Moorside in a tenant's house after hunting. An unsympathetic poet described him:

'A man so various that he seemed to be,
not one but all mankind's epitome,
stiff in opinion, always in the wrong,
was everything by starts and nothing long,
but in the course of one revolving moon,
was chemist, fiddler, statesman and buffoon'.

Many little known esquires and gentlemen rode to Malton for the heraldic visitation of 1665-6. There were many new names, Egerton from Allerston, Horsley from Beck House Grange, Marshall of Aislaby Grange and many more. The Herald later issued a long list of those who had declined his notice to appear, including Will Clement of Bossall and John Heslerton of Hutton on Derwent. The lesser gentry were becoming more numerous. Twenty were recorded in Pickering parish over as many years, most living around the town, but others at Blansby park or in the Marishes. The esquires had name like Lascelles, Conyers, Nandike and Marshall showing their descent from local old gentry lines.

Viscount Fauconberg and Viscount Fairfax were Restoration Lord Lieutenants for the North Riding. They were among the richest families in the shire. Thomas Fauconberg had married Mary daughter of Oliver Cromwell. Pepys described the couple in 1663 at London's Theatre Royal, she wearing a vizard, it being 'late a fashion to hide the whole face'. She rescued her father's remains from Westminster and re buried them at Newbrough Priory.

Sir Charles Duncombe the hugely wealthy goldsmith and banker of London, bought the Helmsley estate in 1695, reputedly for £90.000. He was Lord Mayor of London in 1708. He seems to have been an absentee from Helmsley, where his accounts show payments to the poor, to gamekeepers, and for keeping the park deer, the lodge and a bowling green. The poet Pope commented again:

'Helmsley,once proud Buckingham's delight,
Slides to a scrivener or a city knight'.

The heads of gentry houses could have very different experiences in life. Sir Henry Chomley died at Tangier, where his brother Sir Hugh was governor, presiding over an early colonial venture that failed. James Smith was William Cayley's Steward for Brompton, and wrote the comedy 'Cytherea or the enamouring girdle'. Samuel Marshall from Wrelton Hall managed the Osborne family's Pickering parish tithes.

Luke Robinson expelled from the House of Commons in 1660 lived on among his Puritan tomes at Risebrough for decades. His daughter Lady Boynton complained of her sinful body, but expected to appear and be blessed on Judgment Day. Sir Ranald Graham founded Nunnington hospital and a school in 1688. Gentry ladies without heirs were a major source of charities. Lady Boynton founded a Kirkby Misperton School in 1673. Lady Lumley endowed extensive estates on her foundation in 1657, which supported a Grammar School at Thornton Dale, a primary school at Sinnington and a Thornton almshouse.

Gentle women kept books of recipes. There was more to cooking now. Mary Thompson could make pies with carp, neat's tongues, minced beef, hare or pears. Her puddings were made with orange, bone marrow, rice, kidney, hogsblood, mutton or veale, eels, eggs, not to mention white puddings and sausages. She could make hash or French bread. Her table could carry pickled oysters, soused eels, almond milk cordial and hartshorn jelly. She had notes on how to boil a cod's head, how to make lobsters keep for three months and on pickling gherkins and walnuts. She would make possets, pancakes, and peas pottage. Clearly the storage of raw food was a problem.

Timothy Mauleverer of Ingleby Arncliffe kept the man's equivalent of her common place book. He noted that a horse load of Durham coal cost him fifteen shillings. Practical experience told him that breckon cut brown, a fortnight after Michaelmas, gave better kindling for coal fires than wood chips. He thought rape oil was cheapest for lamps; he used turpentine for taking out grease spots and brandy to wash a wound. He found borax useful to avoid infection, despite 'a little transitory smarting'. To become fair of face, he advised washing with cold small beer. His Uncle Metcalf made his own wax candles and yet had a York coach, lined with blue velvet, and with glass windows on each side that would draw up.

The inside of the great houses was transformed by hanging pictures. Family portraits by Sir Godfrey Kneller, or some comparable painter, were almost obligatory. He painted the Palmes portraits at

Malton and left his paintings of the Duchess of Manchester and Lady Robinson at Welburn Hall. He was paid for pictures at Hovingham hall in 1685. Hugh Cholmley at West Newton was portrayed in armour by Riley in 1674, while the Combers at Newton Hall were painted by Sir Peter Lely.

There was a growing interest in house gardens and orchards. Alice Thornton transplanted cuttings from Hipswell to East Newton 'to set in the rows and walks in front of my house ...for I ever took a delight both in the ornament as well as in the pleasure and profit of it on my land'. Hovingham received fruit trees from London in the seventies. Sir Richard Graham had cherry, peach and plum trees, sent from the capital, for planting at Nunnington. There, the Marquiss of Winchester tried his fruit, on leaving Scarborough spaw in 1683.

Many country gentlemen and their ladies were drawn into the newly fashionable social circuits. They went to York for assize weeks, to see plays and visit the new coffee houses opened at Stonegate and Minster yard, or for race meetings and the assemblies held at Lord Irwin's house. Annually, they visited the spaws to take the waters at Harrogate or Scarborough, and indulged the new therapies of cold sea water bathing. Scarborough was the first seaside spaw and had become the first seaside bathing place. The resort was already a great place of social assemblies and diversions, as much for the healthy as the ailing.

Fashion in clothes and cosmetics was the more demanding for being displayed more often. Mrs. Hall of East Lilling could kill a sheep and complain that it was very fat, but she also wanted a black silk gown from London for the Winter. The widowed Ann Etherington of Rillington in 1654 had a crimson damask petticoat and a black silk waistcoat wrought with gold. She gave her grandchild a needle work covering and five cushions. Lady Bellasiss of Newbrough was remembered by her grand children for the great quantities of perfume that she used.

Most of the gentry followed country sports. James Hebblethwaite of Norton entered his horse Daudler, for the owner's plate, when he and seven others raced horses on Langton Wolds in 1692. He bequeathed his 'hawke and spaniels' to Sir Thomas Norcliffe, and to his man Gabriel, gave his 'setter bitch and all his nets'. Cock fights were ceasing to be a Shrove Tuesday sport, with purpose built cockpits at the inns, advertised contests, professional trainers and heavy gambling. They say that Kilham was the cockpit of the Wolds, while Francis Boynton of Burton Agnes had one of the best breeds of gamecock and his own pit. A ballad

238

'The Fox Chase or Huntsman's Harmony', published before 1680, is said to celebrate the Duke of Buckingham's hounds, and local tradition credits him with starting fox hunting.

More in the Shops

The age of the shop was dawning. Retailers selling local and distant products joined the selling workshop, and the street stall in the market towns, and even in those villages near to a major gentry house. About 1670, York with 2121 households, Scarborough with 514 and Whitby with 335 were major towns and becoming centres for shopping. York was already a shopper's delight, where genteel ladies could buy masks, ribbons and hair powder. It is difficult to realise that Sheffield, Halifax, Doncaster and Wakefield were all still less populous than Scarborough. The local Ryedale market towns were about the same size as thirty others in the county.

Malton had apparently lost its free borough liberties, only retaining a borough bailiff, appointed by the manor lord. In the new world of open trading, it hardly mattered. Grocers were stocking imported groceries in greater quantity, including figs, molasses, lemons, cloves, brimstone, onions and ginger. The towns of Thirsk and Malton had grocers but so did Egton and Gilling while a new Hovingham shop was fitted out with shelves in 1668. John Williamson was grocer at Helmsley in 1674 and John Dent at Kirkby Moorside. A Russia merchant, John Osborne was buried at inland Skelton in 1665.

Malton had some reputation as a spa town now. Thomas Lazenby was the town's doctor of physic in 1668 and there was an apothecary. Richard Denis was the bookseller, almost certainly supplied by Richard Lambert the bookseller at Minster Gate in York. Malton traders included a cattle dealer, Robert Holliday, the mercer Joseph Preston and the haberdasher Michael Pennock. When Thomas Mennell was robbed at the town in 1692, we see something of an ironmonger's stock. He lost razors, buckles and corkscrews, a plain iron, combs, knife and fork, chisel, gouges, spurs, compasses, a two foot rule, inkhorn, gimlet and knife. At Helmsley, there was the hat maker Simon Hamilton, mercer Henry Guist and a Dutch physician Abraham de Groeve. Kirkby Moorside had a yeoman illicitly practising physic. Pickering had Jackson the ironmonger. At the market towns, trade was on a scale sufficient to justify some businesses issuing tokens, during the long shortage of small coin, when clipping was notorious at Scarborough.

Table 32. Some tokens issued in North East Yorkshire, mostly half pennies.		
Malton	- Joseph Preston	(Three Bells, Mercer's arms-1668);
	-A Maddox	(Chickens);
	-Lawrence Dickinson	(Skinner's arms -1670)
	-Edmund Dring	(King'sHead-1666)
	-John Henderson	(Hat & feather, Haberdasher's arms)
	-William Pennock	(possibly a Still-1666)
	-Michael Pennock	(Vintner's Arms-1666)
	-Thomas Galloway	(Grocer & Grocer's arms)
	-John Harrington	(Grocer's arms-1667)
	-Robert Rymer	(Mercer's arms-1667)
	-Will Snary	(Trotting horse)
Kirkby Moorside-	John Thornum	(Thorn bush-1667)
	-A Maddox	(as above)
Helmsley	-John Williamson	(Royal Oak & Stag & hounds-1667)
Pickering	-William Pennock	(Hare and Hounds-1671)
Easingwold	-Michael Woodward	(A man smoking-1668);
	-Thomas Wilson	(Skull & Shield with three crowns-1668)

A Greater Traffic

There are many hints of a growing traffic. The justices were more exercised about road repairs, pressing local waywardens for action, especially on the 'king's highways'. A new stone bridge was made at Sheriff Hutton, on the York-Helmsley-Kirkby Moorside road in 1689. Postal services were regularised. Lieutenant Wade was made sole Whitby post, to collect the letters from the Malton postmaster in 1682. Private gentry stabling at country houses was often extensive. Sir Hugh Cholmley had thirty horses in his stables. James Hebblethwaite of Norton left his grand child 'a bay nag or hobby', a sure sign of affection. Horse thieving and highwaymen increased in the commons at the approaches to York, Scarborough and Whitby. The highwayman

Nevison levied protection money on drovers in the Vale of York until his execution in 1684. The Bracey bridge between Driffield and Bridlingon is said to recall him by his real name.

Table 33. The Guest Beds at Major Destinations in Yorkshire in 1686

York 483		
Leeds 294	Doncaster 206.	Wakefield 242
Malton 195		
Sheffield 119.	Thirsk 110.	Beverley 182
Halifax 130	Hull 199.	Ripon 118
Skipton 72	Northalleton 82	Pontefract 92
Richmond 99	Scarborough 74	Pickering 69
Helmsley60		

Stabling for horses 1686

York 800		
Wakefield 543	Malton 524	
Beverley 460	Leeds 454	Ripon 422
Doncaster 453		
Halifax 306	Hull 349	
Pontefract 235	Richmond 228	Sheffield 270
Thirsk234		

The new kind of Inn flourished along the main roads and in market places. The Duke of Buckingham secured three new fairs for Helmsley.in 1670. The best chance of getting a bed and a stable was at Malton. Edmund Dring's King's Head at Malton, John Thornum's at Kirkby Moorside and Thomas Redmayne's Kings Arms at Northallerton were widely known. The Scots drovers were selling cattle at Malton again in 1664 where Marmaduke Rawdon said that there was 'the greatest horsefair in England'. Drunken Barnaby wrote about that time saying,

> 'To Malton come I, praising th'sale sir,
> Of a horse, without a tail, sir
> Be he maim'd, lam'd, blind, diseased,
> If I sell him, I'm well pleased.
> Should this Kephal die next morrow,
> I partake not in the sorrow.'

Table 34. Main Clusters of Beds and Stables in Ryedale; 1686		
Helmsley	beds 60	stables 136
Hovingham	16	32
Kirkby	33	60
Malton	195	524
Pickering	16	0
Bulmer	3	10
Old Malton	10	19
Oswaldkirk	5	11
Acklam	4	5
Harum	4	5
Hinderskelfe	5	4
Langtoft	3	6
Skewsby	4	8
West Lutton	2	5
Saltergate and Spittle House could put up a solitary traveller.		

Home and Hearth

The reconstruction of old cruck timber houses, within stone cladding, was becoming general. Many of the houses were given lintel stones, with their owner's initials and dates from the 1660's onwards. The great timber crucks still formed a framework of three or more pairs of trees, in bays about sixteen feet apart, joined at the apex to form an inverted V by a saddle, bearing down on a great ridgebeam, the V then made into an A by another cross beam further down. It was the in filling of the walling that changed. A very large cruck house was built at the bottom end of Wrelton village street in 1665.

Stone hearths were placed against a through passage wall, with smoke hoods above, and a salt box and a spice cupboard set in the wall on either side. 'Rannel balks' set in the chimney above the smoke hood, carried a chain with hooks for pots. Sometimes the cruck framework was lifted bodily skywards to give a second floor, giving the walls a new load bearing role. Re-used crucks were often thought, from their signs of earlier use, to be ship's timbers. Thatch remained the main roofing material outside the wolds, but the better houses had pegged limestone tiles. William Marshall at the end of the 18th.century recorded the features of the older houses.

1. The Roman Road on Wheeldale Moor.

2. Helmsley Castle.

3. Rievaulx Abbey.

4. 15th Century Wall Paintings at Pickering Parish Church.

5. Gilling Castle. The Elizabethan Room. A watercolour by Edwin Dolby, 1875

6. Castle Howard.

7. The York to Pickering train passes though Sinnington station, 1953.

8. John Prescott, Deputy Prime Minister, visits Malton during the floods of 2000

Table 35. William Marshall Glossary of Words Describing the Parts of a House.

Bauks-rough chamber in an outbuilding
Beace-cattle stall   Beeld-shelter for stock
Bink-bench at cottage door   Ceiling-wainscotting   and   under
                                drawing for a room
Creel-bier for slaughtering and salving sheep
Dorman-beam of chamber floor
Easins-eaves of house   Entry-entrance or small hall
Fleaks-wattles   Fold garth-farm yard
Gantry -stand for casks   Geavle-gable, or the upright end of a roof.
Heck- rack or entry door   Heynbauks-hen roost
Hood- back of fire   House-sitting room or fore kitchen
Hurn -gap at sides of a wide chimney and the roof
Leer-barn   Linton-main beam of wide chimney
Muckmidden-dung hill   Post and pan-half timber
Rannle bauk-balk across chimney to hang pothooks
Riggen-roof ridge or tree   Shade-shed
Side waver- roof purlin   Steathing-lath and plaster partition
Thack-thatch   Wain house-wagon house
Wattles-rods laid on roof to thatch on.

Many houses were well furnished now. Widow Ann Dobson's Kirkby Moorside house in 1694 had cupboards, tables and long settles in the firehouse, together with a buffet form and two chairs. She had pewter chamber pots, iron dripping pans and a warming pan. The fireplace had a pair of iron racks, a reckon and tongs. Thomas Blackbeard's forehouse at Ness held a table frame, form and long settle, three buffet stools and three chairs, Here were thirteen pewter dishes, two great tankards, salts, a glass case, warming pan, brass candlesticks, chafindish, reckons, fire shovel and tongues. The kitchen had racks, andirons, spitts, kettles, pans, pots and a dripping pan. The parlour held the bedstead, cupboard press and chair. There were other chambers with beds. There was a meal house with 'kimlin' and 'temse'. The low parlour held seven chairs, covered stools, a long settle with cushions, a table and a seeing glass. George Sunley at West Ness was similarly endowed but twelve bushells of wheat and forty bushells of maslin stood about the chambers. Eighty per cent of houses had a single hearth and

A Thatched Cottage at Harum

another nine per cent had two.

Richard Blome in 1675 said that Helmsley was an indifferent built town, but that the houses were of slate and stone. The limestone belt had ample stone, but woldsmen journeyed to Malton and Henderskelfe quarries. A house at Pickering belonging to the Duke of Leeds was repaired in 1738. The carpenter did the bulk of it. A new riggin tree cost £1.12.0, two ribs £1.12.0, eighty spars £4, and the laths completing the roof were £1.5s.0d. The brewhouse, cellar and stable were floored for £10 and racks and window frames installed. A little house and a cole house were added. Inside, the dining room, which had a chimney, was given windows with shutters. The garrets were lathed and plastered, gained a window and some partitions were made. The total cost was £41.10s.0d, then thatching was another £5. A brick chimney was put into the best stables.

Building a gentry house could involve a distant architect, and bring brickmakers and skilled plasterers, or other craftsmen, from York. Ordinary buildings were a more local affair. A few can be dated. Fryton Moor house had deliveries of lime in 1723. The butchers' shops called the shambles in Pickering market place were walled in 1737. Mr. Park marked a tall house I.P. at Keld Head, Pickering and Harriet Hare farm at Helmsley was built in 1758. Perhaps there is a hint of a more general rebuilding as house carpenters appeared and more brick kilns were opened but stone remained the main material in those areas. When the land owner, Sir Charles Hotham had a new smith's shop built at Wilton in 1740, walling and roofing materials were traditional and like the workmen were local, apart from the deals. William Jowsey was the house carpenter, wheelwright and smith in the village and the workshop was built onto a house for his use.

Table 36. Record of the work done in building a smith's shop at Wilton. 1740

John Gilbank mason's work	£3.11.8
John Hauxwell carpenter	£1.16.6.
George Bower, leading stone, lime and sand	£1.5.2
John Hawxwell, deals	9s
Robert Henderson, 2000 nails	5s
William Bower, straw	£1.10.0
Henry Harding, straw	19s
Thomas Audwith, theaking	9s
Robert Brough, serving the theaker	7s

William Jowsey, Robert and Richard Barf,and Kitt at the quarry and at the shop, labouring, 67 days work in all, including making the chimney and the hearth £3.11.9

William Jowsey making spikes, nails, bandes, filling stone and morter, lock and staples for door   11s.5d

---

CHAPTER 6
THE EIGHTEENTH CENTURY. 1714 - 1803

The restoration of the monarchy, the church and parliament in 1660 had changed the balance between the great institutions of the land. The vice-regal Council of the North was abolished. King Charles II retained power but had a fixed annual income, while Parliament controlled taxation. Great noblemen and some gentry bulked large as advisers. His successor King James II was Catholic and attempted to promote Catholicism. The exclusion of his male heirs from the throne was as necessary for the new Anglican church, as for those favouring toleration of Catholics and Nonconformists. The recognition by Parliament of the Dutch Prince William of Orange as King, and Mary, the Protestant daughter of James II as Queen, in 1689, was followed by a Toleration Act.

William's rights as King were more limited than any of his forbears. Parliament voted the King's revenue annually and would take many decisions about its expenditure. Whig and Tory parties competed to serve as the King's advisers, who were slowly becoming the effective government. Catholics and Nonconformists were excluded from office but could worship freely. In 1701, an Act of Settlement brought Mary's sister Anne to the throne but promised the succession to the minor Protestant electors of Hanover, descended from a daughter of James I. Some loyalists to the exiled Stuarts, called Jacobites, planned a Stuart succession after her death but they failed. The Jacobites remained a problem in Scotland, active in the risings of 1715 and 1745.

When the house of Hanover came to the throne, the Whig party, dominated by the great noble families of England came to power for fifty years. From 1721 to 1742 Sir Robert Walpole was the first 'prime minister', of growing significance in the later years of King George I, who spoke no English and had little interest in national politics, but continuing for many years with King George II. Walpole managed the country in a long period of relative peace. The great families enjoyed outstanding wealth, in a period when commerce and industry brought great rewards. Rank remained associated with the ownership of land, where capital would be employed with new effect.

River Navigation.

Improvements to the river Ouse and the river Derwent revived York, and made Malton into an inland port. Farming for distant markets was stimulated throughout a wide area, and several industries were better able to distribute their products. The Malton Derwent Navigation Act of 1701-2 was made effective by investment a decade or two later, about 1720-1725, probably as a result of the acquisition of the principal Malton estate, with the market rights, by the wealthy Watson-Wentworth family. Obstructions in the water course were cleared, and locks, bridges and towpaths built, to allow small vessels to reach Malton. There is an unconfirmed tradition, that only the opposition of the owners of the Flixton estate stopped the navigation being pushed through to the coast at Scarborough. Malton soon gained riverside wharfs to accomodate Hull sloops and Fenton's coal boats with warehouses for goods received and despatched.

The River Ouse Navigation Acts of 1727-1732 initially provided insufficient toll incomes for major improvement on that river, but share issues raised the capital to make the Naburn weir and lock in 1757, which gave a good depth of water in the upper course. Corn ships, keelboats, pinks and 'bully boys' reached the city of York and some went further. This had its effect on a wide area around the city. Sloops and smaller vessels of up to fifty tons burthen, and four and a half feet draught, moved regularly from Malton to Hull. They say that there were fifty or sixty captains on the river, perhaps an exageration.

Out went the corn, particularly oats, for the expanding industrial areas of the West Riding and back came groceries, woollens, agricultural seeds, deals, spices and spirits. The salt boat 'William & Betty' sank in the Derwent on its way to Malton in 1748. Local manufacture was encouraged. Chairs, linen, leather and turves left Malton while flax, deals, glass, coal, hops and paper were brought in. Carriers' wagons from the villages delivered and collected goods at the navigation head. Coal and lime were also unloaded at such small river side landings as Crambe and Stamford Bridge on the Derwent, and Newton on the Ouse.

Malton -'the town of meal and malt'

These were expansion years for the town of Malton, which became the trading centre for a wider country district than ever before. We hear of 332 households in 1732 and 430 families in 1764. The average annual baptisms were little different to earlier decades, until mid century, after which they rose steadily. By 1801 the population was 3047, and it was still rising.

Mark Andrew leased the river tolls in 1720. John Settrington painted a view of 'Malton in Yorkshire' about 1728, from the Orchard Field looking westwards. He showed two ships on the river, but the houses of Castlegate and Yorkersgate seem to have yards rich in trees, rather than the industry which later gave the riverside a character, different to other parts of the town. This impression is confirmed by Joseph Dickinson's 'Map of the Burrow of New Malton' of 1730. This shows three ships below the west end of Yorkersgate, and a hint of an accessway to the water from that street.

The town was still confined within its ancient boundaries, except for the 'cattle market', which had been moved from the Market place, to the west of Newbiggin, outside the walls. The town had thirty two butchers by 1751. Newbiggin had become a long street, a sort of ribbon development into land belonging to Old Malton. There was also a bowling alley outside the north wall. Another rough drawing by Buck, of Malton from the south, showed a town of single storey houses, with the old Eure Lodge, York House and the parish churches of St Michael and St Leonard towering above them. The Derwent bridge had been re-erected in 1700, with three tall arches topped by parapets. Leonard Thompson and Robert Fysh were deputed to see the bridge repairs done 'as easy as may be' in 1730, but it would have to be widened thirty years later.

Most of the town houses were rebuilt at various times between 1730 and 1780. Christopher Dixon was already described as a 'tilemaker' in 1735, at Ryton near Malton, and given the location, this may mean earthenware bricks or tiles. Sir George Strickland's property in the town was bought and added to the Wentworth estate. The agent supervised such elements of the borough and manor courts as remained. Well masters were appointed to look after the three public wells. The town kept four leather searchers and a yarn searcher for the market.

They called Malton 'the town of meal and malt', famous for bread made in brick ovens. A survey made for the Marquess of Rockingham in 1751 shows several houses with kilns. New developments included Andrew's and Mennell's maltkiln, Fenton's wine cellar under the Town's house, Lister's paint house, William Hood's skin yard and Richard Wilson's paper yard. Workshops had opened making spinning

Malton in the Late Eighteenth Century

wheels, breeches and stays. There was a bell foundry, which no doubt did other castings as well. There were several good shops. John Harrison a grocer in 1735 had left enormous legacies and something, as yet unexplained, called Harrison's Folly.

Malton started regular street cleaning in 1748, employing a gardener for the task four times a year. The town streets were paved with cobbles in 1754. Malton traders planned to obtain an Act of Parliament to abolish hawkers and pedlars in 1773 calling them 'the bane of all fair traders'. The town had four hatmakers, supplying what was often the working man's largest single purchase in the year. Between two inns at a corner of the Market Place, Mrs Gaskin built up a trade in linen drapery, millinery, china, glass and tea. Bookseller George Sagg set up a printing press, producing tracts which gave the town political scene, most of what little life it had.

The study of the drift of new industry to the back yards of Yorkersgate and Castlegate awaits a serious student. An industrial quarter emerged. Corn mills were built and then enlarged. They said in 1788 that Malton corn factors made their own prices and some were

Table 37; The Borough of Malton - Households in 1732.

Street	Sites	Freeholds	People with titles of status (& institutions)
New Biggin	24	8	Mr. Watson.Quaker meeting house, Esquire Strickland
Finkill Street	4	2	Mr. Watson Mrs. Lacy
Market Place	45	15	Mr. Watson, Mr Bainbridge, Mrs.Hardwick. Mr.Conyers, Mr.Rymer, Mr. Annison, Mr. Wilson, Mr Fairfax, Mr. Preston, Mr. Mannuel Mr.Hardwick, Mr. Crist, Mr.Pratt, Mr. Harrison, Mrs Walker, Mr. Walmsley Mrs.Taylor, Mrs.Stringer
In Market Place.	10	5	Mr.Mills, Mr. Lister, Mr. Rymer, Mrs.Sewell.
East side	10	2	Prison house, Mrs. Lister, Mr. Smith
Wheel Gate	26	4	Nicholas Harrison's maltkiln
York House Gate	42	6	Mr. Elstob, Mrs Rochester stable Mark Andrew's staith. Mrs. Sherston, Mr. Hick, Mr Hawden, Mr. Stringer, Mrs. Taylor, Mr.Lister, Mr. Harrison's warehouse, Mr. Cartwright, Sir Wm Strickland's coachouse, Mr. Elstob, Mr. John Carr, Doctor Sherston,
Castle Gate	26	8	
Low street	20	9	Mr. Rowintree, Mr. Seller,
Castle Gate	21	9	Mr. Barton, Mr. Burnett, Mr.Lacey
Old Malton gate	30	14	Mr. Croft, Mrs. Carter
Greengate	31	11	
Old Malton gate	15	4	Mr. Burnet.Mrs Rochester stable
Wheelgate	20	9	Presbyterian meeting house Mrs.Rochester
NewBiggin	22	4	Mr. Mills

making three or four hundred pounds a year. Soon Low Street had Priestman's tannery, the mills, maltings, breweries and warehouses cheek by jowl with genteel houses. Allan's had an entry house complete with a retail shop and with a manufactory behind.

The breweries began large scale porter brewing and had their own keel boats for shipment down river. Two breweries that were later well known and are even now well remembered, as Roses and as Russells were said to have started in 1767 and 1771. Thirty five vessels were on the river moving coal and corn and there was a small boat repair dock. The town was described as as 'a nursery of navigation men'. Hannah Wedgwood's foreman William Bull entered a pot house across the river at Norton to make garden and chimney pots. A new workhouse was built in 1789. There was an upholsterer and four staymakers, five flax dressers, and thirty shoemakers a few years later. By 1801, there were four hundred members of Friendly Societies.

On the Road

York was always a great junction for carriers, its many road links to other northern towns, welding the whole into a transport system. The principal roads through the Vale of York were part of the highway spine of England, and gained early public passenger carriages. Malton situated on a navigable river became another terminus for the carriers. As a result of its position on the York- Scarborough road, the town also saw a great many public and private carriages passing through, on their way to the coastal spa and bathing place. Travellers for Whitby could get a moor guide at Pickering. Outside the moorlands, carriers were becoming men with a cart or wagon, instead of a train of packhorses, but the other market towns saw fewer carriers from the villages around them than Malton. John Stockton was a regular Kirkby Moorside carrier by 1737.

There was other long distance traffic, carrying coal. The furthermost parts of the North Riding saw many a cart loaded with three or four quarters of coal from county Durham. Whitby had known coal yards, each side of the river for more than a century, whence the black rock, called 'sea coal' was moved to the alum works. Scarborough imported its own coal but the carrier's charges rose rapidly as you moved inland. West Riding coal now reached Malton on the river boats.

The long distance movement of cattle and sheep was increasing. The Scots and other northern drovers in growing numbers came down the Hambleton drove road in Autumn. They paused at the drovers' inns and cattle stances before dividing. Some took the Oldstead road to the York markets. Others moved on the long Low Moors road eastwards to Scarborough, with some crossing the Vale of Derwent at Wykeham and heading for Hull. Other drovers, as of old, came along the old high street above Ampleforth, crossed the low ground towards Hovingham and came to the great stock markets and fairs of Malton. Animals were moved further between local markets and farms. A Leavening man who bought cattle at Kirkby Moorside, and resold them in 1700, was indited because he hadn't kept them on his own land for five weeks. A Newton on Ouse man took sheep home, across the commons, from Malton market into York vale.

Horse traffic increased generally with more private stables, and more accomodation for post horses and traveller's horses at inns. Guide posts were placed at some crossroads in 1711. Norton bridge was rebuilt in 1700 and widened sixty years later. Bridges on the by-roads across the river Derwent at Kexby, Buttercrambe, and Kirkham all received attention. Yedingham on the Scarborough route was given a stone bridge in 1728 with three arches, two breakwaters and causeway approaches through the low ground. Newsham bridge on the Rye was only rebuilt in timber. Grants were sometimes given to rebuild those on other routes and the year 1732 saw bridges built over the small moor becks about Cropton and Rosedale. These carried some of the Blackamore pannier horse traffic, between Kirkby Moorside, Pickering, Whitby, Stokesley, Guisborough and the dales.

Major improvement of road routes or surfaces was very rare outside York Vale, where the turnpike principle was being applied to raise money for stretches of the Great North Road. Most of the recorded road improvement schemes brought before the justices, were mere diversions to make pleasure parks. Increased traffic meant increased criticism of the traditional parish system of highway maintenance, which did little for the majority of roads. The Pickering to Whitby road was given ten guideposts in 1749, on a route which then went via Sneaton and not Sleights. Others were placed on roads linking Kirkby Moorside, Stokesley and Guisborough in 1757.

There were other perils beside losing your way. Coaches moving between staging inns were advertised as travelling 'God willing', and charged more if there was a guard. A highwayman was taken at Whitwell in 1724, by which time private carriages and Summer stagecoaches carrying spaw goers were frequently seen on the road from Malton to Scarborough. A York - Scarborough Turnpike was formed in

The Stage Coach passes through North Bar, Beverley

1747, offering a prospect of improvement for their benefit, with the by-road from Scarborough to Spital house in Staxton also turnpiked. Beyond Staxon was the dry Wold Road to Beverley. This was either thought adequate or incapable of raising sufficient income. Some road straightening, scraping and the making of cuttings resulted on the York-Malton-Scarborough road.

Changing the Field Crops

Important changes quietly took place in farming. The commonly used local varieties of wheat and oats were replaced by seeds imported from overseas and from other British counties. The slow and hasty oats gave way to Poland, Friesland and Siberian or Tartarian oats. White or Danzig Rye began to replace black rye. Battledore barley disappeared and Zealand, Kent and Hertfordshire wheats supplanted the old white and common red wheats. Seed Catalogues appeared from John Telford of York and quantities were brought up river from Hull.

Parts of Ryedale, the Wolds and York Vale, had already completed the inclosure and division of their arable fields, but the movement continued in several different ways. Early enclosures spread rapidly around Malton at Wintringham in 1718, at Kennythorpe, Langton, Scagglethorpe and Thorpe Basset along the north west Wold edge during the twenties, and at Huttons Ambo, Appleton le Street, and Welburn to the west. Townships with enclosed fields, and those with

253

unenclosed fields could exist side by side. A large dominant estate owner could the more easily bring an inclosure about but, on the other hand, lack of enclosure, was not as inhibiting for an improving owner or his tenant in an estate village, as in a community of freeholders.

Table 38. The Price of Goods in York Market in 1735	
beer, best sort	2s a gallon
beer, second sort	1s "
beer, third sort	6d "³
claret wine	8s a gallon
white wine	6s8d "
carcase of beef, best	£9.10.0
carcase of mutton, best	£1.2.0
a lamb	8s
capon, best	1s9d
hen	7d
pig	2s

Different Men Took Different Decisions

Some villages on the high dry limestone were reduced to two or three farm steads while their neighbours at Lockton, Levisham and Newton remained substantial communities. The shrunken village of Cawthorn seemed to collapse in this period. Mr Conyers sold five houses there in 1705, called Mennel House, Hallgarth, Friargarth and Old house and Lounsbrough farmhouse. By 1722 the little street close had six frontsteads extending westwards, meaning six empty plots. The Middlefield was divided into several closes. The village of Kingthorpe in a very similar terraign was in 1676 said 'judging by the ruins of old buildings, to have once been larger'. The chapel garth had a ruin while the smithy garth and cutler garth were empty. 'There was scarce soil for the plough, yet they usually had good crops'. The township was inclosed in four parts, giving 659 acres of inclosures and 470 acres of common 'the utmost improvement it can be brought to'. Both became almost empty village sites.

At the estate township of Seamer near Scarborough in 1735, the age old farming system seemed unchanged. Three common corn fields with a total of 659 acres were still annually divided into forty 'oskins', or oxgang shares amongst the twenty tenants. This gave each man roughly sixteen arable acres, with which went pasture for forty head of sheep, pasture rights in the oxpasture and five 'day – works' in the ings, for each 'oskin'. This was quite different to Pickering where three hundred freeholders, facing the Crown and the lessee of the Church tithes as the only major owners, continued to steadily consolidate field strips together by numerous exchanges, and had made some into closes within the fields.

Marl, a variable earth, had been used to improve dryer soils on a limited scale for many years. Household waste had always been put back on the land. Dunghills stood about the town and village streets, and where forecrofts or front gardens were taken in, they formed private middens at the front door. A twenty load heap was sold for fifteen shillings at Thornton Dale in 1733. The highly valued pigeon dung, from rare dovecotes, was five pence a bushel in 1748. Sheep grazed the Wold outfields, the stubbles and fallows of open cornfields and the aftermath or fogg of meadows, and dunged as they did so, often controlled by fold bars or hurdles.

Danby and other dales' farmers already knew that their ground was improveable by liming, but they had none and had to buy it from those with kilns in the limestone hills to the south. As inclosure progressed and landowners' attitudes changed, there came an insistence on tenants putting back into the soil, what their crops took out of it. This was written into leases. Mr. Hill at Thornton Dale in 1729 required land to be ploughed and to be manured in a husbandlike manner, and this was 'to be judged by neighbours'. The tenant yokeing his ploughs for wheat and rye was to lay on twenty full coup loads of wholesome manure, or three loads of lime, or pay £2.10s 0d. more rent for every acre.

Little change in equipment is evident in farmers' inventories, though they vary with the terrain. Thomas Williamson at Sherburn in 1730 kept eleven beasts, four horses one hundred and six sheep and two swine. He grew corn and hay. His main implements were his wagon, a wain, a plough and harrows. Crushed gannister or lye sand was fetched from Castleton in Danby for sharpening scythes. A four sided square piece of wood, two foot long with a handle at one end and a point at the other, was smeared with swine grease and the sand pressed into it.

New Breeds

Far reaching initiatives were taken which pioneered the selective breeding of animals. The stallion known as the Darley Arabian, pillar of the stud book, was shipped from Aleppo to Buttercrambe in 1704, and went for training on the Wolds. The Earl of Carlisle raised the Carlisle Turk and the Carlisle Barb. Isaac Leetham spoke of racing blood introduced to develop the various coach, saddle and plough horses. This interest in breeding may have spread from sport to farm.

Scots sheep were seen at Helmsley in 1735 and twenty one Scots ewes joined the Thornton Riseborough flock of three hundred and fifty sheep a few years later. They would also appear among the old Wold and Holderness breeds of the chalk lands. Mr.Hill sent his men from Thornton to distant Corbridge to buy wethers in 1743. Old black cattle were the dominant local breed, although Pickering had some red whies. Squire John Hill at Thornton Dale bought a new prize breeding bull in 1734 to improve the village cattle as well as his own. Nine years later, he bought nine Scots cows and a bull. Scarborough's Martinmas beast fair was moved into long Westgate in 1727 and Hovingham market was revived in 1739 for live cattle as well as grain.

The new fodder crops, clover and sainfoin were at least considered for planting at Wetwang on the Wolds. There was a clover close at Thornton Dale and two hundred bushels of potatoes were produced there by Francis Ash in 1743. A major set back came from 1747 to 1753, when herds generally were seriously depleted by a cattle plague. Desperate measures were tried and failed. A Snainton remedy was one pint of Geneva, with a pint of old verjuice, in a quart of boiling water, given warm, three or four times a day. When the beast began to purge, spoonfulls of sal. ammoniac with a handful of cork burnt to a powder, were administered in a hornful of gin punch. The Thornton Dale Steward gave a good ale cordial mixed with treacle and aniseeds, but all to no purpose. Mr Priestman the Thornton tanner bought all the hides from Scarborough to Pickering and Malton and took a place at Snainton to tan them. A fresh start had to be made.

Butter was the main marketable produce for many farmers. Factors dealing in hams, bacon and butter secured additional Acts of Parliament to regulate the butter trade at York in 1722, and at Malton in 1744. The Malton Butter Act made a staith yard adjoining Yorkersgate into the place of despatch for thousands of butter firkins each year. The eight pound firkins each held fifty six pounds of butter. London provision merchants and cheesemakers took the best, while the poorer grease was sent from Malton to the West Riding. Scarborough's butter market was resited at Low Cross, conveniently accessible for sellers and buyers.

Farmer's wives and farm servants travelled there to supply it from far afield.

A good cow in a common year could produce two and a half to three firkins of butter, as well as a rearing calf, half a hundredweight of skim milk, and some whey. Two and a half gallons of milk made a pound of butter, and one gallon made a pound of cheese. Spring butter was taken to market by the farmer's wife or the dairy maid, but the rest was sent out packed in firkins. The better off cooked with butter and May butter was valued as an opening medicine. Wath's marigold cheese was famous but most 'hard cheese' went to the poor. Farm inventories show five or more cows, wherever good grass was abundant. There was a growing concern with managing pastures and some areas were newly stinted.

Making the Commons Productive

Black Hambleton and Blackamore still seemed desolate to strangers, but the commons and so called wastes played their part in village economy. Their dales produced little corn and that was either oats or 'big', a winter barley sewn in spring .The moors were the home of the black face sheep. The high wold was another sheep country, the wild plants struggling to find a footing in the outfields, as they were joined by warren rabbits.

Gamekeepers were widely appointed in Queen Anne's reign to limit gneral access to game but the great country houses were accustomed to buy many other things, found or caught in the commons and woods. Thornton Dale Hall paid out useful sums of money when callers brought honey, birch besoms, fir cones, walnuts, acorns, bilberies and cranberries .The moor fringe had straw bee skeps set in wall recesses called 'boles' which produced the strong heather honey. Birch was secured for broomsticks, walnuts and acorns for feed, small wood for dead hedging, bog myrtle for gale beer, seaves and rushes for thatch. Ling was gathered by knee padded girls with a toothed sickle, who could cut thirty sheaves a day, good for kindling, for besoms and as bedding for stock.

Cropton manor court was mainly concerned with management of the commons in the early 18th century, now that its fields were under enclosure. Small encroachments were often alleged, and gates not hung, but the main problem was to stop people removing the assets that were there. Thomas Suggit was said to lead stones to Pickering. Nicholas

Cheesman took turves to Appleton and seven Rosedale people graved turves and led them away, all in a single season. The Rosedale east side perambulation in 1787 saw plenty of punch and liquor drunk from a can. People in violent passions challenged each other to fights.

The Thornton Dale steward had to stop people crossing from Whitby side to take turves from Pexton moor. When Spaunton manor bounds were ridden in 1763, the boundary walkers set fire to ten loads, graved up by Westerdale people from the Spaunton commons. They were watched by the sad Westerdale folk, standing at Ralph Cross. A high wind blew out the fire and it took three hours. The main common right to survive some early commons inclosures was the right of digging, or graving for, and carrying away turves and ling.

Timber was in short supply outside the modest areas of coppiced woodlands. These included Dalby where John Wooller counted 369 tun of bark in 1726. Much old wood was felled at Rosedale in 1716, but sizeable hardwood trees were very scarce outside the great estates of the Duncombe family at Helmsley and those of the Earl of Carlisle at Castle Howard. Their great trees were sought by the shipwrights, for the busy ship building yards of Whitby and Scarborough.

Scandinavian deals were being imported in quantity but only a few landowners could take a long enough view, beyond one lifetime, to see profit in new plantations. They were begun in 1702 at Hinderskelfe and Helmsley, while Pockley and Beadlam saw much fencing of young springs in 1710. Lord Harley spoke in 1723 of Ray Wood with the noblest beech trees to be met with in England. An inscription of 1731, at Castle Howard read –

'If to perfections these plantations rise
If they agreeably my heirs surprise
This faithful pillar will their age declare
As long as time these characters shall spare'

The Earl of Oxford witnessed more fresh planting about Newbrough. At Thornton Dale John Hill planted 7600 seedlings in 1737, and within a few years he was supplying young firs and ash to Pickering. Strickland tried planting fir trees on the Wolds about that time and Parson Wyke of Levisham bought firs for the first recorded local shelter belt around his house.

Rabbits were seen as a profitable cash crop on rough commons. Scamridge warren was active in 1666 and both Thornton warren and

Coneysthorpe warren before 1700. Charles Fairfax had the Scackleton rabbit warren functioning by 1727 and Mr. Hill converted the high riggs above Dalby into several warrens, where he had early success with rabbit production on a commercial scale. He stocked nine hundred couple of rabbits on one of his warrens at Flainsey moor in 1742, and sold 1843 couple at 11d the couple making £84.9.5. Nets and traps cost £8.8.0 and the warrener had eighteen shillings a month wages.

The rabbits provided meat and their skins went to Scarborough for hat making. In 1744 Dalby warren sold many at Bridlington. By 1795 Ellerburn warren covered six hundred acres, Thornton and Farmanby near seven hundred acres and there were others not far away at Kingthorpe and Lockton. A self operating system of culling the rabbits was developed. Rabbit types were formed at a gap in the turf wall of the warren, with nicely balanced planks, which tipped a night's cull into the hole beneath.

In the low carrs, the challenge was greater than the response. Meadows and low commons alike were often inundated with water, when the run off from the bare hillsides went into the becks after heavy rains, and this excess met the sluggish Derwent river flood water. The manor courts were always much concerned with keeping the low carr and ing dykes clear, since standing water ruined the grass. The local Court of Sewers ordered the widening of drainage ditches and sewers throughout Marishes and Lund in 1727. John Hill required Thornton Dale water courses and public drains to be made deeper and wider in 1728. A pioneering 'new cut' was made from Wykeham sewer to Brompton beck in1743 and a few years later, Sherburn made a cut through Scab Hook to stop flooding.

A few low commons were separately inclosed and drained. The Earl of Carlisle agreed an enclosure of the one hundred and sixty acre Welburn moor in 1747, previously stinted into fifty eight beastgates. The Slingsby estate owners made an early carr drainage to convert low ground into closes for a single new farmstead built on Fryton moor, at a time when the arable fields on the slopes above remained unchanged.

Wild life was mostly treated as vermin, to be killed to protect the crops. The churchwardens and some manor stewards paid children at fixed and well known rates. One detailed list gives the payments available for hawks, kites, buzzards, scrags, cormorants, ringtails, jays, ravens, kites and kingfishers. Young birds and birds' eggs were paid for by the half dozen. Bigger sums came for fox, polecat, and badger, smaller for hedgehogs, moles and rats, while it needed twelve mice to make a penny.

A Modest Rural Industry

The wider districts of north east Yorkshire had a modest share in the early industrial revolution that was elsewhere gathering force. Iron ore was picked up from cliff fall along the coast from Scarborough to Saltburn by 1721, and was shipped for another century to the furnaces of County Durham. Inland iron working seems to have ceased everywhere, apart from Forge Valley near Scarborough, but this is by no means certain, for the use of iron was increasing. Cinder hills of unknown dates were very numerous until removed for road making.

Ironwork was widely adopted for pot kilps in the chimneys, pokers and coalrakes in the hearths and perhaps for the gille and mash vats used for brewing. John Otterburn at Scackelton had pewter and brass in the house, but the kitchen had an iron fire shovel, broyling iron, dripping pan and tongs. John Bayley at Askew had an iron pot and an iron kettle. Pickering blacksmith Peter Sunley may well have bought his ore locally. His shop held a stiddy, a vice, a spoke tyre, punches, chisels and shoeing tackle, two grindstones, a pair of bellows and a stone slecking trough. Wagons were described as iron-bound when they had an iron rim around the fellies, on the end of each spoke. His stock for sale was seven socks, two axes, seven hammers and seven pairs of tongs. He held two stone and four pound of iron.

A coal working era, over a hundred years, saw colliers employed in the moorland dales, working on a modest scale, to produce a poor quality coal from thin seams. Matthew Foord sank three shafts at Ankness in Bransdale in 1715. Coal was later worked, wherever moorland seams could be found, from Bilsdale to Grimston near Gilling, from Birdforth in York Vale to Fadmoor, Hamer and Goathland. The pits were dug on the high riggs and have left their mark to this day. Small bellpits were worked by one or two men, a donkey and a boy but some colliers moved on to 'pillar and board' working, probably including those at Rudland rigg, where the numerous pits are regularly placed.

The coal was highly valued for working breweries and limekilns, and was sent down to the Vale of Pickering market towns in some quantity. Pitman John Bloomer was active mining coal at Hartoft before 1769, by which time the Harrisons had opened a Rosedale coalmine and Hartas was mining coal on Spaunton moor. Pickering farmers welcomed donkey trains bringing moor coal from Goathland as well as Wilmot leading coals from the wharfs at Malton as late as 1851. There were ten coal miners' households in Rosedale, second in number only to forty five farmers and twenty nine farm labourers.

Stone quarrying became another widespread industry of the limestone hills as the stone was increasingly used in house building and in making dry stone inclosure walls. South country masons inspected the large cut Thornton quarry stone in 1733 and there was talk of shipping some abroad. Mr. Blomberg wanting stone for his house at Kirkby Misperton opened a new quarry at Newbridge behind Pickering in 1746. New Georgian houses were being built for gentlemen, some with cut stone dressings and Pickering already had two glaziers. Specialist malting is said to develop in the 18th century in the countryside, barley previously being malted in farmers' kilns but the picture is unclear.

Much limestone was extracted for lime burning. Hartoft had a limekiln by 1736. Cropton, Lockton and other villages of the moorland edge opened quarries and built kilns to burn the lime for despatch into Cleveland, where there was none. A circular traffic carted lime across the moor into Eskdale, and picked up coal on the way back at Rudland, Hamer Inn house, or Blakey Inn, each of which had its coal pits. Lime roads linked Newton with Goathland, Lockton with Sneaton and Sleights, Cropton with Danby and Hutton le Hole with Castleton. The smaller limekilns of farmers spread throughout the limestone belt. From the west edge of the Wold, plaster was produced at Leppington and sent to barges on the river.

Brickyards at Black Bull, Wombleton and Middleton in the Vale of Pickering were producing by 1785. That year James Rich advertised his Wombleton works, as a well accustomed brick and tile yard of about two acres, with a complete new kiln and tile shop, and a new clay mill. Roofing tiles and chimney bricks found a ready market and walling bricks made their way slowly into house construction. About 1770, pantiles for roofing instead of thatch were sent through Cropton into Danby. There was some revival of pottery making, but at the rough earthenware end of the trade. William Wedgwood made pancheons at Yearsley and others of the name made pots in the Howardians.

Linen

Linen manufacture expanded, both as a specialist craft, and as a second occupation on farms, producing fine linen cloth and coarse servants sheets. Flax heckling, spinning and weaving became the main tasks of ordinary people at the towns of Kirkby Moorside, Helmsley and Pickering, but also at Hutton le Hole and many other villages. Simon Sturdy of Kirkby Moorside was an early clothier and may have been a key figure in expanding the industry. He had another house at Pickering in Birdgate, near the stone bridge over the beck, with George Staines' dyehouse nearby, along with the tenter garth used for hanging the cloths to dry in the sun. Similar bleach fields could be found from Ellerburn to Osmotherley.

A Wrelton man charged at the Cropton manor court for 'raiting' several loads of lime in the Ingdyke, and flooding the common was typical of many cases over several decades. Arthur Young could write in 1771 that the sole local employment of the poor and children at Kirkby Moorside was flax spinning. Sheriff Hutton bought twenty five spinning wheels one year to give employment to the parish poor. Small farmers might have between one and four looms for weaving. Robert Dunning of west Rosedale had both loom and spinning wheel, later in the century. New fulling mills were built on the fast flowing dales streams. Squire Duncombe erected one in Bilsdale in 1708 and another was opened in 1743 near remote Hartoft. By 1730 there was a linen printer at Stillington. Mary Campion at Pickering was owed money in 1737 by distant drapers from Hull, London, Market Weighton, Cawood and Helmsley.

Each town had workers in most of the stages of the process. The Reveleys of Ryegate in Helmsley made shuttles. The Helmsley weavers were remembered for their prodigious thirsts. The bleach garth was in upper Beckdale and dyers' bridge was at the bottom of Castlegate. James Richardson was the bleacher and George Fenwick of Boroughgate was the dyer. Four annual fairs were held for linens and woollens. The 1773 recession in linen led some weavers to migrate, but the trade recovered and linen cloth fairs survived at Easingwold, Guisborough, Helmsley, Kirkby Moorside, Seamer, Stokesley and Thirsk. By 1780 Helmsley weaver John Simpson had prospered enough to own a watch, a silver tankard, Delf plates and a gun.

Rag from the linen trades became the basis of a local paper making industry. The Ellerburn paper mill was rebuilt in 1733 and another opened at Danby in 1764. Byland, Thornton Dale and Pickering had paper mills later in the century. John Hill's Thornton Dale paper of all kinds was much in demand at York and James Boddy converted Pickering Low mill for paper making.

Large manufactories at the ports supplied the Whitby and Scarborough sailmakers with the well spun flax and finely woven yarn, that were essential to withstand the great strains exerted on ships' sails. Robert Campion opened a works in factory fields Whitby by 1776. Caleb Fletcher established a spinning factory at Keldholme, outside Kirkby Moorside, and Westgate in Pickering had a manufactory. Miss Nessfield of Wrelton was reckoned a great catch in 1790. Not only had she £3000, but unusually for the times, she could still spin her own wedding gown.

Corn Mill monopolies were being challenged. Antony Colcote leased the high and low Pickering mills from the Crown. They were ancient soke mills and he claimed that all the inhabitants had to use them. The details aren't known, but freeholder townsmen Samuel Harding and John Jackson protested his claim in the courts. Costs were awarded against him for 'his unjust and vexatious persecution'. Hardly had the local people celebrated their victory, when Harding and Jackson bought out the defeated Colcote and insisted on the very thing, that they had complained of.

Within a few years, broader partner ships were founded to lease the mills, opening the way towards a wider share holding. The partners agreed in 1758 not to use the low mill for dressing leather, or for fulling cloth or linen, for twenty one years. Partner ship agreements would later become common, wherever large capital or high risk was involved, as in porter brewing, and was applied to the first local banks before the end of the century.

More Gentry Building

Vanbrugh in 1721 said that many Yorkshiremen were possessed with the spirit of building. Arden hall was built in Queen Anne's time. Thomas Browne, partner and brother in law of Sir Charles Duncombe, and Receiver General of the Excise erected Duncombe Park in 1713 to the designs of William Wakefield. He changed his name to Duncombe.Thomas Hayes about 1714 built Aislaby Hall with a Venetian window, high kitchen garden wall and a roadside summer house, near to the older cruck house.

Colin Campbell designed the miniature Ebberston Lodge in 1718 for William Thompson, and a lady who legend claims didn't arrive to share it with him. The garden had a water course and cascade set in a planted amphitheatre. From the garden, the house seemed set on the

Ebberston Lodge

horizon with the water vanishing beneath. Hugh Cholmeley at Howsham spent £352 in one year making gardens. Bossall Hall had a rain head of 1726. The Darleys built Aldby Hall in that year, and there were many more. Thomas Worsley, surveyor general of the Board of Works built Hovingham Hall, with a giant riding school at the entry in 1750. Richard Sykes of a mercantile family married Mark Kirkby's co -heiress and gained Sledmere on the partition. Sledmere house was built in 1751.

The lesser gentlefolk added a few taller houses to the towns. In the villages, a new hall could relegate an old manor house into a mere manor farm. Architecture had arrived, in a sense, but it was often a stage away from the designer's hand, more often from the builder's pattern book. Samuel Buck drew sketches of many of the houses, including Thomas Sotheby's fine compact house at Birdsall, the east front with a porch entry beneath a high broken pediment, above steep steps down to the carriage drive. His sketches allow us to see some houses that have gone. No one sketched the majority.

Modest houses, often described as 'neat', with their straight lines, several floors and new sash windows, came to distinguish the gentleman's family residence from those about it. A stylish doorcase, often with a small pediment on columns, could even dignify an older building. There were front and rear rooms, rooms for eating and rooms for sleeping, sometimes cellars for kitchens and attics for servants. The hall itself shrank steadily to become the bottom of the staircase, a good place for a walking stick, an umbrella stand and a coat rack. Not every plan reached fruition. John Sheffield, the new Duke of Buckingham bought the gaunt empty Slingsby mansion in 1719, but he died soon after and the so-called castle went to decay. Mrs Daly sold it to the Earl of Carlisle in 1751 and it remained a ruin.

By mid century, brick was the coming material, sometimes stucco covered. The native timber tradition began its long demise but stone lingered where it was the cheaper material. At Kirkby Moorside, the new High Hall adapted an older timber framed house but the Low Hall below it was new built, though much later. Both were sited in the large demesne close of the ruined castle to the north. To complete the block, another Manor House filled the rest of the site. A wing of the old castle was taken down in 1730, and the stone used to build a new tollbooth in the Market Place.

Parks were changed from hunting arenas, beyond the formal gardens that nudged against the house, into something quite different. The decorative kind of objects which had graced the gardens were placed further afield. Country house landscapes were designed afresh, with sculptures, fountains and other features to illumine and focus rides and walks. The Castle Howard grounds gained an obelisk to the Duke of Marlborough in 1714 and a great Mausoleum in 1745. The undulating walk to the Temple of the Four Winds replaced an earlier geometric plan.

Scenes and selected views were treasured and new ones planned. An entire landscape of surprising beauty and a source of much lasting delight could emerge at the hands of the new landscape garden experts such as Capabiility Brown or Bridgman. The second Thomas Duncombe improved his parkland first with one ride and then another. The Rievaulx terrace was made in 1758 above the Abbey ruins, which now seemed 'picturesque', instead of just derelict buildings. This remarkable mental shift derived somehow from the vista of collapsed Greek and Roman architecture seen on the Grand Tour. Mr. Hill heard from his steward that his hall was to be given the 'Vitruvian scrawl', as the cellars were flagged and a new road made before the Thornton house.

Getting the Wherewithall.

If you would enjoy new pleasures, it is an advantage to be rich. The country nobility and gentry were never richer. Many who had money, made more. Their projects, in their turn, expanded the new professions of lawyers, surveyors, architects and even engineers, who joined them in a relative but real enough prosperity. Sardonic comment was not lacking. An Appleton le Moors house gained an unflattering stone carving on its facade. Three faces were to be identified as the doctor, the lawyer and the parson, with the initials of the sentiment 'the art of living is how to find bread'. Few from the professions have ever welcomed the thought, that the trio were locally explained as 'the three parasites on the back of the human race'.

Much wealth flowed from far distant colonies, that were called the 'plantations' and from the trade with the Indies. Commerce was the great new engine of wealth, and directly or indirectly, most rich people were involved in it somewhere. A few Yorkshiremen, including the owners of Studley Royal, burnt their fingers in the 'South Sea Bubble' but others extricated themselves in time. One local family who built their Hall anew, has misty stories of wealth founded in slave trading. Others more certainly owned estates worked by slaves, and a few were brought back as household servants.

William Marshall of Pickering managed plantations, before returning to become the scholar of his own country's agriculture. There were professional and government openings too. William Ingledew of Nawton was a surgeon with the East India Company. One of the Darleys from Buttercrambe was collector of the Queen's Revenues at Barbados. When Nathanial Chomeley returned from eastern diamond trading, to occupy the family estate, they said of him-

'At Whitby dwells N.C. Esquire,
as great as most are in the shire,
whose honour stands in sore dependance,
with coach and six and grand attendance
and saddle horses stout and able,
stand all day feeding in the stable'.

A place in the home government, or in its expanding administrative departments, including the revenue service could be another source of great income. William Thompson of Ebberston was Master of the Mint, William St Quintin was a Lord Commissioner of the Treasury and Receiver General for Ireland. Mr. Hill of Thornton Dale was Commissioner of the Customs and Sir Thomas Wentworth, made Lord Malton in 1728 and later Marquess of Rockingham, was twice Prime Minister. He gave £200 to built a Malton workhouse for the poor in

1735. Admiral Anson was expected to dine at Castle Howard in 1744, Lord Carlisle having recommended him to represent the borough of Hedon in Parliament. Places were secured by influence.

If nothing else offered, it was good advice for a gentleman to 'find a fortune and marry it.' John Dowker of Salton led Miss Woodock to the altar at Kirkby Over Carr. She was 'a lady of great acomplishments and a fortune of £7000'. Squires Cayley, Osbaldeston and Legard wooed and won the supposedly beautiful but certainly wealthy Digby daughters. When the Earl of Carlisle was absent from Castle Howard, no man was allowed in, lest the daughters fall to some prospector. Lady Wortley Montagu said that it was like a nunnery. The Fauconbergs shipped one young but unsuitable suitor off to Spain, with a captain's commission. Nor was it all one way. Wealthy Whitby merchants offered a good prospect for genteel ladies. Daniel Defoe saw the York Assembly Rooms as a marriage mart.

And Spending the Time

A York house became necessary for the very rich, to allow participation in the season for some, a good place for a confinement with a physician to hand for others and companionship within their class for all. Minster memorials witness to the widows who retired there. Viscount Fairfax was in Castlegate, the Bowers and St. Quintins in Micklegate. Viscountess Preston of Nunnington, daughter of Lord Carlisle, lived at the Treasurer's House in 1721. Since her husband was attainted, they called her Mrs. Graham. Lord Widdrington used the house later. The Darleys had a house in Coney Street. Squire Garforth of Wiganthorpe would build in 1757 at Micklegate.

The parapetted town houses and the new terraces, for country gentry, spread along the street inside, and then outside the walls of York, and into Bootham and the Mount as they would at St Hilda's Terrace and Bagdale in Whitby, and rather later in precincts outside Scarborough. Lead tanks fed from roof gullies by down pipes were made to catch the roof water. Wrought iron gates opened for fore courts to admit carriages. York was acknowledged to be the social capital of the north and it was a lot cheaper than London.

Servants were a problem. At Thornton Dale, the steward, William Wilmott, said that the postilion William had been spoken to many times, but he had stayed in the town all night, seven or eight times and was never in the house till nine or ten. One night, he had quarrelled with his companion over the cards at the alehouse. When servants moved, ladies wrote to each to enquire into their character, work and sobriety. The Fauconberg steward had to send to Thirsk, for some bark to use as packing, because the poor folk had burnt it. His best news for the Viscount was that the servants were all very diligent and free from any noise or strife. Managing servants was a trial to wives and stewards. One of the several reasons for sending young men on the Grand Tour was to break their close links with servants.

Back at the mansion, the paintings multiplied around the walls, the portraits fresh for each generation, but adding in gloomy grandeur, an almost over bearing sense of 'us' for later generations. The third Viscount Preston was painted in the robed grandeur of nobility. One artist visited Mr Ralph Crathorne at Ness one year and portrayed Thomas Worsley's three daughters at Hovingham the next. Phillip Mercier painted the less daunting 'conversation pieces'. The Leeds and York newspapers appeared in 1718, the almanacks and the mercuries a few years later, full of advertisements, national and foreign news and reports of gentry movements, a great aid to leisure and binding the class more firmly together.

Gentlemen adopted French dress styles - periwig, small cocked hat, full bottomed coat, short breeches and blue or scarlet stockings over the knee, square toed shoes with buckles and heels. They said sarcastically of Whitby seamen doing well that some had silver buckles on their shoes. William Thompson paid £10 for a periwig when off to Scarborough in 1733. Tea was the great social innovation, made into a public occasion, but privately consumed as well. Much was made of it. It was 'the broth of abominable things' to some, and 'the tongue tipping cordial to others'. Tea became familiar at Malton and at Whitby in Queen Anne's reign and Mrs. Beal sold it at Thornton dale by 1733. The drink created new habits and eventually a new daily meal; but was blamed for 'the chamber maid's lost bloom'.

While family portraits gave a sense of family history, to the great men and women, mere description served for others. Mary wife of William Wise of High Field at Norton was remembered as 'a good looking woman of middle size, brown hair and fair complexion, round face, beautiful colour in her cheeks, blue eyes, handsome forehead and always had a smile on her countenance. She had a noble and generous disposition. She was very pious and born of second sight. She was an affectionate mother towards her children and a dutiful wife'.

Her husband William Wise was 'tall and small, dark brown hair and middling complexion, a 'gluteel' looking man. He had an agreeable and sensible countenance. He was a man of uncommon abilities, an excellent writer and composer. His chief pleasure was the study of Latin and French, the history of his own country, foreign geography and botany. He knew the species and use of almost every plant that grows and could explain their Latin and Greek names. He studied biography, astronomy and the Bible. He was a man of general knowledge and good understanding. He sold an estate at East Lutton and also the one at Holme because he could not get a proper inclosure in 1770. He bought estates at Norton from James Hebblethwaite Esq'.

This was an age of 'diversion and not staying at their habitations' said Sir Charles Howard. Assize and race weeks gave York a season. The city was given a scene with lamps in the streets, new coffee houses at Stonegate and Minster yard, a Lord Mayors' Walk and the New Walk at the riverside for promenading. Lord Burlington's new Assembly rooms in 1732 offered a county meeting place for dancing and gambling, and the new Theatre four years later completed a series of public places, for the private use of this rich clientelle. The long list of subscribers to the assembly rooms in 1731 included Cayley, Fairfax, Fauconberg, Howard, Legard, Preston, St. Quintin, Strickland, and many more.

For others, a London house was no less essential. Thomas, third Viscount Fauconberg, had a new city house, but he preferred Newbrough, while she liked London. A stay in the capital meant weekly letters from the Steward, with regular despatches of hampers of foodstuffs. One hamper held hare, pheasant, six partridges, two woodcock, duck, teal, two cucumbers and three swine cheeks. In another were 'two Newbrough cheeses and a map of the West Indies'.

Lord Chesterfield considered eating to have become 'the great pride, business and expense of life'. Butter was being used plentifully in cooking and sugar too. Sauces, pickles and ketchups were arriving on the tables, although 'roast beef and plum pudding' were well on their way to becoming the national dish. Cook books abounded and cooking vessels became elaborate in the great kitchens. There was practicality too. The Newbrough butler had to brew four hogsheads of ale for the Fauconberg household on one occasion, then had to brew three more to mix with the old ale, which had gone stale.

Scarborough attracted the same town and country gentry, and each year an extra scatter of national notables, for its spa water and sea bathing seasons. Hardly a season went by without a long stay by a couple of Dukes and a pair of Duchesses. The resort offered another suite of buildings, besides the spaw houses, where the rich could meet, in the assembly rooms, coffee house, theatre and subscription library, which together formed the necessary framework for genteel leisure.

The healthy joined the sick and soon out numbered them. Both fully utilised the sandside opportunities for improving their condition, by drinking heroic quantities of medicinal waters, pints and pints, one after another, and for the hardly less challenging plunges in an ocean, thought the more medicinal if it was cold. Two of the fashionable gentleman's clubs known as lodges of freemasons were formed there in 1705 and 1729. The beach was the promenade, with riders and carriages moving backwards and forwards, in a morning scene of fashionable display.

More rustic spaws attracted a clientelle. Dr. Shaw listed their virtues in 1734. The Newton Dale cold spring was good for strengthening weakness. Terrington Spaw 'worked against rheumatism. Malton iron spaw worked internally by stool and urine. It was good for 'hypochondriac melancholy, asthma and ulcers, bowel obstruction and languidness'. We must presume that these benefits were felt. In sickness, the gentry had little more to expect than those of smaller means, other than the services of the few medical men. Jesse Ness was the apothecary at Helmsley in 1777 and Joseph Chipchase the surgeon. Pickering had two surgeons and an apothecary in 1798. Richard Stephenson described as a doctor at Cropton in 1762, was associated with an asylum at the village, and was credited with having a cure for madness. Vicar John Rudd at Weaverthorpe, who lived to be eighty two, swore by temperance and exercise. The vicars listed the ills that caused deaths in their parish registers for a decade or two, at the end of the century, from 1782 at Lastingham and 1793 at Middleton until 1812. The things that ended life were given simply as sickness at the one, and old age at the other. The clearest agreed cause of death was consumption, with smaller numbers affected by fever, fits, scarlet fever, small pox, typhus or dropsy, asthma, convulsions and chin cough. In these things, we were not divided.

A Christian Education

The old Grammar schools had re-appeared at the Restoration and their masters were duly licenced. Pickering had Nicholas Gray B.A teaching in 1662 and Richard Gray in 1685. They are said to have taught the classics, arithmetic, geometry and astronomy, to Thomas Ward of Danby Castle and his brothers, but English and mathematics must have comprised much of it. Kirkby Moorside Grammar School was in the church or the churchyard, where Thomas Hague, Charles Emmot and Charles Legard followed each other as masters. The Malton schoolmaster in 1697 held Holgate's school and lived in the master's house built in the Priory churchyard.

New schools were founded from the charity of wealthy people. Elizabeth Lady Lumley, widow of Sir George Sandys endowed a Grammar School at Thornton Dale and an elementary school at Sinnington in 1657. Lady Judith Boynton charged Thornton Risebrough estate with sums for a schoolmaster for Normanby and for buying bibles for the poor. William Smithson endowed a school at Kirkby Misperton in 1673 and Ranald Graham at Nunnington in 1678.

These pioneering ventures presaged a wider movement. The Toleration Act issued by Parliament in 1689, made for a society which allowed differing opinions on matters of church organisation. Agreement remained on the need to promote the ability to read the bible, from which all derived their shared faith. Half the people alive were under twenty one but schools were available for very few of them. Churchmen and dissenters still feared the return of Catholicism. The Society for Promoting Christian Knowledge formed in 1698, gave a national focus and central encouragement for the establishment of charitable schools and even libraries. There was a warm response from Archbishop Sharp at York and sufficient local interest to bring an upswing of education to many places.

Within one year, 1705, six catechetical schools were founded within 12 miles of the Vale of York village of Spofforth. The catechism was a simple device, using set questions and answers to assist rote learning. Forty pupils were enrolled in the York charity school. The master taught ten of them at a time for an hour each, while the others worked in the work house. As a result, each boy received instruction for some part of the morning and part of the afternoon. They concluded that the boys came to the schooling with a better will, when it was a relief from a more painful task. Those who proved negligent and careless at the learning had the work house task made worse.

The 'SPCK' commissioned James Talbot DD. the Spofforth vicar, who was troubled by the re-emergence of Roman Catholicism, to write 'The Christian Schoolmaster or the duty of those who are employed in the publick instruction of children, especially in charity schools'. This was published in 1707 and was virtually an official handbook for teachers. The child's mind was seen as a blank paper on which it was a Christian's obligation to imprint religious duties.

The curriculum offered an advance from the alphabet to the hornbook , to reading the primer and the spelling book, and so on to religious books and Aesop's fables. After all that, you might learn to write, and once you could write, attempt some arithmetic. A Snainton pupil calculated that two, doubled thirty four times, gives 34343728368. Talbot argued, with some force, that Latin was irrelevant to those in farming. He required children to come washed. Pupils were not allowed to talk, play or gaze idly about, but were given learning exercises to occupy their minds in the time that they were at school.

The clergyman Robert Ward left a rent-charge to educate ten poor Slingsby children in 1712, the year that Thomas Farside founded the Hutton Bushell free school. Mrs Arthington willed £20 to freely educate four more at Hovingham in 1715, where a school was active south of the churchyard. Charity Schools appeared at places as diverse as Acklam, Newton, and Rosedale in the twenties, usually with a Christian motivation. Thomas Peirson founded Rosedale school in 1720 to educate three from Rosedale East side and two from Hartoft, without charge. Not all the schools had sufficient endowment to survive for any length of time and some needed a few paying pupils to run at all. John Hovington at Snainton taught a school in 1716 with both adults and children, which only ran for the few years that their payments allowed. The Reverend Robert Addison kept a Sherburn school in 1737. Probably, there were many more.

There were horror stories of bad teachers but not many. It proved difficult to get rid of a bad usher at Malton Grammar School in 1717. John Walker the Husthwaite teacher of 1730 was said to be a passionate man. If the stories are true, he put one pupil in a chest, then in a window, then whipped him, then placed him on a cold stone in the church with many boys' hats on his head. He knocked three and a half teeth out of another boy. It was judged that he was of 'little or no discretion to teach'. The influence of the charity schools is impossible to assess. It has been thought that their impetus was over by the forties, when Archbishop Herring's returns for his diocese gave a discouraging picture. In 1747. Pickering had its one public grammar school endowed with £12 a year, where the master 'took care to cultivate the barren brain' and the curate also instructed children in the church catechism. At Cropton a poor man taught six poor children and a few others who paid.

There were few roads to higher education, but occasionally some able pupil was encouraged to seek one out. John Clarke born at Kirkby Misperton in 1706 was noticed by the Rector. He placed him in Thornton Dale School and he was later given one of Lady Lumley's exhibitions to University. He became a schoolmaster at Wakefield and Shipton Schools, then curate of Moor Monkton. Subsequently he was headmaster of Beverley School and in 1751 of Wakefield School. They called him 'little Aristophanes', but he was made known in print as 'The Good Schoolmaster' and was highly thought of, by his pupils. Thomas Lazenby the teacher at Burton Agnes was another able man, author of an early work on book keeping.

It may be a similar spirit which produced a wave of charitable foundations of other kinds in these years. The poor were not increasing and parishes generally found their responsibilities towards the poor manageable. The bequests were modest, useful and were often made by yeomen freeholders. In time, many would be destroyed by inflation. William Lownsbrough set up a bread charity for the Middleton poor in 1720. John Cockerill of Goathland left Thwayte and Beckhole farms to his son provided that he gave ten dozen bread to the Goathland poor every Christmas 'for so long as the world endureth'. Thomas Frank of Hutton le Hole endowed £3.10s a year on the Kirkby Moorside poor.

Sermons and Jacobites

The Church of England remained an influence on many lives, with regular attenders arranged in pews, according to social station, with the poor pew near the draughty door. Pews were a property now. Walter Frankland bought one sixth part of a pew from John Wardell of New Malton in 1727. What influence the church had is hard to assess. The larger the place, usually the lower the proportion who attended church, at least for communions, which were held only four or five times a year. Pickering parish in 1747 had at best a hundred communicants coming from five hundred families. Sheriff Hutton parish contained one hundred and seventy five families with about one hundred and twenty individuals at the last Easter communion. The vicar of Bossall was a happier man. With a hundred or more families, he usually found forty or fifty at each of his three chapels, for communion, at Buttercrambe, Sand Hutton and Flaxton as well as at Bossall church.

In all too many places, the vicar's incomes had been diverted to supporting an absentee, while a curate on low wages did the work. At

Kirkby Moorside in 1743 the two hundred and seventeen families had a vicar who lived in London and a curate at the town, but he was well paid with £33.3s.0d a year. The Lastingham curate had a small farm and rights to turf and pasture. He had planted an orchard in 1723 and now had a score of apple trees, to help sustain him. The parishes bore little relation to the spread of population now, if they ever had. The Middleton vicar looked after Cropton, Lockton, Levisham and nominally Kirkby Grindalythe.

The Independant, Presbyterian and Baptist congregations had shrunk into small fastnesses at the market towns and at the occasional village. Rillington kept a dissenting tradition alive. The Quakers with their tight organisation kept scattered societies at surprising places, including Barton le Street, but the members were in every case drawn from a wider area. The Society of Friends was effective at keeping groups in touch with each other, the members travelling on horses to district meetings, rather than relying on an itinerant ministry. The road between Danby and Rosedale became known as the Quaker road. The Friends seem to have lost any fringe of local hearers. They frowned on their young people marrying outside the Society of Friends. Later, cash help was given to help Quaker children attend their own school at Ackworth.

Fears of Catholicism seemed out of all proportion to their numbers, depth of commitment or significance. They were few enough, lingering only in remote dales like Egton or where a Catholic squire took his servants and a few tenants into his private chapel. As in other periods, political society seemed to need a threat concealed beneath the bed, and the Catholics were it. The Jacobite risings in Scotland of 1715 and 1745 revived the fears. Catholic gentry had their weapons and horses seized in 1715, when the highland Jacobites rebelled. Lord Widdrington of Nunnington was active in the rising. He tried to take Newcastle and after capture at Preston, he was confined to the Tower of London. An oak cabinet, where he was said to have hidden after the battle, long survived at Nunnington.

The second Jacobite rising in 1745 led a youthful rabble to attack a Catholic chapel at Stokesley, but apprentice boys from Whitby on a similar bent, were easily diverted into Lythe public houses. As the Scots marched south to reach Derby, Scarborough turned its guns inland, on rumours of a coastward move by 'Bonnie Prince Charlie'. Local Catholics failed to rise in his support. After the battle of Culloden moor, the loyal associations and volunteer companies were disbanded. New barracks were built at Scarborough in 1746, well equipped for a permanent garrison of one hundred and twenty men under the Duke of Montagu. Helmsley's Catholics were still attended monthly by the chaplain of the Earl of Fauconberg from Newburgh Hall, using a high street room that had been endowed for the purpose. Thomas Fauconberg made Earl Fauconberg in 1756 abandoned his Catholicism and a tradition ended.

Lighter Moments

Popular leisure remained robust. Village lads took pea shooters to church services, and climbed out on to Middleton church roof to mark out the shapes of their shoes in the roof lead. The village year was punctuated by a programme of traditional occasions, more habitual than either pagan or Christian. Village feasts, divorced from any links with saints days, offered a mid- year holiday, with grinning or gaping matches, maids dancing for a ribbon and lads climbing a greasy pole to win a leg of mutton. Men grasped arms and struggled to kick each other's shins with their clogs. At a Cayton Whit Monday fair, they played 'losing their suppers'. Seamer fair in 1734 saw gaming with two thimbles and a button. At Rievaulx feast, they covered the pinfold with sailcoth and installed benches for it to serve as their alehouse.

John Stripe of London listed the games of 'the common sort' in 1720 as football, wrestling, cudgels, ninepins, shovelboard, cricket, ringing bells, quoits, pitching the bar, bull and bear baiting, throwing at cocks and lying at alehouses. That seems about right for the Yorkshire country as well. The bye laws of the manor of Sinnington still required the constable to enquire whether the keepers of public houses allowed carding, dicing, skittle playing, or received the takers of pheasants, hares, doves or pigeons. Sunday football lingered at Hemsley until it was banished to Rievaulx by Vicar Conyers, to disturb the idyllic setting where the poet William Cowper hoped to settle. The Society of Bell Ringers at Helmsley rang 'Hornby's surprise' in 1777. Popular touring-booth theatre favoured the melodramatic. Pickering in 1797 saw the pantomime 'Bluebeard'.

Many traditional things, done at regular times around the year, involved begging round the houses, to find the wherewithal to feast on. Some of the things done had pagan roots and were ancient attempts to deal with evil spirits. Witchwood was gathered annually across Blackamore on St. Helen's Eve and worn for luck. Other occasions

Table 39. Calendar Customs

January-	6 Plough Monday - Young men's 'fond plough' procession in costume, including begging for money.
	7 Distaff Day - Return of women to work. Men-women games.
	20 St. Agnes Eve - Sitting in church porch to see who would die shortly.
	New Years Eve or Day-First footing. Begging for small rewards.
April -	1 Fool's Day - Practical jokes
	24 St Mark's Eve - Sitting in church porch to prophecy demises
Days before Lent	
	Collop Monday - Eat slices of meat and eggs. Last day for meat
	Shrove Tuesday - Eat pancakes. Ball day & races
	Ash Wednesday - Eat fritters. Play tut ball
	Bloody Thursday - Eat black puddings.
	Long Friday - Eat cake, biscuits or buns. Clear up farms
	Easter Eve - Beg and decorate eggs
	Easter Sunday - Men-women games for forfeits
Days after Easter	
	Carling Sunday - Eat steeped peas fried in butter
	Palm Sunday - Gather and decorate with willows
	Whitsuntide - Milkmaids dine and dance
	May Day eve. - Youth to fields in early morning to gather garlands,
May -	1 May Day - Maypole dancing
	14 St Helen's Eve - Witchwood night. Search hills for mountain ash
June -	20 Mid Summer Eve-Bonfires, Summer games
	21 Midsummer Day
August -	1 Lammas day - First fruits offerings
October -	30. All Saint's eve - All Hallows eve
	31 Nut crack night for divining future
November-	2 All Souls Day - Small cakes eaten
	11 Martinmas - Packrag day. Visit home. Oxroasts
	Christmas tide - Wassailing. Gooding, including begging.
December-	26 St Stephen's day - Stephening - The rich give away and the poor beg.
Michaelmas -	Butter loaves, Visit families
Trinity tide -	Home visiting, Eat peascods
Reaping and harvest suppers -	Corn dollies made.

brought a particular food or certain games to the fore, sometimes both, as on Shrove Tuesday morning. Some customs were opposed but if you didn't contribute to the 'fond plough', you might find a furrow made in the soil before your front door. Quakers, called 'broad brims' from their old fashioned hats, tried to stop the Mayday dancing around the Sinnington and Slingsby maypoles in 1708. They sang hymns in opposition to the dancers and players of flutes and drums who had come to crown the May Queen, but they failed.

Rich people went 'poor peopling' at Christmas to distribute charity, and the squires were expected to pay for other celebrations. Mr Hill at Thornton was told by his Steward to give money for drink in the village, on the occasion of national victories, outbreaks of peace and political elections. William Garforth of Wigganthorpe had his steward liberally distribute ale and bread for the multitude when his horse died in 1748. Coxwold roasted an ox with gilded horns for the 1761 Coronation and much ale was drunk. A barrel of ale for the populace was almost a philosophy in itself.

The new forms of hunting became popular but were made exclusive to the gentry. The Thornton Dale steward said he had never seen so many hunt, or publicly course apart from the two gentry families, the Hunters and the Hills. The other freeholders hunted rabbits or set snares for them on the common at night. Mr Hill hunted carted deer before he kept foxhounds. With the deer, the hounds were held back from a kill.

Mr. Darleys pack of hounds at Aldby was one of the first used exclusively to hunt fox. He started to keep hounds in 1733 and sold them in 1765. Within a single year, thirty couple cost him £19.12s. and earth stopping another £21. He kept a huntsman, a groom, a whipper in and a dog keeper, and ranged with them on open ground from Garrowby to Gilling, and Bulmer to Pocklington. His mad dog medicine was bought at Scarborough. Foxhounds were bred for speed and endurance on long runs. The riding became harder and needed more skill, as inclosure hedges ate into the open commons. New plantations and fox coverts gave the fox a chance. The horse riding was itself seen as a remedy against low spirits, indigestion and gout.

Cock fighting was widespread, attracting rich and poor. There were cockings at Malton races in 1739, a 'main of cocks' between Mr Thomas Richardson of that town and the Gentlemen of Scarborough for two guineas a battle and twenty guineas the main. Mr. Hebblethwaite of Norton issued public challenges to groups of gentlemen for cock fights.

Cock Fighting was popular

Thomas Boye's cockpit at Harum was said to be 'fit for a pig'. Vicar Conyers was credited with stopping barborous bull baitings at Helmsley in 1754.

Boys were still rewarded by church wardens for badger heads, and even foxes but mainly for foulmarts, polecats, sparrows and their eggs. This encouraged a hostile view to much wild life, in sharp contrast to the attitudes shown to horses, dogs and even cattle. Prize fight contestants were treated in much the same way. George Stephenson faced 'a stand and deliver', in the company of his patron's second wife. They say that he killed one highwayman and fisted two more. Stephenson passed from the employ of Mr Sykes at Sledmere, to pugilism for the Prince of

Wales. He fought Jack Broughton till he died, at Taylors Amphitheatre, when a large wreath came from Sledmere Hall.

Gentry restraint on the populace was greatest over poaching. The older game laws were thought to be failing, despite the widspread appointment of gamekeepers. Pheasants and partridges were increasingly viewed as the property of those on whose land they settled. Inclosure removed the birds, hares and rabbits, at a stroke, from commons to private land. The 1754 Game Laws were severe and required a game certificate. By 1770 poachers could be imprisoned for long periods or whipped. Gentry shooting lodges at the moor edge began with Darley Lodge in Spaunton built by 1770 and Barmoor lodge in 1783. The Earl of Carlisle rented Cropton moor for shooting in 1778 and appointed its gamekeeper. Luke Smelt wrote to John Piper the attorney, sending a young spaniel, and advised firing a gun to him in the yard, till he found he could stand it. Shooting joined the hunt as one of the exclusive sports.

Lord Carlisle, overseas in 1766, spoke of playing cricket in the late morning. I'Anson of Norton later wrote, that the Yorkshire game was said to have had its origin at Castle Howard, even though cricket had been played from early times at Langton Wold. Buttercrambe played Bishop Wilton in 1803 but village matches must go back earlier than that. The Leeds Intelligencer in 1774 gave an epitaph for a deceased cricketer

'I bowl'd, I struck, I caught, I stop't.
Sure life's a game of cricket
I block'd with care, with caution popp'd
Yet death has hit my wicket.'

A Day at the Races

Horse racing became the popular sport, gathering crowds from far and wide. Thomas Jackson, the Nunnington jockey was better known to his contemporaries than either the pioneer novelist Laurence Sterne of Coxwold or the landscape gardener William Kent from Bridlington. Race meetings united all classes in gambling and spectacle. Three horses might race at a country fair, but Langton races in 1713, saw horses trained by grooms and races run for four miles over an agreed course.

Black Hambleton, west of Helmsley, was the most famous course.

The Heseltine family trained their horses there. The fabulous White Mare of Whitstonecliff was said to be an Arabian horse sent to train in the early days. She proved a strong horse that no one could ride, and she bolted over the cliff into Gormire lake. In a famous race, 'Old Merlin', probably belonging to Sir William Strickland, and ridden by Jerome Hare of Cold Kirkby, beat a New Market horse and shifted much southern money northwards. The first King's cup was raced for at Hambleton in 1715, the cup of a hundred guineas. The race was altered to be run by mares under five years old, of ten stone weight. Thirty horses entered in 1719.

Rules were made to regulate the racing and the betting in 1740. A Statute limited matches raced for money, plate or prizes, to Newmarket and Black Hambleton, clear recognition of its role as the principal northern course. Subscription plates were added in 1749 with encouragement from the Earl of Carlisle and the Lords Fairfax and Fauconberg. Nunnington church has a marble slab to Thomas Jackson, 'bred at Black Hambleton and crowned with laurels at Newmarket'. He made some local fortunes and they said that he died 'in the service of his friends' in 1766. The memorial spoke of him as 'a useful lesson to the humbler part of mankind that men of industry and honesty may rise to glory from the lowest stations and have their memories recorded as well as the great and noble'. A royal order removed the King's plate to York Knavesmire, where improved facilities included a grandstand in 1755, but great popular race meetings continued at Hambleton.

Langton Wold races became regular meetings, with one event a day, but each with three or four heats. Malton and Norton had some of the top feeders. Newspapers advertised the races which gained reputation steadily. Soon there were mains of cocks and assemblies. The horse fair at Malton was linked to the races. Owners of horses were required to make early registration at those Malton Inns with stables. Richard Langley of North Grimston ran his famous horse 'Duchess' and the St Quintins fielded 'Cade' and 'Herod'. Entries widened to include horses entered by Ayrton and Fenton of Malton, Preston of Burythorpe, Sykes of Sledmere and George Searle training for Henry Goodricke of Sutton on forest.

Hunmanby, Pickering and Seamer started regular meetings which began to form part of a programme for the north. Winners becoming well known and listed in published almanacs and racing calendars. Sir William St. Quintin bred the stallion which produced the famous 'Scampston Cade'. Richard Ayrton of Malton's 'Archimedes' won at

Hunmanby in 1773. Even the Pickering meeting on the level Yatts Common north of the town, had entries in 1779 from the Marquess of Rockingham and Mr. Osbaldeston. Hogsheads of port, the patriotic drink, were prizes at the Pickering Port Stakes of 1782 when the Black Swan had assemblies, plays and cockfights during the race week. Langton Wold was in a different class, taking the place that Hambleton had enjoyed in the region and was given a grandstand in 1801.

A Touch of Romance

Love Tokens from Malton

The old proverbs said that 'in love is no lack' but that 'it is hard to wive and thrive all in one year'. The old sayings were full of what a later age would call 'relationships'. Love will find its way but 'there belongs more to marriage than four bare legs in a bed'. Marriages were long delayed but 'Young cocks know no coops' and 'Who weddeth ere he be wise, shall die ere he thrive'. 'Faint heart never won fair lady' but 'courting and wooing bring dallying and doing'. 'Jack shall have his Jill' and 'a good Jack maketh a good Jill'. This was a young society. Among the young, no matter has greater consideration and none offers a less certain result than matrimony. A Snainton woman concluded that 'married life affords but little ease, the best of husbands is so hard to please'.

The village talked when young Shepherd and Nelly Smales were seen cooing 'like a turtle and his mate' in a Cayton back yard in May 1744. That optimist George Shepherd of Eston offered young Jane a handful of raisins for a kiss. A Quaker girl Barbara Priestman left letters for her lover in a hollow tree at Thornton Dale, while mother went to attend the Pickering meeting. The lad called in at the beckside house. The gate clicked and the lover left in haste through the rear window. Asked what she was doing, the Quaker miss replied 'meditating, mother dear'. Sarah, the only daughter of another Quaker, John Richardson at Hutton le Hole was promised to a member of the Society. She absconded in the night to marry a man of her own choice, to 'the great exercise of her father'.

Thomas Brown was the son of the Lastingham vicar. He became the master at Yedingham School and had dialect poems published in 1800. As a young lad, he was the village Burnes. Robin Rawlinson asked him to write a love poem on his behalf addressed to Sarah Ann Twigg. She twigged it wasn't by the ardent lover, but accepted the suit nonetheless. Parson Wyke on his first visit to Ellerburn found the clerk

---

Table 40. The Lost Language of Character, recorded by William Marshall of Pickering;

bonny - pretty, boorly - large but comely, bunchclot - a clodhopper
cankered - ill natured, chubby - full faced, cobby - cheerful
cowdy - frolicsome, daft - inept, donnot - good for nothing
dowley - sick, not brisk, dozzand - shrivelled, dunderknoll - blockhead
fashed - vexed, fond - foolish, gallock handed - left handed
gammestang - idle loose girl, gauvison - oafish, silly fellow
gotherley - affable, kind - friendly, kipper - nimble
misteached - spoilt, naffhead-blockhead, old farrand - old fashioned
pauky - artful, seasonsides - sly, dry fellow, whik – alive

---

and the sexton watching a free fight, across the river, between a husband and wife. He was advised to look and see 'a woman combing her husband's hair with a three legged stool'. The minister with Protestant fervour leapt into the middle, shouting 'hands off scoundrel' and 'retire virago', but they turned on him. Lively gossip claimed that Laurence Sterne was wed to a 'prickly and sharp tongued woman', whose breakdown was due to finding him in the embraces of the maid.

A man in the Byland area had his fortune told in 1797. He was told to mind a fair haired minx who meant him no good. He presumed that this was Alice who 'bore him a spite'. A month later he saw three black cats so he didn't go to market.

Evangelical Revival

An 'Evangelical Revival' swept into Church of England congregations, and the surviving chapels of the dissenters. This could hardly have been predicted and it is not obvious why it occured. Ultimately it would result in the establishment of numerous Methodist societies, which would break away from the Church of England, and recruit from the wider society, to become a great Christian denomination. The movement also created strong local Baptist, Congregational and Presbyterian societies, in the market towns and in a few villages, with wider groups of regularly attending 'hearers'. The evangelicals would form an emphasis and later almost a party, within the revived Church of England.

A few parish churches saw the revival first, but with no idea what was to follow. There were fresh people about, imbued with a new spirit. This often derived from a sense of being awakened, or even converted. The question was often put 'what must you to do to be saved'. Vicar Richard Conyers was already serving Helmsley as the minister in the church living, when he had a sense of being converted. He walked backwards and forwards in the room shouting 'I have found him'. He began to preach with uncommon zeal, and often extempore, round about 1756. Soon he was holding preaching and social meetings all day Sunday, weekdays and every evening. He worried about the unchanged sinners that heard him.

Vicar John King at Middleton, appointed to that living by the heir of old Luke Robinson, was another in the new mould. Popular preaching and social work went together in his ministry. When he catechised the children from the families of his parish, he just tried to explain 'in as familiar and plain a manner, as he was able'. He could be close friends with a Calvinist Baptist of a totally different viewpoint, and he made prominent local people into churchwardens. When he was obliged to leave for Hull, one wrote-

'In mournful strains, permit me now to sing,
And vent my sorrows for the loss of King
Unto a fallen, lost and wretched race,
He preached salvation, full and free by Grace
The naked he did clothe, the hungry feed ,
He was a friend to those who stood in need.'

The evangelical ministers held few of the pulpits, but they pioneered a new way. They won some influential support in their struggle to promote a bible-based, personal religion on the one hand, and to do some good on the other. There was much talk of sin, but also much social action. Conyers started classes at Helmsley for girls, young men and young women. When he married the genteel Mrs. Knipe, 'who dressed in a camlet gown', they said that she bought corn for the poor and every Sunday they fed eighty of them. There was opposition, too. Threats came that 'if he preached his Methodism, his gown would be pulled over his ears'. Instead of that, the vicarage was rebuilt with a new coach house and stables. Squire Thomas Duncombe paid for the bell to be recast. There was some point in ringing it now, and then a new peal of bells was hung.

Conyers left Helmsley after his wife died, aged fifty six in 1774. John Wesley visiting him had worried about the theological tendency of his reading. After his departure, some of his congregation left the parish church to found a Calvanistic church in a backyard behind the high street, linked with the Countess of Huntington's Connexion. Much the same consequences followed the departure of Vicar King, from Middleton parish-

'Ye saints of Hull, come mingle tears with me.
But Middleton I'm most concerned for thee.
Into whose hands thou art now like to Fall,
Is only known to Him who, ruleth all.'

The clergyman who followed, didn't have the way of it. The keener members left to start a Congregational church at Pickering.

Another Parish Church could miss all that, and yet still feel that great changes were taking place. Some installed new galleries to hold more hearers, but others put them up to hold musicians. This began an important movement from dull chanting led by a reed pipe, towards richer styles of music, communally sung, which could prove a stronger root on which to nourish a congregation. Malton St. Leonard's church had Richard Storr for fifty years, to teach the choristers who transformed its music. He died aged 85 in 1817.

'When first a master he was seen.and scarcely was he then nineteen
'Twas here to teach that tuneful art which warms devotion, mends the heart.

And lifts the soul through ecstasy, to taste the joys that reign
on heigh.'

There were those who feared music. Many years later, John
Castillo, a keen Methodist opposed the installation of an organ at
Sinnington church, with satire.

'Ye pleasers of men , I would have ye beware
As Satan is cunning in setting his snare
Bear witness O. tree which the lightning smote
What an host to the old parish church did resort
Whose absence declare their great business here
Was chiefly the new set up organ to hear
Had half of them done what the minister said
What a glorious fire would have quickly been spread.'

A concert was performed at Hovingham parish church in 1836, joined
by musical societies from Kirkby Moorside and Malton.

Methodism

The Church of England
could not contain the
Evangelical movement that
began within it. The great
Methodist missioner, John
Wesley repeatedly toured the
district preaching in parish
churches, but was often denied
entry to pulpits, and would
preach in the open air instead.
You could sometimes reach
more people outside the church
than within it. The preacher
became part of street life, where
many were always looking
for something to do.

John Wesley

Other preachers came in Wesley's wake, and together they had to
elicit a response from local people, who would form a society and make
it work. John Manners of Sledmere wrote to Wesley in 1763. After

much opposition, he had managed to join nineteen in a society at Malton and fifteen at Pickering but he forecast 'a glorious work' at both places. The curate opposed the preaching to a large Settrington crowd. He threatened the Methodists, but shortly afterwards fell off his horse and broke his neck. Some would see that as an omen.

A Malton minister in 1764, reported 'a house appropriated for a meeting house, where a few illiterate people who call themselves Methodists now and then assemble'. The Slingsby minister said his local Methodists disliked the label and attended church, but the Lastingham vicar saw those attending the two Methodist meeting houses in his parish, as a rabble. Parker the 19th century antiquarian retained the sceptical view. He wrote that 'in the earliest years of the Wesleyans, at Helmsley, when their faith was thought to move mountains, an ancient couple were proselytes to the cause. Wonderful as it may seem, though stricken in years, they were newly born again'.

The Methodists were offering something people wanted, and which the Church usually didn't offer. Where the parish church was outgoing, Methodism might be, for a time, delayed. The new preachers showed a 'passion for souls' and many who responded felt 'a strong sense of sin', a feeling of conviction when relieved of it, and 'a determination to achieve the same result by the conversion of others. Robert Venis from Fryup talking to two Methodists at York, thought they made 'too much adoo about religion', but he soon began to feel himself a sinner. By 1761 he had concluded that cards and dancing were sinful. He changed his way of life. His wife said that he was 'righteous overmuch'.

Joseph Pilmoor from Fadmoor and Richard Boardman of Gillamoor in 1769 journeyed to Leeds to hear John Wesley. They brought Methodism to the two villages and, after accepting missionary roles in Philadelphia and New York, they contributed to establishing a movement that two hundred years later, would include millions of United States Methodists. For these things to be possible, it was necessary to accept that salvation was open to all who believed, and not restricted to a chosen few. If this was the driving force for many, there was still space for an inner group, a 'select band' who felt their sins forgiven, or experienced a sense of triumph over sin, separate from the wider members of the societies, and the even wider congregations of hearers. The conviction that there was an 'after life' was common ground. Methodist John Jackson of Lastingham in 1785 looked forward to meeting his relations in heaven.

Early Wesleyan meeting houses or chapels were built at Hawnby in 1770, where the landlord turned the Methodists out of their houses, and at Fadmoor and Westow in 1793. Elsewhere, meeting houses were licenced widely in the cottage meeting phase of the movement, until chapels were built to replace them. John Atlay of Sheriff Hutton, an intimate of Wesley, headed the Dewsbury schisms, the breakaway phenomena that continued to afflict Methodism as it grew to become a denomination. These were exciting times. Young Jackson the artist at Lastingham wrote letters full of Methodist religion, with talk of 'experimental godliness'. Bransdale was said to practise 'a wild sort of Methodism'.

Many middling people became 'serious' and sought personal 'improvement' by study. An 'improvement movement' would extend

---

Table 41. Some Certificates issued for Dissenting Meeting Houses.

1767   Hovingham (Samuell Freeze)
1770   Burythorpe (Richard Wilson); Thornton Dale (John Tweedy); Pickering (Joseph King); Appleton le Moors (John Gill)
1773   Wintringham (Thomas Bacon); Ganton (Richard Wilson);
1775   Marton near Sinnington (George Warne); Sinnington (Thomas Medd); Hovingham (Robert Foxton); Hanging Grimstone (Henry Ireland)
1776   Nawton (David Cussons);
1777   Helmsley, Church Street (William Boys); Kirkby Moorside (John Frank);
1778   Stittenham (John Revis); Barugh (Robert Guthrick); Claxton (William Pearson)
1779   Acklam (Abigail Catton); Burythorpe (Richard Laycock); Settrington (Richard Waller); Nunnington (William Bentley); Stonegrave (Robert Peacock); Middleton (John Lancaster); Carlton (John Wilks); Gillamoor (Thomas Parker); Hawnby; Cornbrough (Robert Hobson); Helmsley (William Fletcher); East Heslerton (James Woodhill)
1781   Flaxton (William Horner); Sheriff Hutton (Methodist preaching house); Harome (John Simpson);
1783   Farmanby (New building);

---

beyond its religous roots. Faith Gray wife of the Helmsley estate Steward, would write that 'the days were occupied in active improvement and the evenings in a way calculated to gratify and improve the mind'. She used the evenings of a November week at Helmsley in 1768 to read the 'Thirty Nine Articles of Faith'. Her friends feared she would 'fall to Methodism', but she remained in the Church of

England. Ministers like Vicar Comber at Kirkby Moorside were just as active, but didn't seem incapable of remaining where they were.

These people, with their evangelical friends, were active in promoting the new Bible and Tract societies, often vigorously supported in a patronal sort of way, by other leisured ladies of the market towns and country halls. You could feel that you were doing something good for people by bringing the bible to them. By 1778 you could subscribe to the 'Universal Family Bible' supplied in a hundred parts. The societies made the bible and the shorter tracts available. The 'good book' spread far afield in penny numbers. Mrs. Gray circulated Hannah Moor's cheap tracts where ever she went. A seaman could write to his wife from his ship off Portugal, that he was glad to hear she was taking in 'the bibble'.

The Sunday Schools

The Sunday School movement brought the children of an expanding population back to church to learn to read - the bible. The Charity Schools were in no position to expand and meet the need. Mr Conyers had run some sort of school in 1769, and Vicar King in 1764, giving an hour a week to catechising children, was running a Sunday school of sorts, but that was another day. The Misses Hill pioneered a school at Tadcaster in 1785. The Archbishop approved a Sunday school at York that year to teach the poor their duty to God, their neighbours and themselves.

The Helmsley Steward, Mr Gray soon aftwards encouraged the spread of Sunday schools 'to promote among the lower classes the knowledge and practise of religous and moral duties, a regular attendance upon the ordinances in the Church of England and principles of loyalty and subordination'. That year a Sunday School for sixty boys and girls was opened at Kirkby Moorside, supported by C. S. Duncombe and in November, another opened at Helmsley, where seventy were soon admitted. Vicar Comber left £3 a year to endow the Kirkby Sunday School.

The beginnings were somewhat visionary. Principal inhabitants were encouraged to act as visitors, assisting volunteer teachers. The realities proved hard but the schools were a success. They minded children for part of the one day of the week that held much leisure. They interfered little with child labour. They helped extend literacy to women and they helped to create 'a nation of the book'. Middleton built a Sunday School building in 1832, for £70, of which £40 came from the

National Society. The young people of the parish taught the school.

More People Abroad and Wider Horizons

A remarkable growth in the number of people surviving early childhood, brought a population explosion in the second half of the 18th century. This would go on for a hundred years, flooding the villages and towns with more people. Growth meant prosperity for some, as an expanding society gave more opportunities, but many had to leave, in each generation, for the industrial areas, the ports, towns and cities and for overseas.

Colonial wars opened up new prospects. General Hale from Tocketts in Cleveland led the 47th regiment, at the Battle of Quebec in 1759. The early migrations that followed, took local people to newly conquered French Canada, whence blacksmith George Hick wrote home, speaking of prosperous labourers. English place names soon spread across that country. More went in the seventies from the moors, small owners, craftsmen, some Methodists, and some poor families paid to go to New Brunswick and Nova Scotia to relieve the Yorkshire poor rates. The ships 'Thomas and William' and the 'Prince George' sailed from Scarborough in 1774.

Others travelled widely in the army and the navy of the colonial age, or found profitable employments in their 'plantations'. Valentine Striker, a rogue found at Old Malton in 1772, had been the world over, in General Oglethorpe's regiment at St Christopher and for five years at Santa Cruz. Ralph Sandwith of Helmsley died in Honduras in 1788. William Hill managed slave plantations at Tortola. William Marshall ran plantations in the Indies, as well as English farms before returning to Pickering. John Webster of Marton rose to become captain of the ship 'Lively'. William Wilson, Commander of the East India Company Marine who retired to Ayton in Cleveland took the view that 'the English had the right to navigate where ever it pleased God to send water'.

John Paul Jones, the naval hero brought an American squadron to harry shipping off the Yorkshire coast, in 1779, during the American Independance War that ran from 1775 to 1783. A Stittenham lad wrote to his Dad from Boston in December 1775, saying the soldiers were starving for want of food and firewood. Many volunteered at York to reinforce Preston's light dragoons at Boston. Whitby ships took the 31st Regiment the next year. A Scarborough transport was sunk at the battle of Yorktown. William Bosville of Thorpe near Rudstone went with the

289

53rd Regiment, and imbibed Republican sentiments, becoming a friend of Tom Payne, who visited his home. His 'Rights of Man' and 'The Age of Reason' were infuential social criticism of a new kind. They were quickly suppressed by the English government.

Clever Men Trying to Change the World

This was hardly an age of reason, but there was emerging a new approach to human experience, and how this could be used. Nathaniel Bailey's Dictionary of 1721 and the Chamber's Cyclopaedia of 1728 classified things known, and made the information accessible for those with books. Dr. Johnson's dictionary came out in 1755. A considerable range of printed books began to enter gentlemen's libraries. They made diverse experiences and ideas comparable, and spread knowledge about methods of doing things. Mr Hill at Thornton Dale had useful works, as varied as Bradley's Husbandry 1726, Atkinson's Navy Surgeon 1737 and Dalton's Country Justice 1742. A more varied newspaper press played its part in providing better information. The York Courant newspaper was locally available in 1736 sold by Mennel at Malton, Stockton at Kirkby Moorside and Mr Parkinson at Pickering.

There was a new curiosity about things, among those with the opportunity to explore them, particularly the gentry, the clergy and other professionals. During 1743 and 1756, 1759 and 1762, strange fossils of ancient creatures were discovered in the alum rock near Whitby. These posed unanswerable questions, for those who accepted old biblical accounts of the Creation of the World. Old habits of mind died very hard. After all, it didn't affect anything of practical importance, whether you believed this or some other explanation of the origin of things. In 1752, January 1st was decreed to be New Year's Day instead of March 25th, and the eleven days between the 2nd and 14th of September 1752, were eliminated. This was practical enough. Men could feel that they had been robbed of time.

The practical approach to solving problems showed greater advances. Local contributions came from Joseph Foord who from about 1747 made moorland water courses, from the higher moors to Griff, Old Byland, Carlton, Pockley, Nawton, Fadmoor, Gillamoor and Lastingham. He was a surveyor, and he used his professional skills to create channels with slow descents, down contours which at first sight might look impossible. Each water course was a considerable engineering feat. By way of contrast, Spaunton had to commission a miner to dig a well at least forty yards deep in 1782, with little certainty that he would strike water.

William Marshall of Sinnington surveyed farming practices throughout north east Yorkshire and published them in his two volume 'Rural Economy'. He then edited surveys covering the entire country, which were published in a series of volumes. He suggested a Board of Agriculture to promote the best practices and before his death in 1818, established the first farm college in the country at Pickering, to further that purpose.

Robert Teesdale, the head gardener for Lord Carlisle at Castle Howard, made a classified catalogue of rare plants in the neighbourhood, some one hundred and ninety seven species in 1794. William Scoresby the elder, born at Nutholm in 1760, who went to sea at nineteen, invented the ice drill and the crow's nest. Francis Nicholson, said to be a weaver's son from Pickering, was known as 'the father of water colour painting' and made contributions to colour chemistry.

Another land surveyor, Nicholas King of Pickering in 1789 prepared four plans for the town's field inclosure. He sought broader opportunities overseas. He sailed on the 'Hunter' for America in 1793, a voyage taking three months. Reaching Philadelphia by stage coach, he wrote that 'this city exceeds my expectation - many elegant buildings', that were the best he had ever seen. After working for a rich American, he became a part time commissioner for Washington, on condition that his father Robert King could take his place the next Spring. He levelled streets and laid out the divisions and squares of the young city of Washington and he mapped the Potomac. His father Robert served as principal surveyor 1797 - 1802 and his son Nicholas from 1802-1812. They made maps of the Ohio, Alabama and Lousiana rivers and of the vast region west of the Mississipi, after the Louisiana purchase. The younger Robert King was city surveyor 1812-1813 and 1815-1817.

Sir George Cayley at Brompton took the view that he should inform himself of the useful branches of human learning, including the practical arts. He did so with some effect. He was a major force in getting the Vale drainage started and was an early promoter of cottage allotments. He experimented with hot air, steam and gas engines, encouraging others to take the ideas further. He pioneered experiments in heavier and lighter than air human flight and constructed an instrument for testing the purity of water. His notebooks show an interest in brick making, rainbows, the breaking strengths of timber, the shrinking of cast iron, artificial hands and kites.

New Private Schools

A few more schools gained endowments in the later 18th century. There may have been more masters teaching at all levels. The Hovingham school was enlarged by Richard Worsley in 1758. Schoolmasters appear from Sheriff Hutton to Farndale. Fee paying schools expanded, some for mere child minding, others to meet the demand for the reading, writing and mathematical skills, increasingly necessary in a widening range of occupations. Mr. Robinson taught classics at Pickering till 1778. Nicholas Cheeseman came back from being a Yarmouth exciseman before 1786 to be the Middleton schoolmaster. Benedictine Refugees from the French Revolution came from Lorraine to Ampleforth where Ann Fairfax built them a chapel and they opened a school in 1802, that would become a major Roman Catholic educational centre.

Surviving school books show the child mind being bent to elementary mathematcs. Peter Kirkby's book of 1771 had the exercise 'Work out the course for a pirate to evade capture by a sloop', given speeds, directions and details of the prevailing wind. John Gibson's book had cube roots, and ways to estimate the number of bricks in a wall. Robert Piper's notebook included the observation that 'a point is the least assignable part of a space'.

John Welborne opened a school on Potter hill, Pickering in 1793, offering grammar, writing, arithmetic, mensuration, navigation, astronomy, and book keeping. His wife would manage 'tambour, embroidery, needle work and reading from approved authors'. Harrison's School at Scrayingham added roots, logarithms and the slide rule, conical sections and trigonometry. Mr. J. Nicholson at Welburn near Castle Howard offered 'English, writing, arithmetic, merchants' accounts, geometry, surveying, algebra, mechanics, astronomy, navigation, fortification, gunnery, fluxions and every other branch of mathematics, requisite to complete youth for the army, navy or mercantile affairs'.

Mr.W.Allan launched his school at Wheelgate, Malton in 1800. His advertisement likened the child mind to a sheet of wax, on which a good impression could be made by a good stamp. His view of the female sex was rather different. He thought that 'they were conceived to form the principal happiness of men and to gently turn their rough manners'. He urged that wives should have a well stored mind, to avoid the husband turning to vice. Hutton Bushell in 1784 had a young ladies school offering framework and needlework. William Ashton, an eminent teacher, opened a school at Malton about 1795 and one pupil eloped with his daughter.

Kirkby Moorside had endowed and private schools. George Easterby was licenced to teach a petty school in 1752. Another master was teaching the 'three Rs' there eleven years later, when there was also a Latin school with eighteen scholars taught by the Reverend George Skelding and an 'old woman's school'. Christopher Hornsey had the petty school in 1771. The 'parish school' was built after raising subscriptions in 1796, at the south entrance to the churchyard, apparently with only four free pupils.

Turnpike Transport

A Gentleman's Magazine writer in 1769 observed that 'We may expect soon to travel through turnpike lanes instead of open fields'. Turnpike Trusts, founded under private Acts of Parliament, charged travellers for use of the through roads, and spent part of the income on such improvements as lowering hills, scraping and straightening the roads. The Vale of York gained early turnpike roads linking London to Scotland, but others joined the farming countries, to the hungry industrial and mining areas of the West Riding.

The York - Scarborough Turnpike of 1752 was different, a response to increased gentry traffic heading for the Scarborough resort but it carried goods traffic as well. TheYork - Easingwold 1752, Malton - Pickering 1765 and Lockton - Whitby 1765 turnpikes extended the network into north east Yorkshire. The York to Oswaldkirk Bank Top Turnpike of 1758 linked inner Ryedale to the county capital. This was continued by private road improvements undertaken by Mr Duncombe, taking the road to Sproxton in 1757 and beyond to Helmsley a few years later.

Ancient king's highways were usually confirmed by Inclosure Commissioners at widths of forty and sixty feet. Provisions were made under the Inclosure Acts of Parliament, and the Awards that followed, for the maintenance of these roads by local highway surveyors. Where inclosures had been undertaken by earlier methods, responsibilties were less well defined but the roads remained as they had been, subject to any repairs required by the justices. Road maintenance was much discussed, with great criticism directed at the usual method of throwing up barrelled earth roads with a limestone cover, the stone eventually sinking into the mire below.

There was considerable improvement of bridges. The important Malton bridge was widened in 1760 giving a better carriage and coach access across the river Derwent. The North Riding Bridge Surveyor, John Carr, a very able architect, between 1772 and 1803, rebuilt most of the lengthening list of county bridges in the North Riding, to quite beautiful and efficient designs. Tilehouse bridge was built in 1773, Ayton bridge in 1775, Sinnington bridge in 1769 and 1787 and Crambe

The Bridge at Kirkham Priory

bridge on the York road in 1798. John Tuke considered the North Riding bridges to be some of the best attended and most numerous in the kingdom.

The enthusiasm for canals led investors to provide much of the country with a major new network of communications, which provided cheap if slow transport for heavy goods. This had little local impact in north-east Yorkshire but Whitby-Pickering, Scarborough-Helmsley and Pickering-Malton canals were seriously canvassed in the last decade of the century. The last two were flat land projects, but all three failed to mature, although estimates were made and some shares issued. Only the River Foss navigation scheme for a waterway from York to Stillington was completed, distinctive in serving a primarily agricultural area. The Derwent navigation gained an extension from Malton to Yedingham, where modest wharfs were built.

There were more horses than ever and great houses gained large stables. The Castle Howard stables were built on a mammoth scale, matching the house, to the designs of John Carr. Along the turnpike and other main roads, the principal inns were refashioned to accomodate more travellers. Their yards were equipped with stables and coach houses, with haylofts, smithies, horse ponds and accommodation for postboys. Their lodging rooms filled with travellers' furniture, wig stands with flea powder and warming pans full of sea coal. Castle Howard was given its own Inn, built across the through road.

The Inns and Alehouses

The great York Inns, the Black Swan, the York Tavern, the George, Etheridges and others, accomodated the genteel coaching and riding travellers making for Scarborough and Whitby. They might visit Malton's New Talbot Inn, to stay over night, the premier inn on the route. Other stages were the Barton Hill Inn, Snainton New Inn and the Yedingham Providence Inn, on the way to Scarborough, or the Pickering Black Swan and the Saltergate Inn en route for Whitby. The Triton Inn at Sledmere was a major halt on the York-Bridlington road. Ganton Dale Inn would become another good quality, half way house on the Scarborough-Beverley run. These were the principal coaching routes.

Vehicles called diligences gave way to regular stage-coaches, running three days a week towards Scarborough or Whitby from York and returning on alternate days. The inns at the terminal points served like later railway stations and expanded their services to travellers. The more expensive coaches had guards. A highwaymen robbed the coach on the Whitby run In 1774, 'a lusty man in a light great coat with black crape over his face'. John Williamson robbed the Whitby mail coach at Thornton moor of £66.2s10d the next year. Besides a growing number of public stage coaches, there were slower vehicles for long distance goods traffic. A heavy stage waggon went regularly in 1778 from the George Inn, York on Tuesdays and Saturdays for Malton, 2d a stone to Malton, 4d a stone to Scarborough, passengers 1s.6d and 3s.6d putting in at the George Inn Scarborough.

Lesser roads gained increasing horse and wagon traffic, including some driven off the turnpike roads by their tolls. The Rosedale Crown Inn was rebuilt by John Page in 1776 as a two storey posting house with stables, on the busy Kirkby Moorside to Whitby road. John Porteous at the Lion inn, Blakey had corn markets and cockfights at this isolated half way house across the moors, attracting well to do Pickering and Kirkby folk to the cockpit, fifty yards off the road and a hundred yards from the public house.

As long as the droving trade lasted, the inns at Chequers, Dialstone, Limekiln House and Hambleton Inn attracted the drovers, and pastured the cattle in their stances. Some delivered Durham coal into Bilsdale and took back oats. They were remembered for eating 'waff', a name for oats, eggs and bacon. Moor edge alehouses at Dalby moor and Allerston moor on the long road to Hackness, must also have relied on the drovers' trade. The townships of Wykeham and Ruston took tolls from droves of cattle crossing the vale a little further east in 1769, heading for Garton, Kilham and Driffield, the markets of the Wolds.

New Malton had twenty five inns and alehouses. Outstanding among the inns was the New Talbot. Sir William Strickland had built a mansion just outside the borough wall perhaps as early as 1684. This was sold to the Wentworth family in 1739 and within a decade was converted into an Inn. This was described as 'an eligible stage to sleep at', for the gentry making for Scarborough. Its landlords were well known figures required to be able to deal with the mightiest in the land. The Malton New Inn had nightly balls during the race week of 1743.

The King's Head in the Market Place was reckoned the principal town inn during 1751. By 1773, the town seemed packed with inns, of which the Angel, the Blacksmiths Arms, the Black Horse and the Royal Oak all had brewhouses. A London horse dealer visiting the Malton dealer, Mr Whitty stayed one Wednesday evening at Nicholsons little public house next to the Royal Oak in Market Place, bedding down with George and Isaac for the night, before leaving for the White Lion at Hovingham.

The Crown Inn at Helmsley in 1725 had eight beds, nine tables and twenty two chairs. By 1736 the numbers had risen to twelve beds, fifteen tables and forty one chairs and there were pictures on the staircase. Thomas Underwood's Golden Lion on the east side of the market place saw the formation in 1767 of the Helmsley Orderly Society. One of the purposes of this Friendly society was stated to be 'to support the mutual love of the members'. The renowned Black Swan Inn was in the market place by 1784.

The Helmsley linen workers were remembered as a hundred thirsty weavers who were served by twenty public houses in 1774. Stories are told of smugglers reaching the town with cheap supplies of spirits. Thomas Thompson found a barrel in a quarry and fetched a gimlet to

The Black Swan Inn, Helmsley

bore a hole. The smugglers returned to remove the barrel. He wondered where it had gone, when he awoke from his stupor.

The Black Swan inn still displays its porch of 1632 at Kirkby Moorside and the Angel Inn in West end was mentioned around 1700. The King's Arms was 'ancient and well accustomed' in 1752. The King's Head was rebuilt in 1760. The list of licencees for 1774 numbers nineteen, include the Wheatsheaf, the Black Swan, and the Hare. TheGeorge and Dragon had been a cruck framed house, but was given a second story and by 1811 had stables, barns and coach houses. The White Horse Inn had a private pew in the church and invested in a post chaise in 1777. There were three alehouses at Gillamoor, three at Farndale and others at Keldholme and Kirkby Mills.

Public houses saw almost every public activity and a good deal that was private, even illicit. Four handkerchiefs, a black hood, a Holland apron and a camblet gown stolen from an Amotherby trunk in 1741 were pawned at a Broughton pub for 4s.6d and a bottle of brandy. At

Sledmere, they said that squire Mark Kirkby had an arrangement with his coachman that they would never get drunk on the same evening, so that one or the other would be fit to drive the coach back to the great house.

Some village ale houses had distinctive features. At the Blacksmith's Arms, in Lastingham, the curate Jeremiah Carter played the violin, having thirteen children to sustain on an income of £20 a year. John Featherstone rebuilt the Cooper house at the low end of Hutton le Hole to become the Red lion Inn in 1787. The Buck inn at Wrelton had its own brewery in 1779 and seems to have been run in conjunction with both a shop and a farm. The shop goods worth £15 exceeded the value of the ale and spirituous liquors at £13.

Some isolated ale houses found enough custom to survive. The old Kirkham Priory gatehouse became an alehouse. There wasn't much of the village left but there was an annual bird fair. A 'Pick and Shovel' alehouse was built near the Hartoft coal pits. A legend claims that the Earl of Mulgrave, upset at having to use the same horses without relays between Pickering and Mulgrave Castle, lent £100 to the Pickering Black Swan chaise driver, to keep horses at Saltergate. Thomas Massenger converted the house into an Inn. Many alehouses took on the title of Inn in these decades, implying that they could feed and accomodate both man and horse.

More to Come Home to

Houses changed, as house carpenters appeared everywhere and communal cruck rearings became a thing of the past. The Pickering jailer at the castle prison was on oath in 1715 to stop the locals pulling the walls down to make houses, as well as to hinder them stealing the rabbits. Most of the houses were still single storey. Foxholes rectory had a mansion house, fifty two feet by thirty one feet, with two large barns and a stable, but also a Foxholes cottage thirty nine feet by fifteen feet. The Lastingham vicarage house, twenty yards by five yards, had a stone floored hall and kitchen, and a board floored parlour, beneath the thatch in 1743 and outside were the turf house, barn, wain house and stable.

Malton's six hundred houses were mostly stone built, but Northallerton was already a brick town. William Marshall of Pickering towards the end of the century, described stone, pantiles and deal as the main building materials of his day. Brick walls were spreading around the lowlands and would dominate the Vale of York and the Marishes.

Brickyards opened at Middleton in 1782 and Wombleton by 1785. Newton on Rawcliff gained its first brick house in 1810. Dales homesteads called Red House recall the time when they alone had the new pantiles. William Watson paid £95 for a gentleman's house on the north side of Pickering Potter Hill in 1779. Both James Harrison and Thomas Mathers were glaziers. John Frank of Bridge Street was making fine furniture.

Table 42. Some of the duties of a North Riding constable in 1788

1.Present names of Popish recusants over eighteen who forbear to go to church and all who do not resort to divine service every Sunday.
2.Inquire into felonies, robberies, hues and cries made and whether the watch had been kept to apprehend felons and vagrants.
3.Inquire what vagabonds and rogues have been apprehended and who has relieved rogues with meat.
4.Certify what cottages have been erected contrary to statute with what inmates.
5.Certify how many inns, alehouse and tippling houses have been kept, whether licenced or not, whether they sell ale and beer according to the assize, who has been drunk, and who has maintained any unlawful games.
6.Present all unlawful weights and measures, and enquire whether the assize of bread has been kept.

Farmers and craftsmen had more in their homes. Hearths had long been well equipped with iron fittings, but a tea kettle, occasionally a looking glass, an iron oven or a corner cupboard make their appearance. Barbara Thackray in 1723 at Pickering had a black russett coat and petty coat, blue pettycoat, best suit of head clothes, best white apron, white cambrik handkerchief and linen smock. John Noble in 1732 had his pepperbox and cheese plate, tin dish covers, funnels, grater and coffee pot, candlebox, toasting iron and looking glass. Christopher Postgate owned a clock in 1738. John Kneeshaw in 1755 had three oval tables and looking glasses. Thomas Coates in 1761 had three Delf plates and Elizabeth Pennock five years later a bedstead with hangings, a brass kettle and a round oak table.

William Hague arriving at Scarborough in 1756 was amazed to see sailors with silver buckles on their shoes and watches in their pockets. They sang a song about Bobby Shaftoe 'going to sea, silver buckles, on his knee' and he did have a season at the resort. John Simpson a Helmsley weaver of 1780 had an inventory of £83 including a silver tankard, pewter, a wanded chair, a gun and a silver watch. The balance of things is better shown by William Skelton of Yearsley in 1780. His clothes were worth £5, his husbandry gear £2, his household furniture £40 and the rest making a total of £218 was beasts, calves and horses.

Tinkers travelled to repair things. Daniel Duck at Danby in 1786 was discomposed 'by hearing of the kettle being broke'. There was some pride of possessions. Helmsley wives had an unusual custom of shewing their scoured pewter in street displays on Good Friday. Money was lent out on bond or hidden in the thatch. A few by saving, sought in good periods to offset loss of earnings in the bad, by modest insurance, placing their small savings in Friendly Societies, formed at the market towns of Malton (1771) Hovingham (1773) and Kirkby Moorside (1777). The Helmsley Orderly Society in 1767 adopted rules to protect the savings of members, and incidentally specified no bad language and no disputes over religion or government, at the meetings to pay in the subscriptions.

The Good Life

The conspicuous consumption of the rich extended to household or personal servants, 'coxcombs in livery' as some called them. The Marquess of Rockingham had sixty two. As Richard Sykes finished his Sledmere house, he told his decorator Joseph Rose that he wanted the old rather than the newest styles, nothing rich and gaudy but neat and simple, suited to a plain country gentleman. He lived that life with the help of housekeeper, butler, gardener, coachman, groom, postilion, chamber maid and cook maid. His horse and carriage made him mobile and there were visits to the county town, the spa town and his house at Hull. He hunted with his own dogs, dined with his East Heslerton tenants, talked with his neighbour the Bishop of Carlisle, and he held the October courts at Helperthorpe and Weaverthorpe.

Grounds were converted into rolling parkland with created views. The Howsham mill was given an elaborate facade to take its place in the view. The half mile Rievaulx Terrace was made by 1757, a rural ride between decorative pavilions. Sledmere was given a fish basin in the park for carp. Christopher Sykes married Mary Tatton and gained a fortune. He began enlarging his house and by 1783 he had moved the village outside his new park and drained the mere. The Gentleman's

Magazine of 1826 lamented the later auction of the fine Sledmere library.

John Dowker of Salton wed Miss Woodcock at Kirkby Overcarr, a lady of great accomplishments and a fortune of £7000. Mr. Blomberg at Kirkby Misperton saddled his estate with a mortgage for £8000, which neither he nor his wife's second and third husbands could ever redeem so the property reverted to the Crown. A youth brought up with the children of the royal household, who bore a striking resembance to the monarch was given the estate. He built a new hall, lodges and in the park, an obelisk to his patron.

Young gentry toured Europe and visited the sights of England, including each other's houses. The Earl of Oxford on tour saw what he called Mother Shipton's house at Sand Hutton, the great inn across the through road at Castle Howard, the Terrington Spa pool and the new planted woods at Newbrough, before riding on to the fine Golden Bell Inn at Thirsk. Local gentry visiting Scarborough for spaw water or sea bathing, stayed in new purpose-built lodgings in the upper town. They also favoured the new local spaws at Hovingham, Sleightholmedale and Normanby. Richard Sykes was at the Scarborough long rooms in August 1752 and would go to the play. The Duke of York made an unexpected visit to take the waters in 1761 and visited Helmsley and Duncombe Park in August. He returned again in 1763, giving a fillip to the York and Scarborough seasons.

They said that it was an age of diversions. They were many and varied. In the year 1757, when the militia riots seem to have led to trouble at both Birdsall and Duncombe Park, Sir George Strickland was said 'to mind nothing but planting children and trees'. John Pearson the Ripon drawing master visited Brandsby. Faith Gray had a strange mixture of 'morality, history and novels in her reading' in 1768. Charles Duncombe in 1786-87 was travelling in Europe. One local landowner in 1792, lost £28.500 at play to Mr Barry, a debt eventually settled at £5.000. Thomas Hayes had artist Francis Nicholson paint 'The Triumph of Brittania' on the roof of his Aislaby Hall summer house. The last of the Dowkers was Vicar of Sinnington, and was credited with 'besting a witch'.

The tax on those using hair powder levied in 1795, fell on those for whom fashion was the corollary of status. The Darleys and Mrs Young paid at Aldby Park in Buttercrambe. The fashionables in the country around Pickering were the Fothergills at Kingthorpe, Vicar Dowker at Sinnington, the Coles and Mr Hodgson at Wrelton and Thomas and Mrs

Table 43. Number of male servants taxed in 1780; Some Ryedale and Nearby Entries.

25.-William Rose (Cold Kirkby)
12.-William Constable (West Newton); Nathaniel Chomley (Howsham);
10.-Earl of Carlisle (Hinderskelfe); Sir William St.Quintin (Scampston)
9.-Thomas Duncombe (Helmsley)
7.-Stephen Croft (Stillington); R. B. Craythorn (Ness); Sir James Norcliffe (Langton) Henry Willoughby (Birdsall);
6.-Lady Osbaldeston (Hutton Bushell); William Read (Sand Hutton);
5.-Francis Cholmeley (Bransby); Earl of Fauconberg (Newbrough); Ralph Lutton (Knapton); William Strickland (Welburn); Thomas Worsley (Hovingham)
4.-Richard Hill (Thornton Dale); Lady Ledgard (Ganton); Mrs.Masterman (Settrington); Rev Mr Sykes (Sledmere);
3-John Belt (Buttercrambe); H.B. Darley (Buttercrambe); Barnabas Foord (W. Heslerton) Miss Fairfax (Gilling); Mr.Hutchinson (Welham-Norton); Leonard Thompson (Sheriff Hutton); Charles Tancred (Arden)
2.-Mrs Bower (Norton); Mr. Blomberg (Malton) Thos Barber (Slingsby); William Cholmley (Whitwell) ; Sir George Cayley (Brompton); Rev William Comber (Kirkby Moorside); Sir B. Graham (Nunnington); Rev Mr Hodgson (Ganthorpe); Mr.Hebden (Easthorpe); John Knipes (Helmsley); Isaac Leetham (Barton le St); Mr Morley (Stonegrave); Mr.Plumber (Lilling); Rev Rousby (Sledmere).

Hayes, Miss Hayes their daughter, the governess and Georgiana Thwing the ladies maid, all at Aislaby Hall. Pickering had itself had a well powdered elite, drawn from the Atkinson, Belt, Kitching, Mitchelson, Piper, Simpson, Waterson and Yeoman families, but Yeoman ran the Inn, and Atkinson the best of the shops.

The Inclosure Movement

Great changes came in farming with the completion, over several decades, of the process known as inclosure. Some places had seen either part or the whole of their fields or commons inclosed earlier, but many had not. A passion for inclosure swept through land and tithe owners. They secured local Acts of Parliament, at some expense, under which professional surveyors mapped the last fields and the township commons. Commissioners of considerable local experience were appointed to divide them amongst those with land in the fields, or rights on the commons. They specified when and how they were to be inclosed.

In place of field strips and common rights, the owner received one or more compact areas of land. By 1780, the enclosure of arable fields was coming to completion, while commons enclosures were proceeding apace, and would go further during the wars with France between 1793 and 1815. Not all the new farms were within a ring fence, for old rights had to be compensated with comparable land, so a farm could still include several scattered closes carved from old field, meadow, car and high common. These could be farmed in whatever way the owner or his tenant chose.

The Cropton Manor inclosure award was enshrined on thirty nine broad skins of parchment. The fields were already under enclosure and this dealt only with the commons, which were shared by several townships. An agreement was made in 1764 and the award was completed two years later. In some places, the process took many years. The new awards were given access roads and their boundary ditches specified. Much of the landscape still bears the straight line stamp of the inclosers, essentially a planned countryside.

There was usually a buying up of common rights before and a buying up of awards afterwards. Some chose to raise money. Others found that they couldn't find the money to meet the legal costs of inclosure. These were allocated by the commissioners among those benefiting. When all was done, the costs of making up drains and fences in a limited time could prove too much, and there were more sales. An Inclosure Act and the Award that followed were the first steps. The land awards were converted into smaller fields, rapidly by larger landowners and much more gradually by others. This was expensive.

The fencing and dyking of his awards under the Sherburn inclosure cost Richard Sawdon £26.5.6. and yet the high wold fields at Sherburn were only flatted and divided. They were left to be managed by stint, until their owners decided to enclose them. A similar approach was adopted for the higher commons in the limestone country, where fencing or walling were not justified by the value of the land. It could be years before some awarded land was actually inclosed.

In isolated cases the older system of management survived. Spaunton kept its manor court, since the landowner refused to have an

Table 44. Some Local Inclosures (including partial inclosures)

Birdsall 1691; Langton c 1650 & c1696; Settringon common 1669, Scagglethorpe 1725; Nawton 1709; Kenneythorpe c1725; Thorpe basset 1718; Slingsby 1754; Wombleton 1753; Hovingham 1754; Sherburn 1755; Skirpenbeck 1758; Brompton 1757; Hovingham 1756; Strensall 1758; Sutton on forest 1759; Wombelton 1754; Kirkby Grindalythe & Mowthorpe 1755; Skirpenbeck 1758; Cropton 1765; Appleton le Moors 1767; Ebberston 1769; Fadmoor 1762; Sheriff Hutton & West Lilling 1767; Snainton 1768; Duggleby 1765; Wharram le Street 1766; East Lilling 1769; Acklam 1769; Huggate 1767; Stillington 1766; East Ayton 1768; Sutton 1769; Bulmer 1779; Butterwick 1771; Gillamoor 1771; Levisham 1770; Fadmoor 1779; Stonegrave West Ness & Nunnington 1776; Terrington 1772; Wigginton 1771; Wilton 1773; East Heslerton 1770; Garton 1774; Croom 1775; Rillington 1778; West Heslerton 1770; Sledmere 1776 Thornton Dale 1781; Cold Kirkby 1789; Kirkby Moorside 1788; Lastingham 1788; Nawton 1784; Sledmere 1787; Sinnington, Edstone & Marton 1785; Felixkirk 1793; West Heslerton 1794; Pickering 1790; Old Malton 1794; North Grimston 1792; Settrington 1797; Thixendale 1794.

Folkton 1802; Langtoft 1801; Ampleforth 1804; Weaverthorpe-Helperthorpe 1801; Huttons Ambo 1805; Leavening 1804; Luttons Ambo 1801; Sand Hutton 1806; Wombleton 1806; Binnington, Potter Bromton & Ganton, Allerston 1818; Farlington 1813; Beadlam 1819; Cottam 1845; Foxholes 1836; Scrayingham 1825.

inclosure of the commons. A few townships retained a small cottage pasture for cowkeeping. The Flaxton vestry continued to annually appoint pasture masters, for their extensive greens, controlling the drains, mowing and pasturing and pindars to take in the strays.

There was a great extension of hedges, dry stone walls and ditches to define and inclose the new smaller fields. This would continue, as they were further sub divided by their new owners. Live hedges were planted, hawthorne and crabtree, where ever they would take. Dry stone walls spread steadily across old commons, the stones carted from nearby quarries, being cheap and durable, and successful where live hedges were slow and difficult to raise. At the quarries, immediately below the soil was to be found a layer up to six inches of slatelike limestone, loose and horizontal which was used for walling. The field walls were usually built double, without mortar, stone laid upon stone up to five feet high, two foot wide at the base and narrowing slightly towards the top stone. They were made using a wooden guide frame. Each yard took more than one small cart load of stone, and walling could cost a shilling a yard. Old Roman roads and ruins were readily robbed for stone, in a practice that continued for decades. Hedging and stone walling became arts of the countryside.

The Improvers

The inclosure movement was encouraged as part of a broader 'improvement' movement, among land owners and some of the larger tenant farmers. An inclosure was seen as necessary before better farming could take place. There were some smaller people who lost out, including those who couldn't afford the process and sold out, and those who lost accustomed rights of access to open fields, pasture and commons, with whatever they had made from them.

Sir Christopher Sykes has been credited with being the great Wolds encloser between 1770 and 1801 but he was not alone. Most of the great landowners were involved. Some were themselves keen hobby farmers, and some had able and committed Stewards. The whole enterprise was a massive investment on which a massive return was expected. Once the landscape had been re-organised, the landlord's investment, encouragement and often enough control was still important.

New farmsteads were built outside villages on new inclosures, many of them model farmsteads, protected by shelter belts of trees against north easterly winds, and with new quadrangular layouts around foldyards, designed to waste nothing. Old village farmsteads often gave way to cottages. Some of the names of the new farms carry a hint of the challenge. One near Sheriff Hutton was called 'Cape of Good Hope'. Others less optimistic have names like World's End or Canada.

The improving tenant farmers, and owners working their own estates, could decide how to farm within their closes. Manorial control and communal decision making ended, apart from vestigial annual checking of the drains. Men like Mr. Cleaver at Nunnington pioneered the new methods, but much of it was trial and error. Others came to them more slowly. Farmers keenly watched the success or otherwise of the experiment around them. William Marshall in 1787 said of Pickering

A Cruck House. Once an Inn, Called 'The Spout House' in Bilsdale

Vale 'poverty and ignorance are the ordinary inhabitants of small farms; even the smallest estates of the yeomanry are notorious for bad management'.

Some changes were not closely tied to the process of inclosure. The sewing of seed had been changing for some time. Instead of scattering seed by hand, or with a simple bowed hand drill, horse-drawn seed drills were widely adopted to deliver the seed in regular lines, more economically and covered by earth. The Rotherham swing plough was in use, and cast iron plates were replacing wooden mould boards on ploughs, just as horses were replacing oxen in the yoke.

Winnowing machines, also called machine fans, were familiar, brought in from Holland for dressing corn after threshing. John Marshall of Pickering made the first. The hand flail would long survive but threshing machines were being made by the wrights. Mr.J Wyrill started making agricultural implements at Farlington north bridge in 1780. In the dairy, lead bowls were replacing those of wood, and the barrel churn mounted on a wood frame with a hand crank was in use for butter making. Most of the farmers on the limestone set up kilns to burn their own lime. William Hartas built a limekiln on Spaunton west field in 1807.

The turnip and clover husbandry put heart into the crop rotations. Oats, barley for bread, sheep and rabbits had been the Wold story. Weaverthorpe had turnips in the field by 1785. A West Lutton four

306

course rotation a few years later was wheat, turnips, barley, and clover or peas. The Wolds were a country of large farms and high corn prices took much of the Wolds back to tillage. Between 1792 and 1820 Mowthorpe was turned into a great corn growing township with shelter belts, and a new upper farm built by 1813. The new fodder crops spread everywhere.

Potatoes were planted as a fallow crop from about 1760, heavily manured, and used to clean the land. The sets had to be changed frequently to avoid the 'curl', but some varieties including potatoes obtained from America were resistant to the disease. From a food for pigs, potatoes quickly became the daily food for every cottager, and the most important article of the diet.

The Earl of Carlisle offered prizes to encourage use of the best breeds. Improvers were few and the butchers demanded weight, but the old black cattle with white faces gave way to newer breeds from Craven, Holderness and the Tees, with attempts made to reduce the bone and increase the flesh and fat.

Tuke reported the same trend for sheep, new rams from Lincolnshire and the Tees district, reducing the bone and offal in the valleys, and the long wooled Wold flocks varied by Leicester breeds. The old black face remained in Blackamore and the moor mutton was highly valued by the Scarborough visitors. The pigs changed over thirty years as they were bred for sale to the bacon maker. A Rillington man killed a hog pig in 1786 weighing fifty one stone. They claimed that the pig had just lept over a gate five feet high -a tall tale, perhaps.

Much of the lower land stayed a dairy country, whereas the only cow kept on the Wolds was to supply the farm servants with milk. Arthur Young visited East Newton and Laysthorpe in 1771 where a farm of one hundred and fifty acres carried twenty cows, twenty young cattle and one hundred and forty sheep but had only thirty acres ploughed.

Cow keepers made a living near the towns, and cottagers might pay a cow herd, for 'coo tenting', to pasture their animals on the broad road side verges which survived enclosure. A good cow was said to give a rearing calf, three firkin of butter, each firkin being fifty six pounds, and a large quantity of skim cheese which was 'eaten by all ranks'. The whey went to feed the pig. Dales farms produced large quantities of four and seven pound cheeses.

Outside the enclosed dairy and rearing farms which had replaced the granges in the low grounds, much of the lowland, spoken of as the east marshes, was over run with sedges. Malaria, locally called the ague, was not unknown. Inclosure improvements of drains in the higher ground were extensive but the flat lands remained in low condition. There was talk of drainage improvement about Hovingham and Mr. Milbourn in 1768 surveyed the river Derwent for a partial straightening of its course, but a collective effort by many landowners was needed. Improvement in one township could never be enough. This had to wait for another day.

A Nation of Shopkeepers

The advance of the retail shop, beyond serving the gentry, is poorly recorded but tea and tobacco found their way. Few villages had a shop even in the early 19th century yet a Thornton Dale shop was already a hundred years old, apparently surviving by supplying a few main families, and a little passing trade. At first gentry purchases were different in kind, and the small shop could only stock many purchases by prior agreement.

Mr Hill in 1733-34 bought a box, a chair and some brandy at Scarborough. A pair of shoes and some glass came from Malton and some sugar was sent to Malton from Hull. This gentleman visited York to see his tailor, to buy tea, drapery, hats and more sugar. From London, which he visited frequently, came mercery, books, pottery and glass. At London in 1746-48 he called at New Bond Street for jellies and syllabub, ice creams, macaroons, marsh mallows and blancmange.

William Pennock of Pickering sold groceries, salt, fir deals, hemp and whalebone by 1704. There seems to have been a grocer continuously at the town from that time onwards. Henry Ramshaw of Robin Hood's Bay set up shop there in 1732. Simeon King was a grocer at Pickering in 1748. With Simeon Hutchinson of Helmsley and other local traders he invested in voyages to the Indies. About 1764 Thomas Atkinson would supply locals with mustard, pepper and cloves. Thirty four years later Thomas Atkinson was the grocer, woollen draper and seedsman in the shop at the head of the Pickering market place. The town with eighteen genteel families could also sustain Roger Hart, grocer, tallow chandler and cheesemonger, Samuel Pearson grocer, woollen draper and seedsman, Thomas Read and George Wood grocers and Thomas Seavers brandy merchant and druggist. One town shopkeeper sank into poverty in the depression after the Napoleonic War, but Lockton had a shop at the east end of a house in 1797.

Some things, often themselves quite small were being made in sufficiently large quantities for wide distribution through many outlets to be necessary. They were sold through appointed agents, who gained cover advertising in the new regional newspapers. Laurence Sterne spoke of visiting the 'Pickering Comissary shops'. The 'York Herald' itself was in 1798 sold by William Grayson the hardwareman at Helmsley, Thomas Robson, the Hovingham grocer, Joseph Garbutt, the Kirkby Moorside grocer and Christopher Dobby, the Pickering linen draper.

Table 45. Specialities in Owen's Book of Fairs 1769

Brompton November 12 Swine, a few horses.
Coxwold August 25 Cattle, sheep, pewter, hardware,linen & woollen cloth.
Helmsley May 19; July16; Oct 2; Nov 6. Cattle, sheep, horses, linen & woollen cloth.
Seamer July 15 Cattle, sheep, horses, boots, linen & woollen cloth.
Kirkby moorside.Whit Wednesday Cattle, horses.
September 18 Sheep,woollen & linen cloth.
Kirkham Saturday before Trinity Sunday; Sheep, brass, pewter, hardware, pots, smallware.
Malton Saturday before Palm Sunday-Cattle, horses.
Day before Whit Sunday Sheep, brass, pewter.
October 10 Hardware, pots, smallware.
October 11 Sheep.
Pickering September 14 Cattle, sheep, horses.
Seamer July 15 Boots, shoes, horses.
Stamford bridge November 22 Horses, cattle, sheep, brass, pewter, hardware, woollen cloth.

York was a maze of shops, twenty five drapers, thirteen haberdashers, hatters and glovers in 1784 and at least fifty other shops. By 1823 shops listed at the city exceeded four hundred and thirty. And yet most country people bought little and what they did buy didn't come from a retail shop. Many things were sold from maker to user. Some made their own candles, spinning fine white tow for the wick, then dipping it through hot scalding wax in a pudding pie pot, repeating in not so hot wax and winding it round on a spinning wheel.

A Yorkshire labourer's family in the 1840's bought a very short list of things - yeast, flour and oatmeal, sugar, treacle and coffee, with soap and candles in very small quantities, occasionally bacon, meat, milk, butter, salt and brimstone, senna and eggs. Durables were confined to a brush, worsted, cotton tape and a hat.

The corner shop at Thornton Dale on the first Saturday, New Years Day in 1831 saw Mrs Hill, from the Hall, buy nine yards of linen for 7s.6d. The blacksmith John Maw called for coffee. Adam Maw bought seventy two yards of ribbon for 2s.2d. Richard Bower the shoemaker called in, for his shagg at 3d. Richard Smith picked up a parcel from Scarborough and Richard Nicholls from the mill bought butter. On the following Monday, John Baker from the Marishes bought twilled cotton and shoe tape, Francis Pearson from Wilton had starch, shag pipes and worsted. James Craven from Allerston bought flannel, shagg and tape.

A quiet rural revolution would make the old market centres busier, taking shops into villages and new commodities into better off houses. The reliance on the shop was growing. By 1865 the village of Thornton Dale would have ten grocers, four drapers, two general dealers, as well as a dozen dress maker and milliners, seven shoemakers and ten tailors. Sam Priestman returning home after seven years away found many changes. In his own home, the scriptures were read daily instead of weekly. Carpets covered the floor where sand used to be. The gardens were more gay. W. H.Coulson of Kingthorpe in 1865 had a wash stand, dressing tables and an American eight day clock.

CHAPTER 7
THE NINETEENTH CENTURY. 1803 - 1900

The Georgian century involved the country in many wars, but those of the later years had different purposes and greater effect. After the Seven Years war, 1756-1763, Britain gained new acquisitions in India and Canada. The War of American Independence created the seed from which another great English speaking country would grow. The War of the French Revolution 1793-1802 was fought against movements that seemed to threaten the roots of society and when renewed against Napoleon, 1803-1815, was of a character previously unknown.

The aristocracy held sway, in Parliament and outside it. Although George III sought to rule, power passed to the ministries, formed, in succession, at intervals, by the Whig and Tory parties. Royal government was over, leaving merely royal influence. The parties competed for a small electorate, edging towards widening the numbers who could vote. Population had moved to new areas which were unrepresented. Economic power had partially moved to others than the aristocracy. New industries, and such commercial activities as banking, were beginning to fuel the lives of millions outside agriculture. The expanding middle classes could not be permanently excluded, even if many were nonconformist in religion.

Georgian order gave way to the great strains placed on national life by a rapid growth of population. As the countryside offered limited new employments, town growth and the spread of new kinds of industrial community re-distributed people around the British landscape. Vast numbers created new cities, and many moved beyond these shores to settle in America and a growing empire of colonies. After 1815, there was a long period of European peace, although colonial wars continued, in pursuit of national, often commercial advantages. As Britain became the banker, shipper, commercial and manufacturing supplier for much of the world, the country for a while dominated the world economy.

War with France

The war with France restarted in 1803. When a French landing was feared, a mass evacuation was planned to remove all farm stock from the coastal districts. Volunteer regiments were formed for local defence, including the Newburgh Rangers led by Captain Bellasis, the Barton le Street Cavalry, the Helmsley Infantry and Cavalry under Captain Charles Duncombe and the Castle Howard Rifles, who met under Captain Viscount Morpeth at the Castle Howard Inn. John Sootheran led the one hundred and thirty six men of the Helmsley infantry.

The largest unit was the Pickering Lythe Infantry, nearly five hundred men under Colonel Sir George Cayley. Sir Mark Sykes troop of Wold cavalry rode into Malton with a band for the King's birthday in June 1804. Major Fothergill of Kingthorpe sent the drum round Thornton to muster his sixty men. He insisted on things being properly regimental. Men of his detachment were fined for absenteeism, and he gave some their marching orders, when they questioned his choice of a serjeant.

Professional troops were deployed but they were not popular, being liable to interfere with smuggling. Regiments were marched through frequently for duty at the coast, where illicit landings were welcomed by large numbers, who quickly moved the illicit tea, spirits and other commodities inland. Townspeople mobbed the officer when a soldier of the 18th Regiment was publicly punished at Malton in 1805. A battalion of the regiment made a visit to Pickering and Malton again in 1808, during which a captain died in a canal boat after attending a picnic at Kirkham. The regiment had a good band which was much appreciated, with flutes, cymbals, triangles, drums and fifes. They had cocked hats and yellow coat trimmings with silver lace. During their stay at Malton they were ordered to change hair styles, henceforth to be cut close to the neck and without powder.

A new Local Militia Act abolished the old volunteers in 1808 and created a new force. Twenty eight days training a year was now required. The first assembly of the Malton Volunteers was in Orchard Field under Colonel Isaac Leatham. They received their colours in June. The next year they did fourteen days' service, during which Cobber Frank, Thomas Douthwaite and Will Fletcher were 'tiled to the Holberys' on the Wolds and punished with the cat.

The real war was fought in many parts of the world and it left many wounded. Shaw of Easingwold and Edward Patterson of Malton were at the Battle of Waterloo. A Danby man was for ever after known as Waterloo Jack, Patterson as Waterloo Neddy. Matthew Grimes of Thornton Dale was in the Peninsula campaign. He was a guard on

Napoleon at Saint Helena and a bearer at his funeral. Overseas wars came home, or seemed more real, with the spread of newspapers.

John Foster in 1809, was on a man of war taking three hundred troops to Portugal. He wrote to his wife Elizabeth, his 'dear partner', as he put it, to explain why he thought she shouldn't be with him, although there were women on the ship. She was struggling to keep going with his young sons, but he wasn't allowed to send her any more money. He wrote, 'my dear partner must do as well as she can'. He asked her to speak to Captain Longster, who might speak to Lord Mulgrave who might get him some advance, beyond his rank of quarter gunner.

The Impress service sent its press gangs to secure recruits for the navy far inland, as well as on the coast. There were hot presses at Scarborough in 1790 and local sailors fought them at Whitby three years later. Lieutenant Thomas Legard was in the service in 1793. Thomas Wilson of Sinnington accepted the bounty for joining the Navy in 1795. George Pearson taken by the Press Gang at Whitby, was wrecked off Brest and kept a prisoner in France for years. Some pride was taken in the successes of the Royal Navy. Robert Ward of Slingsby was a midshipman with Nelson at the battle of Trafalgar. A Nelson Arch was erected in 1806 at Duncombe Park to mark the victory. Machel Foster of Pickering watched the funeral procession for Lord Nelson in London.

The Farmers' War

Farming prospered in an island at war. Output was lifted by more intensive farming, more use of root crops and better rotations. The government paid subsidies on some crops normally imported. Sinnington and Edstone farmers were among those claiming the bounties for growing flax and hemp, which usually came by ship from the countries of the Baltic. The arable acreage increased, taking in land not used for centuries, and for a time this gave very good yields. There was more use of fodder crops, including turnips and clover, while rape was supplying rape oil mills at Keldholme and Ayton by 1813. Bone manurance and turnip husbandry were thought to be improving the thin wold soils. Potatoes, first thought of as a food for pigs, were now the cheap staple food for poor people. Grain prices stayed high until the peace of 1815, when slump and rent reductions returned. The 1815 Corn Law offered some prospect of protection, by excluding foreign wheat until local wheat reached 80s a quarter.

Between 1800 and 1807, the Muston and Yedingham Drainage

project was undertaken, under an Act of Parliament for 'draining, embanking and preserving' tracts of land adjoining the river Derwent, and its tributary the Hertford stream, which ran towards Filey. Over ten thousand acres, mostly old carrland and marishes, in lowland townships from Malton to the east end of Pickering Vale, were reclaimed or improved. The floods of 1799 provided the stimulus. Sir George Cayley was probably the main driving force and he employed a first class engineer.

William Chapman's scheme reduced main river flows, first by taking off much water along the new Scalby Cut to the sea. Secondly, he reduced the volume of water reaching the low grounds, by diverting the flow from other streams through parallel cuts, to the lowest possible point of access in the main river. Thirdly, the rivers were embanked at a distance from their natural course to provide an area for flood waters to expand into. The scheme cost £42.000 but land values rose. An acre tax was levied on areas that benefited, to keep up the works.

Sir George Cayley in 1856 estimated an increased annual value of £1 per acre was obtained at a cost of £4 capital expenditure. Straightening of the course of the river allowed the river navigation to be extended to Yedingham. Throughout lower Rydale, river flood plains were given embankments under more local schemes, to bring all but the worst floods within limited confines. The Earl of Salisbury invested £400 in the drainage of Brawby moor, but found that he could raise rents to bring a return of £200 a year.

Initially, increases in farm output owed little to machinery. More labour was used and not only at harvest time. Some new crops needed close attention, hoeing and weeding throughout the growing season. Harvesting a wider range of crops gave several busy seasons for corn, peas, beans, potatoes, turnips and fruit. Bossall children missed three and four months from school, singling turnips or for harvesting. Servants in husbandry were supplemented by more hired hands, the regulars hired by the year and others by the day, week, task or month.

Farm equipment changed slowly. Gentry estates saw experiments by 'improving landlords', and the agricultural societies did much to spread knowledge of new practices. The tools of the harvest were still the sickle, the reaping hook, fagging hook and scythe. Men unloaded wagons by hand and built ricks, the boys tieing and stacking the sheaves. The improved Dutch plough was seen at ploughing matches. Threshing machines, introduced at Nunnington in 1790, took a long time to completely replace the thresher's flail but by 1841, a water worked threshing machine was in use at Hood grange. Sinnington manor farm saw a demonstration of steam threshing in 1857.

On the home farm at Castle Howard, Lord Carlisle experimented, using bones as a manure to fertilize soil in 1796- 97. Horses were used in a horse mill, with stampers to crush the bones. Jonathan Booth the Hull and Malton millwright replaced the stampers, with toothless rollers in 1804. They say that one of the Sykes family also noticed good plant growth where dogs chewed bones. The Wolds were particularly short of manures. Sir Tatton Sykes in 1810 used bones chopped up with axes, mallets and harrows for the same purpose.

The son, James Booth, a skilled engineer, erected a water mill for crushing and grinding bones at Malton in 1823 and brought the first cargo of bones up the river Derwent. A steam bone mill was built soon afterwards and instead of one cargo of between thirty eight and forty four tons, the two mills run by Booth from Norton Grange crushed two thousand tons a year. A steam corn mill erected at Habton in 1855 was intended for bone crushing.

More new farmsteads were built outside the villages. The isolated Sinnington Manor was built by Edward Cleaver, a noted improver, when he was agent to the Marquess of Salisbury. Near Pickering the Duchy of Lancaster had secured good common land close to the town and erected Scallomoor Manor farm and Hambleton farm. Richard Simpson, another improver, moved to Saintoft Grange before 1790. Two new farms were also built on the low Westgate Carr, and one at Upper Carr, and Brown Head farm on far higher ground by 1827.

At Middleton, the next township, we hear of Moorhouse by 1782, and Henflatts, Keldy Grange, Nova and Brown Head farms in the thirties. At Cropton, Keldy grain, Thackhead or Sutherland and Peat rigg appear by 1811. The same movement can be seen in many other places. The courtyard farm plan, which was widely adopted, allowed the easy collection in the central fold yard of all animal and vegetable residues, leaving nothing to waste. Stock gained better housing, with improved feeding, littering and easier mucking out. All these things needed the cheap labour, which was plentiful. The threshing barn supplied straw, which the livestock turned into manure. At village farms, there was less change in farm buildings, but rebuilding left its mark in date stones, 1771 on a Cawthorne wagon shed, or Hutton le Hole cottages dated 1782.

Commercial gardens producing vegetables and fruit for the market would grow significantly, especially near the towns, as diets changed and population increased. The remarkable Bean family were among the pioneers. John Williamson at the age of nine left Fridaythorpe for Scarborough, where his relation William Bean had his pioneering gardens. From eleven to nineteen, he served his apprenticeship. He was under gardener at Wykeham Abbey and head gardener at Mulgrave Castle, before returning to the resort. At Scarborough, they said that William Bean 'first brought the elegant cultivation of vegetables into notice here, producing everything for kitchen, table and desert'. Both men became naturalists of some standing.

At Leavening another of the clan, James Bean, the gardener at the west end of the village, was a severe but diligent and clever man of business. He grew fine fruit which he took the thirty miles to Scarborough market, twice a week during the fruit season. Leavening was much visited on Sundays to partake of his garden produce. Other country growers from far afield took produce to the town sales at Scarborough while York drew on a considerable concentration of gardens. Gentry houses had their own produce gardens. Seven hundred square feet of glass in hothouses was struck by lightening in 1839 at Castle Howard. Inner Ryedale became a fruit growing district, sending out large quantities to hungry places.

Horse and Carriage

Both commercial and private traffic increased rapidly, tearing up unmetalled roads. Saddlers, wheelwrights and shoeing smiths proliferated, to maintain many more carts and wagons. During 1815, the tolls from three gates on the Malton -Scarborough road yielded £1264. Some of the takings were used to employ the road improver Macadam on the road a few years later. More generally, filling pot holes was the main means of road repair. New highway legislation in 1835 shifted the responsibilities for repairing main roads to the surveyors of highway districts, who used limited rate incomes to employ contractors to do the work, in place of the old statute labour.

Gentlefolk toured the area in private carriages or on horseback. A little private chaise was a great comfort to the gentlefolk at Brandsby Hall, taking their parties to Sheriff Hutton, Crayke, Castle Howard, Rievaulx Abbey and Helmsley in 1803. The next year, Francis Cholmley's wife set off for Scarborough with two daughters on August 10th. He followed, with two more, two weeks later. There were trips to Newburgh, Gormire and Byland and to see the races. The artists visiting them, Nunn and Cotman were fearful of being mobbed, for painting views on Sundays.

Public stage coaches linked the major towns. The Hull -Malton road saw the *Velocitas* and then the *Velocipede*. The *Union* coach ran along the coast road. The Royal Mail linked York and Malton with both Scarborough and Whitby. The Scarborough run regularly saw *The Old True Blue*, *Prince Blucher*, and other named coaches.

'Boat coaches' linked Pickering and Malton with packet ships departing from Scarborough for London and Newcastle and the ports between, which from the twenties included the steam packet boats. A heavy stage waggon ran from York to Whitby once a week.

Transport between Pickering and Whitby was transformed by an astonishing development. This put stage coaches onto rails. Surplus Whitby capital was invested in a horse and carriage railway, which opened in 1836, its one stated purpose being to take coal to the 'interior', meaning Ryedale. A local had complained in 1829 that 'Pickering had never been so dead, some with nothing to live on'. The construction of the railway, essentially a track for stage coaches, changed that. John Foster wrote that he and 'many more were employed pile driving to stop a hill falling in a new beck made up the dale for the convenience of the railway rapidly going up the valley' towards Goathland.

The railway was a considerable engineering achievement, if a doubtful commercial prospect. It caused great controversy as to whether it was a good speculation or not with wildly different estimates circulating. The ageing Francis Nicholson, a supporter , thought that 'the hugger mugger clodpoles of Pickering would do all in their power to cross it, as they did that for the navigation of the Costa with Lord FitzWilliam'. The first coals from Whitby were expected in January 1836. The railway debts mounted but stone, lime and ironstone workings soon developed along its route. Grosmont iron was sent to the distant works on the river Tyne that same year. A Helmsley-Scarborough daily stage coach was begun to time with train arrivals at the Pickering terminus.

Ordinary Lives

Thomas Burton of Salton kept a record of events between 1791 and 1845. He knew his district and noted what seemed important to him. He spoke of Bishop Dowker the Salton butcher, of Mrs Dodsworth of

The Coach Railway, which ran between Pickering and Whitby, leaves Newton Dale in 1836

Malton who died in 1797 aged 102 and of Bartholomew Johnson the Wykeham musician, who had moved to Scarborough, had the gentry pay for his portrait to be painted and who had kept an early billiard hall. They wrote 100 on the coffin of Mrs Wallington of Kirkby Misperton but others told him that she was really 103.

He wrote that surveyor Robert King and all his family went to America in June 1797. During 1800 John Foord an equally notable surveyor was drowned in the River Derwent. The local clockmakers were skilled and well known men, William Dixon at Pickering and Thomas Kidd at Malton. Among the more famous, he recorded Joseph Gray of Harum who weighed twenty five stone. His great events included the balloon ascent made by Mr Adler in 1814 from Minster Yard at York, with the descent at Easingwold, and the death of Thomas Dibdin the London composer of a hundred songs.

A Welburn fellow kept another plain man's guide to the passing scene, noting marriages and burials in 1833, including one at the new Unitarian chapel. He travelled in to a Malton Church visitation and was appointed a churchwarden for the first time. During the Summer, he went to see Duncombe park. In December he heard that there was cholera at Coneysthorpe. The great event was the start of the travels of the 'White Ox' from Castle Howard. A group of shareholders sent this collosal beast as a travelling exhibition, with John Smurthwaite of Welburn as showman. They spent one hundred guineas on the beast and £35 on the caravan. A year later they sold the beast for £150. The next year, the diarist gambled a dozen of wine on the survival of the Castle Howard steward in his post. As to events, John Vause was made coal meter at Crambe landing and in 1835 the county election for MPs saw 9544 vote in the North Riding. The Wiganthorpe steward fell of his horse returning from the election.

National newspapers brought a growing awareness of national and international issues, incidentally adding something to conversation. A typical issue of the Yorkshire Gazette in 1839 carried several columns of national news, about a third as much foreign news, of which a good deal was concerned with America, and another block of parliamentary reports. There were also court reports. Editorials were broad in scope. One copy held a satire on Whitby, stories of steam navigation to India, and an essay on Hindu morality.

Migration from the Countryside

The booming increase of population far exceeded any increase in rural employment and was on a scale never before known. There were more people than could be contained in the local villages or dales, and each generation produced more. They migrated to other districts and to other countries. Gawan Pickering from Lockton arrived in Australia in 1814, but he was 'transported'. During 1827-28, when many industries and farming were in trouble, some overseers found it cheaper to pay the costs for paupers to migrate to America, rather than support them here. A number went to America from Scarborough in 1828, one hundred and fifty in one ship and another seventy a few days later. Many in Pickering talked of going that spring. During January 1830 the Helmsley estate tenants petitioned Charles Duncombe, lately made Baron Feversham, for a reduction of rents. In February they were required to present a humble apology.

Some parishes saw absolute population decreases during the hardships of the thirties. Many emigrated from Pickering vale and from the dales of Blackamore. Robert Merry in 1833 said that there was 'not a township or hardly a family but what had some of the inhabitants and some of their relations gone to America, both labourers and farmers'. Among them were small debt-ridden freeholders compelled to sell up and emigrate, but also labourers who had managed to save the £20 passage money. The Posts, Adamsons, Kings and Tindalls went from Cropton about 1837.

Emigrant ships left Whitby for Canada again in the early forties. During 1841, the 'Acadia' steamship took migrants. John King in the green country of Illinois heard from the folks at home in 1843, that prices had fallen for twelve months but labouring men's wages had fallen further. There was much talk of America. One wrote 'I think we shall most of us have to emigrate'. Two sons of John Boyes left Wombleton in 1851 intending to go to South Africa but hearing of the gold discoveries of 1853 in Australia, they sailed for Victoria. The movement of people continued through the century. William Fletcher as an emigration agent ran assisted passages. In the eighties, the Primitive Methodists established their own settlements in Canada.

Towns and cities offered other opportunities, many of them better paid than farm labouring. There was much going on and many openings for men and women. William Foster went to Whitby. When he was expecting a visit from his Pickering mother, he said she need not buy a clean apron, but he did say 'Pray send my old coat for the young men here seem very respectable indeed'. A girl going into 'service' in London, found many Ryedale folk already there. Her mother wrote to tell her to stay indoors. She soon welcomed others of her family to this city and wrote chattily detailing news of the Yorkshire people that she met.

Some talented young men found national fame. They gained professional training in London, usually after being given connections and other help by one or other of the local aristocracy. They included Matthew Noble the Hackness sculptor, Francis Nicholson the Pickering 'father of water colour painting' and John Jackson the Lastingham artist. John Teesdale left Malton for Birmingham. Watching from a cellar level office in the main street, he observed that 'many of the wenches have very bad legs'. He meant ankles. On his first night out, he met a blooming girl of twenty seven with £30,000. 'I intend her for myself' he said, adding 'Aim at a golden gown and you will be sure at least to get a sleeve of it'. He didn't get a thread, but 'there was still corn in Egypt' in the shape of another girl with another fortune, but then he didn't get her either.

The Harder Life of Poverty

As the populace expanded rapidly in the later 18th century, the number of the very poor grew with them. Overseers of the poor sought to prevent their families becoming chargeable on their parishes. George Hall, his wife, a nine year old daughter and an eight year old son, ordered back to Cawthorne in 1784 were typical of many. Certificates of legal settlement were issued by churchwardens and overseers, virtually a passport to stay where you were, but which allowed you to move because the mother parish agreed to accept responsibility for you, if you became chargeable elsewhere. Pregnant unmarried mothers were a particular problem.

Where they accepted responsibility, the overeers did much good. The Rosedale overseer built a cottage for one pauper costing £9.4s.1d in 1785, but building and thatching another fourteen years later cost £17.10s. They thatched another pauper's house and the school house, led coals or turves and paid for funerals. John Collier was paid 16s.8d to clothe Hannah Solitt in 1789 and Hannah Pierson had 2s.4d for making the clothes up. Shoes cost 1s.6d. Occasionally they bought a peck of corn, two bushels of potatoes for four shillings, or food for a week for someone who was sick, at three shillings. They paid for small pox inoculations and bought an iron range costing 21s.6d in 1809.

There were better decades and worse decades and within them good seasons and bad seasons. As early as 1814, the Worsley agent at Scawton reported 'one real scene of poverty, leaving them entirely, Ma'am to your generosity'. Every bad time, the labourers were paid off. Charity was much sought and much given, but it was never enough. There were soup kitchens at the market towns. A spate of legal settlement cases marked 1817. Overseers of the Poor were continually occupied with moving people back to parishes, where they had a legal settlement, to avoid any possible cost of maintaining them. Edstone appealed against the settlement of Mary Eddon in the parish, arguing that her last settlement was at the Keldholm spinning mill, where she had been hired, and that the overseers there were responsible for her maintenance.

Robert Merry of Lockton in 1818 paid labourers 3s.6d a day. By 1833 it was down to between 2s and 2s.3d a day. 'They had less meat and never a raisin in a cake'. One response to hard times was rick burning. Paupers begged in 1821, saying 'that stack would make a good fire'. There were haystack fires on the Wombwell estate in 1830. In the worst years, the fires burnt at many farms, especially on the Wolds. As the local costs of sustaining the parish poor became overwhelming, new Poor Law Unions were formed in 1834 to serve groups of parishes, with appointed Guardians of the Poor. They tried to replace out door relief with the new workhouses built at the market towns. Winter relief remained annually necessary through much of the century. Malton in May 1857 had six hundred and fifty on out relief and one hundred and twelve indoors. The workhouse came to seem a place of shame, for those who feared they might end there.

Self Help and Mutual Aid

Self-help movements flourished among farmers and prospering craftsmen in the more prosperous periods. Early pioneering Friendly Societies, like the Helmsley Orderly Society, were praised by the gentry for fostering the pride of 'the labouring classes' and helping to keep them from accepting support from the parish rates. They were run by their members, who elected officers to collect regular subscriptions. Once a fund was formed, modest payments could be made during sickness or unemployment. New savings banks, run on a trustee basis,

To the church wardens and overseers of the poor of the township of *Pickering* in the said Riding ;
and to the church wardens and overseers of the poor of the
township of *Aislaby in the said Riding.*

(12)

[Order of removal of poor.]

UPON the complaint of the church wardens and overseers of the poor
of the township of *Pickering*
aforesaid, unto us whose names are subscribed, two of his Majesty's
justices of the peace for the said Riding, that *Anne Shelton*
Single woman

came lately to inhabit in the said township of *Pickering*
not having gained a legal settlement therein, nor produced
a certificate owning *her* to be settled elsewhere ; and that the
said *Anne Shelton is with child and*
actually

~~likely to be~~ chargeable to the said township of *Pickering*
We do therefore, upon due examination of the premises,
adjudge the same to be true : And we do likewise adjudge that the legal
settlement of the said *Anne Shelton*

is in the said township of *Aislaby*

THESE are therefore, in his Majesty's name, to require you the
church wardens and overseers of the poor of *Pickering*
aforesaid, forthwith to convey the said *Anne Shelton*

from your township of *Pickering*
aforesaid, and *her* deliver to the said church wardens and overseers
of the poor of *Aislaby* aforesaid, together with this
precept, or a true copy thereof, at the same time shewing to them the
original. And we do also hereby require you the said church wardens and
overseers of the poor of *Aislaby*
aforesaid, to receive and provide for *her* as *an* inhabitant of
your township.

Given under our hands and seals the *eleventh* day of *August*
in the year of our Lord one thousand eight hundred and *six*.

Thos. Hayes

1806

A Certificate of Removal from Pickering to Aislaby

were encouraged by an 1817 Act of Parliament. One was formed at Malton . Deposits were later made, one night a week, at schools in many towns and villages.

The Pickering Benevolent Friendly Society revised its 1779 rules in 1825. The aim was clearly stated .The 'sole intention is by monthly contributions to establish a fund, whereby the bed of the sick, the house of the lame and the situation of the widow may be ameliorated'. The subscription was 1s.3d a month. During the war period, a number of 'Poor Men's' Friendly Societies were formed. Women joined the 'Dead Burial Briefs', as at Old Malton, with the limited aim of insuring against a pauper's grave and an ill attended funeral. The societies did more than that, often forming a social group that channelled mutual aid, and gave people a broader experience in running their own affairs, beyond the orbit of the family.

They spoke of them as 'clubs'. They provided a measure of insurance, and they could do that better if the fund was substantial. Many of the later Friendly Societies were linked in the nationwide affiliated orders for men called Shepherds, Gardeners, Foresters, Druids and two sorts of Oddfellows. One or the other was present in most villages. The village branches had optimistic titles, such as the 'Hope to Prosper Lodge'. They used modest secret signs and rituals, akin to those of freemasonry. They took over many of the ancient village feasts, to which members marched wearing sashes, behind a banner and a hired brass band.

The Manchester Unity Oddfellows meeting at the Red Lion in Kirkby Moorside in 1838, wore scarlet, white, blue and black robes, caps with feathers and sashes. Their regalia included the Warden's hatchet and they paid five shillings for a Warden's hat. The Loyal Milton Lodge first met at George Peterkin's Rockingham Arms Inn at Wheelgate, Malton that year. Contributions were 1s.6d a month. Brothers were fined a shilling for intoxication. Doctor Colby as lodge doctor advised on the payments made to the sick. They processed to the church on Whit. Tuesday and delegates were sent to quarterly meetings at the Oddfellows Hall, Leavening, the Black Swan Brawby and the Rose Inn, Pickering. They opened a Norton Branch lodge at the Union inn. Some Methodist friendly societies were formed, to break away, due to the close links of the lodges with public houses.

C A Darley about 1803 provided allotments of land at Stamford Bridge for 'the poor with no garden and no pig who stood in Summer evening after work smoking and talking and tempted to the alehouse'.

Thirty years later he thought it 'a very cheering sight to see them and their children in the Spring and Summer evenings busily and happily employed. Nearly all had a pig giving eighteen to twenty five stone of bacon at Christmas and vegetables'. They paid a yearly rent of eight shillings a rood for allotments. Scrayingham in 1833 had three acres of allotments giving the cottagers enough land for vegetables, while the continuance of a cow pasture enabled them to keep one cow. The more radical Chartist movement found a modest local echo. John Watkins tried to form a provision society at Whitby in 1839, and Thirsk meetings aroused local fears. A short lived society at Malton sought to provide members with flour at reduced prices.

National Politics

Freeholders had always had a voice inside and outside the manor courts. They gained a new experience of local democracy, with all its difficulties, in nonconformist meeting houses. Some of these habits found new use in friendly societies, and in elections for overseers of the highways and the poor. The higher government of the county and the country knew little of it. If there was anything comparable, it was confined within the bounds of the elites who governed. The Greek models, that radicals so much admired, were just as limited.

Royal occasions were already celebrated. Three hundred were given a gallon of ale each at Pickering for the 1821 Coronation, while the town gentlemen dined at the Black Swan. Poor families were given a cake, tea and sugar. At Hovingham the band played for dancing on the green. In about 1820 a Salton clerk was moved to shout 'God Save Queen Caroline' at the end of prayers. The King, her husband's effigy was burnt at Malton.

Election politics for the national Parliament were more of an electoral game for aristocratic nominees than a serious pursuit. The freeholders had a vote but little more. The representation was without responsibility to the represented. The result had little direct bearing on the lives of freeholders or anyone else. The more substantial freeholders of the entire county, voted for members of parliament called 'knights of the shire'. In the national Parliament, parties had evolved called Whigs and Tories, closely linked to the great landowners, the mercantile interest, and the country gentry. The candidates were named by their more influential members.

The electors were pursued briefly for the duration of an election.

Pickering with up to two hundred qualified freeholders was worth some attention. There was no dominant great estate in the town. This was not a body of men easily dominated by aristocracy. They had to be 'treated', well treated. When votes were sought, there was a brief chance to get a promise of some local grievance redressed, or a contribution of funds to some local purpose. Beyond that, there were the treats. After the voting, there were the poll books, which told everyone who you had voted for.

An undated letter to a landowner expressed the situation well. He wrote 'when any gentleman produced any arguments to prove that the Tories are strong in Pickering, those arguments shall either be fairly answered or acknowledged to be unanswerable'. The Tories had just spent £50 on the freeholders and 'they only prevailed on four to openly declare themselves'. 'We spoilt their game by giving the first treat'. Lord Carlisle's agent had spent the £50 but 'Lord Carlisle has as much interest in Pickering as Kouli Kan'. Even so, a nearby village proved difficult and so they treated the freeholders at Newton a second time.

The boroughs of Thirsk, Northallerton, Scarborough and Malton had retained the right to elect two members of Parliament of their own. Their electorates were very small, about one hundred for Malton until the Reform Act of 1832. This was called a Whig 'pocket borough', the nomination in the pocket of the major land owning family, who owned the Malton estate. During the elections of 1807, the electors were divided into groups and treated to an evening of free ale at the town inns. The arrival of three twin births in the nick of time saved Malton from being disenfranchised in 1832, after which it was briefly and sarcastically known as 'Happy Malton'. The first Reform Act of 1832 extended the vote to include resident '£10 freehold and leasehold' householders. The Malton electorate was widened to include Old Malton and Norton.

The Blue party working up to another election in February 1835 had dinners for the freeholders, on a Saturday at Cropton. They became 'riotous and drunken', until two in the morning. A few who lasted into the Sunday were finally stoned out of Cropton by the old women and boys. The Orange party planned a treat in reply.

The 1846 election at Malton was still described as a 'farce gone through'. Viscount Milton offered himself for election at Sheriff Hutton Park, attended by a select few. He waited on the electors the next Tuesday, shaking their hand at each door. Banners were unfurled, the band struck up some discordant tunes, and a mob followed in a confused mass to the Talbot Inn. The orange calico banners read 'Lord Milton the

People's Friend and no monopolies'. James Dunlop proposed him at the town hall. No one else stood. He was declared elected and faint cheers were heard. He said that he was in favour of free trade and rain fell.

The Englishman's Home

John Tuke portrayed the local cottages as small and low, with one or sometimes two rooms, both level with the ground or below it, and consequently damp and unwholesome. On the Wolds, they were still made of chalk covered with thatch. Strickland found Wold landowners disinclined to build more, as the rents wouldn't pay to keep them in repair. North Grimston cottages held a room measuring twelve to fourteen feet. The two room cottage rents at the estate town of Helmsley were £1.15.0 a year and their fuel was turf. In some estate townships, building was sometimes stopped and demolitions made, to avoid any settlement of those liable to fall on the rates. A visitor to Appleton le Moors in 1840 saw the village street as 'forty variously shaped houses, a few well built and boasting respectability, but most were such rude structures that the whole village looked outlandish.'

The basic foods were bread, skim milk and pottage, with potatoes increasingly used at every meal except breakfast, but the diet still mainly consisted of oats in the dales, just like the West Riding. The poet wrote that 'In Yorkshire Wolds, we mostly barley eat, for there we have but very little wheat.' The bread flours included rye, but most people in the North Riding, according to John Tuke, ate a bread of mixed grains or 'maslin', a brown bread, which stayed fresh longer. By mid century, white bread was driving out brown and both barley and rye bread had largely gone.

For many, the other most important elements of the diet came from the pig. Every cottage needed a well fed pig, its character enshrined in the popular saying 'a layer of fat and a layer of lean'. Commissioners enquiring into rural conditions found that women and children lived chiefly on bread, milk, pottage, and bacon. Allotments were a great help in keeping the pig fed. The pig could keep the family fed and that was what kept things going. If there was a cow too, the cottagers family life was manageable. As for water, Cropton well took two hundred and forty feet of winding, per bucket of water. At many villages it was fetched in yoked buckets from the spring or stream.

Labourers in cord trousers with a long smock tied around the waist, and a badger skin cap were familiar in the scene. John Oxtoby was remembered in a flitch of bacon coat, broad brimmed hat and chocolate kerchief, his hair combed to his eyebrows. Wold poems spoke of homespun clothing, grey stockings of mixed black and white wool, and a rough hempen shirt. Strickland said that the coarse grey woollens worn by the farmer and his family had vanished, but careful housewives still spun and knitted stockings of mixed wool, and in winter spun flax for a web of linen for sheets and shirts. Smocks lingered but trousers became more common. Boot and shoe making were the principal village industry. Every village had one or more shoemakers. Tailors walked round the farms, carrying their tools making and mending coats, breeches and leggings. William Foster in love in 1843 talked to his intended about 'the Spring patterns coming out' but he was a shop keeper.

Addison said of the village of Leavening that there was much simplicity of manners and absence of pride. 'No one presumed to stand before another in rank or superiority'. He thought that people differed sufficiently in character, to produce an agreeable variety. Many in the village had the same name so distinguishing names were invented. Five Thomas Sellers were Long Tom, Short Tom, Norton Tom, Hallgarth Tom and Butcher Tom. The Richards became Butcher Dick, Hallgarth Dick, Buskill Dick and Scalamoor Dick. There were nicknames. The butcher was the 'Duke'. A farmer who heard that he had the same name as the Earl of Northumberland, and assumed that he was related, was called 'Earl Percy'. Despite the intimacy of the community, no house in the village was occupied by the same family, when he looked back a few decades later. Village communities were surprisingly mobile. There was much moving about, for work, for tenancies and for marriage. Michaelmas Eve was 'the butter loaves feast', when the family came home. Callers helped themselves from a big loaf placed on the table, with a cavity in the top filled with butter.

Life was hard and intimate but neither romance nor light heartedness were unknown. The different parts of a gate were called male and female. The female part was that which made all the noise. Gloom is never universal. One man pleaded

'Share my cottage, gentle maid,
It only waits for thee,
To add fresh beauty to its shade,
And happiness to me.'

328

Weddings were rare and were as much community as family events, when they happened. There was often a long walk to the parish church at some other village. With that ceremony over, young men raced to the bride's house for the ribbon which had replaced the older garter. When the bride reached home, a full plateful of bride cake, broken in bits, was thrown over her head into the street, as she went into the house. The boys scrambled for it. Footraces followed in the evening and the groom was expected to distribute money for healths to be drunk. The Pickering Vicar pleaded for an end to garter racing in 1812. Farmer Peacock of Nunnington wed Miss Mattison in 1810 after twenty years courtship. At Pickering in 1836, John married Phoebe. They went to Kirkby Moorside in the afternoon for dinner and then back home for evening tea. The honeymoon was over.

North Grimstone women worked at weeding or in the harvest times earning ninepence for a day, lasting from eight in the morning to five at night, joined by their children for the same hours at the age of ten or eleven, for between fourpence and sixpence a day, during the thirties. Helmsley women topped, tailed and pulled turnips, spread manure and gathered stones in the Spring, then harvested hay and corn in the Summer for eightpence a day. Their cottage rents were £1.15s a year for a two room dwelling. Rheumatism was common. Men at Kirkby Moorside had wages of £8 for a headman, £5 for a plough lad, £2 for a ten year old boy, while £3 was paid to a dairy maid. Women in harvest had sixpence a day and four pence in Winter. The labourer's house rent was twenty five shillings a year.

Funerals were family and neighbourhood events. The church bell tolled or a messenger was sent around a dale. At Helmsley, twenty or thirty were invited to view the deceased. Some chapelfolk interpreted the destination from the appearance of the departure. Miss Bennett wrote in her notebook-

'Teach me to quit this earthly scene
With decent triumph and a look serene.'

There was the wake, where you sat in the deceased's house for two or three evening hours. Silver tankards hired from the inns were filled from large puncheons of scalded ale with added herbs and sugar. The excellences, defects and good deeds of the deceased were discussed and the tales of long ago retold, with occasional recourse to cake and cheese, and another tankard of ale.

Navy Days

During these centuries of sea-borne commerce, when Britain's maritime adventures captured every boy's imagination, Whitby and Scarborough were magnets offering better wages and a wider world. Their shipyards produced great tonnage of sailing ships, particularly of colliers and later for a while small steamships. Both ports were spoken of as 'nurseries of seamen', just as Malton was 'a nursery of navigation men'. The Napoleonic War made each port into a place of great trade and many Yorkshire ships served profitably as wartime supply and troop transports. The Whitby docks were busy with repair work and the Greenland Straits whaling trade enjoyed bouyant years.

Many men and boys went to sea from inland villages and had done so since the late 17th century. Nicholas Piper of Pickering was master of his own ship, the 'Swallow' calling at Newcastle and at Boston in America in 1762. The Cropton area was home to the most successful of the whaling captains and made notable contributions to their crews. In the year 1789 four out of ten baptisms at Cropton were for the children of mariners. The largest houses in Pickering were built with whaling profits, as inland gentry invested in the ships. A Piper family partnership bought a 251 ton ship, the *Henrietta* in 1775 and equipped it for whaling. By 1824 the ship had secured nearly five hundred whales in forty four voyages. Cropton's Captain Scoresby in the ten years from 1803, in the *Resolution* took 249 whales yielding 2034 tons of oil. The *Henrietta* in ten years from 1807 under Captain Kearsley brought home 213 whales yielding 1561 tons. John Machell a young surgeon from Pickering in 1823 had a chance to go to Greenland with the younger Captain Scoresby. He wrote 'Considering all things I think it is rather an honour to acompany such a man'.

Smuggling was active with many successful landings, despite some offshore chases by the Revenue cutters, and the expansion of the corps of riding officers, and the boat's crews of the Preventive Service. The coastal people thought of it as 'freetrade', unreasonably interfered with by government. Much of the time, this was a highly organised commercial activity handling a large part of the trade undertaken. It was not unusual to read in the newspapers of three hundred gallons of seized foreign gin for sale at the Whitby customs house. A Helmsley man carried casks home by foot on his shoulders. Large scale landings were prepared with men ready to move goods quickly inland to hides or to transhipment points. Gin garth at Baysdale was one such place, Little

Beck and the Blakey Inn were probably others, for goods landed on the Cleveland coast heading for Ryedale or York. The fast steam vessels ended much of the smuggling in the 1830s.

From Mills to Manufactories

The green rural Ryedale landscape does not immediately suggest the great national shift to manufacturing industries of the 18th and 19th centuries, known since as the 'industrial revolution'. Yet, for a space, small manufactories, usually called mills, were active in some surprising places. Rape was milled for oil at Keldholme and Ayton. Many corn mills were rebuilt on a grander scale, with multiple floors and gravity hoists, to cope with the larger crops. Gillamoor mill was rebuilt in 1779, with an overshot wheel worked by wooden slabs instead of buckets, and Howe Keld mill in 1797, on the site of a mill that had burnt down forty five years earlier. Hold Cauldron mill bore the plaque 'Peter Peat 1784'. Some mills, like Newsham mill rebuilt in 1839, installed a steam engine. A steam corn mill was built at Pickering's Potter Hill. Wardell's Pickering windmill was removed in 1839, but a modern paper making machine had been installed in the Thornton Dale paper mill in 1834.

Each market town had its iron and brass foundries. Malton has an unusual memorial to the Malton brass and iron founder of 1837, Arthur Gibson, showing him with bottle in hand. Ralph Yates of Malton followed on the site of Marshall's foundry. They had an early success with flat iron turf plates for domestic hearths. The breweries of the market towns were joined by other breweries at Sheriff Hutton, Rillington, Sherburn, Ebberston, Leavening and Snainton. As most public houses abandoned back yard brewing, these breweries built up modest rural networks of tied houses. Maltings were sometimes run independantly of brewing. Agricultural ropes and nets were made at the towns. The Helmsley ropewalk was in Pottergate running across low field, and Kirkby Moorside had several, one of them surviving late in Dale End.

Linen manufactories were at Kirkby Moorside, Pickering and Sheriff Hutton and at Balk, Crayke, Easingwold and Haxby not far away in 1823. A line thread factory was established at remote Castleton and Lealholm had a paper mill. But this local industry fell victim soon afterwards to the industrial revolution. Cottage hand loom weaving collapsed. Linen spinning and weaving left the cottages for water powered mills, elsewhere in the country. A weaver called Frank left

Hutton le Hole first for York and then for Bradford. The linen manufactories closed. This was a significant loss to the entire district.

Local coal working lingered on. Geology was little understood although William Smith at Hackness and Scarborough had produced his explanation of the stratification of the rocks. Daniel Rivis of Sherburn was persuaded to drill for coal at Cottondale in the chalk Wolds. The workmen put a few pieces in the shaft to encourage him. George Osbaldeston drilled for coals at Ebberston about 1843 with as little result.

Change at Malton

The local market towns of the early 19th century, absorbed some of the growing numbers of people, typically adding half as many again to their population. Malton, Pickering, Kirkby Moorside and Helmsley gained the services of physicians, banks, insurance agents and printers. They saw the establishment of denominational chapels with Sunday schools and many private educational academies. Malton had two new banks, financed by wealthy local gentry and a savings bank. Despite local bank failures in 1810 and 1823, the amalgamations which established the more secure joint stock bank networks, left each market town with more than one bank branch. Bower, Duesbery & co of Malton were issuing notes by 1824. The York City and County Bank opened its Malton branch in the thirties. This was also the age of the small shop, though often they were still part workshop, but increasingly for repairs rather than manufacture. By1823 Helmsley had five grocers, Kirkby Moorside eight and Malton thirty one.

A very few physicians and apothecaries and rather more surgeons had practices which together covered much of the district. Malton, Pickering and Kirkby had the higher status physicians and apothecaries. There were surgeons too at the market towns but practices had been established at Hovingham Lastingham, Slingsby, Snainton, Thornton Dale, Leavening, Sheriff Hutton and Rillington. The boundaries dividing the activities among the different members of these professions are not clear now and may not have been then. Thomas Harrison of Kirkby Moorside described as a surgeon, apothecary and man- midwife certainly prescribed and sold powders, ointments, anodyne draughts, and ninepenny elixirs to customers in a wide area around that town. Pickering had William Birdsall apothecary and midwife and Joseph Harrison surgeon and midwife.

Malton made some show as a social centre, building Assembly Rooms, which at one point included a museum. They were used during the fashionably attended races of 1814. A 'beautiful new theatre' was in part of the Rooms. On the 5th of October, this was crowded with a fashonable audience of four hundred, for Sheridan's 'the Rivals'. A month later, Sieur Sanches, the 'wonderful antipodean' would walk against the ceiling with a flag in each hand, play guitar, imitate birds and pretend to be an orchestra.

Here and there, around Malton, a gentleman or a prospering trader or solicitor built a Regency style house, perhaps covered with stucco, with neat thin glazing bars in the sash windows, and a door case with columns and pediment. The architect John Gibson arrived, fresh from laying out Scarborough's new suburb at South Cliff. He designed villas for the select precincts at the Mount, single houses of some splendour, along the Brows above the river, and several good buildings in the town and its neighbours. The market town churches and chapels, National Schools, cemetery chapels, flour mills, and the country houses, park lodges and Sykes farmsteads, often bore his stamp.

Voluntary societies proliferated at Malton, a literary institute formed in 1838, the Malton Wentworth Oddfellows lodge of 1840, an Agricultural Society staging ploughing matches and a Malton Floritechnical society with a Spring flower show. Members of the Mechanics Institute had a talk on the oxyhydrogen gas microscope in 1841. Lord Morpeth could welcome thirty ladies and three hundred men to a meeting of the Malton Total Abstinence Society. When the navigation froze up in the severe Winter of 1841, cheap flour and coal were supplied to the poor as the mills and gas works stopped. Soon afterwards the railway ended the navigation and a new age for Malton had begun.

The Old Religion

The Editor of the Wesleyan Methodist Magazine could write in 1818 that 'The Methodists, as a body of people, stand on a different ground in the opinion of the world, than they did fifty years ago'. The odium had gone and you now heard it said that 'Methodists are very respectable'. Something certainly had happened, for many of the more ardent members, who wanted to continue the missionary work, left to do that in a new denomination. From the older generation, Thomas Wardell a Wesleyan of Settrington, wrote in his diary in 1819 that he was 'another day nearer eternity'. He bore family loss and sickness with pained resignation, saying 'the lord still keeps me in the furnace'. Life's trials were 'Job's messengers', following one another in quick succession. He read Paley's 'Natural Theology' in 1827. By 1837, he had read the Old Testament eighteen times and the New Testament twenty two times.

There was more active Wesleyan Methodism. The Pickering Wesleyan society had built a new circuit chapel at Hungate in 1812. The circuit sent out remarkable men as missionaries. George Piercey was the first Wesleyan missionary to China and James Calvert the 'Apostle of Fiji'. Eleven years later, in 1823, they saw all the signs of a revival around them. Several villages in the circuit doubled their membership in three months, joined by people of all ages and every description of character. The revival apparently started at Lastingham. There was talk of children converting parents, husbands wives and wives husbands. Letters sometimes record this almost forgotten phenomena. Bethiah Pearson would write to her children 'pray for thy mother' and 'beg the almighty to work a change in thy father; his faults are ever so great'. Before this revival was complete, other things were happening - there were schisms, disagreements and breakaways.

Rosedale saw the Anglican minister Robert Skelton raising funds at a crowded meeting to form a Bible society in 1825, but over the next ten years, six Rosedale houses were registered as Nonconformist meeting places, including Bell End and Pryhills house. Methodist chapels were built to replace them at Thorgill and in Rosedale east in 1836. A year later a new Anglican church was built costing £665 to accommodate nearly four hundred people. Here was some competition. John Castillo the Methodist lay preacher wrote 'A dialogue between Rosedale Bob and Hartoft John arising from a speech by the Archdeacon at a Bible Meeting in the New Church'. When a new school was built in 1856 someone still said of Rosedale and Hartoft 'They were a century behind their neighbours in elementary knowledge'

Primitive Methodism

A new religious movement made great local inroads, deeply affecting towns and villages alike. The founder William Clowes visited the district in 1820. The Primitive Methodists, popularly called 'ranters', broke away from traditional Methodism, to revive missioning in open air meetings, offering a kind of 'crowd religion' well suited to the open air character of the times. A man or woman would join a crowd, where they wouldn't cross the door of a church. Their zeal to convert sinners and a plain spoken approach offered excitement, appealing to many that the more staid churches could never have attracted. Preachers recruited from the congregations spoke in dialect and gave extempore prayers and sermons.

Praying companies sought dramatic conversions in the field. Jane Ansdale and six others from 9.30 one morning, preached to thousands at a Pickering 'camp meeting', with five praying companies 'wrestling with sin in the valley', as women sang gospel songs. By 1835, they had 326 members attending at nineteen places in Pickering circuit. The title of a Wrelton sermon in 1846 was 'What must I do to be saved'. A man at a Fryup love feast said that 'his heart turned over in his belly'.

As societies were formed, they centred on unpretentious cottage gatherings, very lively and well adjusted to what people really felt and needed. A Hartoft man wrote in 1829, 'We are seven of us, Methodists, no chapel. Wherever a ray of divine love darts down on us, there we worship God'. The Primitives soon built chapels at villages, and even at hamlets where never a church had been before. They had hearers far in excess of their members. On Trinity Sunday 1851, many feasted at 'the Prim's cathedral'- Roseberry Topping, their drink soup and their food nuts.

The Wesleyans saw fresh schisms in 1849, and other break away groups were formed for a time. Eventually most villages had Wesleyan and Primitive or Reformed chapels, with services three times a Sunday and sabbath schools, bible groups, sewing circles and activities every evening. A 'Bible belt' culture spread among rural working people, offering a remarkable framework for thinking. Some spoke as if bible characters were known to them. There was much talk of sin and many conversions. Those who died were said to 'have gone to a better place'. It wasn't hard to believe there had to be one. There was also much talk of moral and social improvement.

The Improvement Movement

The broader improvement movement had lost none of its force. Nor was it entirely middle class. Sledmere Hall built up one of the finest libraries, until Sir Tatton Sykes sold 2690 books in 1824. Meanwhile, the Cottager's Companion found readers as avid as those who devoured the Mechanic's and Arminian Magazines. A different approach was emerging to that of John Wrightson the widely consulted 'wiseman', who lived at Malton and died going through Hovingham on his way to jail. A wealth of new knowledge was available for those who would study it. A sense of virtue in doing so, appeared among middling people. In 1828, a Malton youth urged his sister to become 'accomplished'. She was already a teacher but with a brother's patronage he wrote 'You are studying music, try French'.

The Kirkdale cave was found in July 1821, full of animal bones from previous eras, that seemed once again to provide compelling evidence which contradicted prevailing views of the age of the world. The younger William Scoresby of Cropton wrote the classic essays on magnetism. At Brompton, Sir George Cayley's prolific mind produced papers on flight, finned missiles, caterpillar traction, tension wheels, sloping theatre floors and much more. He wrote for the Mechanic's Magazine. William Smith the Hackness Agent from 1828 to 1834, discovered the stratification of the rocks. Richard Spruce of Ganthorpe, prepared a list of the flora in the Castle Howard area with nearly five hundred entries, and went on to explore the flora of the Amazon.

Whitby gentlemen opened a botanic garden in 1812 and a Literary and Philosophical Society in 1823. Scarborough Philosophical Society was formed five years later. Country gentlemen bought telescopes and microscopes, filled cabinets with rock specimens and read widely. Mr. Bean at Scarborough opened a private natural history museum. Mr.Watson at Brawby and Mr. Parker at Wombleton had museums in which they placed old seventeenth century furniture, gentry paintings and such curiosities of the past as querns and flints.

George Calvert of Kirkby Moorside with the help of the parson recorded the local folk lore. An observatory tower was built at Oldstead in 1838. Mr. Hill at Thornton Dale kept a collection of curious animals for which he was offered a live wolf from Canada. 'Pot-hunting squires' like Lord Londesborough excavated burial mounds for urns and arrow heads. Squire Thomas Kendall at the Pickering Low Hall had a great prehistoric stone coffin in the front room. Mr. Clemishaw of Easingwold in 1852 made a wooden watchman who would turn, fire billiard balls, ring two alarm bells and say 'fire'.

The newspapers and the new magazines helped. The thin 18th century newspapers, the York Courant, Chronicle and Herald were joined by the Yorkshire Gazette in 1819 and they thickened, printing reports of activities, thoughts for the time and discoveries. Reading rooms were founded to give access to books and newspapers, with occasional public 'penny readings' for those who couldn't read. Mutual improvement societies and mechanic's institutes spread with similar purposes. This would culminate in a new drive for a different kind of education.

The attempt to broaden the appeal to wider groups was an uphill task, for there was little leisure yet for attending classes. Public adult education appeared as single lectures. The Earl of Carlisle, addressing a Mechanics Institute in 1850, thought this was like 'attempting to support life by administering a series of excitements'. The Malton Mechanic's Institute founded in 1838 reported apathy two decades later. Some succeeded better. Ishmael Fish had a class at Welburn talking about electricity, with glees sung at intervals by the Malton Singers. William Foster, a Congregationalist liked what they called 'a missionary meeting', with accounts of far off places. He walked from Pickering to Kirkby Misperton, to sit down to tea with two hundred, when a converted native from Madagascar was expected.

More was probably learnt by people reading books on their own, other than the widely read bible, tracts and Sunday School prizes. John Watson said as much. His mother was a teacher in a Malton Sunday School and gave him a taste for reading. When he was apprenticed as a farm and household hand with a clergyman, he read by the fire during the long winter nights. He first became acquainted with politics and theology when he was nineteen. He became a radical reformer.

The number of secular works published, grew rapidly and they offered the stimulus to change things. 'Hints for Home Comfort' offered a different wisdom – 'Always lay your table neatly whether you have company or not' and 'Dirty windows speak to the passer by'. But there was good advice – 'When sheets or chamber towels become thin in the middle, cut them in two, sew the edges together and hem the sides'. 'A flannel petticoat would last twice as long turned backwards before the front began to wear thin'.

Isaac Cooper recalled the stranger beliefs, previously held strongly at Helmsley. 'To turn a beggar from the door would bring bad luck', surely an echo of the mediaeval Christian virtue of hospitality. 'Walking through the churchyard by the public footpath on St Marks eve was to be avoided'. There were once reasons for that too. 'An old woman covered with pins and needles was reckoned to come from the castle ruins in the dark'. They brought Spink of Beadlam over to lay the ghost. Some thought it requisite to give a pair of shoes once in your life to a poor person. A few believed that Arthur and his knights waited below

Freeborough Hill in Cleveland. Farndale was still blamed for having several witches. If you met one, you had to speak first, or not at all, or she had power over you. John Wrightson and the Wise man of Scarborough had been sought out to cure cattle, know the future, or to show how to avoid being balloted for the militia.

The New Schooling

The early educational movements have been under valued, swamped in the memory of the later 19th century changes. The education available was very varied, but what was on offer did expand and could be adequate to the need. Samuel Priestman, a Quaker born, was luckier than most. He had three years at a Dame School, three years with a clergyman where he learnt the catechism, three years at a Boarding School, where he recalled learning about ghosts and hob goblins at night. He thought sisters exerted a petty tyranny over brothers, which he returned in full later on. He was then apprenticed to learn milling at Thornton dale for seven years and in 1820 went to Leeds to run a mill on his own account. He built the Kirkstall Mill.

The British and Foreign Schools Society was formed in 1808 by Evangelicals and promoted interdenominational schools. The National Society was founded in 1811 and sought a church school in every parish. There was a spirit of competition between the established church and nonconformists. By 1818 a fairly high proportion of the younger age groups received some elementary education. By 1823 Pickering had its endowed free school, a ladies boarding school in Hungate, an industry school and six private academies. The Methodist conference in 1833 concluded that a Christian way of life needed Christian teaching. The Methodist attempt to provide their own schools would prove a major challenge, stimulating Anglicans to greater efforts.

Fresh charitable endowments for schools still came from landowners. Endowment usually brought a measure of supervision and the school was unlikely to be a mere child minding establishment. C S. Duncombe founded a charity school for eighty free scholars at Helmsley by 1822 and another was established by Lady Feversham for girls in1832. This was apart from the market place grammar school which took fee paying board and day pupils. Lord Feversham built low mill school at Farndale in1829. Lord Middleton endowed Leavening with £40 a year in 1832 with part of the sum reserved for the education of girls. Lord Hotham built a school at Wilton in 1836 allowing the master

£10 a year. Duggleby School was built by Thomas Croft in1838 and West Heslerton school in 1850 by the Rector and Mrs. Langley. There were several more in the district.

Some schools and their teachers were certainly valued. Thomas Wardell of Settrington praised his schoolmaster, 'a farm servant who had raised himself to be a successful teacher'. He not only taught his scholars, reading, writing, spelling and arithmetic but when required instructed them in mensuration and even in navigation. 'He was a man of unquestionable and undeviating attention to his calling'. The master at Leavening was engaged by half a dozen farmers. He was a good penman, took great pains and saw improvement in his pupils, despite a crowded schoolroom. Pupils of the Welburn dame school presented Miss Bramley with a butter cooler on her retirement, to thank her for managing a large company for twelve years.

Mr. Bearcroft's School at Kirkby Moorside showed a different picture. The terms in 1807 were £15.15.0 a year for boys under ten, another guinea if older. The education was two guineas; entrance half a guinea and washing £1.5.0. Pupils brought their own bedding, towels and table utensils, or paid a guinea to hire them. Quills and a penknife were required. Two months were vacations. William Bearcroft from Pockley was highly thought of. He taught John Jackson the portrait artist. He wrote 'Practical Orthography', published in 1824, a work on the art of teaching spelling, by writing, using dictation, exercises and making collections of difficult words. His prospectus offered English, Latin and Greek, penmanship, arithmetic, accounts, dividing commons and open fields, geography, natural philosophy, mechanics and astronomy. Gabriel Croft the educated Congregational minister opened an academy at Pickering, where some students were prepared for the nonconformist ministry, and for many years, he held a free school for poor children.

Malton Grammar School in 1827 attracted between twelve and twenty scholars, who either lodged or dieted in the master's house. When he decided to take no more boarders, the number was down to four. The usher taught a school for the 'three Rs' with twenty or thirty pupils partitioned off, who paid nine shillings a quarter. Since he didn't attend readily, no one was very happy. There were riots at Old Malton in 1835, when some locals asserted that the master was making the school into a sinecure by only teaching classics and only for inhabitants of Old Malton. A school society was formed and applied to the British and Foreign Schools Society for a master. One testimonial had fifty eight signatures and marks, about half of which were said to be in the same hand writing.

The national government showed a growing interest in education after 1832, and some funds were made available as grants for building schools, for the poorer classes. As the number of schools increased, the monitorial system was applied to teach growing numbers of pupils. This used the skills of those who had learnt something, to teach to others who hadn't. An important step was the establishment of the National Society Teacher Training College at York in 1841, which was soon sending out trained teachers. The Committee of the Privy Council for Education began making grants to schools, subject to annual inspections in 1839. Pupil teachers began to replace monitors a decade later. The poor law commissioner in 1843 thought that what was learnt was soon forgotten. He had doubts if book knowledge was of the value which it was the fashion to suppose. Although infant schools were more numerous, he thought that what the children of the poor learnt, was of little use to them.

At Play

Leavening children played football, trap ball, tap and taw, and shinnow, at noon in front of the school, and played cricket at the Wold end in the evening. At night, they could see the stars out of the chimney without leaving their seats around the hearth. The children played 'manna minetail' at Helmsley, boys and girls catching each other around a ring. Robert Frank of Hutton le Hole recalled boyhood life. As a lad, he fished in the pool, sat, sang and talked on the green, played cricket, raced down the street, rambled the woods and climbed the hills. There were games of fives, 'send the ball against the wall', and 'knur and spell'. High points were November the Fifth, or Gunpowder plot day and sheep shearings, when farmers helped each other and had a substantial dinner to follow. The pleasures of the Wolds were described, at the time, as 'men climbing a greasy pole for a leg of mutton, women tied in sacks racing for tea, snuff or sugar, football, skittles, quoits, wrestling, cock and dog fighting, bull and badger baiting and robbing hen roosts at night.'

Blind Jack Allen, the musical whistler of Malton, challenged the harmonious, from all over, to matches for cash stakes in 1836. A better music was becoming general. As the military bands faded from view, town and village brass bands were formed. The new brass instruments were expensive, but Malton had a good band by 1837. Will Foster played clarionet, Hardwick Spurr an instrument called the serpent, Tom Allison was on the kettle drum and there were bugles, bassons, trombone and fifes. When Pickering race meetings were revived between 1839 and 1842, John Castillo could write-

'There's bands of music, colours flying
Hams and legs of mutton frying
Nimble waiters on the wing,
To sell 'em drink and hear 'em sing.
There's gambling tables, orange stalls
Spice and nuts and dancing.'

Table 46. Early Notices of Local Bands.

1820's   Helmsley

1830's   Helmsley Brass; Pickering; Malton wind; Malton Brass; Leefe's Quadrille

1850's   Bilsdale; Farndale; Gillamoor Brass; Malton Band of Hope; Drum & Fife; Smithson's Saxhorn; Rosedale; Herr Schmidt's band; Moxon's Quadrille; Helmsley Brass; Kirkby Moorside; Slingsby; Bilsdale; Malton Saxhorn; Malton Philharmonic;

1860's   Brawby; Malton Quadrille; Malton Rifle Volunteer; Thornton Dale Quadrille; Rillington Brass; Thornton Dale Brass; Harum; Malton United; Pickering Brass.

1870's   Slingsby; Gibson's Brass; Malton String; Foxholes Brass.

1880's   Helmsley New; Rosedale; Castle Howard Reformatory Drum & Fife; Hutton le Hole; Terrington; Thornton Dale Temperance; Skaife's Pickering; Norton Brass; United Christian Army Brass; Malton Brass; Norton Temperance; Drum & Fife; Farndale; Bilsdale; Hawnby; Rievaulx; Stape.

1890's   Pickering; Sherburn Volunteers; Scampston; Rillington; Malton Rifle Volunteers; Malton Orchestral; Malton Temperance Brass; Thornton Dale Temperance; Smith's Pickering; Kirkby Moorside Temperance; Lastingham; Cropton; Butler's Helmsley Quadrille;

1900's   Appleton le Moors; Rudland; Hawnby; Harum; Malton White Star.

Parliament reduced the cost of the publican's spirit licence from five guineas to two guineas in 1825. This led many houses to stock spirits - the notorious dram-shops. Reformers viewed gin and other spirit drinking as a national disaster. In order to reverse the trend towards more spirit drinking, the beer duty was abolished in 1830 and the retail sale of beer opened up to any ratepayer, who would pay the one guinea excise licence and produce sureties. Beerhouses were freed from control by the magistrates and within a few years, a great many new beer houses opened. Four opened at Pickering in 1831, one at Smiddy hill, the Red Lion in Eastgate and two more in outlying places.

Railways

The railways transformed the nation. People came to feel that those who lived before steam trains were from another world. The pioneering Stockton - Darlington railway was extended to a hamlet called Middlesbrough, as an outlet for Durham coal. It became the fastest growing town of Victorian England. The genteel founders banned fireworks, gunfire, sliding, loitering, bull and bear baiting, throwing at cocks, and dangerous football. Ten years later a 'wizard queen' was advertised swallowing knives. The railways changed things. An early mineral line was developed at Kepwick using gravity and horses to take limestone, from quarries at the west end of the Hambleton Hills, a thousand feet down to kilns near a turnpike road.

Meanwhile, railway networks using steam engines were forming in York Vale, the West Riding and indeed much of England. The 'Railway King', George Hudson and his York and North Midland Railway Company constructed a York - Malton- Scarborough branch in 1845. The Scarborough resort received a great fillip, as it attracted even more of the expanding middle classes, not only from the north but from London, who came to stay for long holidays, but unexpected numbers of the day trippers from the working classes, for one day treats. Twenty five hundred people, including children of four Sunday Schools, went on the July day trip from Pickering in 1853.

Hudson converted the Whitby-Pickering line to steam traction, linked it to the Scarborough line near Malton and built a new seaside resort on the Westcliff at Whitby, which gained an instant respectable appeal. Railway architect G.T. Andrews designed elegant stations with wrought iron and glazed roofs and great archways for giants to go through. Old Hannah of Levisham lay on the floor and moaned, when

342

she made her first train ride to Whitby. Queen Victoria, Prince Albert and the royal family arrived at Castle Howard station on a visit in 1850.

The railway station became a terminus for the wagons of village carriers taking country produce, eventually including churns of milk, transhipped to distant markets. Some were gipsy style caravans, and others more like an omnibus. Passengers would travel with them cheaply, sharing the 'butter-women's talk'. Distant products became locally known, as each region exported its own specialities. When the Welburn carrier delivered a goose to the wrong house, they ate it. It didn't all happen in a day, but Huntley and Palmer's biscuits, Reckitt's starch, Sunlight soap, and Cheddar cheese became known, far beyond their old precincts. Mass production of patented and popular products was given an undreamt of prospect. Nottinghamshire boots and shoes would replace the products of that most common of all village craftsmen - the shoemaker.

The local railway network filled out. A rural Thirsk - Malton line opened in 1853 amid wild enthusiasm. The Gilling - Helmsley line of 1871, was extended to Kirkby Moorside in 1874, and to Pickering the next year. A Pickering - Seamer line opened in 1882 and Scarborough was linked to Whitby in 1885. A York and Market Weighton railway ran via Holtby. The Malton -Driffield line achieved a considerable engineering triumph with the construction of the long brick lined Burdale tunnel.

The consequences of having a railway system were legion. The railways became major country employers. An army of station and line staff included signal men, porters, plate layers and liveried station masters. Every boy wanted to become an engine driver. Plate layers walked a stretch of line, daily checking rails and banks. Signalmen controlled level crossing gates and supervised a length of line. Every station gained a coal yard and so people bought grates to replace turfplates.

Short pleasure excursions on the railway brought fame to surprising places. Some villages around York enjoyed a brief holiday heyday. There was an 1849 railway excursion to Newton on Ouse, and others to Beck Hole near Goathland, Egton Bridge, and Rievaulx Abbey. Thornton dale was throng with visitors from Malton, Whitby and Scarborough in June 1855. Trippers from Lastingham and Appleton reached Slingsby in August 1865. The locals were amazed when two stripped for a fight in front of Swann's blacksmith shop.

The opening of the Helmsley railway in 1871 saw the navvies, full

343

Old Inclosures of Kirkby Moorside Town in the mid 19th Century

of ale, but conducting themselves with great propriety, and a new flush of visitors at the town and at Rievaulx abbey. It was easier to emigrate on the railway, with a shorter voyage via Liverpool instead of Hull. It was simpler to join the California gold rush of 1849. Along the lines, many a possibility emerged. A Marishes housewife saw a fresh opportunity within her grasp. She absconded with a young wagoner on the railway train, taking her clothes and money, and leaving her husband the three children. By 1879 Gilling was the railway station for Ampleforth College and for Hovingham, which had its own sidings to load estate timber. They say that the station sold 13,516 tickets in 1896.

Larger than Life Gentlemen

Robert Frank of Hutton le Hole had seen the social divisions widen. Men spoke of 'two nations between whom there is no inter course'. He said that the forty years to 1863 had brought 'the rich in lofty days, the poor reduced low'. A 'due subordination of rank' had long been assumed by many who had some rank. Now, it seemed that the gaps were widening.

Certainly, aristocracy was sometimes treated with incredible deference, as if Godlike. A young wife tied up a chair with blue ribbons, because the Earl of Carlisle had once sat upon it. When the newly wed Lord Londesborough turned up at Seamer, 150 men would discharge his horses and hand pull the carriage into the village. An extra-ordinary vast monument to Lord Feversham was built at a charge of £800, supposedly at the cost of the tenantry, in 1869, to dominate Helmsley market place. Somewhat later, after the Scarborough shipbuilding Tindall family moved from Knapton to Kirkby Misperton Hall, village boys took off their caps and girls curtseyed to the Tindall daughters, who gave them tracts on morality and religion.

The local 'quality, nobility and gentry' were the subject of much gossip. Ancient local families, like the St. Quintins and Stricklands were joined by the successful from commerce. Their characters were assessed and their eccentricities talked up. Mr. Blomberg who settled at Kirkby Misperton, was brought up by King George III with the Princes, who he markedly resembled. He gained rapid preferment. There was mocking too-

'Come all you brave gallants and listen my song
Of the Lord of Fitzwilliam the broad and the strong
As home from the Tavern he wiggles and reels
With his old canty consort close up on his heels'

Others entered history as characters on the grand scale. George Osbaldeston bought Ebberston Hall in 1824. He removed the lodges from each side of the house, intending to build larger wings. He was known as 'the squire of all England'. He was the sportsman personified, better at the chase than the turf, but with achievements in cricket and tennis, and fame for exploits as an oarsman, shot, gambler and duellist. As his finances worsened, he tried anything, including a fruitless search for minerals on the estate. He started limekilns and brickworks at Ebberston in 1847. Local tradition claimed that he sold the furniture item by item at the Grapes Inn, and in 1848 he sold the estate. His solution was traditional - a rich widow.

Sir Tatton Sykes was a comparable personality. He attended all the race meetings and some said that he was the finest rider in the world. Around the middle of the century, he was mainly occupied in building up his stud and his flocks. He had over three hundred head of horses, yet he hired carriage horses from the village inn. His sheep breeding was successful. He built many Wold schools. They say that he ruled his young family like a tyrant, with rules for rising at dawn, no hot water and the whip.

Younger sons pursued careers. James Anlaby Legard, a fourth son, volunteered for the Royal Navy at thirteen. He fell overboard while in Cork Harbour. In the West Indies, he caught yellow fever. He was a first Lieutenant, when Admiral Codrington destroyed the Turkish fleet in Navarino Bay, the only significant fleet action between the battles of Trafalgar and Jutland. As a mate on a ten gun brig, he surveyed the Dardanelles and was seconded for a time to the Turkish navy. He settled at Kirkby Misperton in 1852, and started deep drainage of his estate.

The gentry were expected to make a contribution and they did so. Ann Bellwood of Sinnington Hall left £300 for the poor, the interest to be divided among them at Christmas. W. St. Quintin of Scampston Hall kept Christmas in the good old English style. 'He entertained all the labouring tenantry on the estate to supper in the mansion with his amiable lady. There followed an evening of innocent mirth and merriment.' Lord Feversham at Helmsley in the Winter of 1864 had two prime fat shorthorns, sheep and deer given away. There were clothing and coal distributions. The young ladies from Aislaby Hall read the Bible on Sunday afternoons to old Nanny Boddy, who was often in bed, wearing her night cap with a huge white frill round her face.

Criticism could break through. At Castle Howard in 1895 they said that 'While the Earl paints, she governs'. He was a friend of the pre-

Raphaelite artists. His wife was an abstainer from strong drink. She was reputed to have emptied the house wine down the drain and closed the public houses on the estate. This was not a popular move, but the fraternities, societies and sunday schools found their way for treats into the grounds, some from the West Riding.

Captain Legard at Kirkby Misperton opened a reading room for labourers, but also had a plan for firing cannon at poachers. Squire Baker at Ebberston was a mighty hunter but unusually taught in the Sunday School. A neighbour parson once upset him by preaching on the text of the rich man and Lazarus. London merchant shipowner Joseph Shepherd built Appleton le Moors Hall, and then a school and schoolmaster's house. New Squires from industry and commerce, like James Walker, the Leeds clothing manufacturer who rented Levisham in the sixties, continued the old patronal tradition. Mrs Walker had house meetings for village youth twice weekly.

Table 47. Some local Owners of more than 3,000 acres of land in the North and East Ridings. 1871

		Acres	Gross Rent
Earl of Feversham	Duncombe Park	39.312	£34.328
Sir Tatton Sykes	Sledmere	34.010	£35.870
Earl of Carlisle	Castle Howard	13.030	£14.502
Lord Middleton	Birdsall	12.294	£14.778
Sir George Wombwell	Newburgh park	11.911	£13.044
Sir Digby Cayley	Bropton Hall	7785	£7842
Rev. John Hill	Thornton Hall	7632	£4475
MCD. St.Quintin	Scampston	7033	£10244
Sir George Cholmley	Boynton Hall	24408	£30544
Mrs R Norcliffe	Malton	3472	£4262
Sir James Walker	Sand Hutton	3580	£5241
Thomas W.Rivis	Malton	6654	£8265
Mrs. Lavinia Barnes	Gilling Castle	3348	£3147
Sir Charles Legard	Ganton Hall	6407	£7751
Mrs.F.Shepherd	Kirkby Moorside	3791	£4421
Earl Fitzwilliam	Wentworth Woodhouse	2976	£13420
Rosedale & Ferry Hill Iron Company		2231	£4536

The rentals of the landed interest increased generally, at least till the seventies. In many places, a squire was still head of the village and there were many stories, either of his interest and kindness, or lack of it, his eccentricity and his family. Death duties began in 1894, bringing heir loom sales while rent incomes were falling.

Village Life

Thomas Parker drew a different picture at Harum in the 1830's, where there was no squire. Until 1810 the inhabitants had been mainly employed in weaving cloth. After that, the industry migrated elsewhere, and it was farming for which the place was remarkable. He wrote that 'the present generation of Harumites, though civil to strangers, are high in the fields of extravagance and dress, forgetting that their ancestors wore hempen shirts'.

The experience was not uniform. There were hardship years, when rural revolt simmered in the Wolds. This was a large farm country with big tenancies, and many absentee owners, and it was the tenant farmers property that was attacked rather than the estates of landowners. There were hay stack fires at Cowlam in 1857, at Duggleby in 1860, and more stacks burnt at Huggate, Boythorpe, Butterwick, Settrington and Wintringham in 1864. One Wold incendiary was caught at the Coach and Horses, Rillington, but Snaffling Jack and Sweep Harry escaped.

There was progress, in good periods. The better off Victorians had a great belief in progress. It came in very small ways. A public pump could end many hours of winding. One Thornton dale house gained a two seat toilet plank, carved 1861. A new public pump was erected four years after. New brick houses spread through the low country, but when Sledmere village was rebuilt in brick, it marked the start of a change of material for houses throughout the high Wolds. Much of Kirkby Moorside was rebuilt in brick after 1850.

Fruit growing, plums, pears and apples helped the cottagers at Aislaby, Middleton and Wrelton, to meet their high rents. Much of Ryedale would later send fruit by rail for jam making. Small savings for bigger purchases were helped by a Blanket club. Mr Preston's bequest added a few rewarding shillings, for the regular sixpence depositors, among the one hundred and sixty five savers, in the 1859 Norton Clothing club. When Norton opened its penny bank, ten years later, one hundred and twentysix depositors turned up to place a total of £4.2s.5d. The average deposit of one hundred and sixty savers in the Pickering Savings Bank in 1860 was eleven shillings. The Thornton Dale

Independant Order of Druids in 1872-3 paid out £95 to some of their two hundred members, but had £1394 still deposited in a bank.

A Malton Dispensary was formed about 1832, and in 1854 dealt with two hundred and eighty patients, but little more is known about it. Some of the Friendly Societies appointed a doctor, virtually creating a limited health service for their members. Otherwise, the doctor was called on if you could afford him. The practices of the physicians were mostly established where they would remain. They were in reach by foot and horse and had to respond in the same manner. Dr Alfred Hartley of Malton was known as 'Killhorse Joe'. Letters reached him from Duggleby and Grimston, asking him to come. Another wrote saying 'his medicine did some good'; Jane Brown wrote from Habton wanting a box of pills. His patients came from as far as Ganthorpe and Appleton le Moors. He developed a lifelong belief in the value of fresh air and good water.

These men were highly regarded and much spoken of in their day. Old Dr Bostock of Malton used a trap drawn by a Wold pony. Dr Lascelles died at Slingsby in 1884 after being the village and district physician for forty six years. Dr. Scott at Thornton Dale handled the flue epidemic of 1888. They said of Dr. Robertson at the same village that 'he gave his medical skills although chances of payment were poor. He did a lot of doctoring for nowt'. The Barugh blacksmiths, grandfather and grandson Bowes, pulled out teeth with their crab claws.

Many people drew on the patent medicine vendors. Carbolic began its career as the popular disinfectant in the fifties. Mr. Mosely, visiting Malton regularly, could offer patent terreous artificial teeth, fitted 'with the stumps left in'. The travelling Doctor Lamb regularly visited market town inns to relieve people of their worms.

The new literature of 'Necessary Knowledge for Young Women' was urging fresh air, skipping and dancing. Grandams stuck by their own medicinal recipes, some still replete with such unusual objects as snails, roast mouse ,or hairy worms to be hung in flannel bags around the neck. Many villages had a chalybeate spring, valued as better water than most, and credited with medicinal qualities. Normanby Spa gave out sixty gallons a minute and like the spring on Salton village green had a strong smell of sulphur. Eye wells were visited for small cures.

The Boards of Poor Law Guardians brought some services to the very poor. They could appoint a medical officer at a fee of £20, but with 1s.6d for each vaccination, and 10s for midwifery. Malton Board of Health issued notices for precautions against cholera. They said that you should avoid excess drink, unboiled water, tainted meat, unripe fruit, raw vegetables, fasting, getting wet and great fatigue. Small pox vaccination was done, at Helmsley in1872. The town had outbreaks of scarlet fever, of measles in 1889, influenza in 1891, cholera in 1892, typhoid in 1893, small pox in 1893 and typhoid again in 1895.

Many village populations shrank after mid century, with young families leaving. The exodus became a flood in the seventies. Some village houses still had large families struggling to make ends meet. Cottages were later recalled, with sentiment, as homely and friendly, where 'none sought the unattainable in this world'. There was virtue in 'keeping yourself to yourself', but curiosity as to what was happening on the far side of the wall. Families bought flour weekly from the mill or the shop for home baking. Men stood at the smith's door to watch the sparks fly and to talk over local events. These included rolling pace eggs at Easter, the first boiling of peas on a July Saturday, and mell suppers with much spiced cake. There were Sunday school prize givings, choir treats and Winter magic lantern shows. 'Wolds lassies in turkey red stockings' went to Malton market, where street stalls sold sweets, hot stew and peas near the church.

Life was later recalled at a long thatched cottage at the corner of Shop lane in Aislaby. This 'cruck house' had 'beams rising from the ground and braced together higher up'. John Chapman a farm labourer threshed, with a flail, the gleanings brought in from the fields by his wife and daughter, probably in the threshold or cross passage behind the hearth. The family kept a cow, which the children tented around the road sides for grazing. The crucks had been raised, but there was little space upstairs under the thatch. There was a great risk of earwigs dropping in the beds, so they had a 'shut up bed' downstairs, within large cupboard doors, which could be closed in the day time. John Chapman earned nine shillings a week in Summer and eight shillings in Winter.

Childhood

John Tate, who later ran Newbridge quarry, as a boy tied bands for sheaves in the harvest field, on his grandfather's farm at Pickering, when he was eight. He was in regular work at twelve leading bricks. He later claimed 'they do not know what work is now compared with years ago'. Childhood was short and if children's work at any stage could contribute to family survival, then it was taken for granted. Orphans were absorbed into families or apprenticed out to farmers. A salutary message to one was 'Do what your Aunt tells you and God will love you'.

Another side of childhood was well remembered. West Heslerton children delightedly scooped, when a West Heslerton grocer spilt a cask of treacle over the main street in 1855. Kirkby Moorside lads still threw birds' eggs at one another on the 29th of May, and gave up bird nesting for the season. Shrove Tuesday brought out the whips and tops. Malton lads about 1865, bored holes in water butts and took garden gates to throw in the river on Christmas Eve. Stone throwing for a wager had two lads break five panes of glass in Yedingham church school one, Christmas Day. Young maids swung on 'the ding dong' gate from Coneysthorpe into the Castle Howard grounds. William Hall of Lockton remembered the mell suppers 'with spice loaf galore, and rum in the tea' and the mornings of the 14th of November when the boys rang the church bells. He recalled the riding of stangs and the burning of effigies.

Young lads dropped peat down widow's chimneys. Girls had wood hoops and sticks and boys iron ones, bowled with hooks, that they ran for miles. A Wold's boy chased hares, thinking them witches. He skated on the village ponds, poached rabbits, kept hawks, and at the age of fifteen shot birds with a gun. Most of the lads played marbles with 'clay bumblers or taws', costing a penny a dozen, or used the glass alleys which kept the fizz in pop bottles. They collected crab apples, or old rags and bones from anyone who would part with them, to raise money, or to exchange for rubbing stone to go daily whitening hearths or front steps. Punch and Judy shows were seen at hirings. A few might get snap cards, some draughts, merrills or dominoes. Foster at Pickering wrote to tell his kinfolk of 'Billy having a ride in Fred Pickering's new cart'.

Table 48. John William Grayson of Pickering's Twelve Golden Rules for Boys; December 1887

Hold integrity sacred. Observe good manners. Endure trials patiently.
Be prompt in all things. Make good acquaintances. Shun the company of the idle.
Dare to do right. Fear to do wrong. Watch carefully over your temper.
Never be afraid of being laughed at for doing right. Fight life's battles manfully, bravely.
Use your leisure moments for study. Sacrifice money rather than principle.

The War with Russia.

A British army was sent to fight Russians in the Crimea on the Black Sea in 1854. An Old Malton man in the 88th Regiment wrote describing the Turkish and Greek ladies, but he had the wit to add 'give me the maids of Merry England'. John Snowden of Gilling, a Royal Marine, wrote from Sebastapol camp after spending five hours with his brother, a Grenadier Guard. He was in hospital sick with the fever and he died of it within a few days. Lieutenant Swaby of Hawnby fell at Inkerman and Robert Nelson of Malton in the Balaclava charge. On that famous occasion, GeorgeWombwell of Newbrough Priory was ADC. to Lord Cardigan commanding the Light Brigade. The general sent six hundred cavalry riding up a valley into direct gunfire. Young Wombwell had two horses killed under him, and was taken prisoner during the charge. A shell burst enabled him to seize a loose horse and he made his escape.

A cannon was placed in Yorkersgate, Malton inscribed 'captured at Sebastopol, by the Allied armies, 1856'. Miss Bilton of Huttons Ambo had sent seventy-two pairs of warm stockings to the soldiers. Miss Thornton's school children at Sheriff Hutton had made them Winter clothing. The peace was well celebrated with great drinkings. Hovingham had flags, thirty rockets, thirty serpents and approaching forty Catherine wheels, mostly made by a local inventor, who let them go bang and whiz on the green while the band played. The hamlet of Kirkby Mills saw twenty people take a cup of tea and 'sumptuous viands' in the middle of the street. The tea was laced with rum and several guns were fired. Appleton le Moors consumed much nut brown ale, and forty times forced the blacksmith's anvil to rocket to a great height using gun powder.

In the peace that followed, in 1859, local rifle corps were formed at Malton, Pickering, Helmsley, Slingsby, Wyedale and Castle Howard; part of a national movement to supplement the professional army. The corps functioned as a sort of popular men's club, with bands and uniformed parades, target shooting unhindered by any game laws, a drill hall to learn manoeuvres and gymnastics, a sense of purpose and an annual away-holiday at camp. Shooting suddenly became a sport that was encouraged. Shooting butts were raised in Goodham dale at Helmsley and in Newton Dale. The 1863 prize shoot held at Pickering butts, instead of the camp site at Strensall common, brought competitors from each of the Corps to display marksmanship. In 1878, the head quarters of the north eastern military district was settled at York. The army took over Strensall common in 1881 as a permament Summer training ground for regular, militia and volunteer troops, received in numbers of up to ten thousand men. Annually between May and October, it became usual to see rows of conical white canvas tents.

Rural Leisure

Some of life's themes are almost eternal. Old hands later recalled that the young man who put an arm round Jenny Johnstone at Malton Crucalty Fair, knew that 'she had the neatest foot and prettiest ankle in Malton'. Mr.Prince at the George Inn, 'inspired by the tender passion, planted a kiss on the fair attendant'. She struck him on the head with an empty porter bottle. There were more subtle pressures to alter popular behaviour. The Crucalty fair in the Orchard Field was criticised by 'our generation of sober sides' in 1858, for there was dice at halfpenny a toss, oranges three a penny and gingerbread. The Huttons Ambo race for the brides garter was changed to a race for ribbon, with less hanky panky. Middle class folk frowned on wife sales, lingering as an amicable working class form of divorce. A Wombleton man in 1855 went to a market cross to part from the woman he had lived with for sixteen years. An Oswaldkirk man paid two shillings and sixpence and departed with Mary.

There was romance as well, strongly expressed in rural song and verse. 'Shout baby shout and clap thy hands, for father on the threshold stands'. Mr. W. Storr, the Sinnington grocer in his 'Native Poetry', wrote-

'When toiling hard to earn my bread,
With weary limbs I homeward tread.
Who's watching there to see me fed,
My wife.
And when I have arrived there,
Who, for me, places, my arm chair,
And with sweet smiles beguiles my care,
My wife.'

The 1856 annual Rosedale 'gypsey party' was pure romance. Not a gipsy was present but three hundred people took tea at a picnic with a brass band. Picnics took fashionables into fields for tea over a fire, and insects in the sandwiches.

Most town treats were in the open air. Pickering castle yard opened annually, as of old, on Easter Day, with rural sports and a fair in Castlegate. Circuses could bring the village to town. There was booth theatre. Malton Cattle market in 1856 saw 'The castle spectre or the haunted oratory' and a farce 'John from York and Paddy from Cork', the box 1s, pit 6d and gallery 3d. 'Doctor Mark and his little men' appeared at Kirkby Moorside. Malton church bells rang when 'Blink Bonny' won the Derby and the pubs stayed open all night, but the Langton Wold race course was closed in 1861, 'due to a parson', they said, and a landowner planted trees across the best gallop at Hambleton.

The visits of a cloth packman, the spectacles man, the sweep, the tinware tinker, and hawkers of china were events in a village. The high points of street life included foot races, which could break out after a challenge at any time. Some were advertised. This brought out the local champions and there was much gambling. The 'West Heslerton nightingale', Mrs Hesp won by a yard over 'Lilly of the Valley', Mrs Potter in 1855. Boddy raced Atkinson on the Hartoft road in 1858.

'They tell a tale in Bilsdale, where no one ever braggs
About a race from Stokesley show, Twixt Wood and Jackie Naggs
It wasn't for a ladies love, the lads had got more sense
'Twas for two pints of Bilsdale brew. The total cost three pence.'

Village feasts lingered but some were virtually taken over by friendly societies, and even by the temperance movement at Slingsby. On the first Sunday, Monday and Tuesday after July 6th, at Oswaldkirk, 'one who can act the fool best' was chosen 'Lord Mayor' and a man in woman's clothes became mayoress. This was surely a vestige of the mediaeval King of Fools merged with the feast,day and morrow of the local saint. Nunnington feast on August 3rd saw farm and cottage feastings, and traditional gin and water, with spiced cheesecakes at the public house. Duggleby Ball Day was described as 'comely youths, and buxom maids playing their annual ballgames on Shrove Tuesday' in 1894. Schools saw their attendance drop on such annual occasions as the Ness Club Feast, the Nunnington temperance flower show, any missionary meeting, and at all times of harvest. An Appleton farm threshing in 1855 saw twenty boys compete, the winner ending the days of one hundred and eighty mice.

Floral and Horticultural Society shows proliferated and proved enduring. The gentry gave prizes to encourage cottage gardening, with the aim of keeping families off the parish rates. Normanby had its society by 1855, Rosedale not till 1871, but the dalesmen added wrestling in the Cumberland and Lancashire style, greasy pig catching and contests at throwing two stone sacks. One year the Castleton publican and other Danby raiders decamped with the leg of mutton, shaken from the Rosedale greasy pole.

Bilsdale had a hedging and ploughing society. Spaunton Cottage Husbandry Society by 1860 could urge members 'Never let a weed run to seed, for one year's seeding is ten years' weeding'. The Spaunton show always kept a strong farming element, with three hundred horses and cattle on the field one year, besides the tent for flowers, fruit, butter and eggs. W. F. Shepherd of Dowthwaite gave a prize for the best cultivated garden and the cleanest cottage in Hutton le Hole. Miss Darley gave one for cottage botany.

Raising and racing pigeons, rearing fowls and other small animals gave rise to something not always seen at the garden shows. The Pickering Industrial, Poultry, Pigeon, Rabbit, Cat and Dog Show Society could display at one Gala, 200 dogs, 400 pigeons, 200 poultry, 196 rabbits, 30 cats and 1400 needlework entries, representing 'industry' in 1894. Prolific fowl were made famous in the press. Bethel Waind's fowl laid an egg for twenty successive days, then two for two more days.

Music took a great leap forward with choirs and brass bands, then quadrille bands. This brought new entertainments in public halls, including smoking concerts, and the brass bands became an expected feature at every open air event. The Malton Brass Band was joined by the band of the 10th Royal Hussars, when Captain Whelan of Huddersfield ascended in his balloon at the Malton Gala. Dalespeople 'of all classes' heard the Rosedale band in 1878. When the new town clock was declared open at Kirkby Moorside in 1894, the temperance band played 'Oh God our help in ages past'. Brass band competitions drew more widely. The Pickering 1899 brass band contest drew on Kings Cross and Halifax competitors. Mr Moone ran a Helmsley Quadrille band as well as the brass band in the fifties. He made the Bachelors' Ball an annual feature of Helmsley social life. Pianos were rare, but spread slowly to become a selling feature in boarding house advertisements. A gramaphone was heard at Malton in 1899.

Many villages had cricket clubs, forty years before there were football clubs, although Appleton le Street Cricket club played its first game as late as 1887. The newspapers made new heroes from cricketers.

The Maharajah of Nawanagar, popularly known as Ranji, was well known in Ryedale, regularly visiting his old tutor. He scored two centuries in a match against Yorkshire one year, and his season score in 1900 was only beaten by Hammond, Hendren and Sutcliffe. The Earl of Londesborough took county matches to Scarborough, where he had a marine villa, and a Cricket Week, later a festival resulted, in reach of many by rail. Bowls was introduced at Malton in 1883. The new rubber ball brought bounce into other games.

Colonel Chomley in 1860 allowed tenant farmers to shoot rabbits on his land for six weeks a year. Gentry shooting of the moors, late in the century, became grouse driving, the shooters behind rounded hummocks, with a line of drivers rousing first class birds, bred to shoot at. Heather moors were burnt in a controlled way to provide fresh shoots as feed. Several had moor edge shooting lodges, like Bumper Castle in Bilsdale built for the Duke of Rutland.

Changing Minds

The market towns established Mechanics or Literary Institutes which offered small libraries and lectures. Pickering Mechanics institute was formed in 1853 and Helmsley Literary Institute began in 1855 with seventy members 'to reduce the Redan of vice and the Malakoff fortress of ignorance'. The Habton Young Men's Mutual Improvement Society heard Captain Legard on astronomy. The Pickering Glee and Elocution society of 1869 favoured light readings, mixed with songs, like 'Break it Gently to my Mother'.

A parallel movement sought reading rooms for villages. When the Gilling reading room and library opened in 1853, twenty nine enrolled in three classes. The rules decreed that no ladies and no improper books were to be allowed in. A village shepherd could say 'let me look at Dick Cobden', a radical leader of whom he heard something and read nothing. A Castle Howard Itinerating Libraries Scheme served several villages with borrowable books left in safe hands. Helmsley had a Mutual Improvement Society. The first Kirkby Moorside spelling bee was in 1876. At Levisham, Mrs Walker had boys and girls to a Sunday afternoon school to hear bible stories and sing hymns, where 'In summer the young men learnt temperance and manliness in the gardens'. Many saw their first local newspapers in reading rooms.

Local and national newspapers had a richer content with more pages and now came the Daily Mail. Russells the Malton newsagent supplied such magazines as Punch, Titbits, Funny Folks and the English Mechanic. Advertising expanded too and a few grasped its possibilities. H. Ludlow of Kirkby Moorside urged you to remember 'the tonsorial artist, cranial manipulator, capillary abridger and facial operator who could adjust hirsute appendages with ambidextrous dexerity'. Rural conversation always rejoiced in oddities from nature, and rural newspapers stayed close to their clients, reporting much of ordinary life. R. Hardy's Aylesbury duck started laying early in January 1896 at Harum and by late June had laid one hundred and twenty three eggs. This was worthy of remark.

There were several campaigns to change minds, more unified over the whole of the nation, in the railway age. Progress in one area was held up as an example to others. The sixpenny monthly, 'Boys Own Paper' costing sixpence a month could show 'a dunce turned into a donkey'. Handbooks for girls claimed that 'they should chew, champ, bite, bruise and crush their food well before swallowing, should sign the pledge, always wear flannel next to the skin and rise early to bring roses to the cheeks. Tight lacing was 'abominably wicked - remember the Black Hole of Calcutta'.

It was not all good sense. There were always competitors in the field with fashionable enthusiasms, for mesmerism, phrenology or reading personality through bumps on the head, and table moving, the cause of much 'surprise and wonder'. Ghosts survived it all, in many minds, into the new century. R. W. Crosland met believers, who had seen the Hamley Lane ghost bobbing over the road at Appleton le Moor. A nun with flaming mouth lurked on the Cropton Road. Welburn Hall, like many a wainscotted mansion, claimed its ghostly cavalier and a grey lady. There was an excessive proportion of monks, and gentry among the ghosts, but an ethereal sow and a litter of pigs appeared at Wrelton.

National associations employed specialist agents who built up expertise at fostering the aims of their movements. The Bible and Tract societies early in the century and the big Friendly Societies, paved the way for the Primrose League and other political associations towards its end. An Early Closing Association was formed in 1842. Shop assistants at Pickering were said to acquire the 'untiring habit of perpendicularity during an average of twelve hours a day'. The young men at Kirkby Moorside managed to get the shops to close at eight in the evening in 1856. This was no mean thing. The great stress placed by many middling people on 'respectability', replaced old rougher gentry models of behaviour. If something became respectable, it was widely adopted. Most of the popular games were civilised, or made respectable, in the Victorian age by giving them rules, although the sports of the aristocracy were not all tamed.

United in little else, most of the churches stood together behind the powerful temperance movement. In the end, one way or another, this achieved much success. At Malton in 1838, men called Gaff Hook, Irish Sweepcrack and Jacky Mousetrap had broken up a teetotal meeting. The movement to abstain from spirits gave way to the movement to abstain, or at least limit drinking of ale and beer. Cheap tea made these practical propositions. The tea feast began to replace the ale, particularly for women and children. The small village of Brawby had a Prohibitory Liquor Association, as well as a brass band in 1858.

Luttons Ambo had a Band of Hope. Like many elsewhere, they took pledges from those promising to shun the 'demon drink'. The children learnt pledge songs such as 'Father, won't you try' and 'Father, lean on my arm'. The comic temperance drama 'The Trial of John Barley Corn' could always get an audience. The Sherburn Sunday school tea meeting saw a hundred adults take 'the exhilerating beverage'. The children sang 'Ye happy muses, what a delight to see, a social company drinking tea.' It was temperance rather than abstinence that made headway. By the nineties it was recognised that a change in habits was taking place in the countryside, though this had a long way to go.

Great Industries

Joseph Bewick showed Grosmont ironstone, discovered along the line of the Whitby-Pickering railway, at the 1851 Exhibition. The main iron seam had just been discovered further west. Iron working would dominate Cleveland, Eskdale and other moor valleys for many decades. There was work to be had, often for attractive wages. There were forty five mines at work by 1883. Glaisdale and Grosmont for a time sustained blast furnaces. Teeside iron-masters built country mansions and shooting boxes. Labourers drew 2s.6d a day and yet there was talk of their wives being extravagant in their dress, and butchers' carts going round the houses every Saturday.

Within Ryedale, a thick deposit of high yield magnetic iron ore was found at Rosedale in about 1853. Isaac Hartas formed a company with a handful of local and York investors. The ore was taken in wagons

Iron Ore Calcining Kilns at Rosedale

to the Pickering railway sidings, until a mineral line with its own locomotives was made northwards over the crest of the moors in 1861. Stationery engines pulled the ore out of Rosedale, and later Farndale, up inclines, to the moor top railway terminus on the west side of the dale. A moving sight was the delivery of the three boilers for the Rosedale incline in 1860 -

'Who ever beheld so grand a troupe, of horses in a team
As those which worthy Lovell owns, almost as strong as steam.
Equipped as if for battle meant, they dragged with ease along
The massive boilers poised high, the wonder of the throng.
Famed Wrelton cliff, so steep and long, their power could not defy
Well marshalled and well mettled, they would conquer or would die.'

The moor line ran to Ingleby junction, where there was a long incline down into Cleveland. More works were established on the east side of the dale and great calcining kilns were built at Rosedale to reduce the weight and hence the royalties payable, for movement across the moortop estates.

Early extraction of the iron by quarrying, gave way to drifts and shafts, equipped with ventilation fans and winding houses. The quiet valley of Rosedale was transformed. Between 1851 and 1871 the

359

population of the east side rose from 373 to 2041 people, and that of the west side from 175 to 798. Terrace housing was built on scattered sites near the workings, for miners and railway workers. This brought a new kind of community to Blackamore. Good wages attracted miners from near and far. There were railway communities too. By 1861 the west side had forty three railway labourers besides a platelayer and time keepers.

Other neighbouring industries changed. The alum industry ran down as cheaper production methods were adopted elsewhere. Wooden ship building ceased at the ports. Whitby built steamships for a time but more were employed in the new jet manufacture. By 1873 the town had two hundred workshops with fifteen hundred hands, while two hundred miners sought jet inland, as far as Rosedale and Farndale. Changes in the industries of the countryside were less dramatic. A number of tanneries closed about mid century, but the industry was not labour intensive. The Pickering Hungate tannery was up for sale in 1851, a large establishment with a bark mill and some eighty pits and cisterns. Other new industries, for several decades, provided an important element of rural life.

Three branches of the Carter family made farm machinery at Kirkby Moorside, each with their own foundry. Christopher Carter's horse-drawn threshing machines were replacing the flail by 1841 and would later be adapted for steam engines. Sootheran and Carr at Pickering in the fifties made a range of equipment, and sold the Cambridge patent roller for clod crushing. This consisted of wheels with thin cutting edges, rotating on a round spindle. Weighill's Albert Foundry specialised in making grinding mills, rollers and cultivators. Barker of Nawton made the smaller agricultural machinery. Russells of Edstone and Kirkby Moorside would secure the royal appointment for their corn hoe. John Thackray made agricultural implements at Brawby. William Wood produced distinctive ploughs at the Fangdale beck forge.

A Leeds blacksmith started Yate's Malton iron foundry in old barge building sheds. This firm produced horse drawn ploughs, turnip cutters, hoes and seed drills that were bought far afield, using Middlesbrough iron and West Riding coal, brought first by river and later by rail. Croskills of Beverley, better known than most, offered their patent mill for grinding vegetables at twenty five bushels an hour, along with reapers, mowers, binders and rakes. The steam thrashing machine was shown at Sinnington manor farm in 1857. It would replace horse threshers and made the hexagonal gin houses superfluous.

Not all the machinery makers had foundries, but the iron and brass foundries at the market towns, along with Isaac Hartas's foundry at Wrelton and the Providence foundry at Langtoft, helped to make iron into the universal material of the day. It was much like plastic in a later day, used for everything from door stops to drain covers, iron garden railings to pig troughs. Cast iron was very durable. The Wrelton foundry had an eight horse power steam engine and made castings for mines for the Rosedale mines. Weighill's foundry at Pickering Market place, restarted by Albert Dobson the Wrelton smith in 1879, functioned well into the twentieth century, as did Fletcher's Park Street foundry and Henry Carter's Cyclops iron and brass foundry at Tinley Garth, Kirkby Moorside.

One of the greatest changes in many homes was the installation of the iron kitchen ranges, which replaced the open hearth and the brick oven. The coal heated iron ovens spread steadily, in several varieties. The 'Yorkshire range' had an open firebox at front and a damper controlling a flu that linked the firebox to a hot air oven, with hobs and a boiler. The closed range or 'kitchener' had a metal door.

Yorkshire market town gas works came with the railway, usually developed by the Malam brothers, who later sold out to shareholder companies. The gas works at Pickering was developed in a smart architect- designed building, suitable for scientific equipment, next to the railway in 1847. The image of gas making changed and the Pickering Gas and Water company formed in 1876, moved their gas works away south of the town centre, while also opening a water pumping station at the prolific Keld Head springs. Christopher Carter brought gas to Kirkby Moorside in 1859. Norton gained a gas works in 1878. Castle Howard estate had its own steam engine by 1857 to supply fountains and stables, a flax mill and its own gas works at Coneysthorpe. Other estates had similar plants. When James Walker rebuilt Sand Hutton hall in 1885, he installed his own gas plant.

Lines addressed to Mr Christopher Carter of Kirkby Moorside, 29.10.1859

'What useful things you've brought to pass.
Who would have thought of glowing gas
If you had not, I say ?
In church and chapel shining bright.
In every street a welcoming light

A substitute for day.
A perfect master of your trade.
The great gasometer you've made
By mathematics true.
Displays that gravity of thought,
Which engineers in vain have sought,
Intuitive in you.'

Wherever the railway went, quarries and brickworks could prosper. Eyre and Stringer's and Thomas Wood's brickworks at Pickering were two of many. Slingsby and Ganthorpe brickyards produced drainage pipes, 'pantiles', two inch by twelve inch bricks and clay pots in 1869.

John Hart's chair making business stopped when he emigrated from Beadlam, leaving six dozen new armchairs for the stock sale but Porrit's Ryedale saw mills and steam joinery works was formed in 1867 and became the largest maker of pigeon lofts. They met a new demand for small wooden buildings on farms and allotments. Besom making expanded at Stape for suppling to distant industrial workshops, and there was a small factory in Pickering.

Many water mills were rebuilt, with several pairs of stones in buildings up to six storeys high, to make good use of gravity shoots for moving corn and flour. Scampston mill in 1853 had a drilling machine, a lathe, and a portable smith's hearth. Hodgson the Scampston millright and engineer re-opened the Foston mills in 1860, adapted to use both steam and water. Newsham was a steam corn mill by 1855 and there were others. The large Malton Biscuit mill was formed in 1868. J. H. Wise the Malton bone crusher sent steamed and milled bones as fertilizers, all over the Wolds, as well as guano nitrates and super phosphates. A gleaming steam engine, in a plastered room beneath a tall chimney drove a bone crusher for Windle's, near the Pickering railway yard. Kettons steam corn mill was on Potter Hill by 1871. Already the smaller and more remote corn mills began to give way to the roller mills, some sited locally but others were at the ports.

Craftsman's Work

Many of the small craftsmen were employers in the workshops attached to their houses. With their working families, journeymen and apprentices, they made a considerable body of people. Shoemakers were amongst the most numerous, but towns and villages held a wide range of crafts. Birdsall with less than 250 people had blacksmith, shoemaker, joiner and basketmaker in 1840. Rillington with 724 inhabitants could employ three blacksmiths, seven boot and shoemakers, three butchers, four tailor-drapers, and five wheelwrights. Malton had people making chains, clogs, nails, linen, tobacco pipes, boats and three dyers. Kirkby Moorside had people making clogs, candles and machines.

Table 49. Some Market Town Craftsmen in a Directory of 1840			
	Malton	Kirkby Moorside	Pickering
Bakers	9	4	
Basket makers	3	1	
Blacksmiths	5	4	7
Boot & shoemakers	21	20	11
Braziers/tinners	6	3	
Butchers	12	6	
Coopers	5	3	
Curriers	4		2
Glovers	2		
Gunsmiths	2	1	
Hairdressers	9	2	3
Hat makers	3	5	6
Joiners etc	14	10	10
Milliners	13	2	7
Painters	6	2	3
Plumber/glaziers	3	2	4
Roper	4	3	2
Saddlers	6	2	4
Stone/brick	8	6	7
Tailors	15	10	11
Turners	4	1	
Upholsterers	4		
Watchmakers	7	3	4
Whitesmiths	5	3	
Wheelwrights			9

The 1896 day book of Pickering wheelwright Jacob Taylor tells of the work done by James, Jim and William Taylor. Some was done in the shop and some out at the farms and gentry houses. The work was skilled and diverse. There was timber felling, three days in February, and then leading it back with hired horses for sawing and dressing the wood. Much of what was done was joinery, but they were wheelwrights and cartwrights too. They hung a foldyard door at Kingthorpe farm and put in two new house doors. Miss Ansell's school needed a form, a new school table and a bay window repaired. The craftsmen made a coffin, a letterbox, axe shafts, naves, a wash tub, water closets, a cover to put over a lame pig and even a summer house. They repaired floors, cucumber frames, corn drills, hay rake teeth and garden rakes. The cart wright work was as varied. William went to Leeds to see a basket cart and then made one. Fletcher's butchers cart was mended, though the shafts were fractured and the axle tree had to be set straight. They made wheelbarrows, navvie barrows, road barrows and repaired the station cab from the White Swan, a blacksmith cart, the vicar's dog cart and some waggonettes, a shooting cart and a water wagon. Then there was the office work - confined to 'writing up bills'.

A new craft called photography burst upon the towns in the early railway years. Kaim and Goulldier opened a photographic and daguerreotype portrait gallery near the Primitive chapel at the back of Malton's Finkle street in 1855. Likenesses were offered daily, nine till four, whatever the weather, with prices two shillings and sixpence to fifteen shillings. The station itself welcomed a new 'chorographic portrait gallery', open eight till six, where Mr Gutenberg claimed a fixing process to make pictures as durable as marble. Mr Bankes in Finkle Street offered colloidotype portraits, beautfully tinted likenesses. Esha's Grand Photographic Gallery tackled buildings, landscapes, animals and made ivory miniatures, prices four shillings to ten guineas. Mr. Boak, fresh from King's College London, called three days a week from Driffield to Pickering, to take carte de visite photographs. He would finish in oil, crayon or water colours. A shop window at Boak the printers in 1864 showed a splendid picture of twelve young men and the Reverend Worsnop of the Primitive Methodist Young Men's Christian Association. Thomas Boxell moved from a site near the station to Potter Hill in 1875, offering portraits for sixpence.

Domestic Service

The main alternative for women to work in the field was

domestic service. This assumed abilities at a multitude of tasks. Miss Richardson at Kirkby Moorside kept written house rules for a domestic servant.

'Rise at 5.30 in Summer and 6.30 in Winter.

First, look after the dairy and see the calves fed. Within one and a half hours get the breakfast on the utensils with the utensils put away straight after use.

For Monday as soon as possible after breakfast make a pie or pudding for the men, setting it in the oven at the proper time to be ready at twelve precisely. Spend the morning washing the sitting room, allowing a few minutes to tidy your self against dinner.

On Tuesday and Friday mornings bake bread. Make a large bowl of bread first thing. Leave it while the clothes are folded for the iron and the copper made ready for dinner. While the first bowl is in the oven, prepare another. Make the dinner for the men. Tidy the sitting room and yourself with all ready on the table precisely at twelve. Any spare time to be spent making repairs what is wanting in your own clothes. Ironing begins immediately after the dinner is cleared.

Wednesday morning as soon as breakfast is over, make a large bowl of stiff pastrie for standing pies. Despatch these as quick as you can. The time they are baking make a pie and pudding for the men or anything else that may be wanted. Sitting room and self tidy against dinner to be on the table at 12 o clock. Mend the clothes and stockings that have been at the wash. See the cream in the churn.'

And so it went on. Saturday brought more pie making and hanging clothes in the air. On Sunday morning, she was to tidy the sitting room, prepare dinner and make the boys ready for church. That was the mornings. One lady recalled going into service with Mr Kneeshaw a jeweller in Pickering, a kind man, but his wife gave her 'several whackings as well as her £2 a year'.

Farming Change

Machinery would eventually replace much farm labour,

including children's work, but the change was long delayed. Increased yields for a long time meant increased labour. The numbers of horses on farms continued to rise and the number of workers in busy seasons stayed high. Hirings became massive occasions in the railway era, with crowds at Kirkby Moorside, Helmsley, Malton and Pickering, Seamer and Sherburn. They were popularly known as 'mops' or 'sittings'. The 1856 Sherburn hirings were thin due to migration, but Malton hirings in 1857 were busy, described as the 'mop fair for the deserted Wolds'. Critics complained of young people herded and handled like cattle, and once hired, open to the 'miserable enticements of penny theatres and the alehouse'. It was claimed in1867 that ten thousand men and three thousand five hundred women were at Malton hirings. Farm lads asked each other the key questions 'Was it a good bait house?' and 'what are their horses like?'

The Ryedale Show formed in 1855 was alternated between Kirkby, Helmsley and Pickering. The shows did much to encourage a spirit of competition among farmers, particularly for stock. The Yedingham and District Agricultural society held their seventh annual show in 1861. There were several others. At the country shows, many new breeds were seen, as cattle were more easily travelled. New tools and machinery were demonstrated. The equipment on gentry and large tenant farms did grow, but long exceeded that available elsewhere. Wharram Grange farm by 1854 had a machine fan, blowing machine, weighing machine, horse roller, straw cutter, turnip cutter and an oil cake crusher. Captain Legard at Potter Brompton in 1860 had twelve ploughs, one for paring and one with iron wheels, and he had three different drills. Thomas Hoggard Hall, a man proud of his descent from Captain Cook, took the first reaper, to Lockton, not a self binder, just a little horse reaper with women tying sheaves behind it.

A Thorpe Basset farm had a thrashing machine, with mill and straw cutter fixed and a ten row corn drill. Machinery became more widely known, but adoption came very slowly, after demonstrations on the smaller farms. Threshing machine owners hired out their machines. A steam thrasher was used at Hovingham in 1855, the farmer killing three hundred and three rats from a single stack. Large numbers of gentry and farmers attended the trial of a two horse grass cutter brought from Banbury in 1863. When Fowlers of Leeds demonstrated a 'steam drag' at Thornton Dale, the newspaper reported that this 'amazed the rustics gathered around'.

Much effort was put into ploughing out the old ridges and furrow of open field, although a great deal remains evident enough. In dairy districts, a hot Summer parched the ridge, while the furrow by winter was rich in the wrong grasses. They could be lessened by ploughing alternate ridges. After the repeal of the Corn Laws in 1845, government drainage grants were introduced to begin a long process of land regeneration. Rye and Derwent drainage schemes were launched that year. By 1880 much land throughout the district had been under-drained with tile pipes or the cheaper stone gulleys. The payments of tithes in kind was steadily replaced by carefully calculated rent charges, fixed in relation to recent corn prices. The rent charges eventually declined in value and were progressively bought out in the next century.

Slater's of Malton by 1854 issued seed catalogues and lists. The use of artificial manures spread with the railway, including superphosphate of lime and ammonia. Cleething and Bell of Yorkersgate, Malton were sole agents for London superphosphate in 1855. By 1865, Sidgewick and Leefe at Hovingham could supply Peruvian guano and soda nitrate while Peacocks at Catter Bridge stored phosphates and crushed bone. At Thornton Risebrough, Mr Smith re drained and then tried liquid manure as a fertilizer, with a large tank and water carts constantly leading it to spread over grassland. Oil cake came regularly from Sinnington mill. The Yorkshire Patent Manure Drill and Agricultural Implement Company at Kirkby Moorside claimed the most perfect artificial manure drills ever invented in 1898.

The great ram show farms included Fairfield near Skelton, originally built to breed race horses, and Lund court near Kirkby Moorside. Duncombe Park held the famous Feversham herd of shorthorns with annual catalogue sales. Sir George Cholmley, Sir Tatton Sykes and other landowners were noted breeders, but many of the new prosperous tenant farmers were cattle men. Sam Wiley's pure bred short horns and his Leicester herd were famous on the five hundred acre Brandsby Warren House farm. He hired pedigree bulls including some from the pioneering Collings breed and Bakewell tups for his sheep. Even his white pigs, known as 'Wileys' were notorious. His bean crop achieved by wide drilling was said to be a sight worth seeing. Manufactured linseed oil cattle cake was widely used. The building of cow houses to reduce the loss of condition from wintering out brought in ashphalt damp courses, new gutterings, and stalls. Weight was the principal goal. Brawby's White Swan announced that Mr. Cammidge had fed his sixteen month old pig to a weight of forty four stone. Large numbers of fine fat cattle were sold to Kirkby butchers, who found a large trade with the Rosedale miners.

The Palm Sunday horse show at Malton saw stables visited for a week before the day. The influx of dealers included foreign buyers, looking for half bred horses, combining blood and vigour, as well as chargers for the armies. The British army buyers from Woolwich Arsenal sought horses suitable for pulling artillery. Hunters, carriage and cart horses, and other horses for riding, were all bred for the purpose. Powerful horses were bought to pull the brewer's drays and London and Manchester sent for cab horses. Great numbers went annually for export. F. H. Sterricker of Westgate house, Pickering made Cleveland Bays internationally known, sending many to America. In 1899, he received the highest price ever paid for a two year old coaching stallion sold to the King of Italy, and proudly mounted the royal coat of arms on his house. Pickering and Malton for some years held annual parades of entire horses.

A watercress farm was begun at Keld Head about 1880 by Mr Hainsworth. The cress thrived in the lime rich soil, in great rectangular green beds, hand harvested and selling about 20.000 boxes a year with twenty bunches in a box, despatched by rail to distant cities.

New trading arrangements were pioneered in these years. A Brandsby Agricultural Club began to buy milk from farmers in 1894, converting it to butter or cream, and selling back the whey as livestock feed. This was a farmer's co-operative with profit divided according to the quantity of milk sent to the dairy. By 1909 the Brandsby Agricultural Trading Association, BATA Ltd. was also curing pigs and selling hams as far south as London.

Churches of England

The 1851 Religious Census showed that the Church of England had already lost much of its connection with the poorer majority. Churchwardens struggled to keep up village churches and would be blamed for cheese paring economies, by the late Victorian romantics, who sought buildings mediaeval in spirit. Mocked as 'the

Tory party at prayer', the church enjoyed a strong alliance with aristocracy, and with growing respectability, was able to win over many middle class people, and those who served them or aspired to be like them. In an incredible new movement, country gentry and their ladies poured money into rebuilding and decorating the rural parish churches, some of which seem to have been little used. Their stained glass memorials filled the windows. Almost every Anglican church in the district was elaborately restored between 1860 and 1890, some twice. New vicarages were often vastly built for gentry sons, who had 'taken the cloth'. The twenty seven room rectory at Kirkby Misperton had more far relevance to the needs of its genteel occupant than those of the parish he served.

And yet, the Church of England renewed itself, again and again. Since the vicar enjoyed a freehold and was difficult to unseat, parishes had local histories as variable as their ministers. Each minister meant a fresh start. The church often responded to a local challenge. The establishment of a Wesyelyan School at Pickering brought an Anglican School into existence within the year. The Primitive Methodists missioned Marton near Pickering and in 1852 opened a small chapel, with services, tea meetings and people saved. An Anglican mission room was licenced the next year. There were high and low churches, the one favouring services that veered towards Catholicism, the other more evangelical. In one, you saw the 'stations of the cross' and smelt incense. In the other the Commandments board provided bleak decoration, and a black letter instruction, as to what you should and should not do.

The church did have great rural reformers. Charles Norris Gray, vicar of Helmsley started in 1870, with a mere thirty five communicants, but once again established Sunday Schools, a tract society, three services a day with large congregations, a parish magazine, soup kitchens, choral services, a rebuilt church and several new outlying chapels. He was not beyond taking on his patron, the Earl of Feversham, when he thought action was needed and he urged early closing on unwilling shopkeepers.

Church music saw some change with small orchestras supplied by whatever local talent was available. Ebberston had a band of cellos, violins played by two men from Snainton, clarinet, flutes and on a few special occasions a cornet. The land agent who sat in the squire's pew thought them 'operatic'. The introduction of new organs and choirs later in the century brought better music and sometimes more participation for congregations. Down-town missions had a hard struggle to muster support, despite some success with 'muscular Christianity' and church football clubs in the eighties. Newbridge quarry near Pickering and the navvies building the Burdale tunnel each had their own mission.

Methodists and Others

Methodist congregations grew steadily in number and influence. Many a small village had two Methodist chapels. Wesleyan chapels built in the first quarter of the century were rebuilt in the sixties and seventies. Primitive chapels spread widely in the same period, plain buildings within which a full social life was available for members. The chapel services had great gusto, reinforced from time to time by big circuit open air, camp meetings. The Primitive Methodists developed the Elmfield College at Heworth to train their ministers, but the ministers only stayed local for a year or two, so that much strength remained with the active laymen. Many dependable officers emerged who ran circuits, societies and classes, which offered activities every evening and weekend.

There were revivals; Wesleyan and Primitive, some in the 1858-68 period which affected all denominations, bringing in a generation of laymen who would remain important for decades. Joe Hesp of Pickering would kneel down and pray with anyone found washing their steps on a Sunday morning. Methodism warmed slowly to better music. Potter Hill Primitive Chapel was long satisfied with Joe Hesp's box of whistles, rising to a harmonium with a one tune book and no music. Before the Moody and Sanky hymns became popular, they used no anthems and sang a few chants. No-one could read music, until a minister started a 'tonic - sol- fa -class.'

The open air tradition was sustained. The Kirkby Moorside Primitive Sunday School in 1859, on Good Friday, marched the streets and at intervals formed a ring to sing a hymn. Ninety scholars had tea. Cropton was remembered as a 'mighty cause' with open air love feasts on August bank holiday Sunday afternoon, later in the century. Come the evening, the congregation and preachers marched happily down the village singing rousing hymns. Sheriff Hutton love feasts until the turn of the century were mainly member's testimonies, followed by sponge fingers and water. The Rosedale

370

The Methodist Chapel at Marton

Primitive Choir in 1894 gave a service of song entitled 'Kitty and Joe at the Hartoft chapel'. Sober-sides hearing a Primitive congregation singing about 'Zachie' and the Lord 'coming to his house for tea' were apt to be sore amazed and a little shocked.

The Independant or Congregational churches revived at the four market towns. With more democracy than others, they gained a strong middle class support. Nationally they were something of an elite. Locally they were strong voices, if given to schisms. Things could get rough. J.Foster wrote 'We had a row on Thursday night at the chapel gates. They didn't get in. One fellow got his head hit with a stick by Tom Yearsley. A rough one. Our side, seeing that done, went up and struck Tom over his eyes, blocking one up, which soon quitted him. John Riddle got desperately handled and the Wilkinson roughs tried several times to beck G.Fletcher, but were hindered by the large lot of quarrymen, masons & c on our side who protected George first rate. We got the victory that night'. The opposition broke in again the next day. Street missioning was renewed at the towns late in the century, by the Salvation Army.

Taken together, the many strands of Victorian nonconformity were immensely influential, mostly standing for improvement and reform, close to liberalism and favouring education and social progress. They spoke of 'the Nonconformist Conscience'. And there was religion. The Yorkshire evangelist Thomas Langton about 1886 was praised in verse

'He hails from Malton full of fire,
A John Bull, plainly spoken
And all those who hear him, oft enquire,
The way to joys unspoken.'

Local Government

A Lockton man was charged with sheep stealing and transported in 1814. A Scampston man was sent to Australia, the next year, for stealing a bushel of wheat. A law of 1816 stated that any man caught with nets at night was liable to seven years transportation. This practice of deporting serious offenders to empty countries was too easy a solution. Parish constables had served well enough at keeping some order when life was more local, though the magistrates for a couple of centuries had appointed Captain Constables to combine their efforts. Many villages had their 'hoppit', a hole in the wall or a cellar, in which to throw the town drunk over night. Something more seemed to be required in more populous and more mobile times. Now pickpockets arrived at country fairs and markets by rail and were gone again in a short space.

Associations for the Prosecution of Felons were formed to protect property. The Kirkby Moorside Association recruited thirty eight members in 1817. The Black Face Sheep Breeders Association of 1820 was particularly concerned with sheep stealing from the moors .A wider association formed for Ryedale in 1841 wanted to pursue felonies of all kinds, whether acts against persons or property. A Cleveland Association formed in 1839 with a large membership, employed two police officers with horse pistols stationed at Stokesley and Guisborough but it was dissolved in 1842. A Malton Association was formed in 1843 and a York Association formed by Leonard Thompson, the squire of Sheriff Hutton, covered Buttercrambe. None of the associations seemed to last very long. Some of the most serious offences were committed in shooting affrays between gamekeepers and poachers.

A County Police Act in 1839 authorised the formation of paid police forces and a North Riding constabulary was eventually formed in 1841 with fifty men. The numbers were very small to cope with large country areas. Kirkby Moorside gained a new prison and constables' residence at Tinley garth in 1851. A new Malton lockup was opened in 1853 and a Great Edstone constable bought handcuffs in 1856. Pickering built a police station with lock up and justice room around 1863. Willaim Robinson was made Superintendant constable in 1857 with three men, one for Malton, one for Slingsby, and one for Welburn. In the East Riding Norton police were re organised in 1857 with Norton as head quarters for the north east Wolds or Buckrose district. John Consit at Norton had six men, at Weaverthorpe, North Grimston, Rillington, Westow, Sherburn and Sledmere. Young men of five feet eight inches or more height were sought as constables, with pay at eighteen shillings a week and serjeants twenty one shillings. The Superintendant had a horse and cart. Some parish constables lingered till much later in the century.

The principal punishment was hard labour. William Beck was sent for four years penal servitude for the theft of a pair of boots at Malton in 1851. Fowl stealing at Stittenham was more modestly judged that year, when six vagrants slept in Hornseys barn and took twelve fowl, rewarded with two months hard labour. Public demand wanted more. Corner loungers at Pickering assailed departing churchgoers with obscene language and sods from the graves in 1856. There were the letters 'Can't the police do more'. The constabulary made efforts to take offenders 'in the act', despite their small numbers. The Gaming Act of 1845 had made wagering agreements void, but that was for the rich who could go to court to try to enforce them. P.C. Snowden built an elevated observatory on Caulkless Hill from which he spied gamblers in a secluded part of Hovingham and he was able to arrest six. Nor was the attempt to reform young offenders lacking. The Castle Howard Reformatory for the reform of North and East Riding juvenile offenders was opened in 1855. The attempt to reform eighty inmates at any one time was attempted, by a regimen centred on spade husbandry, and it was kept going for over a hundred years.

The Great Town Clean Up and the Birth of Local Government

Malton and Helmsley were estate towns, with a dominant landowner, but at Malton the owner was an absentee, represented by his estate agent. They said that the Earl of Feversham owned all but three of the Helmsley houses in 1881. Kirkby Moorside had been an estate town but since the 17th century at least, had a dozen significant freeholds. The Earls of Feversham acquired the estate and continually bought in properties, but the family never counted for as much there as at Helmsley. Pickering with hundreds of freeholds never liked squires and vigorously resisted the attempts of the outstanding families to play the role.

Inevitably, it was the new local government bodies not the estate owners, who carried through early public health reforms in the towns. The market towns, together with Norton and Rillington, established Boards of Health which offered the first significant elements of local government outside the faded manor courts. The estates were influential on the Boards and sometimes dominated them.

Malton had cholera deaths in undrained houses in 1831, 1849 and 1853. The Malton Bye Laws of 1855 firmly interfered in people's lives in the interest of public health. Occupiers of tenements were required to white wash, or other wise keep clean all the interiors. No offensive smell was to come from them. They were to clean, or sweep footpaths, and channels in front of a house before nine daily, whenever notice was given by the Inspector of Nuisances or the Town Crier. The deposit of refuse in the streets was banned, except for building materials. Specifically prohibited were fish offal, ordure, dead animals, blood, bones, manure, glass, china, dust, ashes, slops, orange peel, carrion, tar and dirty water. A drainage scheme for the town was begun in 1856 by the Board of Health and the main drain was put down Castlegate in 1865.

Pickering Board of Health was formed after several town meetings on August 11th 1863. Under the powers of the Local Government Act, it could levy a rate on properties. Thomas Mitchelson was elected to the chair and his members listed like a roll call of the local gentlemen. They met in the Savings Bank room and with some advice from Malton settled on a procedure. Officers were a Clerk, a Treasurer, a Highway Surveyor and the Inspector of Nuisances. Enquiries from central government received tardy replies or none at all. In the year 1875 the Board spent £274 of which £133 was for salaries, £75 for lighting public lamps and smaller amounts on public pumps, the clock and a fire engine but many nuisances were dealt with, by order, rather than expenditure.

The Helmsley Nuisance Removal committee was active in 1856 laying drains. With the co-operation of the new Earl of Feversham, two years later, they had the market place drained, some slum buildings removed and the beck partially arched over. An estate survey of 1868 found that 256 Helmsley houses included 66 that were thatched, 156 tiled, 34 slated. Much of the tiling was old but of the thatched houses 29 were old, 13 bad and 3 both old and bad. The seventies brought an enthusiasm for running water in lead or cast iron pipes but open gutters had yet to give way to pipe sanitation.

Norton Board of Health was a vigorous body which levied separate highways and lighting rates. There was no dominant estate here. The members had to approve plans for many new building layouts with drains as the village expanded into a town. John Wise a small land owner, opening a stone quarry on Langton road was promptly told to fill it up.

A better Helmsley drainage scheme was installed in 1895 after the existing scheme had been indited for its failures. Locals remembered the last time when the 'Vardy Wardens' stopped annually inspecting the drains in 1899. Vardey may be short for 'view day'. Each house had to put out two buckets of water at the drain grate. The wardens poured it down. If it cleared that was good. Suspect chimneys were apt to have an armful of straw fired in them.

Drainage improvements never completely resolved the flood disasters which wasted some of the lowland from time to time. During November 1878 as the floods receded, the railway was stopped from Rillington westwards. At Malton, the Board of Health dray and a small army of cabs plied around town in the shallower waters but Norton and low town held a network of planks on bricks. The foundations of the old Malton vicarage were sapped. Springs bubbled up in tavern cellars. The Waterworks stopped and a water cart went round. A pig arrived by water at one house so they sent for the butcher. Mr. Hickes at Cawton lost sixty sheep. Brawby and Salton were deeply immersed. People were living upstairs, relieved by Vicar Abbey on horseback,and Captain Scoby in a boat.

Cleanliness is next to Godliness

Excessive claims for soap were already familiar. 'Harper's Twelve Trees' soap powder advertised in the Malton Messenger in

1860 was supposed to bring the great domestic revolution. This offered laundresses, 'clothes washing without rubbing'. There was no need to retain the old barbarous disgusting process. 'This powder would save time, trouble, money, firing, soap, tongue and temper and entirely abolish the female slavery of the tub'. All you need do was boil for twenty minutes and hang them up to dry. A penny packet was equal to two pounds of soap. Advertising had come of age.

Martin Dodsworth in 1860 offered his patent elastic washing machine and churn at £2.12.6 . This was a variation on a theme, widely used by several inventors. Sootheran and Carr at Pickering offered the much admired patent wrangling and wringing machine from Tindall's of Scarborough. Some wit observed that-

'My Kate, she was a bonny wife.
There's none more free from evil.
But, until now on washing days,
She was the very devil.
But now the kittens on the hearth,
In fun and sport do play
When they did jump with many a thump,
All on a washing day.'

Other older methods of washing clothes were more generally used. The static bucking tub was a deep round half barrel, where the water was poured through layered linen. The 'dolly tub and peg' with its fibre legged stool was a far cheaper innovation. This beat dirt out by driving the water round against the wall of a corrugated tub. The fancier copper bottomed 'posser' pumped and sucked the water. Hot water was a problem. A copper could take half an hour to heat. Water from Kirkby beck had to stand overnight after storms. They boiled clothes in a copper, then scrubbed them, then put them in the peggy tub. The boys would use a mangle to get much of the water out.

The Countess of Carlisle offered £400 towards a water supply scheme for Slingsby in 1894. After the 1898 typhoid scare, there began the conversion of privies to closets. A Kirkby Mills boy later remembered that one day a week the street was filled with the contents of ash pits and toilets for farm wagons to take for compost. There were no toilets and no running water. John Read the Malton plumber would install flush toilets for those who could afford them. Thus began another change in thinking. Helmsley had sanitary, laundry and dress making classes in 1892 where they said that 'Cleanliness was next to Godliness'. Good soap and tin bath tubs were great innovations. A Pickering household eagerly awaited delivery of a carpet sweeper in 1898.

The New Shopping

The market town shops brought the products of the industrial and railway age. In the larger shops, grocery separated out from drapery. William Snow at Butcher Corner in Malton by 1860 was one of the better known, well placed stores. His Christmas offers of cheap drapery included mantles, jackets, shawls, dresses, and some black quilted skirts at 5s.6d each. He sold the stuffs as well, in great bolts and the ribbons by 1860, that might make something ordinary look brighter. Dress making and millinery were major employments for women. Hopper and Searle the grocers in Christmas 1872 had Whitby gingerbread and Stilton cheese. Sewell and Conning in Yorkersgate sold French plums, muscatell raisins, Melton Mowbray pies and fancy candles.

Specialists in the town of Malton included Spiegelhalters in Yorkersgate where members of the family since 1820 had supplied spectacles throughout Ryedale, and now made watches and sold jewellery. The grandmother and grandfather clocks, locally assembled, with brass and cheaper painted faces soon gave way to cheap mass-produced German and American clocks. Leefe had a fancy repository with workboxes, tea caddies, watch and ink stands and the new electro-plate goods. W. G Fromm offered almanacs and a photographic souvenir of the Cropton murders. A sewing machine at Taylors cost four guineas.

Crawford's at Pickering had American organs and harmoniums, melodeons, thimbles and pewter tea sets available on the 'easy payment system' by 1897. English the chemist sold a celebrated sheep dip of his own manufacture and really good teeth for half a crown. Pape's tic mixture was good for face ache at 1s.6d a bottle. Fentress's supply stores had everything in hardware, trunks, bonnet boxes, wringing machines, fire irons and bedsteads. Coopers the ironmongers sold cycles, lawn mowers, straw mattresses and prams.

The Village Shop, Lastingham

Once a village shop was opened, there was every pressure for it to trade in as wide a variety of products as possible. Anything offered was cheaper by the cost of going to town or paying the carrier. Many stores began after mid century. The railway brought the commercial gentleman or traveller pushing new wares. Some town shops took on the wholesalers' role. Only a few commodities were yet in the small packets and tins which stacked high would later fill the windows. The shop keeper's main activity was breaking down bulk into saleable portions, offered in whisps of paper or vessels taken to the shop. Matthew Simpson at Nunnington was more tailor than draper but by 1863 he was well aware of fashion, offering the Chesterfield, Cambridge jackets and poncho capes.

The grocer learned to have cotton bags for flour, jars for treacle, tins for soap and triangles of blue and red paper. The butter and lard stood in barrels, the tea in sheet iron tins, treacle in square tanks, sugar in wood casks and much more in open sacks. The village shop would be well remembered for its counters, shelves, the floor and the rear living quarters stacked high with baskets, sacks and boxes. The whole merged in a distinctive and memorable odour. Here was a social centre, almost a newsroom and in hard times perhaps a fount of credit. Mrs Goodwill the Sinnington postmistress and shop keeper was sufficiently valued to be presented with a purse of gold and a timepiece by her customers in 1892.

Clarkes at Thornton dale in 1861 sold Malton Derwent biscuits, hams, bacon, lard, Cheshire and Cleveland cheeses, gunpowder and gun wadding. There were onion, carrot and radish seeds, 'warranted to grow', and Tigar's manures. Rillington shops were recalled in reminiscence. There was Temple the grocer, who also sold organs hung from the ceiling. William Bradley, who had started with a basket, was grocer, draper and post office. He sold shoes and was agent for Bibby cattle feed. You took a jar to get to get some treacle from his casks and if it ran over, you shovelled it up. There were big boxes filling a room with Bryant and May's matches, and bags of butter and eggs which he took up into the Wolds. Hodgson's shop showed advertisements for Colman's starch and mustard. His ceiling was hung with salted pigs bought from the cottagers, and the front of the house was always full of cattle cake.

Advertisers

The retail shop that broke bulk was not to last for ever. The packaged goods would win in the end, but it was a long process. The railway started the change, bringing both branded products and regional specialities in greater quantity than ever before. The grocer's shop at Newbiggin Malton in 1859 had Carr's and Reckitts biscuits and the new Scotch marmalade. Thomas Hudson the Greengate druggist and spirit merchant had London gin, Jamaica rum and Taylor's liquid for the toothache at a shilling a bottle. Hoppers in Commercial Street, Norton sold local gingerbread at 3s a pound and Derby cheese at 8d. Bellerby at Pickering and Longbotham at Malton sold Horniman's tea.

As national manufacturers and wholesalers grew, the dignified award of a local agency for the smaller items of grocery and patent medicines, gave way to the scramble for trade. In the first edition of the 'Malton and Norton Gazette and General Advertiser' in 1855, Arkwright Brothers of London 'begged respectfully to inform the inhabitants of Malton and its vicinity that they had appointed Johnson Brothers, wholesale and retail tea dealers, sole agents for the sale of their fine Arabian Mountain Berry coffee'. By 1868 as tea duties were reduced, and a fall of sixpence in the pound widened the potential market, Dawson at Gilling, Hartley and Bartliff at Malton and a Pickering book seller had branded tea and Ellerby's the distributors advertised, inviting new agencies.

Not all grocers carried tea in the early years. It needed the fast tea clippers and the new plantations opened in Java and Ceylon as rivals to Assam and India to make tea cheaper in the sixties but it was the advent of Mazawattee in 1884 and Sir Thomas Lipton's drive to get Ceylon tea 'to the masses', that by 1900 had six pounds a person, of the 'cup that cheers but not inebriates', being consumed every year. Tea was susceptible to faking and adulteration and suppliers advertised to claim their product was free and uncoloured. The grocers opened the tea chests, and sold the tea in paper twists, but Hornimans even in the fifties was obtainable in packets. Ellerbys offered packeted coffee, distinguishing breakfast congou at 2s.10d a pound from lapsang souchong at 3s.3d and No 1 and No 2 coffees at 2s.4d and 2s.8d. Taylor's at Malton, Moor the Hovingham draper, Strickland at Kirkby and draper Betts at Helmsley sold the coffee from bulk at 1s and 1s.8d.

A machine for 'impregnating water with fixed air' had been displayed at Petergate York in 1777. Schweppes waters were on sale there by 1809 and by 1838 could be had at Horsley's chemist shop at Malton. The development of *fizzy pop* saw air cylinders and pipes installed in market place backyards. John Swain at Pickering and Tate Smith at Malton were among those who pioneered 'aerated waters', the 'pop' that was so popular with the young and had the full support of the temperance and abstinence movements in the eighties. The public analyst was engaged to swear that the drink was pure and wholesome.

Other shops long kept other back yard manufactories. The Nawton stores as late as 1895 had Lipton's and Brooke Bond packet teas, but they cured their own hams and sides of bacon. The shop keeper rendered down lard to offer it in seven, fourteen and twenty eight pound zinc buckets. He made his own baking powder. His advertisement read – 'anything you want, cheap'. What he didn't have, you could get from Harriet Jackson, Nawton's ironmonger and hardware dealer.

The Tailor's Workshop

Arnold Leadley was apprenticed to a Helmsley tailor who employed eight men. They marvelled when the first sewing machine arrived. Only the master was allowed to use it. The apprentice ran errands, lit the fire, learnt to make button holes and to sew on bits. At Kirkby Moorside, the master tailor usually did the measuring and cutting out. Master and men sat cross legged, working from six in the morning till eight at night in Summer, and seven to seven in winter, using gas light when day light faded. They had short breakfast, dinner and tea breaks and only worked till five on Saturday afternoon. After five years, an apprentice could make anything, although jackets and breeches were thought of as specialist work. All tools were supplied but you had your own scissors. There was much to learn, 'how to use boxcloth for leggings, felted till it was an inch thick, water proof and strong as leather'. In this workshop, they didn't favour employing travelling tailors, the famous 'knights of the needle', saying that they drank, took Sunday and Tailor's Monday' off, and that they were always talking, telling stories.

For the clothing shops, it was the distant sewing machine with its 'ready mades' that would change it all. Already in the 1850's, draper John Atkinson at Church Street, Helmsley claimed to supply the 'fashionable' goods in ladies mantles, shawls, furs and gloves. Miss Carr annually visited London about 1863 to bring the latest shapes to her bonnets. Woods at Malton and Pickering had the 'Spring prints'. Towards the end of the century, Hawsons at Pickering still had the cloths in great bolts, rough and ready serges, forty five inches wide at 8d. a yard, habit cloth forty two inches wide at a shilling a yard, but the showroom was stocked with the leading lines of the season. Careful buying of what might sell had to take account of minor fashion changes. Ready made shirts were offered from 7s.6d, with corsets, millinery and furs. Hawson opened a new 'bespoke' department at Pickering towards the end of the century. The Leeds Clothing Warehouse was a branch establishment with overcoats, suits for men and boys, and always a good supply of odd garments, hats and caps. Sootherans at Malton in 1854 had advertised 'strong working clothing for the industrious man but nothing for the idle and lazy'. Hawsons by the nineties called themselves 'the people's clothiers'.

New Local Government

Elected County Councils were formed in 1888 and took over much of the administrative role, long exercised by magistrates. It was a long time before the elections produced any candidates from a different layer of society. Local government responsibilities were expanded, along with powers to raise rate incomes and became subject to the supervision of inspectors and auditors appointed by national government. Where government grants were made, direction of policy came from the centre. This was particularly important in education where an inspectorate worked to raise standards. Urban and Rural District councils were formed in 1894 and slowly gained both powers and rate income.

Parliamentary seats began to be contested by candidates of different persuasion, and with a secret ballot, Conservative and Liberal Associations were formed in the eighties to get the vote out and to disqualify as many opposing voters as possible. Broadly speaking, Methodism and Liberalism were linked, the Church of England and Conservatism. The sentiments spread to the local elections, held every few years. When Pickering's John Calvert discovered that the Board of Health, comprising eight conservatives and one liberal, was to be replaced by a new Urban District Council, he canvassed for more candidates and had three more liberals elected.

A rise in civic consciousness, combined with central government pressure, to put baths, wash houses, slaughter houses, street lighting, libraries, burial grounds, and education on the public agendas, as well as highways and drains. There was much keen discussion, but lack of rate income and unwillingness to raise it, regularly inhibited action. Helmsley District Council brought in a five minute rule after two reverend members were found to talk endlessly. Another member commented that 'they only worked one day a week.'

Parish Councils and meetings were also established, though with very few powers. The new parish meeting set up in Stonegrave old schoolroom in 1894 elected the Reverend Pitman to the chair. The overseer Thomas Stamper remarked that 'this being an important event in the local government of England' they should all record their names. There followed talk of the bad taste of the polluted church yard well. James Jefferson said 'he didn't like it at first but he had got used to it.' A year later, it was condemned by the public analyst.

Education

Private educational academies became numerous, as the middle class expanded. The old Grammar schools became very like them, as the value of their endowments shrank and masters took on paying pupils to make the income up. The old Pickering Grammar School was advertised in 1864 for young gentlemen to learn the classics, mathematics, Hebrew and French. Robert Merry Owston attended and learnt by rote, the 'proofs of mercy in one hundred and twenty biblical passages', as well as the 'compositions of gases'. He later applied what he learnt with practical effect enough, as a much respected man. Thomas Goldie a pupil at Malton Mount Academy in 1888 tackled Euclid, translation of Greek into English, the square on the hypotenuse, the causes of the war of the Austrian Succession and '238.7 multiplied by 14.1'.

Many new schools were built during Queen Victoria's reign, usually with a church leaning. The Methodist School founded in 1856 at Pickering was challenged by an Anglican National Society school formed in 1857. Slingsby gained its National school with teacher's house attached in 1860. The Helmsley Methodist Day school grew out of the Sunday School and had 70 pupils in 1890. There was a rush of new school building in the seventies and eighties, despite the widespread belief that work done in life was not helped by what the school could teach. Work and school were different worlds and the purposes of the one were not clearly related to the other. The proportion of the lower age groups attending some kind of school became quite high.

Teachers struggled to meet the requirements of Government inspectors, and so to retain the government grants that became available. They faced a changing body of pupils, of a broad range of ages, often over crowded into a single class. There were great problems in achieving discipline, obedience and even cleanliness, let alone the literacy, some numeracy and the general knowledge that resulted. Some of it was child minding. Some was the struggle for a manageable classroom situation, in which anything educational could happen at all. The Thornton Dale school log book in 1863 recorded that several boys had contracted the habit of smoking - so the master took their pipes from them. Scarlet fever, whooping cough and diptheria haunted the children's schooldays.

Nunnington school in 1863 had poor attendances on the day of the village club feast, Kirkby Moorside fair and the Stonegrave feast. Only half the pupils turned up on the day of the Pickering Wesleyan anniversary tea. Hirings and days following the hounds made attendances thin. Girls were kept at home nursing. The boys were out singling turnips in July and doing field work through August. Winter brought the struggle for heat. Miss Dannat arrived at the school about 1870 and stayed for forty three years. Often there were seventy but sometimes only sixteen attending in the converted cottages. Children were admitted at the age of five if they could say the alphabet and recognise letters. The pupils cleaned the school, lit the fire and brought water from the river.

Sheriff Hutton school in 1881 had 'no fire again this morning' on December 9th. The attendance was down to nineteen on the day before. The teacher wrote 'The parents will not send their children to be starved in school.' She bought fourpence worth of coke and made a fire. Long after the principle of compulsory education was introduced, the struggle to make it real went on. The Parish Magazine for 1896 advised that Wombleton people were not famous for sending children to school regularly. A system of prize giving was introduced. The maximum possible attendances in the period was 411 and the highest scorer was Agnes Smith with 389. A boy asked why he was not at school, said that he thought that *the fever* was coming. That year, the government grant for the school was down due to poor attendance.

The Wrelton British School opened in 1879 with Miss Lightfoot appointed teacher at £5 a year. The government grant received was £8.7s.8d and roughly two thirds of this went to the teacher. A sale of old furniture raised a useful sum, but the managers deferred spending anything buying new school books, so the Treasurer resigned. There were five nominations for free scholar vacancies. Parents had to find fuel, home lesson books, a copy book, pens and slates. Thomas Dowson painted the school inside and out one year, put a front on the bookcase the next and in 1884 a bolt on the coalhouse door. The school closed for harvests, when it was cleaned. A sewing teacher came in and canvas, calico and darning cotton were bought for darning exercises. When Mr. Irving was teacher, there was an unsatisfactory Inspectors' Report and he was told to improve or else. He gave three month's notice. In 1891 the Managers accept the Government circular on free education and gained an extra grant of £10. The Government Education Department wanted the school enlarged. The grant was down the next year and the struggle went on.

Villages with a Difference

Hovingham was one of several Yorkshire villages which carved out a distinctive role as modest spaws. The village had chalybeate, sulphur and rock water springs. The railway increased the number of people who stayed at the three inns and several small boarding houses. Investors felt sufficiently encouraged to build a new hotel in the village and a spa villa about a mile westwards with an open veranda, and a modest pump room among walks and lawns. Dr. Simpson of York said that 'Hovingham water both soothed and invigorated' - a happy combination. The springs 'improved the tone, induced sleep, fostered good digestion and were good for lamesness, rheumatism, gravel, debility and nettle rash'. Robert Swan ran an omnibus to York on Wednesdays. Two surgeons and the Worsley Arms welcomed 'families of rank and respectability'. Sinnington a village without a spa became a modest holiday resort. In the 1886 season a Scarborough family stayed at the Cross Keys Inn, an officer of the 18th Regiment and his wife and the Ward family of Leeds at Friar's Hill, and others at Mallory's Pansy villa and Terrace house.

Villages on the Earl of Carlisle's local estates were known as 'the Castle Howard villages'. They had their own Brass Band, the 'Rose of Castle Howard Friendly Society', a separate branch of the Bible Society and a district corps of Rifle Volunteers. The Castle Howard Temperance Association in 1908 sent speakers to many villagers. The Countess laid out cricket pitches in her villages, and engaged a professional cricketer to go round each evening to give coaching. Legend says that she insisted of them running for sixes in her inter -village competitions. One of the villages was Coneysthorpe. This boasted a pretty frontage to every cottage and it was said that 'in no Yorkshire village was the love of flowers more evident than Coneysthorpe'.

Many of the bigger villages had a small middle class, including the better off farmers. They were strong on 'respectability'. A Wesleyan tea meeting at Barton le Willows sat one hundred and thirty down, including 'the elite of fourteen townships'. Those who did well lived well. They gave their houses names and they filled their houses with fashionable things. Indian carpets were all the fashion in 1896. A Cropton farmer had rooms full of furniture. The dining room had a mahogany cheffonier, mahogany couch, six chairs and an easy chair. There was a pantry under the stairs and a rear outhouse for the copper and the mangle.

Masons the Pickering grocers offered a picture to frame and put on your house wall for fourteen tea coupons. Things finished with, went to 'white elephant' stalls and jumble sales. These were not what they became later. The Rillington jumble sale of 1896 was a Winter tea, concert and glee party event. They heard 'Dearest maiden fare thee well', 'Hail smiling morn'and 'give a man a horse he can ride' sung by Mrs. Harland. Miss Calam recited 'The Jackdaw of Rheims' and someone else sang 'What are the wild waves saying'.

There was another world. James Chapman married at Scrayingham in 1889 had two shillings a day, for several years. His wife and nine children were fed on bread and lard. A son remembered that they had beef once a year at Christmas and that was given to them. He recalled fifty years later that they sometimes divided a bloater in four. There was the charity of 'hand me downs', clothing cast off from further up the social scale.

Norton was indeed a village with a difference, which almost became a town. It gained a few gentry houses early in the century. The church rebuilt to serve them in 1814 had small windows high in the walls, in the style of the time, and was reckoned to look like an asylum. The opening of the railway and some factory development near to it, weakened the social appeal but the village enjoyed remarkable growth. The main street was part of the turnpike road. This became 'Commercial Street with many excellent new houses and good shops'. 'Norton is an improving place' somone said in 1851. It was indeed a new kind of place, chiefly an industrial dormitory, but with no market town roots.

Two years later, eleven brick cottages were built in Providence Row and for some decades Norton continued to gain more new housing estates. A new street was laid out adjoining the Driffield railway in 1860. The emerging town had a strong industrial basis with steam bone mills, Brand's brick and tile works, a coach building business, maltkilns, a laundry and the Dacca Twist saw mills and water works. In the country around were the famous horse breeding and racehorse training stables of John Scott and others. There was much social life with a Lilly of the Valley lodge, Sunday School processions behind brass bands, the 1865 Chrysanthemum society, the reading room of 1899 and the new courthouse of 1902. Thomas Baker came in 1887 to publish the 'Norton Chronicles'.

There was a separate Board of Health and later an Urban District Council.

Market Towns

Franchise Terrace, Pickering

While farming was buoyant, the market towns did well, servicing the populous countryside. They were full of shops, and barbers, and shoe repairers and other services, not least the ale houses, some of which offered an afternoon bed for a 'market Monday'. Each had a cattle market, all eventually with railway links to the wider world, as well as retail street markets. Public buildings multiplied, market halls and town halls, court rooms and police stations, denominational churches and chapels, sometimes rebuilt for swelling congregations. There was some growth of select areas in the towns, the Mounts as they were called at Malton and Pickering. Like the Brows at Malton, they gained very solid houses with rooms for servants, attics or basement, for the usual offices, sitting, drawing and music rooms and parlours. Stout garden walls framed the pleasure grounds, the terraces and their summer houses. They had plumbing and slate roofs instead of pantiles.

Pickering gained two day schools in 1856 and 1857, a Gas Company in 1859, a Board of Health in 1863, a Congregational chapel in 1867, the Potter Hill Primitive Methodist chapel, to sit six hundred in 1875, a police station in 1878, an Infants' School and a large Post Office in 1893, an Urban District council in 1894 and 'house numbers' in 1901. Jubilee trees were planted in 1898, giving the town streets the character they still possess. Twenty five village carriers came in on market day. There were sixty three railway employees and a good many working for the post office. The Volunteers had a Market Place Drill Hall with an armoury. Four large Friendly Societies held annual parades. There were Fancier's. Football, Cricket and Tennis Clubs. They said that in Pickering, 'Methodism counted for everything' and that the town was Liberal. New terraces appeared in Westgate and Eastgate in the sixties, and Franchise Terrace later marked the extension of the vote.

The Widening Horizons

Agricultural depression came in the late 1870's and afterwards, with farms unlet and rent reductions on the Wolds. The American prairies were sending grain, and refrigerated produce began to arrive from Australia, New Zealand and the Argentine. Employment had been shrinking since reaching a peak in 1851. Migration to the industrial areas and overseas had long been substantial. Labourers at Middleton in 1872 sought wages of ten shillings a week with victuals, eighteen shillings without, hours six to six with a half hour for breakfast and one hour for dinner. Emigration became a flood, to Iowa and Nebraska and further west temporarily leaving the 'America Widows', often dependant on the parish. William Smith of Thornton Risebrough wrote 'a Yorkshireman's Trip to the United States and Canada 1892' to ease the path for others. The Methodists developed their own well-organised migration schemes for those seeking land. J. Jaques and other emigration agents, arranged for monthly parties to assemble and go in groups. One Thursday a through carriage to Liverpool was attached to the 10.15 train for his party of forty eight, drawn from Pickering, Malton, York and Leeds, with sixteen starting from Rillington.

Families spread widely and links were lost. Thomas Wardel in 1870 had a son at Langton on forty acres butchering and keeping a grocers shop and nine children. A daughter and her husband were at Norton with seven more. Their eldest son being clever, was in the gas house office st Scarborough. Three other grand sons had wanted to go to America that spring but hadn't enough money. A son was already there and a brother. An orphaned grandson decided to go when he was twenty three, on a vessel with one hundred hands on board and fourteen hundred passengers. On arrival he took the train from New York to Illinois. The grand father said that he hoped to meet him in heaven. Mr. F. Watson of Nawton went to manage a hackney stud in 1908 and died in the Argentine in 1923.

Those who stayed home had their horizons changed as well. The Foxholes annual trip to Filey in 1889 took scholars and parents from the church Sunday School in gorgeously decorated waggons. They left the village at a quarter past six and arrived at the coast at ten of the clock. Every one did what they liked but they joined together for dinner and tea. They were back at Foxholes by ten. If that was exciting for children, the railway could do as much for adults. The Marton annual Wesleyan choir trip in 1894 went to Studley Royal and dined in the Temperance hotel. Shopkeeper, J.M.Foster went shopping in London in 1886. He found dull Indian carpets all the fashion and bought one with a green ground and goldbrown flowers. He wondered where all the people in the city were going. He thought it would be poor sport watching the faces at the local flower show compared with all the gentry and nobility in Hyde Park.

Mother heard the Christy minstrels. She saw Indians weaving at the Colonial Exhibition and heard the great preacher Spurgeon address a congregation of five thousand at Westminster Abbey. Back at home, Annie had just done nine jars of strawberry jam and made six quarts of preserves. Foster went to Brighton and thought it more fashionable than Scarborough. At Manchester, he saw some very fine shops and most beautiful goods exposed for sale in them. He found the Grand Hotel nicely carpeted and he just had to touch a button in the bedroom wall and the light flashed -electricity. And it stayed on. Digby Cayley installed electricity at Brompton High Hall just after that.

Gentleman Thomas Harrison of Thornton Riseborough sent his daughter Hilda in 1892 to a school at Tynemouth. She lost ten marks for leaving her books in the passage, and another day lost her garters and so couldn't go to school at all. Her next finishing school was at Chausie de Charleroi, Belgium She wrote home in 1893 saying that they were allowed to speak English on Sunday. They had walks on Saturday when they were allowed to buy sweets. It was coffee and rolls at eight, bread and butter at four fifteen. She thought some of the other girls didn't set a good example by their manners at meals. The teacher wote to the mother with an account of progress. It all served her well. A letter from Mrs Dyer at Manitoba to Mrs Harrison in 1910 told her that 'Jack at Minnesota has won your daughter's heart at our little prairie town'. Jack had begun planting trees and digging for his new house.

CHAPTER 8
THE TWENTIETH CENTURY. 1900 - 2000

Britain had become a populous country in Queen Victoria's reign. The United Kingdom in 1821 held 21 million people but by 1901 would number 42 million. Another decade would add three million more. And yet, many more had gone overseas. A massive empire had been acquired but the war with the Boers in South Africa had already revealed the high costs, and moral bankruptcy, of a policy of trying to control it by military force. Germany and other countries were challenging the commanding international position that Britain had enjoyed, based on its industrial and commercial wealth.

The home Parliament had widened its representative role, by extending the vote to the middle classes in 1832, to town ratepayers including many artisans in 1867, and to country householders including some agricultural workers in 1884. It would not be until 1928, that all men and women over twenty one secured the vote. The House of Lords remained a seat of aristocracy, and the House of Commons had a long way to go, before it acted as if it represented all the people, by serving their interests.

Liberal and Conservative parties competed for the support of the electorate, with policies that edged towards material improvements, but they had yet to seriously challenge the establishment. Social reform had hardly begun.

The country had become urban and industrial rather than agricultural, although the numbers employed in farming were still considerable. Inside Yorkshire, it was the West Riding above all, which seemed to epitomise the age of the great coal, iron and steel, engineering, textile and other manufacturing industries, although Hull and Tees side had seen comparable growth. A great shipping fleet and the railway system transported their products world wide. Great towns sprawled where villages had been. Smoke filled the air. Middle class people spoke proudly of progress, the 'Nonconformist conscience' and respectability.

Old Ways of Life

The empire was expanding to its limits, when Jack Myers and fourteen other crack shots of the Pickering Volunteers returned from the Boer War in 1902. They found that little had changed. Two thirds of Pickering people were said to be poor. Men's work was hard physical labour, dawn to dusk. On the small farms, it was all hand work. Hay and corn were cut by hand with scythe and sickle. Bog peat and surface turf were dug for fuel, and bracken gathered to bed animals. Those in farm families worked for each other. Everyone knew everyone and there was mutual aid among farmers at threshing, hay making and sheep dipping.

Sacks were made to hold the maximum a man could carry, twelve to eighteen stone, varying with the crop. Women and children sewed seeds, picked stones, fetched water and gathered kindling. Women's fingers were always busy, washing, sewing, mending, making butter, bread and cheese. Mark Ward left school at thirteen for good, and after a week of Winter snow cutting at Wharram Percy, he left that too. He ran away to join the Royal Navy. Every cottage in Aislaby still had a dirt floor, which they polished with milk, to make them shine. There were no earth closets.

Many kept pigs, fed on barley, boiled potatoes and scraps, one to fatten to pay the rent, and one to kill and salt down. Spare eggs and butter were taken to market. Rudland Rigg farms above Kirkby Moorside had thirteen or fourteen extra men for dinner on threshing days, for beef, gravy and suet puddings, home grown vegetables and a great pan of potatoes. They milked by hand, and some milk went into the separator to churn for butter. Children were taken from school for any busy season. Home cured hams hung in the room and skimmed milk stood in a large jug on the table.

Nothing was wasted. Food scraps went in the pot. Anything found was a bonus and horse droppings were quickly shovelled up to manure gardens. Cottagers without land tethered cows along the roadside verges. Moor dale communities were still closely knit. Folk stood at their door to gaze at a stranger. 'Poor people had the greatest abhorence of the poor house'. A Rosedale woman said that 'all food was home made'.

A Kirkby Moorside man later recalled his boyhood during these years. The youngest children all wore petticoats and long hair till they were five, then went to school in braces. His father had £1 a week, thought of as very good money, to keep six boys and four girls. He kept a garden and the youngsters all sold the produce round the houses. The Saturday distribution ended with a visit to Mrs. Sleightolme's grocery, where they bought everything needed except flour. They went to Boddy's mill for two stone of home wheat flour which made fine bread with a 'kissing crust' overlapping the side of the baking tin.

The pig in the garden sty was killed at Christmas providing 'scraps', made in a large pan hung on the reckon over the fire. The pig's bladder was filled with hot lard, and cuttings gathered for brawn. The sides, hams and chaffs were salted for three weeks, cured and hung to supply bacon and ham for the rest of the year, but one ham was sold in April to buy a new pig. Occasionally, they bought liver, rabbits and beast hearts and in winter ate home made stews and soups. They all fished for trout. Mushrooms were plentiful since there were many horses about. Morning milk was cheap with the cream taken off. The rent was 2s.6d a week.

Those in regular, well paid employment subscribed to friendly societies, clothing and coal clubs, to offset recurring periods of hardship. Doctors were expensive, although several were remembered for their free work among the poor. A Kirkby man remembered that 'we had to keep away from the doctor because they weren't free'. Yet the chances of surviving childhood were improving. Some remembered different times when 'there were always babies in the house'. A few diseases were losing their epidemic significance, but childhood was a peril to pass through, although death rates and the size of families were both falling.

Some working people were getting worse off in these years and more than a third were said to live in poverty. Forty per cent of army recruits were found to be unfit. Illness caused frequent family crises. If Newton on Ouse had meazles in 1912, its neighbour Linton had chicken pox. Norton lost one hundred and eighteen people out of 3850 inhabitants in 1918 to influenza or similar. Many who survived the world war, were killed by the pneumonia epidemic of the next year. Winter was always a testing time when bad weather could stop work and income. Soup kitchens for the poor were normal in the market towns.

Plenty of perils remained and little to alleviate their impact. Malton's small old hospital opened in Cemetery lane in 1905. One voluntary District Nursing Association in 1911-12 sought to raise funds, for Nurse Bingley to pay 2545 visits to eighty seven patients in the year. Proprietary medicines sold at Helmsley included Coverdale's Nitkill to clean a head. Aspirin was a new and valued alleviator of pain and good false teeth were a lot more common. One farmer at Ebberston said his daughter carried a ton of potatoes in her mouth, that being the price of her false teeth. She was the first in the village to wear them. Arthritus caused a Fadmoor family to give up their farm.

Old age was only reached by a few and usually meant a permanent descent into hardship. An event of enormous significance came in 1908-9 when old people queued at post offices to receive the first non-contributory old age pensions, five shillings at seventy years, or seven shillings and sixpence for a couple. A Pickering woman said that it was the first money that she ever had, that she hadn't worked for. She had certainly worked for it. Charles Metcalfe at Ebberston expected little from the scheme. He judged that 'it is all officialism and will be more, when Lloyd George's insurance bill passes.'

In One Place or Another

Few girls stayed in service at one place for more than a year, but once married, women stayed in that work all their lives. Week after week, the same things were done on the same days- washing, ironing, bedrooms, baking, cleaning and sewing but nothing on a Sunday. Many men stayed in the same work for decades. John Walker's ancestors had been cobblers at Kirkby Moorside since 1777. Cabinet maker Arthur Wood continued his father's cabinet making business started in 1863. He was in the choir for sixty years. John Mould of Castleton was a butter 'badger' for forty two years till 1914, moving his horse and flat cart round the moor edge farms buying butter, which he sold to shops and miners. Harry Mortimer of Brawby took his thresher and meadow reaper around lowland villages for forty years.

Most villages were rich in specialist skills, each having several different craftsmen, who served wide areas full of scattered farms. Their walk to work was often heroic. Travelling tailors were called 'knights of the needle' but they had no horses. Master bootmaker John Calvert of Pickering would take the train to Forge Valley, then walk round the farms above Hackness to measure farm workers for hand sewn boots and do it all over again to deliver them. John Raw slit clog soles from alder logs in the woods at Dalby until 1914, drying them in large honeycomb piles, then carted the clogs to the Thornton Dale rail station for despatch to the mills of Lancashire.

Other men walked great stallions around the farms. John Stork of Kirkby Moorside, son of a miner killed in a Rosedale accident, joined the post office at fourteen. His deliveries at Rosedale started at 8.25 and it took him two hours to walk there. He would later remark that 'Postmen don't know they are born now' compared with 1895 when the snow lasted from New Year to April. There were commonly three winter weeks of no movement in or out of the dales. Their scene was different to ours, a bare landscape where the hills had few trees and the roads were mostly earth tracks. At 'a goose village', the gaggle met you in the road.

The Shop on the Corner

Table 50. Village Shops in Ryedale. 1937

45 - Norton

10 - Thornton Dale.

7 - Rillington

6 - Swinton, Sherburn, Hovingham

5 - Ampleforth, Leavening, Stamford Bridge

4 - Langtoft, Terrington, Sheriff Hutton

3 - Amotherby, Cropton, Farndale, Settrington, Huttons Ambo, Hutton LeHole, Lastingham Lockton, Nunnington, Rosedale, Slingsby, Welburn, Westow, Wombleton

2 - Allerston, Bilsdale, Barton le Willows, Duggleby, Farlington, Flaxton, Hawnby Heslerton Kirkby Misperton, Sledmere, Gilling, Thixendale, Harome, Langton, Luttons, Marishes, Nawton, Oswaldkirk, Scagglethorpe, Staxton, Stonegrave, Thorton Le Clay, Wintringham

1 - Acklam, Birdsall, Appleton le Street, Broughton, Barton le St, Brandsby, Bulmer, Barugh, Claxton, Coneysthorp, Coulton, Ebberston, Fadmoor, Foston, Ganton, North Grimston, Habton, Kirkby Grindalythe, Kirkby Underdale, Knapton, Ness, Newton, Normanby, Rievaulx, Scampston, Scrayingham, Salton, Scackleton, Skewsby, Thorpe Bassett, Harton, Weaverthorpe, Wharram, Yearsley, Yedingham.

Even quite small shops still combined vestiges of craft manufacture with wholesale and retail sales. W. Searle of Norton, boldy claiming to be the oldest grocery and provision merchant in the East Riding, sold flour in five, ten and twenty stone lots. The advent of paraffin lamps, using an oil by-product, dealt a blow to the tallow

This Invoice from 1897 Might Have Taken a Year to Pay

chandlery of William Marfitt, sited behind his prime shop site at the head of Pickering Market Place. It can be seen in the Castle Museum at York, an industry in itself. Many people expected the supplier to wait up to a year for his money. Thomas Harrison of Riseborough paid his grocers' bill half yearly. One bill was for £10.13s.0d and included one hundred and twenty stone of flour. 'Bero' self raising flour offered a recipe book to buyers.

Pickering had sixty six shops in 1911 and a weekly produce market of street stalls. They opened at eight and closed at seven, except on Sundays. Sixteen of them were grocers. In the drapers' shops ready mades were replacing made to measure. The new general hardware stores introduced a type of shop that has lasted - Fentress's supply stores offered everything - mail carts, brooms, sewing machines and furnishings in the market place. Shop facades became distinctive as plate glass and window shutters were installed. Butchers favoured the tiled shop landscapes still to be seen at Norton and Thornton Dale. Thomas Taylor's high class grocery at Castlegate Malton about 1900 had a boldly painted fascia board stating in large gilt letters that he was an 'importer of foreign and colonial produce'.

A new venture sought to offer working people goods at the minimum price. A Pickering Co- operative Society was formed by fifty six local men subscribing £65 in 1898, operating on the mutual aid principle. They opened a shop at 31 Potter Hill. By 1910, they had sold goods worth £37,000. They acquired bigger premisses in Southgate in 1915 and made extensions in 1928. Other Co-operative societies and branches spread around Ryedale and the Wold fringe.

A Better World

Ideas about a better world were familiar enough, but had long focused on charity, moral improvement, the reform of drinkers and blaming the poor for their own misfortunes. Pickering had one public house for every 232 people, Kirkby Moorside one to 194 and Malton one for 159 in 1906. About a third of families weren't doing too badly, including freeholders, professional people and a growing body of 'annuitants', sometimes listed as 'private persons'.

Many other people were still very poor, their family life a continual struggle to match low income with essential spending. Compared with modern times, a much wider group were poor, in the more general sense used at the time, since they had few possessions, nothing to fall back on and received little of what is now taken for granted. The front room, sometimes the only room, held a thin cast iron basket grate, designed to thrust forward a few sparse coals between the grill and the fireback so as to maximise the radiated heart. Next to it was a 'tidy betty' to hide the debris in a pan. A heated stone was kept to put in the copper or a tin tank for hot water. Even in prospering farmsteads, toilet facilities could be merely -women to the byre and men to the stable.

A new approach to public health made slow progress. House building away from old sites had polluted wells and streams. Many swore by the old wells but the new medical officers of health and local government surveyors swore at them. Old hands argued that the water had done them no harm but the graveyards told another story. Cropton was given a supply of piped soft water, with street taps, by Squire Gill in 1899 at a cost of £1150. Few could and even fewer wanted to pay that sort of money. The long struggle for better piped water supplies was fought village by village over decades. Water supply schemes spread along the limestone hills up to world war one. Main drain sewerage had to wait a little longer.

In the photo: VISCOUNT HELMSLEY, M.P.
3 Mayos LAYING THE HON! MASTER, C.W. SLINGSBY DUNCOMBE, FOUNDATION STONES, CHURCH INSTITUTE KIRBY MOORSIDE AUG 29. 1912

Laying the Foundation Stone of Kirkby Moorside Church Institute

A remarkable social experiment by a Joseph Rowntree Trust in 1902 created a complete new garden community at New Earswick, with well designed, sanitary and well built houses at twenty five shillings a week and a model community hall. Elsewhere, better water and a public hall in a town was most of what could be achieved. The Earl of Feversham gave Helmsley its market hall and courthouse in 1901. A library was pioneered at Canons garth in 1902 and moved into the court house six years later. The purpose built 'institutes' provided by gentry at a few fortunate villages went beyond the old reading rooms, offering facilities for several activities at once. Thornton Dale Institute cost about £400 and was erected as a memorial to the Squire, the Reverend J.R. Hill with separate reading, games and smoke rooms. The Kirkby Moorside Church Institute was built in 1912.

For some, the better world meant their children doing better than they had. Charles Metcalfe about 1910 spoke of that kindly Wesleyan Thomas Bailey whose three sons had been educated at the local village school seventy years earlier. One had become a land surveyor in Monmouthshire, another an architect and large scale contractor at York. The third started as a schoolmaster and ended as cashier of a large bank at Hull.

For others the better world meant following the fashions. Metcalfe recalled the old females in their coal scuttle bonnets, their only ribbons for tyeing. Now 'farmers' wives, who are always complaining of bad times, must not only have these, but must have their fine costumes, pianos, drawing rooms, and all kinds of luxuries, not to their discredit I may say.' Next it was ostrich feathers and artificial flowers. High life fashions went far further. A Wrelton Hall wedding in 1894 saw Miss Florence Hebden in a white satin boddice trimmed with 'point de Venie'. Mother was in 'euale de niu' and a striped silk. Unfortunately, two people gave the same present - silver serviette rings.

Changing Opinions

An old world was slipping away. Many young people went abroad into a British Empire, which had come to span one fifth of the globe. The local newspapers were full of their doings. At home, more people left the villages than stayed in them, and old viewpoints changed. Many villages and the dales had shrinking populations. The newspapers had broadened the interest in national politics. Liberalism enjoyed its greatest local triumphs with landslide voting in 1906. A Labour party formed in 1900 offered a more radical alternative, but made slow headway. Militant suffragettes were active in pursuit of voting rights for women, with meetings at Thornton Dale. Some at least, seemed to think that the world could be changed.

Among the churches, the great Victorian growth in the number of members and their fringe of attenders had never kept pace with the growth of population, but it had made for big congregations, with large male as well as women memberships. Now the numbers were beginning to slip, but confidence was unchallenged, since churches and chapels were still large and local influence was considerable. Bible based opinions were heard all the time, although the new popular newspapers were making other opinions common, and religion shrank within their pages. Church and chapel were still full at harvest festival but there were fewer revivals. Yet, a Methodist mission at Thornton Dale could still net fifty new members in 1903. The Mutual Improvement Society had another fifty meeting regularly.

The new local councils for Urban and Rural districts, despite their limited powers, drew on well known local people as councillors and generated outspoken debate, which local newspapers reported in detail, giving an appearance of vigorous democracy. People spoke their mind in many ways. The Huntington mole catcher heard a preacher say that men are not possessed by devils. As was his habit, he said aloud 'Aye

Edwardian Fashions in Kirkby Moorside

but they are'. A letter was found in the road at Appleton. It read 'Will G.C. be good enough to keep that long tongued busy body of a Vera in her place. She is nothing but a lying mischief making hussy'. Older methods of social control faded. The last stang riding at Flaxton about 1917 was against Henry Lunn who had prosecuted some boy thieves. Twenty years later, a local thought that 'the reason stang riding wasn't done any more was that there were too many bad uns to do it to'.

The New Grammar Schools

Seven hundred children attended Pickering Sunday Schools in 1906, rather more than attended day schools. School Boards had been appointed to bring compulsory schooling to all and new schools were established in areas of need. A Pickering infants school was added to its stock in 1899. Stape a community of small holdings above Pickering was given a school in 1896 built for sixty five children. School attendance officers, were appointed, popularly known as 'kiddie catchers'. Mrs Menzies on a typical day presided over forty two.

Rudland School was moved from a chapel, near old coal pits above Kirkby Moorside, into a new building, when Rosy Teasdale joined at age five. Many of the pupils walked two miles to meet a strict teacher, in

Hovingham School

a building with high windows so that they couldn't see out and an open log and coal fire. She left at thirteen for work. The boys at a Kirkby Moorside school spent the first week endlesslessly writing their name, and the second week, their address. 'You never forgot what you learnt', recalled one lad.

The new Pickering Grammar school built in 1904 was planned to serve thirty six pupils of whom fourteen had free scholarships to win and the rest paid five guineas, a fee which was beyond most pockets. Although the numbers educated by the two teachers in two classrooms was increased to seventy, this was a highly selective system for the very few. Malton Grammar School was also refounded in the hands of governors under the North Riding County Council in 1910 but with a contribution from the East Riding to costs and pupils. This was made co-educational, a novelty at the time. The school opened with three full and three part time teachers educating twenty seven boys and thirteen girls.

Technicals

The change that new technical knowledge would bring was only slowly appreciated. A clergyman exagerated when he told T. M. Foster that 'when he was a boy you had to put your shoulder to the wheel, but now you have to put your thumb on a button'. That was in 1898. His sense of prophecy exceeded his grip on the present. Old hands scoffed at 'new fangled' inventions. A sceptical housewife recalled the 'talk of electricity that it would be as cheap as water and as for margerine, I'd rather give you lard'.

Mr. W. Ellerby taken on at Slingsby as a road man in 1899 saw little of technology until a steam roller was introduced in 1900. His task, before and after, was to break stones, with a hammer, until they would go through a two inch ring. He supplied them at 2s.6d a ton or 2s.4d a day. Most of the countryside work was still hand work. Suits were made at local tailors. Most workers in farming were capable at a vast array of practical tasks, able to make ditches, fell trees, lay hedges, erect gates, build fences and much more, the women no less so, from domestic to dairy work, but with few of the aids later taken for granted. Moor men kept a stack of gathered bracken for animal bedding, boot wiping, and covering potatoes. Each man was expected to teach the next generation.

New technology when it came was not always of general use. But things that didn't change faded away. Arthur Boddy's roller flour mills at Kirkby Mills and the Turnbull's modernised roller mills at Sinnington and Allerston outlasted many other corn mills, which turned to a bit of sawing. Aymotherby mills were destroyed by fire in 1911. Sproxton mill stopped in 1918. When Bransdale mill ceased working in 1935, it was said to be the last oatmeal mill in the moors.

The bicycle proved a great boon in the countryside. W H Smith had an exhibition of them at Malton in 1899, the year that the gentlefolk of the Pickering Cycling Club met at the Kings Arms Inn with a bugler to lead the way. The Dunlop tyre had come in the eighties and the free wheel soon after. Robert Dobson at Pickering could supply cycling machines with free wheel and pneumatic tyres before the end of the century.

The National Telephone Company functioned at York as early as 1886. Malton and Easingwold had sub-exchanges by 1911, connected to the city. Next year the service reached Pickering but a few shopkeepers, inn keepers, doctors and gentry were the only subscribers for some years. Yates of Malton claimed that their home washing machine of 1907 did in two hours what seven people had previously done in two weeks. This was not entirely good news for domestic servants. Few had the washing machines but the Ryedale Laundry started at Kirkby Moorside about 1900, used modern methods and made their woven cane laundry baskets known far and wide.

A new power source came first to gentry houses. Crayke castle had some electricity by 1887 and Captain Catlet at Malton by 1893. Rosedale East Mines had a generator installed by the Carlton Iron company in 1900. An electricity supply agreement was reached for Malton in 1899 and the first power generator for Malton and Norton was built in Pasture lane in 1904 by the Cleveland and Durham Electric Power Company. Mains electricity reached several villages in 1919 but only a few houses benefited. Far more people experienced such novelties as the eight day striking clocks, sold at sixteen shillings each, by F. Turnbull the Helmsley watchmaker, the machine made nails which replaced those of the blacksmith and the new packaged breakfast foods like 'post toasties' or the tinned foods that offered a hope of food preservation beyond the weekend.

Motor cars came first to rich gentlefolk and physicians. One belonging to a Leeds engineer passed through Norton in 1897 stopping for an hour at the Royal Oak where it caused a sensation. Dr Kirk at Pickering had a motor cycle in 1903, and cars were seen at the town the next year. Thomas Frank bought a car in 1906. The Model T ford came in 1906. Robsons of Malton advertised De Dions in 1907 and Dr Bostock bought his first car there. Thomas Dosser at Slingsby had ridden penny farthings as a boy. A watchmaker turned motor engineer, he made his first sale, of a Ford to Dr Fisher of Aymotherby in 1910. The Yorkshire Automobile club filled Helmsley market place with cars for the first time in May 1907. Henry Butler at the town advertised as both cycle and motor maker, but also offered an open Humber with Dunlop tyres and padded seats in 1912. F. W Skaife had a cycle and motor garage at Pickering, advertising pure shell motor spirit with every can sealed in 1910. North Yorkshire police had some cars by 1916. Motor buses began to link villages to market towns. Robinson's motor coach ran between Pickering and Kirkby Moorside by 1922.

Time Off

Time off work was limited but there were steps forward. Sunday was observed as a day off and many shop assistants won an extra Wednesday half day in 1911. The Sunday, even for many with little religion, remained a quiet day. Middle class folk went for walks in best suits. Railway excursions made it easier to do what ever you did with time off - some place else. This became easier still, as the United Bus

Company starting with four vehicles in 1912, steadily spread its services on rural routes, and others did likewise.

Large towns gained first what smaller places wanted later, and going to town for treats became a wish for country youth, while the town went out to the countryside. Malton Baptist church took their annual excursion to rural Slingsby in 1912. Mass Sunday school excursions ran from the towns to Scarborough, which had a roller skating rink in 1909, and a 'People's Palace', offering twelve hours of entertainments for sixpence. This was at a time, when Sheriff Hutton boys still had a months 'holiday' in the potato field.

Music halls were attracting large town audiences, and village shows, even those run by chapels, mimmicked their famous favourites. Father Suggit and his two sons in the Gilling orchestra played the sheet music hits. Kirkby Moorside had its 'nigger minstrels'. Norton had 'penny pops' concerts at the Salvation Army Hall. Thornton Dale in 1903 saw Oxlee Grabham's magic lantern shows and a lecture on 'the advantages of emigrating to west Canada instead of finally emigrating to an English poor house'. Older survivals and some folksy revivals included the Lockton tar barrel play, the Terrington Plough Monday processions with garland dancers, and the Slingsby sword dancers. Rosedale had a fancy dress ball and many village sports were on Shrove Tuesday. There was a Whit Monday horse procession at Malton till 1914 and Christmas mummers lingered at Kirkby Moorside.

'Physical jerks' and 'drill' exerted a fascination, where numbers of people did the same thing at the same time, in a regimented manner. Temperance demonstrations were enlivened by 'tambourine drill'. Hundreds of skaters appeared on the Castle Howard lakes in cold winters, a surprisingly popular activity on other ponds, using home made bone skates. Leisure, in the modern sense, where you pick a pleasure and pursue it, was still a middle class affair. Kirkby Moorside gained golf links in 1907, and was hit by the auction bridge craze, while Malton enjoyed international success at curling. Boy Scouts and Girl Guides were started for the young in 1908 and 1910. Progressive head masters introduced novelties to their schools, the first violin lessons at Malton Wesleyan school in 1908 and swimming lessons four years later. Many things that made the headlines had no impact in ordinary lives but newspapers were widely read. Village reading rooms offered the papers, a few books, a good fireplace, a place to go other than pub or chapel, all usually managed by villagers themselves.

World War I - a National Disaster

German troops marched through Belgium into France in August 1914. Britain had promised to defend Belgium and sent a professional Army Expeditionary Force. They were forced to retreat but stopped the enemy on the river Marne with heavy losses. Lord Kitchener made his famous appeal for volunteers which brought a massive response. The British 'dug in' at Ypres, forming the first trenches, which made wretched soldiers' homes for most of the war. Trench life would continue for years with its lice, 'trench mouth' and attrition. A regiment of Scots Greys arrived at Kirkby Moorside in the Spring of 1915, each field gun pulled by six horses. The lancers ate bully beef and hard biscuits. They smoked 'Wild Woodbine' cigarettes. Next day they practised a charge at Appleton Common. Within a week, they were off to the front line.

There was a vigorous naval war, to keep open the shipping lanes, which now brought the foodstuffs and much else that was necessary for national survival. George Cholmeley of Thorpe Basset was killed that year in command of the British submarine E3. On 16th.December. 1914, in the early morning, two German battle cruisers fired two hundred shells into Scarborough. They claimed that pots danced on the table at Rillington during the bombardment. The Royal Naval Air Service flew from Seamer race course against raiding German airships and submarines. The war spread around the globe. Lieutenant Porter of Helmsley was among the local men killed trying to land at Gallipoli in Turkey.

Casualties in the deadlocked trench warfare of the Western Front in France mounted steadily. All men of military age were registered in August 1915 and conscription of single men between eighteen and forty-one was introduced. By 1916, 248 Pickering men were in the army, eleven in the navy and ten in the Royal Flying Corps. Captain Liddell won the Victoria Cross over Ostend. A Pickering father wrote to his son of his immense gratitude saying 'If you young chaps were not out there fighting for us.....'. Already twenty five of them had been killed in action. Dr. Murphy wrote of seven thousand friends dying in half an hour on the first day of the Battle of the Somme. A generation was lost as men were slaughtered in the mud under machine gunfire .On the first of July 1916, 57,470 British men and more Frenchmen were lost. A Hawnby clergyman lost three sons in this war.

Lord Feversham raised and trained the Volunteer battalion of the

Yeoman Rifles (21st KRRC) at Duncombe Park. They left Helmsley in 1915 and spent three months in the trenches at Ploesteert, retrained during August and attacked on the 15th of September.1916. Of the original thousand who joined the Helmsley battalion in 1916, 395 died in the first battle of the Somme. The Earl was killed with many of his men. After five weeks in France, a lad wrote of shells flying over head one day as he approached the lines. The next day, his officer wrote that one had landed near him, killed three and wounded eleven. Sydney Foord with the Scarborough Pals gun battery fired scarce ammunition in short bursts, from a nine foot by seven foot dug-out holding twelve men on 'rations fit for slimmers'. Balloons hung in the sky to direct gunfire. Just above ground level, floated a new weapon - phosgene gas. In no time at all, the walking wounded came streaming down the communication trenches. This was another sort of war.

Women replaced men in many home employments, including factories making munitions. When the men marched off, a Pickering letter spoke of 'such a weeping- mothers losing their sons and husbands'. Country houses like Duncombe park, Welburn Hall and many others, became hospitals for the huge numbers of wounded and shell- shocked men. Local people were warned of the dangers of injudicious treating of soldiers. Village egg collections were made for them and cash gathered for Xmas presents for the forces. Grannie Middleton at Lockton knitted a sock a day through the war for soldiers. Fathers sent Boot's vermin powder to sons at the front. As the casualties of the 'Western Front' mounted, conscription was introduced.

'We never had a war so near us as this' wrote a mother. Airships called Zepplins bombed York and flew over Pickering to drop bombs at Rosedale and Teesmouth. A sale of fruit and vegetables was taking place at Kirkby Methodist Chapel and the children ran out to see the airship 'like a great sausage flying to Middlesbrough'. Townsmen went up and set light to some heather, in the hope of making the raiders think that they were over the steelworks, and some bombs were dropped. At the quiet village of Sinnington, Mrs Stead remembered saying 'Faither faither, come out, there's Zepplins running about all over'. Lines of Observer Corps posts were opened including those at Stillington, Stamford, Brandsby, Strensall and Ganton. Defeat came closest as German submarines sank great numbers of merchants ships, making food scarce. When all was over, there were not many families without loss. Many women were widowed and many were obliged to remain single. The war memorials still stand in village and town.

Farming Decline

Farming sank back from its highly profitable war time prosperity. Corn prices dropped. Appleton common had been cultivated by German prisoners but now returned to waste. Many Wold farms stood empty on the great estates, and vacant farms could ruin an estate. Birdsall estate in 1932 had two to three thousand acres unlet. Many tenants accrued massive arrears. Other farms went out of condition. Much arable land went out of cultivation between the wars, although dairying, root crops, sugar beet, market gardening and more intensive livestock farming did well. The World was no better for the war and much of the countryside seemed to be in a kind of slump.

Robert Mennell of Foxholes, an invalid, collected the cows at the village to take them round the lanes, blowing his horn every day, outside the farms. This 'cow-tenting' on roadside verges, which made it possible for families to keep a cow, was stopped in 1922, after outbreaks of foot and mouth disease. The Statute hirings of men and women in market places ended in 1924, with new Acts of Parliament to regulate farm workers' wages. Old hands recalled the Malton hirings without sentiment – 'the old farmers out for some cheap labour'. 'They would barter the men down to the last halfpenny'. The wages stayed low despite the Wages Boards set up to improve them, and the number of farm labourers steadily fell.

During 1922, the National Union of Agricultural Workers called for a minimum wage of fifty shillings a week. The National Farmers Union thought thirty five shillings might be possible. Rosedale mining ceased in 1926. Between 1929 and 1932 there was a general slump in activity and much unemployment. Some people left the countryside for the colonies under the Empire resettlement scheme. 'Wold rangers' still filled the demand for seasonal labour on the Wolds, loners who lived rough and drank three gills day, and might pinch some small item so that they could get sent to prison for Christmas. Herbert Day recalled the strict time-keeping for other Wold workers, men rising at five to have horses ready for work before a six-forty breakfast. The wagoner was the time keeper, but Ingersoll self winding watches reached the shops in the twenties and at five shillings, were in reach of the lads at Martinmas. At Foxholes, the men met to talk of a night in the cobbler's hut.

Stericker of Pickering was making Cleveland Bay horses world-famous and few could forsee the day when farms would run without horses. There was still a horse for every ten people but there were signs

A Fowler Ploughing Engine

of change, where men of capital were willing to make them. A Fordson tractor on iron wheels was tried at Hagg House farm in 1922 and another at Mowthorpe in 1929. Mowthorpe high farm used a four-course rotation; corn, seeds, and roots, entirely with horses until 1930. Sugar beet was tried in 1932. Yields of barley and wheat were four to five quarters an acre and oats eight quarters, said to be typical of the wolds.

The Ryedale Internal Drainage Board began the improvement of low lying land. Veterinary effort reached new heights in 1927, with the saving of the wooden legged cow at Musley Bank. Leeds University pioneered farm education, with cheese making classes in Rosedale in 1929. Two thousand chickens were kept in a single unit at Thornton Risebrough. A Malton and District egg society was formed in 1930 to grade and market eggs. The Brandsby Agricultural Trading Association moved to Malton in 1934, using rail links there and at their Aymotherby compound feeds mill, to supply widely. Lilly, a Jersey cow at Normanby beat Abigail of the USA in the world rankings for milk yield in 1935.

Great House Life

Many attitudes were changed by the purposeless slaughter of the war, but the society to which the serving men returned seemed little altered. Rigid class divisions remained. 'High life' and 'carriage folk', remained the focus of popular newspaper interest, although 'showbusiness' was edging in. The local newspapers were full of gentry doings in country houses, at hunts and balls, cocktail parties and private court tennis. They still employed many, gave charity to others and patronised the Church of England. Girls still went 'into service' at the bigger houses. A lass who took a bus from Malton's Green Man yard to Bog Hall farm on the Castle Howard estate at the age of seven, would remember, with pride, delivering milk to the Howard girls' nannie. A genteel Old Malton family of two adults with four children, employed two housemaids, a nanny, a butler, housekeeper, hallboy, cook, kitchen maid, a man, two gardeners, two nursery girls, a governess five times a week and a woman to help the kitchen maid occasionally. They say that a wing was knocked down in 1935 in order to reduce the staff needed.

Newcomers from industry and trade replaced some old gentry families or by marriage helped them survive. Some gentry were much admired. China coast engineer, James Twentyman, at Kirkby Misperton Hall gave the village a Constitutional club and gave Pickering a fire engine. Sir William Worsley of Hovingham captained Yorkshire at cricket in 1928 and 1929. Lord Hawke another famous cricketer, lived at Huttons Ambo. Arnold Toynbee the world historian lived at Ganthorpe House in 1939 and Sir Herbert Read, the art critic a little later at Stonegrave.

Nonetheless, the old way of life was slowly slipping away. Manor lords counted for nothing now. The Leavening manor court could still be seen at the Hare and Hounds, after viewing the drains in 1927, but others just faded away. The income from fines was insufficient to buy the jury a drink. Some estates broke up. The Beningbrough estate was sold around 1916. Gilling Castle became a preparatory school in 1922 and Duncombe Park turned into a school three years later. There were many more like them.

Malton was an estate town and was run for the Earl FitzWilliam by the agent Colonel Diggle. His word was pretty much law. The Countess Fitzwilliam and Viscount Milton would occcasionally pay a visit, when a great fuss was made. On one famous occasion in 1922, the bells were rung, and a thousand gathered on Orchard field, to present a silver salver and a porringer from the tenantry. Some spoke of the estate town as 'a leasehold desert'. When the council planned to build its first batch of council houses, arrangements were made for them to be absorbed into the estate within the year. On the other hand, the Earl donated the site for the new cottage hospital, for twenty four patients.

Faith Shaken

At the other end of the social scale, another group were much talked about, for whom life was a different kind of struggle. Some were called 'characters'. Those long recalled at Pickering, included Slim Jim, who lived at a common lodging house, Limpey Joe, Catty Willy, Billy Tweet, Dafodil Fanny and Dafodil Kate. The Wold rangers lasted into the thirties, living on a diet of bacon cake, raw onion, pies and curd cheese cake. They were a reserve labour force that didn't have to be housed. These loners could bed down in a wood, hedgerow, barn or hayloft. They were remembered as Cloggy Sam who could tap dance, Mad Halifax, Long Lena, Three fingered Jimmy and Horsehair Jack. John Bowes, the Great Barugh blacksmith remembered other travelling men. Canary who had been a butler at Knaresborough but travelled threshing and poaching. In an innkeepers barn, he bored a hole in a barrel and supped it with a straw. Happy Jack ate hedgehogs. These characters were joined by some men, shell shocked during the war.

Faith in religion was shaken by the world war. If some found solace, others found scepticism. Yet church and chapel still set the framework for much respectable living. Services were still well attended and Sunday Schools full. The numerous clergy were judged by their visiting, as much as their sermons. Many Anglican clergy still seemed too tied to the established order of things. A parishioner thought the new Pickering vicar of 1937 'a nice gentleman but he had a private income and was getting a curate to do the work'. She added that 'With no preaching I suppose he will stay for ever'. Another Vicar, Mr. Bundle, was poor and worked hard but having no private means had to do without a curate. A third vicar managed to form large men's discussion groups. A Barton le Street rector asked 'have servants souls?' no doubt rhetorically.

Methodist societies seemed to have greater influence, almost everywhere and had always offered ample participation in sewing circles and prayer groups and bible classes, something every day, should you need it. Pickering Wesleyan Methodist Society had one hundred and fifty six committed 'members', who had fought vigorously for a nonconformist section in the new town cemetery. Many of them treated Liberalism as a natural extension of their social duties. Many others went to the chapel, for whom 'membership' would have seemed an ambition to attain.

Queenie Johnson who arrived as a thirteen year old at the White

Swan inn, Newton on Rawcliffe in 1919 remembered the Chapel Anniversary teas, with adults forming 'kissing rings' for group singing. Even the Wesleyans weren't the biggest church. An observer wrote that in Pickering, 'Primitive Methodism was everything'. Taken together, all the Sunday schools had attendances far exceeding adult membership of churches and chapels. They raised generations in a bible based morality. When a school teacher retired in 1932, after twenty years, they said that Miss Teasdale's 'Christian virtues were an enobling influence on children's lives'.

The Ways of Life

By 1928 the birth rate was lower than was ever remembered. With smaller families, the money went a little further. A Prudential insurance agent claimed in 1920 that working people were getting three times the wages of pre war days but everything was very dear. Some were doing better. Some were not.

Frank Tasker remembered Kirkby Misperton village as it was in in 1927, with no electricity, gas, running water or water closets. House lighting was by candles and a paraffin lamp. Fresh water was carried by pail from the communal pump near the hall gates, and rain water from a tank at the back door. Baths were taken before the fire in a zinc tub, with hot water from a small boiler in the kitchen range, if you were lucky or endless kettles if you were not. The lavatory had a wooden board with a hole in it, poised over a pit at the top of the garden, limed frequently to remove smells, and used with torn up newspaper. Acklam villagers took their buckets a steep climb to the spring until 1935, when Norton Rural District Council built reservoirs supplying water to street pumps. This put 3d a week on the rates. The Sinnington postman walked eighteen miles and more a day.

Women worked in homes and on farms, in domestic service, dressmaking, laundries and shops. At home, women triumphed if they obtained a sink with a tap. They rarely met fresh people or ate food that they hadn't cooked themselves. After long hours on her feet the working woman's leisure was sitting down to sew. Sunday high tea was a weekly high point but 'a cup of tea' was a repeated daily salvation. The calendar was punctuated by such things as the boiling of peas on a July Saturday. There was an outing once a year, a holiday never. These things were remembered without affection in later days, though some were unhappy when change left them time on their hands. They liked to 'keep busy'.

411

Some few saw their standard of living rise in these years with more furniture, clothing and food, distantly produced commodities made famous by advertising such as Cherry Blossom boot polish, Sunlight Soap, Reckitt's Blue and ready made clothes bought from multiple shops. Red Flannel

A CHEERFUL OLD SOUL.

IT IS possible for a woman with increasing years to continue to do laundry work. Thousands who would have been laid aside under the old system of washing have proved what Sunlight Soap can do in reducing labour. The cleansing properties of

SUNLIGHT SOAP

save years of arduous toil. Reader, prove Sunlight Soap for yourself; by giving the best article a trial you WILL DO yourself A REAL SERVICE.

drawers slowly gave way to lingerie. The 'bra' arrived as corsets were laid aside. Men aspired to own a watch, worn like regalia with the chain across a waistcoated chest. The Gazettte in 1932 carried large advertisments for Exide batteries, Cadbury's dairy milk chocolates, Lactogen for babies and Shredded Wheat. A new estate built at Mauldon Avenue in Pickering offered the English dream - a three bed room house for £395, paying 11s.8d a week.

Childhood

Small boys in the thirties played football and cricket and when the season for each came round, brought out their whips, tops, hoops and roller skates. They flicked the new cigarette cards showing sporting and stage heroes and heroines. They played marbles along the gutters. Cycle rides with a bread and jam sandwich and pop for a snack, took older lads to adventures in fields, that somehow never seemed to belong to anyone. Comics and 'twopenny blood' adventure magazines were devoured. They told stories, where Britons with names like Biggles, Carruthers and Standish acted as if they believed that Britain was 'top dog'.

A Pickering boy in the twenties had a halfpenny pocket money on Wednesday and a penny on Saturday. His father taught him how to hold a ferret by the loose skin at the back of its neck. He took the mongrel dog out to catch rats, toured the country side climbing all its trees and took birds eggs in Spring, bringing them down in his mouth. The vicar caught him exploring the high church roof. Good moments were the trips to Taylor's shop to buy fizzy sherbert or gobstoppers and visits to the new Castle Cinema.

Some Lockton schoolboys read about hypnotising rabbits and they tried it, successfully catching a mesmerised rabbit, which on examination turned out to have its paws caught in a snare. They made Meccano models of speed craft, dropped pebbles down the village well, and met the film actor Charles Laughton, walking from his holiday cottage. Three youths gambling on cards in the Scott's Hill quarry at Norton deputed one as the guard with a peculiar whistle, but were caught just the same. Some Great Barugh lads convinced the village, that a white sheeted ghost had been seen in the village pond on Mischief Night in 1929. Foxholes children playing 'Fox Away' would race back to school when the foundry bell rang, telling the foundry men and them too that they had five minutes to get to work.

High days for boys at Kirkby Moorside included the 1st of March horse parade, the Martinmas hirings on Wednesday after the 5th of November, and the visiting fairs. There were men who would challenge you to tie them up in a way they couldn't get out, a fellow who put a sword down his throat and barrel organ men. The stalls included 'aunt sallies' a cake-walk, boxing booths, Burnside's coconut shies, and one year a tent of moving pictures, three pence for ten minutes. Christmas was not just mistletoe and Japanese candle lanterns, sugar pigs and frumenty wheat given by the miller. It was the time when a new suit and boots were bought, and put away for their first outing, when the Sunday schools made their anniversary journey, on the decorated wagons, for the trip to Scarborough. In the Wrelton Nursing Association Carnival fancy dress contest, Miss Margaret Turnbull won as 'Saucy but quite OK' and Stephen Welford as 'England land of the Free'. Spelling bees were all the rage.

Phillip Brown recalled with pleasure, from his boyhood, the savours and scents as you opened the door of Tommy Taylor's, a blend of coffee roasting, ham, bacon and cheese. The grocery in Castlegate, Malton was said to have been established in 1700. Now, the upper shelves held giant red and gold tea canisters. Below were fourteen pound tins of biscuits with glass covers. A white coated assistant worked under the eye of James Taylor, who emerged from a small office, spectacles on head. The manually worked ham slicers went 'woosh woosh', raising a mild fear. Mr. Drake's window on the low side of Finkle Street until it was demolished in the late thirties, had an array of offal, black pudding, savoury ducks, brawn and faggots. Up some red brick steps was Lance Murray's world of schoolboy wonder, full of Meccano, train sets, scale models and clock work toys. Behind a wicket gate in Newbiggin, Mrs Linley's cottage gave up more odours of the baking of 'sally lunns and fat rascals'. The converted railway carriage where the Misses Read and Oldfield ran a dress making business, with its leather sash operated windows, three doors, and notices warning against improper use of the alarm cord, was a boy's idea of heaven.

Fred Marwood at Leavening left school at the age of twelve to work from 5.30.a.m. to 8.p.m. for £13 a year with ten days off at Martinmas. Young Hammond at Kirkby Moorside worked from six to six with his grandfather, a market gardener, packing seeds in sheets of brown paper. The family formed an assembly line on a long table, with name and price written last. It took an awful lot of packets before a hundred weight of onion seed was done. Bert Thompson later looked back on Rosedale when 'everyone had good gardens, quoits was played near the beck. There was a football ground without a net, so you sometimes didn't know if Farndale had scored or not. Benny Walker could kick a ball. You could get 1s.6d for a couple of rabbits in 1937. At the Abbey, children feared the saddler who told them –'I'll cut yer heads awf wi me knife'. Everyone in the dale had a nickname: Revell, Skitter, Cork, Gash and Gobble - some were terrible nicknames.'

The Three Rs

Schooling in the three Rs' - reading, writing and arithmetic - had become general in the early years of the century. The attendance officers chased up the truants. The County Councils took over supervision of the schools from the local school boards and the voluntary school managers in 1902. Church schools kept a little autonomy but became rate supported and subject to inspection. A rise in standards was soon evident. With entire generations attending, discipline was harder to achieve and sanctions were severe. The Pickering Methodist School book recorded one stroke with the cane for playing with a ruler, for rude noises, a trick played on teacher, impudence or splashing ink, and a rising scale of more strokes for worse offences.

School closures were already known as the roll of pupils fell, in shrinking villages. Old Byland school ran from 1833 to 1932, by which time there were only nine pupils. Conditions were still hard. Slowly, modern stoves and electric light were installed but hot water and inside toilets lay in the future. Ink could freeze in the ink wells at Malton Greengate School. The head master wrote that despite many difficulties 'cheerfulness would break out'.

414

School and family papers reveal the sense of mission that inspired many school teachers. Henry Gillespie, head master of a Malton school took pupils to the Wembley Empire Exhibition in 1924 and to Sedburgh to see a total eclipse of the sun in 1927. Sinnington school had that brilliant woman Lillian Ratcliffe about 1932, teaching thirty pupils from five to fourteen years, all subjects including book binding, needlework, art, plaiting the maypole, country dancing and plays. She bought a gramaphone and took them for nature walks. The schools eroded dialect and some grown ups complained of the new 'jack is as good as his master attitude' replacing older ideas of 'the place to which it had pleased God to call you'. Most houses still had children living at home but they left school early for work.

For a very few, ambitions were becoming realisable. School was not generally prolonged into youth but new secondary scholarships announced in 1930, allowed a few to stay longer at school. A few of the few reached the Yorkshire College, which became Leeds University. The small group of Grammar School children, as they left, leavened the broader society, feeding the expanding professions, and clerical jobs. As adults they read the new popular paperbacks, including the sixpenny Penguin books of 1935 and the Edgar Wallace thrillers. They were much pre- occupied with giving their own children a good start.

Voluntary Action

Many things were achieved together which could never be done singly. Friendly societies still offered a great deal of practical insurance. The Co-operative movement had 3433 members at Malton by 1939. Churches and chapels provided social services for their members and sometimes charitable work for others. Other voluntary groups ran ambulances to hospital, provided Red Cross and St John services and supported Fire Brigades. Fund raising was widespread for the cottage hospital and the highly valued district nurses. Allotment gardens became more usual. Their assemblage of huts, in the corrugated iron age, where tools could be kept and tea made, provided a bastion of masculine escape from crowded households.

New societies were formed to improve living conditions and leisure. The Women's Institutes spread rapidly around the villages and towns after their launch in 1915, with 130 societies in the shire by 1925 and 334 by 1936. They offered all women an evening out and many members gained new opportunities in drama, music, travel and the arts and crafts. Rillington had one of the earliest institutes pioneered by the doctor's wife. They produced a historical pageant in Scampston park. Pickering and Kirkby Moorside WIs jointly performed Macbeth in 1927. Norton W. I .had an ankle competition where a woman recognised all the ankles, except her husband's. Rosedale W. I. in 1939 performed the play 'Tyrrany and Tea Cakes'. Over the years, the Women's Institutes pressed for such rural improvements as public telephones, bus services and shelters, all great boons in their day. The regular meetings gave women a night out away from men, a chance to run their own events and an easy programme of light leisure.

The Co-operative Guilds did much the same in their towns and villages. A married woman who went to their evening classes, recalled her husband's disapproval. He told her 'you are wasting your time'. When he became ill, she became a teacher of needlework for ten years, and kept him. Reading rooms had often deteriorated after the arrival of the billiard table and were mostly thought of as a place for the men.

A new movement began founding village halls and institutes. Sheriff Hutton village hall built as a war memorial in 1920 had a bowling green and tennis court. KirkbyMoorside memorial hall came three years later. Aymotherby village hall opened in 1930 and a model hall at Hutton le Hole, with a stage, in 1939, using stone from the old Rosedale bank engine shed. Bowls was played in Pickering Castle from 1912 to 1926 when a ground was laid out in Ruffa Lane. Great Habton Village Hall was built in 1936 for £373. Most of all, there was much enthusiasm for dancing. At Norton, the Empire Ballroom in 1927 had a six hour ball where 387 danced to Midgley's orchestra.

New Horizons for Local Government

There was a growing realisation that necessary things would not come without action that no individual alone, or any voluntary society, could manage. On the other hand, opposition to rate paying was probably the strongest political sentiment. The Urban and Rural district councils were centred on the market towns, with Norton, Rillington and Flaxton, north east of York, in a district where city overspill populations were beginning to settle. The Councils proved to be effective vehicles for country voices but action beyond immediate problems was undertaken slowly and with different degrees of progress.

Medical Officers of Health annually drew attention to problems of water supply and sewage disposal, of health and housing. Dr. Porter in the twenties regularly condemned the water for drinking, which first passed through a 'living churchyard' at one village. Pickering sewage works opened in 1933 and the Malton - Norton sewerage scheme in 1935. Malton in 1928 was said to have 54 uncharted wells. There was progress but it was very scattered. Kirkby Moorside gained a new water works in 1925, Wintringham its water main in 1929. Sewage was seeping into Kirkby Misperton wells and the pump for the water was closed in 1930.

In some areas, about a third of the existing houses were rated 'unfit for human habitation'. The new local authorities were allowed to build a few cheap houses, the best with three bedrooms and a copper. It was a major innovation when ten council houses were built at Kirkby Moorside in 1933. Sinnington rate payers petitioned the Rural District Council, arguing that some of the village houses were unfit for human habitation and asking that water in the pump near the village inn should be analysed. An inspector found that thirty eight out of one hundred and forty seven houses were not reasonably fit, and eight were positively injurious to health. There had been a meazles epidemic and there was no systematic scavenging. They started a hospital contributory scheme that year, collecting three pence a week from those who joined. Two years later, ten private tenants still slept in one room at Helmsley.

John Bowes the Barugh blacksmith still drew teeth with his crab claws, when a Kirkby Moorside Orthopaedic Hospital opened in 1925. The Malton cottage hospital founded back in 1905 during the year 1936 admitted 634 patients. Birth control advice was made available at York that year, and quietly spread elsewhere, another silent revolution. Camps for the unemployed were run in Helmsley Park and Dalby forest in 1935. During 1938 both infant welfare clinics and milk-in-schools schemes were pioneered in Ryedale. A Kirkby Moorside man recalled 'We had to keep away from the doctor because they weren't free', although Dr Tetley once came to cure his skin blisters with a lime wash. His mother's remedies, serving for many ailments, were brimstone and treacle and sliced onion in vinegar. 'We could all eat onions like apples' he said.

New Technology

Nobody spoke of 'new technology' but there was much of it about. The nation seemed taken up with its least important aspect, which was 'speed' in all its forms, including the pursuit of land, water and air speed records. Locally, it was more mechanical movement, rather than speed, that was evident from the internal combustion engine. An early tractor at Kirkby Moorside was met with the judgment 'Theym stinking things, they al niver poush hosses out. There are a lot of things they can't do.' Malton in 1922 decided to charge 6d a car, for parking in the market place. Dodgem cars entered the travelling fair grounds in 1928. Motor boats on the river Derwent in 1935 worried the fishermen.

Radio was better known, operated from batteries. During a demonstration of wireless telegraphy at Malton in the early twenties, E.K. Spiegelhalter received messages from ships at sea, the Eifel tower and Annapolis. Listeners to a wireless in the Ceylon cafe Malton in 1923 marvelled at hearing the Messiah sung from Newcastle. Crystal sets gave way to valve sets, with loudspeakers for family listening. The BBC began regular broadcasts, making news bulletins a part of the daily framework. They revived all forms of music and offered fresh entertainment for children and wider worlds to adults.

Ron Scales invited to hear his first wireless, heard of Amy Johnson arriving by solo air flight in Australia. Norton Bethel Male Voice Choir sang on the radio in1938, the same year that Helmsley had a harmonica craze and stopped ringing the six.a.m. bell. There was local debate as to whether the unemployed should be allowed to have radios. Alfred Rogers of Allerston in 1939 was convinced that 'all wireless sets should be hit with a hammer'. William Harker of Marton, of a family who had formed string bands, thought that jazz was 'nobbut queer stuff' and John Tomlinson who ran a septet in the village thought 'all the new tunes were much alike'. A 1939 Saturday afternoon on Northern Radio featured 'Top Hat', adapted from a Fred Astaire and Ginger Rogers film, a Billy Cotton band concert and the news. This was an important new pleasure, in the home.

Fad Sleightholme at Kirkby made ice ceam, sold for twopence a sandwich and was the first local man to put a slot machine outside his shop. This was for cigarettes - Wild Woodbines - a penny for five. Mr. Sturdy pioneered an early fish and chip shop but trade was too slow. An automatic stamp delivery machine was installed at Malton post office in 1927. A few inns gained hot and cold water, and tried steam heating and cooking. Oil fired boilers and water softeners lay ahead. Marishes Women's Institute had a sewing machine demonstration in 1930. The machines were still not generally owned and sewing circles were a common social activity. A Scagglethorpe man made a river bicycle using balloons in 1935.The new gas water heaters appeared in 1939.

Oil shales were reported at Nunnington, Sinnington and Great Edstone in 1923, but the search had only begun and its day was not yet. The Northern Counties Electric Supply Company after two decades replaced their Malton 'power station' in 1922. A new power station was built at Norton and started generating electricity in 1924. The National Grid switched on in 1926 made the transport of electricity nationwide and began to make electrical power ordinary. Norton had an all electric house built in 1927, a marvel on the Welham Road, with fires, geyser, washing machine, cooker and vacuums, all electrically powered. Lamp bulbs were given away to encourage buyers. York railway station received loud speakers that year. Robots were discussed for Malton as early as 1929. We know them as traffic lights. Electricity reached Hovingham in the thirties although acetylene gas may have run a small plant before that and it arrived at Howsham in 1938, 'a wonderful day'.

Somewhere about 1927, Captain Kingswell's aircraft looped the loop over Malton. Lord Grimthorpe of Easthorp Hall took up flying four years later, going up from Castle Howard and Sherburn in Elmet. He had his own 'Puss Moth' machine and built another with members of a Malton Gliding Club. Sir Alan Cobham's flying circus visited the area in 1931. Frederick Slingsby, a furniture maker and others, formed the Scarborough Gliding Club in 1930. He built his own glider the next year. A glider crashed at Saltergate in 1932. Lord Grimthorpe, Nevile Shute and others hit upon the Sutton Bank site at Black Hambleton, which became home for the Yorkshire Gliding club. That year, the news bulletins announced that Flying Officer Mole was attempting to break the world gliding record at Sutton Bank. A Scarborough Aero Club plane landed at an East Heslerton drome in 1934, the same year in which Scarborough race course saw intermittent use as an aerodrome. The Heslerton drome had a club house and a hanger.

The Motor Car

Private motor cars remained scarce, despite the Ford. The Morris Minor launched about 1928, was sold at the Norton garage. By 1939 Robson's of Malton could offer an Austin for £128. These vehicles were beyond the pockets of all but a few, but commercial traffic began to motorise early. As the tradesman's van replaced the carrier' s cart, old hands complained 'You can't get nothing fetched now'. Pickering had to water the market place after dust storms were created by charabancs, and then banned them from parking there. The Post Office experimented

A Charabanc convoy stops in Thornton Dale

with motor cycles, instead of bicycles for country postmen in 1930 but it was too expensive. A visitor asked for the cobbler at Newton on Rawcliffe in 1933. The answer was 'We aint yan, only a motor van atcums yance a foot neeight, to tak beats awa ti mend and ee wor here yisterda'.

Bus services linked York with Ryedale, in the twenties, ending the Ampleforth college dependance on the Gilling railway. Local motor bus services joined the villages with market days in town and to some railway stations. The weekly bus from Rosedale to Pickering was remembered as 'packed like sardines'. Charabanc trips became popular for visitors with excursions to the six miles of dafodils on the Farndale banks, to the attractive town of Helmsley in the shooting season, to pretty villages at Hutton le Hole, Sinnington and Thornton Dale, and to the Rosedale hill climbs.

In time, blacksmiths' shops became garages or died out and village wheelwrights struggled. Alfred Rogers of Allerston, aged 78 in 1939, recalled road traffic killing the smithies, where he had worked as a boy, from six to six. William Sleightholme from Marton, about 1932, taught many their motor engineering. A network of petrol pumps spread to feed the cars. A fire destroyed pumps at remote Chop Yat in upper Bilsdale in 1936. The alteration of the roads to serve the vehicles would take fifty years, but a Sinnington bypass was made in 1938 and Baxtergate at

Whitby became an early one way street.

A Bit of Sport

Childhood was still skipping, playing hopscotch, marbles, tops and hoops, but with the weekly chores of fetching water from the pump, and taking the radio battery to be recharged. The main interest of many young men was village sport, and the important thing for many young women was young men. Football and cricket had their local village leagues, their matches far more important than those between distant county and national teams. Fourteen villages competed for the Malton area Challenge cup in 1922, but the flight of the young to bigger towns for better wages, soon reduced the number of local teams. A Sinnington hockey club formed in 1926, but Ebberston football club was wound up in 1930.

There were genteel innovations including games for young women. Gilling launched a ladies' hockey club in 1929. Tennis was thought a bit uppish, because few had courts or lawns. Pickering had six private courts but both Norton and Whitwell had their own clubs to make facilities available by 1938. Ganton, Malton and Kirkby gained golf courses and Pickering an indoor swimming bath. Slingsby Social club in 1937 was doing badminton, telepathy and 'keep fit'. Of a different appeal were the homing pigeon races of a Weaverthorpe club. North Grimston was still noted for quoits in 1938. A Bradford club began Rosedale bank hill climbs in 1924, which drew big crowds for several years.

Many old fashioned village occasions were basicly sports days. These had the potato race, three legged race, tug of war, arm bending, musical chairs and one mile cycle races for men and women. There were even hat trimming contests at Coneysthorpe sports in 1925. Public houses enjoyed a rebirth despite the wartime reduction of beer strengths. Club feasts were fewer but hot pie suppers lured domino players. Darts, the gatepost craze of the thirties, moved into the public houses, still largely a man's scene, with sawdust, spitoons, smoke, bets taken and talk of football.

A newly fashioned phenomena saw each younger generation adopting styles and behaviours for a few years, which scandalised their elders. There was shocked talk in 1920, of flappers with hair down over their ears and paint on their cheeks. Ryedale mothers worried about their daughters using 'lip rouge' in 1939. Music fashions came and went rapidly. The new gramaphones spread the new music. The lively village of Salton had a Foo Foo band.in 1932 and the Salton Players performed 'Tilley of Bloomsbury' in a dutch barn for three hundred people. Leavening dances to an old piano had seen farm hands in knee breeches and leggings with 'beetle crushers' teaching each other to dance the valeta. One lad tipped a pound of Epsom salts into the tea urn. A Brandsby Football Club flannel dance meant less formality, but dancing shoes were still required for the Oswaldkirk dance of 1922, where it was bad behaviour to dance with the same woman twice. Crazes for livelier dancing brought quicksteps, foxtrots, 'black bottom', and eventually reached swing and the jitterbug. The 'Lambeth Walk' and the 'Chestnut Tree' were danced at Lockton in 1939.

Village brass bands vanished as populations shrank but dance bands replaced them. The Scarborough 'Rhythm Weavers' played for Marton Cricket Club in 1936. Lady Beckett's hunt ball at Kirkby Tollbooth was in a different class. A fashion for fancy dress dances swept the thirties. Thirty couples judged at a Marton Fancy Dress Ball included entries as Turkish lady, Pirate and Gypsy by ladies and Mandarin, 'Willie from Stape' and 'a Chinaman' by the men. A Sinnington masked dance had an accordion band and Helmsley had a harmonica group. Timothy's Kirkby accordian band toured village dances in 1939. Pianos were bought for village halls. Ukeleles paved the way for the guitar, and a stable boy from Commercial Street Norton, called George Formby achieved national fame playing the ukelele in films. The Pickering Musical Society formed in 1919 and drama groups including Pickering, Barton le street and Thornton Dale 'players', began practised public stage performances that have continued ever since.

Fantasy Dream Worlds

Kathleen Macquoid's novel about Helmsley told of a 'rags to riches' village girl who won the squire. 'It may so happen, It may so fall. That I'll be leddy o' Duncombe Hall'. The romance, the dream moved to a more beguiling arena. The new cinema, initially known as the 'flicks', because it was like that, showed films without colour, often staccato and with local piano accompaniment. The silent screen captured the young of the towns. Here was an escape into a dream-like world of illusions, of handsome men and pretty women, who always wore clean new suits, of cowboys to cheer and Indians to boo, of space ships and cartoons, and epics and romance. The Exchange picture hall at Malton showed Charles Chaplin in the silent film 'A Dog's Life' during 1922, the seats 5d, 9d and 1s.3d. Spiegelhalter of Malton took films to the other Ryedale market towns.

Talking movies came in 1927. Thirsk had the Gaiety and the Ritz, Malton the Majestic and the Palace, where Ramon Navarro appeared in 'The Prisoner of Zenda'. Pickering had the Castle and the Central cinemas. William Sturdy built an early 'talkie' machine at Kirkby Moorside. Cinema comfort leapt ahead with push up seats and sweets to buy. The York Odeon opened in 1936, a splendid new cinema with seats for nearly two thousand and Scarborough had several giant movie houses. Charles Laughton, an actor from the town, won an early Oscar for his film performance as King Henry VIII. Imaginations were carried into new worlds, rich in American influence but an English film making industry supplied something different, with many actors, who felt obliged to speak with BBC accents. People laughed at American voices in strange places but the language changed again. A Ryedale village woman in 1937 was heard to say, 'O.K.baby'.

Work Outside Farming

The farming basis of the countryside remained but the role of agriculture as the main employer was ending. A woman in 1935 said that 'prices kept going up in Pickering but work didn't get any more plentiful'. Most new jobs were at the distant cities and towns, where many went to find them. Teeside with its great iron and steel works offered a strong lure on the far side of Blakey moor. Oil prospecting began on the North York Moors in 1935, though without early success. Potash salts were found in 1939 at Aislaby in Cleveland, basis of a future industry.

Rosedale iron extraction ended in 1926 after decades of working on a contracted scale. Rural corn mills and tanneries were closing too, as corn and hides were trucked away to the ports, but the roller mills at Helmsley, Kirkby and Easingwold lasted a little longer. Small mills lingered grinding farm feeds or working saws. A new bacon factory opened at Norton in 1935 and the Bower's and Malton Farmer's Bacon plants drew on a wide area to produce thousands of tons each year. Fred Slingsby developed a sailplane works at Kirkby Moorside. Quarrying continued for roads and houses but much lime was sent to Tees side for industrial use. Burdale quarry between 1925 and 1938 employed twenty men, based on a Nissen hut. Grinding and screening equipment to produce agricultural lime was installed at the Hovingham building stone quarry in 1932.

Kirkby Moorside had large scale brickworks. Light mineral railway lines were used at Hovingham and other woods for timber and at Pickering quarry for stone. Fish hatcheries were founded at Keld Head in 1931 to produce coarse fish, later adapted to produce trout. A new Forestry Commission founded after the war to produce national reserves of standing timber, progressively planted 50,000 acres of the North York Moors and dales, mainly at the eastern end of the limestone hills.The straight lines of conifers rose on marginal land and land out of cultivation. The early plantings gave poor results until the RLR plough was produced at Russell's of Kirkby Moorside in 1943. This cut a deep furrow through the natural underground iron pan, which had inhibited root growth.

World War Again

Preparations for a war with expansionist Nazi Germany began in the late thirties. The Royal Air Force was enlarged with new 'fighter' aircraft and new air fields including Linton on Ouse and Thornaby. Two thousand men camped at Heslerton anti -aircraft camp for one exercise, when the pilots of eight civil aircraft from Church Fenton decided not to drop bags of flour between eleven and one at night. The famous Spitfires were seen at Church Fenton airfield in May 1939. War games were held in 1936 with an army landing at Bridlington, which fought a battle between Malton and Market Weighton. The Duncombe Park army camp of 1938 held the Yorkshire Hussars and a Helmsley troop disgusted to be posted to their own home town. The Hussars kept their horses despite being mechanised. Army infantry units began to receive rapid firing Bren guns.

While the peace talks took place at Munich, a Malton cinema showed a film entitled –'how to put on your gas mask'. Village meetings to promote air raid precautions took place from Pockley to Thornton Dale during January 1939. One hundred attended an Air Raid Precautions lecture at Habton. Sirens to warn of attack were first tried in April and the biggest army manouvres ever, were planned for north Yorkshire in September. An early Radar Station was established on Staxton Wold.

War broke out that month. Air raid shelters were half buried in backyard trenches, the first known 'kits' arriving as a set with spanner, nuts, bolts and corrugated iron sheets. Grosmont railway tunnel became an air raid shelter and Battersby chimney was blown up as a likely guide for enemy aircraft. Police and air raid wardens wore 'tin helmets'. Evacuated children from Hull and Middlesbrough were billeted in homes at Ryedale towns and villages. One lad, continually asked to wash his hands, remarked 'It isn't an evacuee she wants, it's a duck'. Gas masks were issued to all and carried everywhere, until folk tired of it. Windows were blacked out nightly and you were fined for showing a light. Black out accidents were common. Fire watching enlisted those between eighteen and sixty. Sandbag walls guarded public buildings and schoolshelters. The coast was closed. Barrage balloons flew near Middlesbrough and searchlights broke the night sky above the moors.

The army went to France and into Belgium but was rapidly bypassed in May 1940, when the German armoured divisions broke through, and defeated the armies mustered against them. After a retreat to the beaches at Dunkirk, many soldiers were rescued but others became prisoners of war. France collapsed and Britain expected an invasion. Home Guards were formed and given battle dress. They had few weapons at first but the United States sent old rifles and machine guns. The Royal Air Force held its own against German fighter and bomber attacks, removing the threat of immediate landings. An air attack on Yorkshire airfields late in 1940 brought down a Junkers 88 near Duggleby howe, the pilots greeted and helped out by six villagers. In expectation of invasion, the Home Guard established a hide at Red House farm near Wharram, in which to go to ground and re-emerge as a resistance.

The war economy picked up rapidly and by 1940 there was full employment, the first time for decades. Scarcities were everywhere and yet some newly employed men bought their first suit. German submarines made heavy attacks on shipping causing great loss. The American 'lend lease' programme saved the day as British resources ran out. Rations were fixed at twelve ounces of sugar, four ounces of bacon and four ounces of butter per person a week. Increasing numbers were conscripted into the army, navy, air force and merchant fleet. Women took over many of the jobs they left. It was a nation at war. When troops were billetted on locals, they received three shillings a night for officers, sixpence for men and twopence, if the man had no bed.

When the German leader sent his huge armies to attack Russia, the possibility of a victory re-appeared and collossal German losses in the east were the most decisive factor in bringing that about. British soldiers

Kirkby Moorside in the 1920s above and 2003, below.

opened up battle fronts against the Italian colonies and eventually cleared Abyssinia and Libya. The Japanese attack on Pearl Harbour in 1942 brought America into the war and made eventual victory certain. British forces retreated into India and many became Japanese prisoners at Singapore. After landings made in 1942, Anglo-American forces together swept the Germans and Italians from North Africa.

The R.A.F Bomber Command launched a sustained air offensive against German towns, in which local men fought and died. Wombleton airfield was later taken over by the Canadian air force. Their Halifax aircraft had trouble getting off the ground fully loaded and the moor edge claimed many victims. Hambleton Gallops west of Helmsley gained a dummy decoy airfield to divert raiding German aircraft. Others were placed on Blackamore to divert bombers from Teeside. A passenger train fell in a bomb crater near Coxwold. Four bombers straddled Kirkby Moorside station but the bombs didn't explode.

A North Riding RAF squadron flew escorts for shipping. Here lay the greatest threat as German submarines made heavy inroads on North Atlantic convoys. Food imports fell by half, requiring a crash programme to expand arable cultivation, managed by War Agricultural Executive Committees. Land fertility committees raised farming yields and standards with subsidies, and control of scarce cattle nuts, poultry foods, and fertilizers. 'Dig for Victory' allotments appeared everywhere. Local children collected rose hips to make syrup. Curiously, the nation's health improved with subsidied milk, vitamins, orange juice and cod liver oil distribution, widespread use of such foods as 'spam' and dried egg, and the more equal distribution of basic foodstuffs brought by rationing. The Women's Land Army reported that they had killed 27,141 rats in 1943 in the East Riding of Yorkshire. Some of the girls worked in the Castle Howard park, after it was ploughed up.

Iron railings were taken from gardens and gates for making weapons. The radio unified the nation, its bulletins the main gauge of what was happening for years, when what was happening was rarely good. Italian prisoners in 1942, and later Germans taken in North Africa, came to the Eden prison camp north of Malton. Much of the North York Moors became a battle training ground to prepare for the return of British, Canadian and American armies to North Europe, with detachments from many nations who had been exiled here, including many Polish servicemen. The Helmsley station master Ernest Leaman counted 3.000 tanks through in one year. The Welsh Guards stationed at Pickering from 1943, trained in 'Cromwell' tanks on the moors. On one occasion they were given the local task of recovering an escaped lion, walking the streets of Pickering. The 22nd Dragoons regiment from 30th Armoured Brigade lived in Nissen huts for eighteen months in Duncombe Park, training with 'Cruiser' tanks on the Hambletons.

Second Army manouvres, on the Wolds and in the Vale, preceded the great move southwards, preparatory for the landings in Normandy. King George VI came to inspect the Guards Armoured division at Langton. The 22nd Dragoons re-equipped with 'Sherman' flail tanks, led the D-day landings, clearing mines from the beaches. The sailplane works at Kirkby Moorside had produced many of the troop carrying gliders, used on D Day and again for the air borne landings at Arnhem in Holland. Teeside works produced the concrete and steel sections for the Mulberry harbour units used in the landings on June 6th. The armies fought their way into Germany which collapsed in 1945. Other local men served in the hard fought campaign up the spine of Italy and in the Burma jungle, fighting in the Far East. On August 6 1945 an atomic bomb was dropped on Hiroshima and three days later another on Nagasaki which led to the surrender of Japan. Young men and women returned home to another life and yet the war seemed to define the life of several generations for years to come. The country was bankrupt.

Social Improvement

The British economy was shattered by the war, with overseas investments, export markets and much of the merchant fleet lost. Ever greater austerity was invoked for the peace. The nation was urged to 'Export or Die'. The fresh meat ration was reduced to sixpence a week in 1948. There was little sugar till sweet rationing ended in 1949. Derationing of meat had to wait till 1954. Well fed families had eggs or a cereal with milk, and bread and butter for breakfast, meat, potatoes and another vegetable followed by a pudding for lunch, and bread butter & jam for tea. Some did better than that and some didn't do that well. Houses were short, and some disused army camps became local 'squatters' parks'. 'Holidays at home' gave the first Carnival weeks in 1949. Post war austerity only slowly receded.

The social achievement of these decades was notable. Some had been planned under the war-time coalition government. They were brought into being by a Labour government. War time taxation levels were retained and government spending was higher than before. Free school milk and dinners introduced in 1946, were a boon when rationing included fats and bread. Child allowances came in 1947. National Insurance schemes were adopted and a National Health service was launched in 1948, with health care for all, regardless of ability to pay. Both dental treatment and spectacles were provided free, bringing quick improvements to many lives. Market town libraries were opened.

Progress wasn't all a result of government decisions. People turned out to be fitter on the leaner diets. Scientific developments gave major steps forward. Chest X-ray vans came to the towns in 1956 and welfare clinics shortly after. The use of 'antibiotics', notably penicillin, saved many lives and transformed many illnesses. When the local physician, Dr Murphy retired at Pickering about 1967, some sixteen hundred people gratefully subscribed to his retirement gift. He later remarked that 'before penicillin there wasn't a lot we could do'.

The 1944 Education Act offered primary and secondary education for all, abolished fee-paying and fixed eleven as the age for leaving primary for secondary education, with an 'eleven plus' examination to decide which kind of secondary school pupils should go to. New secondary schools were built, teacher training improved, and the number of teachers increased. Malton had Grammar and Modern Schools but the Pickering Lady Lumley's School served for a time as a bilateral school. The Ryedale county modern school opened at Welburn in 1953. Over several years, libraries, equipment and playing fields were improved. Many village primary schools were single teacher schools, in buildings over a hundred years old. Many were closed and children were taken by bus to a smaller number of better equipped schools. In the 1960s, the eleven plus was abolished and mixed ability teaching adopted in comprehensive secondary schools. Two decades later a national curriculum was enforced by central government. The over all result was a dramatic improvement in levels of education, the years spent in school and the number going on to higher education.

Village Life Not So Long Ago

A farm at the Wold village of Acklam in 1947 had only an oil lamp for lighting. The village had only four houses which possessed water closets and water taps. Many homes had earth or brick floors and low ceilings. They were remembered as 'never any better for cleaning but they were warm'. The nearest doctor was at Malton. An Acklam woman was asked if she ever had a permanent wave or used make up. She replied 'my husband likes me as I am and he's the one that has to look at me'. A villager from Coneysthorpe, in the Howardian Hills, later recalled that 'you were able to walk up and down the village and that there was always someone you would meet for a chat'. Later on, he didn't feel that was the case. The reading room had papers and sometimes a dance. The anual picnic on the green was a high point of village life.

A Cropton girl raised in the period was bathed in the tin tub. She and her sister once dropped it. They slept three to a bed, using candles to go to bed and they once set the bed on fire. The toilet was reached by a cold journey outside, day or night. On mischief night they painted the toilet seat with tar. Mother sat with sick friends and baked for them all. All the children in the large family went to Sunday School and 'this gave mother a break'. Things were interdenominational in a practical sort of way. It was 'best dress for Church in the morning, followed by Chapel Sunday School in the afternoon'. New dresses were made for the Chapel Anniversary, and 'that was it for the year.You didn't have to grow very fast'. The pig killing was an important time. On threshing days, they carried the chaff and killed rats.

After school, there was cricket in the street, rounders, fox- off and making dens in trees. The best room had a piano which mother could play. They sang songs like 'Whistle while you work', from the film 'Snow White' and jingles like 'Attlees got it, Churchill wants it', a comment on the succession of the Labour government. Now and again they heard a concert party. A great aunt from Bradford came and gave them 'threepenny bits'. Winter brought sledging on Cropton Bank and a Nativity play. They rolled eggs on Easter Monday and kicked the can on Round Hill. They sang around the village street to raise New Year money. As the girls grew up there was Brownies, Guide camp at Elleron, tennis club and daily journeys to a distant school. On the Sunday school outing to Scarborough, they had thirty minutes in a boat on the sea.

Many villages and dales were declining rapidly in the post war decades. Rosedale east side shrank from 297 to 203 people between 1951 and 1961. There had been 2041 people in 1871. The village of Aislaby shrank from 166 to 66 between 1871 and 1961. Many houses were demolished. Others became the weekend cottages or holiday homes, which could yield a better return than a local tenancy. Village schools became too small to sustain and the fewer children were bussed to distant schools. There was a drift into the market towns but they only just held their own. Some villages on the bus routes had a different experience. Thornton Dale had ninety three houses built between 1968 and 1972.

Table 51. Population	1931	1951	1961	1971
Pickering urban and rural areas	9349	9567	8939	9363
Malton urban and rural areas	10300	9877	9507	9222
Kirkby rural area	4907	4785	4407	4175

The Ryedale population was ageing, with fewer children and young people, but with more in the older age groups. The doctors noticed it first. The village of Allerston had seventy houses about the village in 1970, of which two were empty and one was a weekend cottage. Thirteen of the seventy were new houses or bungalows built in the previous five years. Sixteen village families still farmed. There was a shop, a public house, a church and a chapel, a mill and two craft workshops, but no school. Half the houses had the telephone and more than half the households ran a vehicle. The village population of one hundred and seventy included thirty eight old age pensioners. Many villages were not quite what they once had been, but most were still there. The changes would go much further.

The Cold War

Britain slowly withdrew from its military and administrative involvement in a vast 'empire' and from the world wide commitments acccepted as part of the Second World War. A series of military and political crises punctuated these decades and local men saw military service in Greece, Malaya, Korea, Germany and elsewhere. Attitudes to the process of disengagement were very mixed but the country could no longer pay. The army, navy and air force were steadily reduced in size and changed in character. There was a slow acceptance that Britain was a small country instead of a great power. A whole wealth of careers were lost in colonial administration. Edward Harrison came back from hard experiences with the Methodist Missionary Society in China. A Nunnington-born man returned from service with the Crown agents for the Colonies in twenty one countries, during which he had helped to introduce mechanical cultivation to several parts of Africa.

A new kind of blight came with the revival of mutual hostility between the communist countries of Russia, its satellites and China on the one hand and the capitalist west on the other. This was called the 'cold war', experienced as a 'wartime atmosphere in peacetime'. A Pickering man had seen Britain's first hydrogen bomb explode over Xmas Island in 1957. The threat of a general conflict, perhaps including the use of the more destructive new weapons, hung over several decades. The War Department of the national government took over huge acreages of Lockton and Helmsley moors for tank training and air force bombing ranges. A 'nuclear bunker' was built near Goathland for recording fallout after any nuclear attack on Yorkshire.

By 1963 an impressive early warning station, visible as three gigantic white globes, and employing over five hundred people, known as 'Fylingdales', was in operation on Lockton high moor. This was designed to give sufficient warning of a missile attack, to allow devastating retaliation, and consequently to deter any such attack. It had its opponents. Peace campaigners and nuclear disarmers periodically camped in protest at the gates. The Cold War atmosphere only ended with the collapse of the Soviet Union in 1989-1991. When the three great white 'golf balls of Fylingdales, were replaced by a pyramid structure for tracking satellites in 1991, there was almost a nostalgia for the old shapes, though not for what they represented. Fylingdales also heralded dramatically, the future, more general, arrival of 'high technology'.

New Ways of Getting About

Traffic jams appeared on bank holidays in Ryedale during 1950 as petrol rationing ended. Movement of the products of farm and factory rapidly changed from rail to road, and from horse and cart to motor vehicle. The Pickering-Scarborough rural railway line closed in 1950 and the railway lines to Kirkby Moorside, Helmsley, Gilling and Pilmoor ended over the next decades, until finally the Malton and Pickering to Grosmont line, linking with Whitby closed in 1965. Only the York-Malton-Scarborough line remained within the district, supplying visitors to the still popular seaside resort and providing a railhead for central Ryedale. The age of the transport hauliers followed. Slater's fleet of waggons from the Marishes, Smith's of Pickering lorries and Cook's bulk milk carriers from Kirkby Moorside seemed to be everywhere, with the vehicles of factory and farm, and suppliers from

Pickering in the 1930s, above and in 2003, below

outside the district. Vehicle capacities rose to twenty tons and then higher. The first motorway, the M1, was made up the spine of England in 1959 as a new national road system, characterised by rapid movement, began to replace the rail network.

Local roads had evolved for local purposes. The major through roads were few and they passed through the towns and villages not around them. Many roads had more roadside verge than track, and both rural roads and 'unadopted' urban roads were rutted earthen tracks. Kirkby Moorside was the first Ryedale town to be given a bypass in 1949. Keldholme near Kirkby was given a by-pass in 1963 and in 1967 the hump backed Yedingham bridge was replaced by a new flat bridge. Despite mounting pressure for road improvement, the local councils hadn't the funds to deal with minor roads, beyond filling a few 'potholes'. When the Castleton to Hutton le Hole road was improved in 1954, many without cars of their own, thought it excessive. Car ownership spread rapidly, including the many 'mini' cars of the sixties. Opponents derided the 'worship of the motor car'.

There were still many without access to a car or motor cycle. The pedal cycle was the general local means of travel and it was the motor bus that linked villages to market towns. There were few of them and you knew your timetable. Three buses a week went to Pickering from villages to the west. The Saturday night bus was 'the pictures bus', timed to suit cinema goers. Bill Robinson ran from the White Swan yard. The bus was packed with Wrelton folk, who used to race from the cinema. One villager recalled going to Fusco's fish and chip shop, where for 2s.6d you could get as much as you could eat in the back room, but he said, 'we had them in a bag'. For ten shillings, you could have 'a grand night out', provided that you didn't miss the bus. United automobile services went further afield, linking Ryedale to the coast and the cities, as well as providing a local service, 'smokers at the back'.

Changing Rural Industry

There were never sufficient jobs to employ young people growing up in the district. 'There's nothing for them here', was a common remark. A steady stream went to wherever the jobs were. For a time Malton and Pickering had employment exchanges and even youth employment bureau, but they vanished along with other branches of government and social services to distant towns. Other people came into Ryedale to live and some travelled daily to work here. No longer were jobs expected to be near the family home though a minority found otherwise. Trains and buses took some to the confectionary firms, Rowntrees and Terrys, or the regional British Rail workshops and offices at York. Dale Electric, Plaxtons coach body works, and McCain International Foods, producing potato chips, at Scarborough were in reach of some people. There were opportunities, across Blackamore, at Teeside, at Imperial Chemical Industries, in production from 1950 and in potash extraction at the new deep Boulby mine from 1973, but the ironstone mines and the steelworks closed. Expanding car ownership, further divorced place of work from place of residence. For the majority, education became the preparation for some place else.

The Ryedale economy changed.The market towns had lost their tanneries, roperies and many smaller workshops and yet an amazing diversity of small businesses remained. The collapse of old rural industries continued. Farm and railway employment rapidly declined. Pickering lost its stock market in 1965, though Northern Butcher's kept a Hide and Skin collecting centre. Several of the local corn mills dropped out of use, that at Raindale moved to a Museum in York. Wharram quarry sent out Wolds stone until the railway line closed in 1958. Wath quarry sent thousands of tons of limestone by rail to Dorman Long's works in the fifties. The closure of the last iron works in 1964 ended the demand for limestone as a flux. The Forestry Commission had begun as a major employer and a forest workers' village was built at Dalby in 1949 but forestry soon ceased to be labour intensive. The Rose's and the Russell and Wrangham's breweries at Malton were bought out and phased out. Behind the scenes, there was already evident the shift from primary production and manufacture towards the service trades. By 1959 57 % of insured people in Pickering, Helmsley and Malton employment exchange areas were in the service trades.

Other industries did well. The district held many small employers rather than a few dominant large works. Hargreaves quarries at Pickering employed thirty quarry men extracting stone for road making in 1966. Human stone breakers had given way to a crusher which dealt with twenty four tons at a time. Half a million tons went to the Malton bypass. Slater's at Thornton Dale built up a large business, quarrying limestone for conversion to ground lime and flour for use in cattle and poultry foods. Burgess Feeds Ltd at Thornton Dale mill made the famous Gold Medal plain flour but was sold in 1963 and adapted to produce over seventy thousand tons of animal feed compounds a year.

Table 52. Some Employees at Firms in Malton, Pickering, Kirkby Moorside Urban and Rural Districts in 1969

	Pickering	Kirkby Moorside	Malton
Clothing Factory	102		
Sawmills	47		
Egg Packing	37		
Nurseries	76		
Forestry	112		
Builders etc	50		53
Garages	42	14	60
Coal distributors	14		
Road haulier	10	15	
Hotels	35		
Transport	154		
Feeds	69		
Brickmaking		28	
Micrometals		14	
Agricultural engineers		72	27
Joinery		55	
Sailplanes		104	
Forge		17	
Laundry		32	
Hospital		94	
Agricultural merchants			188
Builders merchants			40
Mineral waters			23
Plastics			24
Abatoir			9
Brewery			47
Food processing			174

Bricks were produced in quantity at Kirkby Moorside. Thomas Tate Smith, a firm, going back to 1888 at Malton expanded production of the popular soft drinks and mineral waters, which now found their way into plastic bottles. Several nurseries expanded. There were new pig, egg and poultry rearing specialists and two Malton bacon factories. The building trades, road haulage and vehicle repairs grew busier. The

Early Warning station and Flamingo Park Zoo were major new employers.

Two exiled Czechoslovaks had established Saw mills at Pickering in 1940 and there were several estate saw mills. Joseph May & Sons founded clothing factories, employing women in 1950-51 at Pickering and Norton, when Leeds was short of labour. The Ryedale Printing Works formed at Helmsley in 1954, later expanded and moved to Kirkby Moorside. Westlers moved to Amotherby, producing canned goods for caterers. The Malton Mineral company at Castlegate mills made trace element minerals. Palethorpe Sausages at Helmsley employed thirty or so. A few surviving crafts were notably successful in adapting to meet more specialised demand, including Wilf. Dowson of Kirkby Moorside, the wrought iron smith at Kirk Forge and just outside the district, Thompson's the woodcarvers of Kilburn, whose fine furniture, bearing a carved mouse, remains renowned. The diversity of employment gave some strength, since not all industries were likely to suffer trouble together.

George Russell had moved to Ryedale in 1848. He took the Salton blacksmiths shop the next year at a rent of £7 and made ploughs, corn drills and scrufflers. A son moved to Kirkby Moorside about 1890 and built up the works of the Yorkshire Patent Drill Company at West End. The 'Kirkby Moorside root drill' was the basis of their business into the middle of the 20th century. Other companies formed by the Russell's family developed root thinners, light root drills for sugar beet, and rubber tyred carts. In 1934 the Kirkby Moorside glider factory was built and Slingsby sailplanes was made a separate company. The Russell famous RLR plough solved the forestry problem of penetrating iron pan which had seriously limited the value of early plantings. The firm pioneered a wide range of new agricultural equipment. Russells of Kirkby by the seventies produced elevators, spaced seed drills, powered tool carriers, bale carriers and other specialised equipment.

First Steps Towards Conservation

A Yorkshire Fisheries Board hatchery opened at Pickering between High Costa Mill and Keld Head springs, on the river Costa in 1947, with fifty four ponds, each able to be isolated, and their water changed every twelve hours, for restocking the Yorkshire rivers. The Forestry Commission planting of the poorer valley slopes of the tabular hills had begun to creat a green canopy, mainly of conifers, since 1921. This gathered pace in the post war years, as more marginal land was acquired. The 'smokeless zones', started nationally in 1952 began to clean the very air we breathed and the appearance of the buildings we lived in. The Teeside industrial district to the north was still sometimes covered by a pall of smog and the froth of pollution in moorland streams made them look like a sink over charged with washing up fluid. There was high though invisible air pollution.

Some 554 square miles of Blackamore were designated as the North York Moors national park in 1952 with the aim of conserving the heather moorland, old woodlands, the coast and farmland. This was only national in the sense that it had national recognition and it was not a park, being almost entirely privately owned, but much of the moor was open, being managed for sheep grazing, and by burning and cutting to increase the grouse population for shooting. Some other areas were partly accessible by footpath and road. About a third of the park was in Ryedale. This was principally a planning control device, not a means of increasing public access. The body given responsibility for running the park, the county council had actually opposed its establishment. A battle was fought to prevent a reservoir being established in Farndale, but TV masts in Bilsdale west moor, road improvements, new toilets and picnic areas were managed in the interests of conservation.

Down on the Farm

Farming techniques changed in the peacetime decades. Prices stayed bouyant for many years and with the support of government grants and subsidies brought about a technical revolution, which gave bigger output per acre, and good returns from stock. High Mowthorpe farm was bought in 1949 by the government to become an Experimental Husbandry Farm, where new developments were tried out under controlled conditions. The Ministry of Agriculture in 1964 opened an advisory office at Pickering, to serve nearly five thousand farms in a broad area. New land was taken into improved pasture and cultivation, including six per cent of the remaining moors by 1975.

High yield crops were encouraged by the use of new strains, supported by chemical fertilizers and weed killers, and with protection by pesticides, fungicides and herbicides. Renewed investment went into farm buildings for drying and storing grain, siloes, Dutch barns, new ways of housing stock, wood sheds instead of stone byres, with corrugated iron and weatherboarding replacing thatch. Better fodder crops, silage making and electric fences changed pasture management. Many farms in town streets and later village streets closed.

Dairying was important on and below the limestone hills Milk marketing boards operated guaranteed prices subsidising dairying. Fresh animal health measures brought a new science based stock farming. Milking machines came onto farms. Refrigerated tankers moved milk. Milk separating, churning and cheese making moved to the factory. The famous dairy herds included those of R. Baker at Giverndale head, Major Ringer's Ayrshires and Jerseys at Sinnington Manor, Mr. Baldwin's Guernseys and Ernest Aconley's Newton on Rawcliff herd of British Friesians, all well known at the Dairy show.

Horses disappeared from the farmyard. Mechanisation of field work came with the general adoption of tractors and combine harvesters. Men no longer lived in. New equipment was steadily adopted, including more developed tractors, and lifting gear that would take twenty times the old balers. A Marshall tractor appeared at Cropton in 1947. A Fordson tractor in 1965 was £295. The machines became more powerful and more expensive but a contractor might lift a crop in a few hours. Men were needed less and the farming population continued to shrink. Small farms became family businesses again but there was talk in the seventies of barley barons, supported by a bouyant beer market on the Wolds. There were probably a few beef barons too, as the beef burger became a national addiction. The growth of food canning and freezing expanded the field cultivation of vegetables.

New Ways of Life

Houses had not been built during the war years and the peace brought shortages in the market towns. Private and council building expanded in the fifties and was sustained for several decades. New council housing estates spread around the towns, often with a distinctive character of their own but houses remained scarce. Many proved as strong in 'neighbourhood' as any village. A handful of selected villages saw some new building. By 1966, Pickering rural council was managing 173 council houses in fifteen villages out of a total stock of 1781 dwellings.

A new problem was that more housing was needed for fewer people. The Pickering population fell between 1951 and 1961 by 143 to 4193 people, and yet between 1955 and 1959, a hundred new houses were built. Since the size of households continued to shrink, more

Yorker's Gate, Malton around 1910, above
and the Market Place in 2003, below

houses were needed than ever. As late as 1976, a Malton councillor stood for election on a ticket of reducing waiting lists for council houses. When a Pickering working man who had been married for thirty five years got a modern bungalow in June 1977, he had been on the waiting list three and a half years. He said that it was 'a grand council house. There was an inside toilet but you starved to death in the kitchen with a draught. They've cleaned Pickering up a lot the last year or so'.

It is hard to imagine that in 1951 of the 4336 people living in 1298 households in an urban district, 48% had no fixed bath, 25% no water closet, 25% no kitchen sink, 22% had no piped water and 4% no cooking stove. A government policy of 'improvement grants' steadily fostered the modernisation of older houses. A do-it yourself home improvement movement added many more, small but important changes to home life. Evening Institute classes flourished, to teach you how to do it. The Scarborough Technical College from 1951 offered new chances within reach, for pursuing studies beyond what the local evening Institutes could do.

As electricity spread, urban street lighting was changed over from gas, and you no longer sent the children with the accumulator weekly for recharging. Household shopping bulked larger in family budgets. There were mangles with rubber rollers instead of plain wood. Linoleum and carpets were bought as never before, and furniture and furnishings. Lavatories that flushed with water and even the occasional hot water system appeared. Over twenty years, inside toilets, and bathrooms or showers became almost universal. By 1971 most families had a television and a vacuum cleaner. Some even had a washing machine and a refrigerator. Within a few more years, many had both a washing machine and a refrigerator that included a small freezer. It was not the things themselves that mattered, but that they changed lives.

Homes became more comfortable, less bleak and more personal. Mechanical cleaners and washing machines reduced housework, making the old carpet sweepers seem modest indeed. Food storage by refrigeration altered shopping and cooking habits. Few grew all their own vegetables or kept a pig. The spending priorities shifted, with each decade as living standards rose. There were gramaphone records, canned fruit and condensed milk, even ice cream in the fifties. Pasteurised milk, pressed beef, fish fingers, remarkable trousers like overalls called 'jeans', and 'home perm kits' that wrapped women's heads in tiny rollers of a morning, marked the sixties. A by product of oil called 'plastic' which had appeared in 1909 as bakelite and in 1910 as

441

celophame appeared in a multitude of guises in the post war years, producing cheap households goods, and toys, with a revolution in packaging.

Cinemas still gripped the nation, although the giant screens, and such novel viewing as cinerama made little difference in the small local cinemas. A steady flow of A & B pictures, with news and advertisement slots, were offered in programmes which changed twice weekly. Some films like 'On the Waterfront', 1954 and 'Bridge over the River Kwai', 1957 seemed memorable, but it was the steady flow of drama, fantasy, adventure, horror and comedy, that added new dimensions to the imagination.

Television changed all that, enriching the options available for leisure at home. The British Broadcasting Corporation had started a television service in 1936 but no one had sets to receive it. A few television sets were available by 1951, when the Queen's Coronation was watched by many, invited to social parties with those who had. Commercial television began shows with accompanying advertisements in 1955. Within ten years, ownership of television sets became general and households commonly had their sets on for family viewing, twenty five hours a week.

For some years, enormous audiences watched the same things. A colour television worth £250 was a prize for a Ryedale playground association event in 1969 and they spread rapidly too. There were people who had their sets on for company, and one or two who spoke to them. Family viewing required seats and sofas, with arm fittings to carry the coffee and the beer. The access to sport, to shows for children, to nature programmes, to films, to famous comedians and to quality productions made for television, collectively offered a cultural leap forward, and a race of new heroes and heroines, called 'celebrities'. Quizzes, party games, conjurors, and a variety of other fillers held their own, while international news came home as never before.

An early local event to be televised was the novel 1953 Traction Engine Derby, a race of monster machines, organised at Pickering. Dorothy Sleightholme became a regular presenter of cookery programmes in 1959. Black and white soaps called 'Emergency Ward Ten' and 'Z-cars' for some years became almost national obsessions. Cinema going plummeted to a more modest role and radio took a back seat, although pirate radio stations enjoyed huge music audiences, to which new local radio stations eventually responded, including Radio York in 1974.

**The Malton and Norton Amateur Operatic
Society perform 'Calamity Jane' in 1974**

Leisure outside the home - the 'evening out' - was often divided, between men and women, and between different age groups. Public houses still had working class and middle class bars, or 'best ends', but one or two town houses pioneered a bar for the young. Domino drives and bingo gave many a regular treat in a friendly crowd, whether arranged by churches, pubs or clubs. Young people in these decades found that higher wages left some money for freer spending. Less crowded houses sometimes meant a room of their own. The 'youth culture' seemed amazing, with its own music and clothes fashions, not least 'rock and roll'. Young farmers' clubs held lively dances and occasionally a big name band came to a giant marquee. Enterprising volunteers arranged new Youth Clubs on the one hand and Older Peoples Clubs on the other, which spread to most sizeable communities, the last with such strange titles as Evergreens, Elderberry, Over- Sixties or Darby and Joan.

Pickering Women's Institute choir sang in the Royal Festival Hall at London in 1950. Like many others, the Welburn and Bulmer Women's Institute during 1969-70 held a monthly evening meeting, with a social half hour, talks on spies and old glass, and demonstrations on the use of latex foam, cooking, patchwork and herbs. There were small competitions, easy to take part in, for mincemeat, trifles, sponges, scotch eggs, a bowl of bulbs or a pretty ash tray. There were produce and handicraft guilds and outings. Football and cricket clubs were as vigorous as ever, but the leagues were smaller as shrinking villages saw some clubs abandoned. The market towns saw new clubs formed for the new enthusiasms, for bowls, judo and yoga.

The bigger villages Sheriff Hutton, Norton and Thornton Dale, like the towns, had drama groups. There were voluntary movements which in many places established the first children's play groups and less frequently play areas in the sixties. Volunteers established museums at Hutton le Hole, Pickering and Malton. Railway enthusiasts from inside and outside the district formed the North York Moors Railway Preservation Society in 1968, one of the most successful voluntary efforts, the area had ever seen. Within a year sidings were re-instated at Goathland and steam engines arrived at Pickering railway station.

Traditional Yorkshire ham teas, sausage and mash and boiled cabbage lost some favour. The better off ate more fruit and meat, the others more bread and potatoes. The desire for something tasty seemed to almost give the preference to artificial flavours. Fish fingers and many other quick- frozen and quick dried foods entered the diet. Cafes changed names to become wimpey and coffee bars. Eating out was becoming a treat. Battery chickens brought cheap chicken and chips in a basket at cafes and public houses. It was not all gain - a chicken with a solid backbone became hard to find. Fish and chips survived as the pioneering fast food, with several shops in each market town and others at spaced out villages, but the first Chinese takeaways appeared.

Social differences were probably as definite as ever, but as people became better off, they mattered less, until in the end they hardly mattered at all. Country houses proved difficult to modernise and to run without cheap servants. Some ended like Risebrough Hall with a fire in 1952. Some were demolished: John Carr's WiganthorpeHall in 1955, Welham Hall in 1957, Dalby Hall in 1961, John Carr's Sand Hutton Hall and Easthorpe Hall in 1971, to name a few. Oswaldkirk manor house became the Malt Shovel inn. Howsham Hall in 1958 was converted to a boy's school. Malton Lodge became a hotel in 1996.

New Ways of Government

During 1971, the old currency of pounds (£), shillings (s) and pence (d) was replaced by a decimal currency of pounds(£) and new pence(p). The farthing or quarter penny and the halfpenny vanished along with the florin (2s), the half a crown (2s.6d) and ten shillings paper notes.

Britain joined the European Community in 1973, an international association, which enacts binding legislation on its members and seeks to harmonise economic development and to raise living standards. The 1992 Maastricht treaty envisaged further moves towards a single market and common policies. Periodic negotiations between national governments involved a kind of horse-trading in particular advantages. The directives that embodied the new rules meant that some lost and some gained from the deals that were struck. The redistributive policies gave some grant aid to north east Yorkshire. The agricultural policy was widely perceived to favour French farming at considerable cost to Britain.

Neither the economy, the road system or other parts of the 'infrastructure', nor many other matters were any longer primarily local. Decision making was moving away from the locality. A new Water Authority in 1974 took over the management of the various water supply and sewerage schemes. The river Derwent was a major source of Yorkshire drinking water. A County of North Yorkshire was created in 1974 with responsibility for police, fire services, ambulance stations, hospitals, road modernisation, education and libraries, social services, care for the needy, and environmental services. These broad functions were not markedly different to what the North Riding County Council had managed before, but there were some significant shifts of responsibility, especially for roads. There was talk of strategic planning and behind the local changes, there emerged a growing tendency for more direction from central government.

The existing Urban District Councils of Malton, Norton and Pickering, and the Rural District Councils of Flaxton, Helmsley, Kirkby Moorside, Norton, Malton and Pickering were abolished and with them much of what had been local democracy in local government. A new Ryedale District Council was established, one of eight within the county responsible for housing, local planning and development control, environmental health, food safety and hygiene, refuse collection and other services. A large office called Ryedale House was built at Malton and opened in 1978, with the aim of concentrating staff in one place with modern office facilities. Despite efforts at public consultations, there was a loss of local involvement in local government. Press reporting of discussions at the older authorities had been detailed and lively. This largely ceased to be the case.

More than eighty Parish Councils were retained with slightly enhanced responsibilities for footpaths, bridleways, local lighting, parking, parks, allotments and children's playgrounds. These became significant channels for consultation. The Middleton, Aislaby and Wrelton Parish council in 1976 discussed planning applications, cycling on footpaths, play areas, advertisement signs, the burial ground, use of the old Sunday school building and the change of use of Wrelton Methodist Chapel. The next year, there were road improvements, best kept village contests, tree planting and siting a seat, street lighting near old folks bungalows, salting roads, the drains at Wrelton back lane, road widening, bus tokens, a scrap car dump and commons registration. This was local government.

The new Ryedale was initially 394,926 acres, within which 72.535 people lived, and it included areas north east of York, where old village communities were experiencing very rapid growth, with many young families, whose employment was in and around York. Huntington in the commuter belt was the largest community, with 8.224 people and there were seven fast growing villages which looked like approaching the size of small towns. They already held two to three thousand people each. They were unlike either the old towns or the villages in character, sprawling out from village centres, in expanding housing estates. The district was an artificial creation and the reasoning behind it was soon abandoned. Further local government changes in 1996 reduced the area to 580 square miles with a population of approximately 48,200. This meant that a third of the population was transferred to York. The largest communities remaining were Norton, Malton and Pickering in a traditional rural area.

Thirty one conservation areas were registered in Ryedale to protect the built heritage and over two thousand buildings were 'listed'. This kept the character of the market town centres, which were seriously at risk. The Howardians Hills gained recognition as an area of outstanding natural beauty. A growing awareness of the need for care of the natural environment was heightened when a nuclear explosion at Chernobyll in Russia in 1986 scattered radio active fallout over northern Britain. In 1989 came the switch to unleaded petrol. Plastic bag waste collection replaced dustbins in the eighties. Local quarries were selectively renamed as civic amenity sites. Wild deer re-appeared near Pickering in 1981. The final disposal of the growing mountains of household waste and recurrent lowland flooding remain unsolved Ryedale problems. Yorkshire societies had already created nature reserves and seventy volunteers might be found from the Yorkshire Naturalist Trust bracken beating around the Bridestones. Several sites of special scientific and other interest were given some protection. Among several nature conservation ventures was a small nature reserve created by voluntary effort at Sheriff Hutton castle.

The Start of Rural Tourism

Fred Spencely was a Rosedale veteran. In 1966, he could remember when the dale had four grocers and there were five railway engines at Bank Top. The population was down to 151 people on the east side and 83 on the west side, instead of the hundreds when the mines were working. He said that 'this was still a good place to live. The blacksmith cuts your hair and we get every flake of snow that falls'. He thought that 'the new caravan and camping site had brought more people to the dale' and he welcomed that. 'There had been only ten children at the village school, but now there were twenty five. Miner's cottages had been done up for weekend use. Now there were two guest houses and four or five farms taking residents.' The story would often be repeated, over much of the district, in the years that followed.

The remarkable growth of tourist visitors to Ryedale proved to be beyond all expectations. Foreign holidays, in hot climates at new resorts easily reached by cheap air transport, substantially reduced the numbers of staying visitors at Scarborough and other Yorkshire seaside resorts, although tripper tourism remained strong. There was a parallel national growth in inland tourism for second holidays, together with more motor car touring and more day tripping in coaches to rural places. Together, they gave a much needed boost to the Ryedale economy, in the face of shrinking factory and farm employment. This was not always welcomed, at first, by those used to a different world.

Caravan camps multiplied in the seventies, at Coneysthorpe, Kirkby Misperton, Nawton, Pickering, Thornton, Welburn, Wrelton, Yedingham and elsewhere. Some said that caravan camps were a blight on the landscape. A local headmaster observed that they were cheaper than hotels, and gave people a holiday, who might otherwise not be able to afford one. Young people used the cheap youth hostels at Malton, Wheeldale and Farndale, and the fine purpose-built hostel opened at Helmsley in 1964. Holiday cottages were bought for a song in many shrinking villages and let for the season, remaining empty for the rest of the time. Hotels were upgraded at Helmsley, Kirkby Moorside and

Helmsley Market Place 2003 above and All Saints Church below

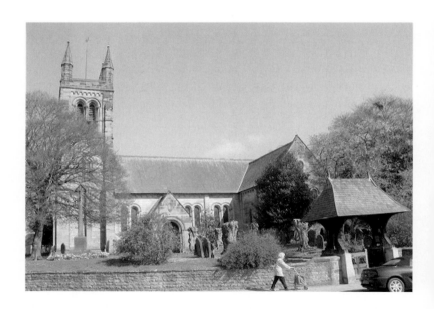

Eden Camp

Pickering. Public houses gained strongly by supplying bar-meals, and over two decades under went a revolution in appearance. One conversion in 1978 took ten gallons of paint. A Thornton dale inn gained a squash court and a riding school. Rural potteries appeared. Hotels found a rather substantial number of overseas visitors.

Pentland Hick showed considerable foresight when he began the Flamingo Park Zoo, in 1962, around a bankrupt country club at Kirkby Misperton, as a day tripper attraction within reach of the cars and motor coaches of the populous West Riding. Within a few years he added a fun park, while the zoo claimed the first dolphins and killer whales shown in England. Flamingoland developed into a 'theme park', where the only observable theme was having fun, immensely popular, with car and coach parties for day trips and for a large caravan population. The North York Moors Railway Preservation Society re-opened the line to Grosmont in 1973 taking steam engines through eighteen miles of moorland dales. The line proved immensely popular and Pickering joined Thornton Dale and Helmsley among the most popular destinations for visitors.

Countryside tourism played its part. Jim Hingston ran 'acorn camps' for the National Trust in Bransdale. Footpaths whose original

449

purposes had long been forgotten were revalued for ramblers and some efforts made to keep them open. Pickering Civic Society produced a town trail in 1975, a year when a new caravan site was proposed for Black Bull, near the town. A trout lake and farm was opened at Pickering where you could feed or fish for the fish in 1971. A windsports centre opened at Wombleton airfield including mircolight flying. The Forestry Commission abandoned its policy of excluding visitors and opened forest drives, walks, residential cabins and picnic sites. The Cranedale study centre opened on the Wolds at Kirkby Grindalythe. The Wolds village of Thixendale by 1989 had a tea garden, tea room, farm house bed and breakfast and cottage crafts as well as the Cross Keys. An Indian restaurant appeared on the York to Malton road.

Some of the attraction was in the heritage, some in the scenery. Nunnington Hall passed to the National Trust in 1952. Sledmere house opened to the public. Castle Howard, always a major tourist attraction, became better known through its use as a setting for such famous films as 'Brideshead Revisited', and added a costume gallery, gift shops, plant centre, adventure playgrounds, cafeterias and concerts in the park. Duncombe Park, restored in 1986, was a late addition to the list of open country houses, amidst parkland and near the Rievaulx terrace and temples. English Heritage in the nineties transformed the experience of visitors at Helmsley and Pickering castles, and at Byland, Kirkham and Rievaulx monasteries, by better interpretation, basic facilities and re-enactments. The Eden Camp modern theme museum near Old Malton pioneered a unique display of the history of the Second World War.

The Changing Place of Industry

The moors, the dales, the vales and the oceans were all scoured for new sources of energy. Oil riggs appeared at High Dalby in 1967. The North Sea oil was found shortly afterwards. When it began coming ashore in 1975, oil provided a major boost to the national economy. Young local men travelled far to join the oil industry. Drilling for natural gas started in 1952 and this was found at Grosmont in 1954. A large gas field was found under the North Sea in 1966. Jack Wigley of Kirkby Moorside laid long distance piping for natural gas across the moors and over farm land from Whitby to Malton. An extensive processing plant was built at Pickering in 1971 to deal with the gas from the Lockton field, but technical problems caused its removal almost as soon as it had been built. After the conversion to natural gas, the giant old gas holders at Pickering and Kirkby were removed in 1984. The exploration by Kelt UK spread to test wells at Kirkby Misperton in 1992. The extent of the Ryedale gas field was realised in the next year and Knapton became the site of an electricity generating station, using gas turbines to produce electricity.

By the seventies, every local authority in the country was trying to encourage 'light industry', but nationally, manufacture was running down. British industry steadily ceased to play the part in the world and the national economy that it once had. The siting of new factories and workshops was footloose, less linked with any local advantage, but attracted to low rural rents and low wages. The Government sought to influence their siting and to create jobs, by forming small factory and business parks near the towns and some villages, from the 1960s, equipped with basic facilities. This policy eventually succeeded, improving the evironment and achieving some economies. There were still losses to the local economy but there were also gains. Brick making ceased at Kirkby Moorside in 1975. Pickering Sawmills closed in 1989, due to pit closures and cheap imports. Bower's Malton Bacon factory, one of two at the town closed in 1990. A mensware factory at Norton employing 160 people closed in 1998.

Long established firms made notable contributions to the local economy. Norton Bright Steels was established in 1919, when Cris Chouler left a West Riding firm to set up on his own account. Bright Steels Ltd at Norton became the largest producer of bright drawn steel flats in England, employing around 140 people at a five acre site, extended in 1986. The family business takes pride in the long service of its professional staff. The bright steel bars are cold finished in drawing dies to accurate dimensions and shape, and with a good finish.

Two brothers Frank and Wilfrid Ward of Sherburn worked for their farmer father until they were thirty. They went into making farm buildings with designer H D Griffiths in 1949. By 1965 they had 170 on the payroll and were making large wide span steel industrial buildings, which they do to this day. Boythorpe Crop Stores in 1984 employed sixty three folk at Weaverthorpe making great containers from steel sheets.

The Malton Bacon Factory goes back to 1932 when the Yorkshire Farmer's Bacon factory was established from Sherburn in Elmet. After seventy years activity, it has become the largest employee in Ryedale, with two to three thousand employees. The firm gives employment to people from a wide area outside Ryedale as well as within it, including

Scarborough and York. Indeed, the story is told of people from overseas arriving at Leeds station and asking for 'the Bacon factory'. Its suppliers come from great tracts of rural Yorkshire, and the firm specifies high standards of hygiene and quality, as a major player in the wholesale market.

Derwent Plastics of Stamford Bridge opened a Pickering works at Westgate carr in 1969 employing 145 to make plastic mouldings for household goods and components of many kinds. This was acquired in 1977 by McKechnie Vehicle Components.

Christopher and Johnathan Shaw started MicroMetalsmiths making precision castings at Kirkby Moorside. By 1972 they were making components for the concorde jet aircraft. Slingsby Sailplanes in 1969 became part of Vickers Ltd. Torva Sailplanes opened at Pickering in 1971. The Slingsby Engineering Company made flight refuelling equipment and pioneered under water remote control vehicles, including miniature submarines. Slingsby Aviation made the firecracker training aircraft. Europa Aviation from 1991 supplied the firefly two seater training aircraft in kit form. Thompson Automation at Malton specialised in solving enginerering problems and in 1987 were making package equipment for production lines. Spritebrand at Pickering made system scaffolding for the building trade. Page Cycles made parts for mountain bikes at Edstone.

Where Goes Farming?

Specialised production farming grew. A pheasantry that started in 1953 at Cropton was by 1974 incubating 50,000 eggs yearly to supply shoots all over the country. More pig units appeared in the eighties. Kirkby Grindalythe manor farm had a pig fattening unit for near two thousand pigs in 1988. There was venison farming at Studfold farm, Ampleforth, the red deer herd raised from fifteen to two hundred and fifty within five years. Supermarkets and large suppliers to supermarkets tended to dominate much farming activity, out of market, with contractual agreements.

The generally bouyant farming years ended. There were farm mergers in the eighties and nineties when farm incomes were falling, especially for hill farms. The workforce dwinded further. 1984 was the year of the milk quotas when dairy farms were told to cut back because of over production in Europe. The common agricultural policy subsidy system had rewarded intensive farming. Guaranteed prices gave beef, butter and grain mountains. 1992 reforms gave lower guaranteed prices for grain but subsidies for land planted and for land set aside, where there was a surplus. Livestock payments per head of cattle and sheep were maintained. By 1996, farm incomes were said to have halved in real terms over ten years. Policies of minimising instead of maximising output and diversifying lay ahead, with a new stress on countryside conservation.

A major development came in 1998 when the ministry of Agriculture, Food and Fisheries sited the Central Science Laboratory near Sand Hutton on the Malton-York Road, bringing five hundred people from five sites together, for research into agriculture, the environment and food, but especially plant pests and diseases.

The Changing World

Nationally it appears that real household disposable incomes nearly doubled between 1971 and 1997. Over the fifty years to 1997, prices rose twenty fold, but average men's wages rose fifty times, and women's a bit more than that. There is no reason to doubt that Ryedale shared in the general trends, although even in 1999, average weekly earnings were only 70 % of those for the United Kingdom. Over thirty years, there was a profound change in living standards, unparalleled in earlier history, here as elsewhere in the country.

At first, not everyone welcomed all the changes. By the seventies, you could hear that 'people live better now than then, but you know people less. The villages were livelier with their own children in them. You can't beat your own food, there's nothing like a nice piece of fat bacon or home made Yorkshire puddings'. And 'men retire, we women plod on'. Raymond Hayes thought Hutton was livelier in the thirties than now, and there was the commonly heard opinion 'that you used to know everybody. You can go up there and not see anybody now'. To some extent, it was just a nostalgia, but there were real changes taking place. Some villages and dales seemed a bit empty. About a quarter of the people lived in the four market towns. They were growing and pretty lively. 'Incomers' had another opinion, quoting the old myth that it took you twenty years to get acceptance. They just didn't realise that those they were talking to, had mostly only been here five minutes themselves. In most places, there are far more incomers than natives of long standing.

Many newly married couples made early starts on home purchase, and more used 'hire purchase' or 'never never' payments to secure home equipment, from the start of marriage instead of saving to buy later. Flush toilets were soon taken for granted and with the passing decades refrigerators, washing machines, televisions and telephones came to be seen as essential. Clothing was cheaper and more was spent on leisure, including eating out. Fly mows replaced lawn mowers in middle class gardens. The eighties and nineties brought compact disc players, video recorders, camcorders, and satellite dishes to add choice in home entertainment. The electric razor was seriously challenged by the throwaway razor, and almost unbelievably towards the end of the century, the camera by the throw away camera. As the century ended, children were acquiring mobile phones. Many houses held a computer and the children had computer games players. People could talk without meeting.

The gap widened between high and low income groups, the latter including the large and growing groups of single parents and many pensioners. Wealth was even more unequally spread than income, but people seemed to care less, while their own living standards improved. Class differences persisted but were less of a pre-occupation. The pattern of tennis, boating and fast car for the one layer, chapels, posh newspaper and intense concern about their children's education for another, and the pub, pool, darts, football, bingo and gambling for a third was never the whole story. But if there was a new pattern for leisure, it was increasingly geared to age rather than class. Shorter working weeks meant that weekends and evenings offered significant time for the car, television and hobbies. Holidays with pay gave more chances for 'getting away from it all'. The rarer pursuits spread, if not to everybody, at least far wider than before, as golf became a popular sport, foreign holidays a popular destination and the car a near - universal possession.

Families stayed small but changing attitudes and greater freedom, including use of birth control pills after 1961, made many marriages less enduring relationships. Health authorities issued guides to healthy 'relationships', including the avoidance of the new disease called aids. A 'women's movement' registered a shift in decision making. Marriage break down became grounds for divorce in 1969 and divorce was soon as un-exceptional here as elsewhere. The number of divorces began to match the number of weddings. The conventions of Christian marriage were less frequently sought and by 1995 church weddings were becoming the exception instead of the rule. Many young people spoke of partnership, rather than marriage. Relationships replaced courtship for some. Many undertook living together before marriage. Single parent families became more numerous.

There were more older people. Old age, like other periods, became a stage of life, one in which there were four times as many widows as widowers. Life expectation had once been forty seven. Now it was seventy seven. For those fortunate in health, older years were taken more lightly, and became an age of opportunity. The breadth of opportunity depended on good health and the financial means available. Some had state pensions and some had occupational pensions or other provision. People lived long enough to get the new illnesses of the older years. Homes for the very old became an industry.

A considerable flourishing of voluntary societies came during and after the seventies in the towns and larger villages. Some were for the age groups, mother and toddler groups, playgroups, parent-teacher associations, guides and beavers, cubs, scouts and brownies, youth clubs and dinner clubs for the elderly. Many were for the enjoyment of sport - indoor and outdoor: bowls, badminton, billiards, bridge, cricket, football, golf, hockey, the hunt, microlight flying, pigeon flying, shooting, squash and tennis. Hobby groups included choirs, dance, dogs, flowers, allotments, painting, photography, music, yoga and keep fit. A distinct group of voluntary societies sought to alleviate or to raise funds for the alleviation of the problems of children and animals, of the handicapped, disabled and those with such problems as cancer, arthritus and spina bifida. Social groups like Round Table, Freemasonry, Lions, Rotary, the British Legion, Toc H, Working Men's Clubs, WRVS and church groups often had charitable as well as social aims.

A Better Road to Travel

From 1971 to 1984 Bill Bishop and near two hundred County Council workers presided over a dramatic upgrading of rural roads. They made them suitable for motoring, in the face of the relentless build up of traffic. Car ownership rose to include 80 per cent of households. A Malton bypass was finished in 1976. The eighties saw some stretches of moorland road straightened. Seamer bypass came in 1987 and so it continued. Parking restrictions came to the towns - the notorious yellow lines, ugly but necessary. Coopers shop moved from Pickering market place to a site with better car parking. Pickering tried a one way system in 1998. New backland car parks were made at Malton. Rustic garden centres proliferated. Car showrooms appeared in the countryside,with ranks of cars offered at prices it was hard to believe anyone could possibly afford. Even huge car boot sales took to the fields. Retail warehouses moved to out of town locations near Scarborough and York. Local supermarkets found compromise solutions, not always ideal.

Compulsory seatbelts were adopted in1983. Bus companies were privatised in 1986. School buses taking children to school became the most regular of the services. There were so many cars that public transport on minor roads became slight, leaving a problem for those without cars, and an opportunity for taxis and delivery services who filled the gap. A moorsbus service pioneered access to the National Park.

Bridges had to be upgraded to take the strain of giant container lorries of up to forty tons, and double decker buses in the nineties. There is an unsolved disjunction between the huge lorries and the traditional market places. The through roads, the A 64 (York Scarborough), A170 (Thirsk Scarborough) and the A169 (Malton, Pickering, Whitby) and the A166 gained the sophisticated road markings heralding a safer age. One railway line remained through the area, Scarborough and Malton to York. Roads to the coast still jam in the holiday seasons.

The Shifting Shop

Town and village retail shops steadily vanished after the sixties, in food, clothing, shoe repair and tobacconists. Small ladies-wear shops survived, while household goods and fancy goods suppliers actually increased. Thomas the Baker started in 1991 at Helmsley, soon had twenty shops, in market towns. Smart public betting shops replaced 'hole in the corner' betting. Yet, the spread of market place charity shops was the silent witness to many a retail departure. The emergence of small supermarkets, which challenged the grocery trade of smaller shops proved to be merely a stage. At Malton and Pickering, they were soon replaced by bigger supermarkets. Malton gained two supermarkets and Pickering one. This was only another stage as they too were challenged by developments outside Ryedale. There are stages yet to come.

Really large supermarkets at York and Scarborough, some in retail parks, lured the car drivers further away. The Clifton Moor shopping centre opened in 1988, and the Monk's Cross cluster of supermarkets and other large retail stores at York in 1995. Scarborough gained several supermarkets in town and out of town, and the large retail warehouses lining Seamer Road, which had not developed within Ryedale itself. The out of town sites allowed easy delivery, ample parking and gave customers wider choice, more comfort and price reductions.

Helmsley kept a more traditional shopping centre but with an early emphasis on serving visitors, with high quality shops. Kirkby Moorside had a smaller scale supermarket, open from eight in the morning till nine at night, on Sundays and Bank Holidays alike. A woman who had lived at Kirkby Moorside for sixty years remarked in 1990 that 'over the years, more houses had been built and a few shops shut'. Her main complaint was that 'to get to York, you have to get a bus to Pickering and change'. Of the local supermarket, she said 'The Spar is good for most things'.

The Good Life

By 1989, Ryedale was said to be one of the top ten most desirable residences in Britain. Pensioners and others from the cities, especially in the south of England found that they could sell their house for a good price, buy one in Ryedale for a much lower price and enjoy the difference. The cost of living was also substantially lower. A strong demand emerged for houses. Demand eventually exceeded supply and house prices rose rapidly in market towns and attractive villages, but without altering the advantages for buyers. Estate agents and building societies proliferated in the market towns. Young local couples marrying had to look elsewhere.

Eating out became more popular as a treat, as part of a holiday, as a regular meal for pensioners and as part of the life-style. National food fashions changed the opportunities available. Malton enjoyed an Espresso coffee bar in the seventies but later gained Italian and Mexican restaurants. Pickering cafes and inns were joined by Indian and Chinese restaurants. Rural restaurants and inns established reputations. Public houses everywhere abandoned chicken in a basket for wider menues, at every level. If 'fish and chips' held its own as the first 'take-away', 'curries' and a 'chinese', moved from being an adventure of the sixties, to a new century commonplace. Among the very young, the beefburger in various guises, won and retained an appeal.

Home eating probably saw changes just as great, with health food cults, fast food, frozen food, and ready cooked meals challenging traditional sausage and mash; roast beef, potatoes and cabbage, or

Yorkshire pudding with onion gravy. A European element entered the diet, with the widespread use of pastas, quiche, and pizzas and the foods of five continents, with stir fry and much else. The microwave opened the way for fast foods at home, and the word 'cooking' began to change its meaning, as women returned to work outside the home, and some men entered their kitchens.

Sunday became one day off in the weekend, as the appeal of church and chapel steadily waned. Attendance waned faster than membership as the fringe hearers vanished. There was probably a marked loss of religious faith. The voice of the churches was less often heard. Christians seemed to become a minority, less than fifteen per cent on optimistic estimates. Religious thinking seemed to lose its significance, remaining for most as only a few vague beliefs, perhaps called upon in times of stress. Anglican parishes were amalgamated and despite lay help there were fewer services and more locked churches. Numerous Methodist chapels were converted to private houses. Roman Catholicism had re-emerged in Ryedale in the century but seemed to experience similar trends. What went on in churches was becoming a culture unknown to those outside.

The premises used for leisure needed upgrading to match the rising standards of the home. Inns, hotels and public houses were dramatically improved, as they ceased to be primarily 'locals' and catered for all comers. It was not long ago that a woman wouldn't go into a public house without a man lest her reputation suffer. Soon , it would be the other way round. A visitor to a pub in 1963 found a cheerless table in a bare room, where he waited while the landlady served her husband's dinner and eventually offered him a bottle of beer. There have been few greater changes than those in the character of public houses.

Facilities for sport and leisure saw manifest improvement. The swimming pools at Helmsley and Norton were joined by a new pool at Pickering. Ampleforth College opened its sports facilities to wider use. Norton gained a leisure centre with indoor bowls. Pickering a fine new Sports centre. A few sizeable villages had clubs for bowls, billiards and badminton, and rather more for tennis. Playing fields, playgrounds and village halls were improved but the end is not yet. The old reading rooms, church halls and altered industrial buildings are sometimes dismal enough, in contrast with better conversions like the Kirk theatre at Pickering, and the Helmsley Arts Centre. There is not a lot of open countryside outside the moors. Simon Thackray pioneered 'The Shed' as an exciting centre for pioneering arts and entertainment at Brawby and

Ryedale gained its first resident professional theatre company when Alan Avery founded 'The Northern Lights Theatre Company' in 2001.

Tourism has gained from imaginative use of what was there, as well as from new initiatives. Market place tourist information centres proved a boon. The North York Moors Railway organised popular Wartime re-enactment weekends. They regularly feature 'Thomas the Tank engine' for children. The line and hence the district gained from its use in Television's Heartbeat series, which made Goathland into better known 'Adensfield', and more recently in 'Harry Potter' films. Elsewhere, traction engine, trucking, motor cycle, car and other rallies proved considerable attractions. A large roller coaster was installed in 1986 at Flamingo Park and the rides have proliferated. A narrow gauge steam railway opened at the old station house at Ampleforth. A Wolds foot path was established after long negotiations. Caravan parks invested in hard roads, good standings, main water, toilets and shops. A caravan park at Ebberston pioneered a family history centre. Several farms diversified to establish riding, walking, mountain biking, catering and other rural activities. Eden Camp founded as a war museum in 1987 by Stan Johnson proved to be a major visitor attraction.

A positive move towards quality craftsmanship in home workshops brought developments that were a boon to the tourist trade. Small breweries were opened at Cropton and Malton. Craftsmen and women made jewellery at Easthorpe, art candles at Hutton, pottery in the Marishes, at Kirkby moorside and at Hinderskelfe, woodcrafts and cabinet making at Ebberston, quality clothing and walking sticks at Helmsley, cane chairs at Leavening, felt products at Gillamoor, stone fireplaces at Hovingham, garden ornaments at Nunnington, fine furniture at Pickering and knitted woollens at Barton le Street. The Rosedale glass gallery quickly won praise. In 1986 a Norton man extended his chimney sweep service to cover weddings. Racing Stables, long the life blood of Norton, spread to more places than before, and proved they could produce a winner or two.

The market towns replaced their old surgeries with new health centres. Women have returned to work outside the home, often incidentally giving grand parents a new role, making the change practicable, but in other instances needing day nurseries. They say it is a more child centred world, but computer games apart, it is hard to see it. Eternal testing blights the school system and it takes a long time to raise funds for a children's playground. A skateboard park or two have lately appeared.

459

The influence of 'high tech' has gathered strength. Pickering had only four hundred telephone subscribers in 1955. The automatic telephone service began in 1963, replacing a row of operators at Malton in a year, in which local councils had rows about 'one arm bandits' and fluoridation. Transistor radios rent the air in the same days as the bikini appeared - the minimal bathing costume. In 1972 a Pickering girl left for Manchester University to take a computer degree. It seemed an unlikely thing to do at the time. The next year a dinosaur's footprint was found near Pickering station. Then there were pocket calculators. Within ten years, there was a row of computer books in the local library. The Midland Bank installed self - service cash machines in 1989, and older people tried desperately to remember their pin numbers. Cassettes were giving way to discs. By 1993, they say a third of houses had a home computer. Then, the older generation discovered them and everyone was taking the courses. When it all started, most men had worn hats or caps, now there was hardly a hat or cap to be seen.

Ryedale people live in a wide diversity of circumstances. Here is a countryside, which outside the five market towns, is very thinly populated by national standards. Single houses, hamlets, dales and villages, large and small offer new variations of personal and communal life. Town, village and dale news-sheets, e-mail and mobile telephone communication, supplement the car and the local paper. A glance at one issue shows a parish council mapping footpaths, a car boot sale for a church fund, a theatre club visiting the Alan Ayckbourne play at Scarborough, a darts knockout at the pub and a stall on the green raising £273 at bank holiday. Barton le Willows in 1999 was down from nine farms to two, no shops but five new houses and three barn conversions. The fish and chip van called on Fridays but there was a playgroup and aerobics. Acklam in 2001 had sports, carol singings, pie and peas suppers, and wine and dinner clubs.

Norton has become the growth point of Ryedale, an unrealized change, stretching back into the last century, when it grew from a village to a town. In 1801 there were 615 people but towards the end of that century there were 3,700. Now Norton is the largest community in Ryedale. If it lacks the presence of Malton, architecturally, shop-wise and socially, it none the less has the employment. There have long been moves to merge the two communities, and as long as there have been those moves, there have been others to resist them. Nontheless, as Norton firms adopt Malton names, and official pamphlets speak of the two places as Malton-Norton, the change may one day dawn.

Commercial Street, Norton. Malton.

Commercial Street in Edwardian 'Norton, Malton'

The four market towns of Helmsley, Kirkby Moorside, Malton and Pickering, are distinctive and each is a hub of retail and social activity. Town centres have just about managed to retain their character, a credit to those much criticised people who exercise planning control, while continually under threat from the needs of cars, lorries and commerce. If their attraction goes, the tourist and residential functions go with it. Malton has just launched a 'town centre initiative'. The core of each town needs guarding, and so far they have been guarded well. They are still let down by the occasional 'shop front horror'. Socially, few communities can be more alive than a Yorkshire market town, not big enough to be impersonal, but large enough for a diversity of enthusiasms. More than half of the people live outside the towns, but look to them for much that is needed, for many villages now have neither shop, chapel nor public house.

Individuals flourish in communities and out side them, but can have remarkable effect, in a thousand different ways. George Howard of Castle Howard was Chairman of the B.B.C. - few posts cast a wider net. George Baxter was the hermit of Rosedale, a recluse for forty years, who fired shots at any who came too close. Peter Easterby of Habton was said to have raised thirty winners, again, in one year, a valued contribution. A long series of remarkable men, Les Maw and Clarence Cartwright among others have led local bands at Malton, Swinton,

461

Young People of Ryedale in 2003

Pickering and Kirkby Moorside to competitive success, community regard and fun for their young players. Wilf Ward of Sherburn founded the Isabella Court Day centre for the handicapped in 1989.

Mrs Elizabeth Shields of Firby astonished local pundits when she was elected Liberal MP for Ryedale in a 1986 bye-election, turning a hopeless position into a 5,000 majority, after much spade work by her supporters. She was the first Liberal MP since 1905. Her stay in the House was to be short-lived, Ryedale returning to its traditional Conservative stance, electing John Greenway as its MP in the next general election, a position he has held since, despite National swings to the Labour Party at the close of the century. Local politics is dominated by Conservative, Liberal and Independent councillors with the Labour Party, despite determined efforts, making little headway, even losing its only Ryedale District Councillor, Gary Hobbs, in the 2003 elections.

In the autumn of 2000, Ryedale was again reminded of its vulnerability to the weather when heavy rains and melting snow on the moors swelled the rivers to overflowing. The beck at Pickering burst its banks and homes in Sinnington were flooded for the first time in living memory. The worst effects were felt in Malton and Norton where the area round the bridge flooded extensively, ruining homes and businesses and providing dramatic pictures for the national media of water lapping against the edges of the station platform. The rising tide of water swept down the Derwent and contributed to flooding in York. The Prime

Minister, Tony Blair, visited York and the Deputy Prime Minister, John Prescott, donned his waders to inspect the damage in Malton. Once the floods had subsided, extensive flood protection schemes were put in place at Malton and Old Malton and the A169 between Pickering and Malton was raised to bring it above water levels. Some blamed global warming, others farming methods on the Moors.

I asked two friends at Middleton, a main road community close to Pickering, to say what changes had come to that village over fifty years. They spoke of the labouring jobs in farming, nearly all gone due to machinery. Farm land near the village had been sold for building, and further away, hedgerows have been taken up to form huge fields. There are more retired people now, partly because younger couples can't afford to buy property and partly because there are few jobs locally for them. There has been a huge increase in traffic, which passes through the village. Quite unusually there is still a shop and a post office, pretty well used, and a shop at the garage. Both the vicar and a local doctor live in the village. There is little crime and no vandalism.

Some of the characters have gone. Mr. Sid; G.B; Johnny Harrison and Jim Gill. Some say that some of the old village spirit has gone with them. There were lots of children in the seventies, but fewer in the eighties and nineties. Now there are children in the village again, but they are not out and about so much, perhaps due to computers, play stations and television. Parents seem less willing to give up time for community events, even for their own children. The old Sunday School room has lately been reclaimed for use as a youth club, fully equipped, but is anyone willing to run it? Village events attract less interest so that Carnival floats, the Guy Fawkes bonfire and village pantomimes have stopped. Some changes are due to excessive insurance premiums. Yet, the fewer community do's are well attended. Volunteers still clean out the village pond, the football team is going strong and the village hall is well used by a variety of clubs including the Women's Institute and an embroidery group. Every village will have a different story, and every resident a different way to tell it.

Landscape, employment, income, community allow people to flourish. Many say we we are healthier, better fed, better educated, better housed and better off. Ryedale was never richer and yet its traditional basic industry - farming - is in flux. Some farmers 'diversify' to supplement falling incomes, a fancy name for finding some other way to make money. Local unemployment remains low, but the last recession brought temporary shakeouts from industrial firms, which were no help to confidence. Tourism, retirement and dormitory living for those who work elsewhere, continue to grow.

Much of the fame of Ryedale consists in other things, in an unusual range of nationally known places, most of which enjoy rural settings. Flamingo Park and Eden Camp, the North York Moors Railway and Castle Howard, Rievaulx Abbey and Pickering Castle are widely known. Ampleforth College, Fylingdales, and the Central Science Laboratory are establishments of national stature. Sutton Bank Gliders, the Ganton Golf club and the moorland shoots near Helmsley have been pioneers in sport. Much of the delight of Ryedale is in none of these things. Ryedale is fortunate in a beautiful landscape, populated by some real communities. That has been its history. Long may it remain so!

Appendix 1

British Monarchs

House of Wessex
Aethelstan 927-939
Edmund 1 939-946
Eadred 946-955
Eadwig 955-959
Edgar 957-975. the peaceful
Edward 975-978
Aethelred II 978-1016. the unready.
Edmund II 1016

House of Denmark
Cnut 1016-1035
Harold I 1037-1040
Harthacnut 1040-1042

House of Wessex
Edward 1042-1066. the confessor
Harold II 1066

House of Normandy
William 1 1066-1087.the conqueror
William II 1087-1100. Rufus
Henry I 1100-1135

House of Blois
Stephen 1135-1154

House of Plantaganet
Henry II 1154-1189 (& his son Henry 1170-83)
Richard I 1189-1199.
John 1199-1216
Henry III 1216-1272
Edward I 1272-1307
Edward II 1307-1327
EdwardIII 1327-1377
Richard II 1377-1399

House of Lancaster
Henry IV 1399-1413
Henry V 1413-1422
Henry VI 1422-1461 & 1470-1471

House of York
Edward IV 1461-1470 & 1471-1483
Edward V 1483
Richard III 1483-1485

House of Tudor
Henry VII 1485-1509
Hen ry VIII 1509-1547
Edward VI 1547-1553 (but House of Suffolk-Jane 1553)
Mary I 1553-1558
Elizabeth I 1558-1603

House of Stuart
James I 1603-1625
Charles I 1625-1649

Between the kings
Commonwealth 1649-1653
Oliver Cromwell. 1653-1658 Lord Protector
Richard Cromwell. 1658-1659 Lord Protector
Commonwealth 1659-1660

House of Stuart
Charles II 1660-1685
James II 1685-1688

House of Orange
William III 1689-1702
Mary II 1689-1695

House of Stuart
Anne 1702-1714

House of Hanover

George I 1714-1727
George II 1727-1760
George III 1760-1820
George IV 1820-1830
William IV 1830-1837
Victoria 1837- 1901

House of Saxe-Coburg -Gotha. (renamed Windor in 1917)
Edward VII 1901-1910
George V 1910-1936
Edward VIII 1936
George VI 1936-1952
Elizabeth II 1952-

A GUIDE TO FURTHER READING

(abbreviations -YAJ for Yorkshire Archaeological Journal; RH for Ryedale Historian; CT for Bulletin of Cleveland and Tesside Local History Society; NYCRO-Journal of North Yorkshire County Record Office.; SADAS for Transactions of Scarborough and District Archaeological and Historical Society)

Books dealing with the county or substantial areas of the county

Eboracum. F. Drake 1736
Topographical Dictionary of Yorkshire T. Langdale 1809
A History, Directory and Gazetteer of the County of York. E. Baines. 1822
Historia Rievallensis. W. Eastmead 1824
A new and complete History of the County of York. T. Allen 1828
History, Gazetteer and Directory of the East and North Ridings of Yorkshire. W. White 1840
Collections relating to Churches and Chapels within the Dioceses of York and Ripon. G. Lawton 1840-42
Vallis Eboracencis T. Gill. 1852
History & Topography of York & the East Riding of Yorkshire. J. T Sheahan & T. Whelan 1855-6
History & Topography of the city of York & the North Riding of Yorkshire. T. Whelan 1857-59
Guide to Ryedale G. Frank 1875
History, Topography and Directory of North Yorkshire T. Bulmer 1890
History, Topography and Directory of East Yorkshire T. Bulmer 1892
The Golden Vale of Mowbray. E. Bogg 1909
Victoria County History. Yorkshire. W. Page 1913 Ed
Victoria County History of the County of York, North Riding W Page. 1914-23 Ed
The Early History of the North Riding. W Edwards 1924
The Rural Landscape of the East Riding of Yorkshire 1700-1850 A. Harris 1961
A History of Helmsley, Rievaulx and district. J. McDonnell 1963 Ed
Life in the Moorlands of North East Yorkshire. M. Hartley & J. Ingleby. 1972
Yorkshire Wit, Character, Folklore & Customs of the North Riding. R. Blakeborough 1973

The Ryedale Story. J. Rushton. 1986
The North York Moors. Landscape Heritage. D. Spratt & B.J.D.Harrison. 1989
Coxwoldshire. D Wilkinson 1992 Ed

Prehistory
Early Man in North East Yorkshire F. Elgee. 1930
Iron Age Sites in the Vale of Pickering.(YAJ 30) M. K. Clark 1931
The Archaeology of Yorkshire F. Elgee & H W Elgee 1933
The Excavation of Staple Howe T.C. M. Brewster. 1963
The La Tene Culture of East Yorkshire. I. M. Stead. 1965
The Parisi. H. Ramm. 1978
The Arras Culture. I.M. Stead. 1979
A survey of Archaeological Sites in Humberside N. Loughlin & K.R. Miller 1979
Prehistoric and Roman Archaeology of North East Yorkshire. D. Spratt. 1982. Ed
North East Yorkshire Studies. Archaeological Papers R. H. Hayes 1988
Linear Earthworks of the Tabular Hills of North East Yorkshire. D. Spratt 1989

Roman
A Romano British pottery at Crambeck, Castle Howard. P. Corder 1928
The Defences of the Roman fort at Malton. P. Corder 1930
A Roman Villa at Langton near Malton P. Corder & J.L. Kirk.1932
Roman Yorkshire. F.R.Pearson. 1936
Malton-Norton: a Roman fortress and town. N. Mitchelson 1950
The Roman Pottery at Norton. R.H Hayes & Sir Edward Whitley 1950
Wade's Causeway. R. H. Hayes & J. C. Rutter 1964
Derventio: Roman fort and civilian settlement. L. P. Wenham 1974
The Archaeology of Malton and Norton. J. F. Robinson 1978
The 1968 to 1970 Excavations in the Vicus at Malton. D. Bailey 1997 Ed
Excavations on the Roman Villa at Beadlam Yorkshire D. S Neal 1996
Cawthorne Roman Military complex. (R H 1998-9) G. Lee. 1998-9

Anglian and Scandinavian
The Battle of Stamford Bridge. F. W. Brooks. 1956.
The Place Names of the North Riding of Yorkshire. A. H. Smith. 1969
The Place Names of the East Riding of Yorkshire A. H. Smith 1937

The Viking Century in East Yorkshire A.L. Binns. 1963
The Early Charters of Northern England. C.R. Hart 1975
Domesday Book: Yorkshire. M. Faul & M. Stinson Eds 1986
Yorkshire from A. D. 1000 D. Hey 1986
The Northern Counties to AD 1000 N. Higham 1986
The Kingdom of Northumbria AD 350-1100 N. Higham 1993
Viking Age York R. Hall 1994
Oswald. C. Stancliffe & E. Cambridge Ed. 1995
Archaeology at Kirkdale L. Watt. J. Grenville & P. Rahtz. 1996
West Heslerton: the Anglian Cemetery. C. Haughton & D. Powsland. 1999
Blood Feud. R. Fletcher 2002

Mediaeval
The Norman Conquest of the North. W. E. Kapelle 1979
Domesday Book. A.Williams & G. H. Martin 1992 Ed
Castles of North Yorkshire. M. J. Jackson. 2001
The History of William of Newburgh. J.Stevenson 1856 Ed
The Royal Forests of England. J. C. Cox 1905
Conquest, Anarchy & Lordship, Yorkshire 1066-1154. P. Dalton 1994
The Northerners. J. C. Holt 1961
Rolls of the Justices in Eyre for Yorkshire 1218-19. D. M. Stenton 1937. Ed
The Survey of the County of York taken by John Kirkby. R H Skaife 1867. Ed
Yorkshire Inquisitions. W. Brown 1892. Ed
Yorkshire 100 and Quo Warranto rolls. B. English 1996. Ed
Walter Daniel's Life of Ailred, Abbot of Rievaulx. F.M. Powicke 1950. Ed
The Religious Houses of Yorkshire. G. Lawton 1853
Monasticon Anglicanum. 1722. Roger Dodsworth & William Dugdale
Yorkshire Abbeys and the Wool Trade. H. E. Wroot 1930
Mediaeval English Nunneries. E. E Power 1922
The Monastic Orders in England. D. Knowles 1940
Rievaulx Abbey. P. Fergusson & S. Harrison 1999
St.Gilbert of Sempringham & the Ghilbertine Order. R. Graham 1901
History of the Knights Templars. C. G. Addison 1854
Abstracts of the charters in the Chartulary of the Priory of Bridlington. W. T Lancaster 1912
Kirkham Priory from foundation to dissolution. J. E Burton 1994

Notes on the religious and secular houses of Yorkshire. W. P. Baildon Ed. 1895
The Monastic Order in Yorkshire 1069-1215. J. Burton 1999
The Monastic Grange in Mediaeval England. C. Platt 1969
Monasteries & Landscape in North East England. B. Waites 1997
St John of Bridlington. J. S Purvis 1924
Moorland and Vale farming in north east Yorkshire; the monastic contribution in the thirteenth and fourteenth centuries. B. Waites 1967
Early Yorkshire Charters. W Farrer 1914-16. Ed
Charters of the Honour of Mowbray 1107-1191. D.E Greenway 1972
Thurstan, Archbishop of York. D. Nicholl. 1964
Henry II. W. L. Warren 1973
Yorkshire Lay subsidy 1297 & 1301. W Brown 1894-7. Ed
History of the Duchy of Lancaster Vol 1 R. Somerville 1953
Thomas of Lancaster. 1307-1322. J.R. Maddicott 1970
The Honor and Forest of Pickering. R. B. Turton 1894. Ed
Ayton castle. F. C. Rimington & J. G. Rutter 1967
The 1377 Poll Tax returns for the North Riding. (CT) B.J. D Harrison
The Wool Trade in English Mediaeval History. E. Power 1941
English Industries in the Middle Ages. I. F. Salzman 1923
The Peasants Revolt of 1381. R. B. Dobson 1970. Ed
The Lost Villages of England. M. W. Beresford 1954
North-Eastern England during the Wars of the Roses. J. Pollard. 1990
The Crosses on the North York Moors. T. H. Woodwark. 1976
Mediaeval Parks of of East Yorkshire. S. Neave 1991

Tudor and Stuart Times
Yorkshire Monasteries .Suppression papers. J.W Clay 1912. Ed
Lollards and Protestants in the Diocese of York 1509-1558. A. C. Dickens 1959
Monks, Friars and Nuns in 16th Century Yorkshire. C. Cross & N. Vickers 1995
Brittania. William Camden 1695
Yorkshire Chantry surveys. W. Page 1894-5. Ed
The Yorkshire Gentry. J. T. Cliffe 1969
The Visitation of Yorkshire in the years 1563 & 1564 by William Flower. C.B.Norcliffe. Ed. 1881
The Visitation of Yorkshire in 1584-5 & 1612. J. Foster 1875. Ed
The English Reformation. A. G. Dickens 1964
500 Hundred Points of Good Husbandry. T. Tusser 1580

The Pilgrimage of Grace & the Exeter Conspiracy, 1538. MH & HR Dodds. 1917
The Itinerary of John Leland in or about the years 1535-1543. L. T. Smith 1964. Ed
Tudor York. D.M. Palliser 1979
Itinerary in England. J. Leland. L. Toulmin Smith 1906-8 .Ed
The Diary of Lady Margaret Hoby 1599-1605. D. M. Meads Ed 1900
The Memoirs of Sir Hugh Cholmley. 1787
Dugdales Visitation of Yorkshire. J W Clay 1899. Ed
Archbishop Grindal's Visitation of the Diocese of York 1575. W. J. Sheils. 1977. Ed
The Council of the North. F. W. Brooke 1953
Yorkshire Fairs and Markets. K. L. McCutcheon 1939
Descriptions of East Yorkshire. Leland to Defoe. D. Woodward. 1985 Ed
The Journeys of Celia Fiennes. C. Morris 1949. Ed
Quaker Social History. 1669-1738. A Lloyd. 1950
Yorkshire Quarterly Meeting of the Society of Friends. 1665-1966 W. P. Thistlethwaite 1979
Witchcraft in 17th century Yorkshire. J. A Sharpe 1992
The Eure family. (NYCRO. vol 7) T. E. Barker 1980
The Autobiography of Mrs. Alice Thornton. C. Jackson 1875 Ed
Agrarian History of England & Wales Vol. 1V. 1500-1640. H.P.R Finberg and J Thirsk 1967. Ed
The Farming and Memorandum Books of Henry Best of Elmswell. 1642. D. Woodward Ed. 1984.
The Visitation of Yorkshire, 1665-6. Sir William Dugdale 1859
Yorkshire Puritanism and Early Nonconformity. B. Dale 1909
Northern Catholics. 1558-1790. H. Aveling 1966
The Puritans and the Church Courts in the diocese of York 1560-1642. R. Marchant 1960
The Memoirs of Sir John Reresby. A. Browning 1936. Ed
Yorkshire Composition Papers. J. W. Clay 1893
Quarter sessions records. North Riding. J. C. Atkinson 1884. Ed
George Villiers, 2nd. Duke of Buckingham 1628-1687. W. Burghclere 1903
Yorkshiremen of the Restoration. J. S Fletcher 1921
North York Militia. R. B. Turton 1973
The Open Fields of East Yorkshire. A Harris 1959
Richard Cholmley's Book. (NYCRO) M. Y. Ashcroft. Ed

The Great and Close Seige of York. L.P. Wenham 1976

The Hearth Tax List for the North Riding of Yorkshire 1673. Ripon Historical Society 1991

A Place of Great Importance, Scarborough in the Civil War 1640-1660. J. Binns. 1996

18th Century

Planting and Rural Ornament. W. Marshall 1796

A General View of the Agriculture of the North Riding of Yorkshire. John Tuke 1794 & 1800

A General View of the Agriculture of the East Riding of Yorkshire. Isaac Leatham 1794

The Good Schoolmaster. Thomas Zouch 1798

Papers & Diaries of a York Family. 1764-1839. Mrs. E. Gray 1927

The County of York, surveyed in 1767-70. T. Jeffreys. 1771-2

Samuel Buck's Yorkshire Sketchbook. I. Hall 1979. Ed

Archbishop Herrings Visitation returns 1743. Ed P. C. Walker & S.L. Ollard 1928-31

Archbishop Drummond's Visitation Returns 1764 C. Annesley & P. Hoskins Ed. 1997 –2001

An Historical and Descriptive Guide to Scarborough J. Schofield 1787.

Tour through the whole Island of Great Britain. D. Defoe 1724-6

A Six month Tour through the North of England. A Young 1771

The Rural Economy of Yorkshire. W. Marshall 1788

The Agricultural Revolution in the East Riding of Yorkshire .O Wilkinson 1961

The Letters of John Wesley. J. Telford. 1931. Ed

The Journal of John Wesley. N Charnock 1909-16. Ed

Real Improvements in Agriculture. Thomas Comber 1772

York-Oswaldkirk Turnpike Trust, 1768-1881. J. Perry 1977. Ed

A history of Banks, Bankers and Banking in Northumberland, Durham and North Yorkshire 1755-1894. M. Phillips 1894

Poverty and the Poor Law in the North Riding of Yorkshire c 1780-1837 R. P. Hastings 1982

The Charities of Rural England. W. K Jordan 1961

East Yorkshire Friendly Societies. D. Neave 1988

The Moor coal of North Yorkshire. (CT) J. S. Owen

Universal British Directory. 1793-8

Lime roads in the Whitby district. R. F. Moore 1972

<u>19th-20th Centuries</u>
A survey of the Agriculture of Yorkshire. W. Harwood Long 1969
A General View of the Agriculture of the East Riding of Yorkshire. H. E. Strickland 1812
Practical Arithmetic. W Putsey 1830
The Costume of Yorkshire. G. Walker 1814
Piety among the Peasantry: being sketches of Primitive Methodism on the Yorkshire Wolds. H. Woodcock. 1889
History of the Primitive Methodist church. H. B. Kendall 1919
Report of William Chapman, engineer, on the means of draining the low grounds in the Vales of Derwent and Hertford. W. Chapman 1800
An account of the Arctic regions and History of the Northern Whale Fisher. W. Scoresby 1820
Church Rides in the neighbourhood of Scarborough. J. Fawcett 1848
A Month in Yorkshire. W White. 1859
Celebrities of the Yorkshire Wolds. F. Ross 1878
County Folklore Vol. 2 (North Riding, York and Ainsty) Ed Mrs Gutch 1901
Return of Owners of Land. Local Government Board 1873 –1875
Lime Roads in the Whitby District. R. F. Moore 1972
Farm Workers in Open and Closed Villages 1841-1891. J.A. Asquith 2000
The Rural landscape of the East Riding of Yorkshire 1700-1850. A. Harris 1969
Report of the Assistant Poor Law commissioners on the Employment of women and children in agriculture. 1843
A Yorkshireman's trip to the United States and Canada. W. Smith 1892
The Emigrant's guide to Upper Canada. J. Mewburn 1830
The Black Face Sheep Keepers guide. 1897
The Yorkshire Wold rangers. A. Antrim 1981
Essays in North Riding History, 1780-1850. R. P. Hastings 1981
More Essays in North Riding History, 1780-1850. R. P. Hastings 1983
Yorkshire Forests. Forestry Commission 1966
England's Oldest Hunt. J Fairfax Blakeborough
The History of the Countryside. O. Rackham 1986
Ryedale. A report on the district. CPRE 1951
Howardian Hills, area of Outstanding Natural Beauty. NYCC 1997
To Farm is to Live. N. E. Kirkwood 1999
Eden Camp. The Peoples War, 1939-45
Horse Farming through the Seasons. H. L. Day 1991

Ryedale Local Plan 2002

History of Buildings
Buildings of England. Yorkshire North Riding. N. Pevsner. 1966
East Riding Water Mills. K. J. Allison 1970
Cruck Frame Buildings in Ryedale & Eskdale. R.H.Hayes & J. G. Rutter 1972
Buildings of Britain. 1550-1750 D. Hey 1981
Mediaeval Buildings of Yorkshire. P.F. Ryder 1982
Vernacular Houses in North Yorkshire & Cleveland. B.J. D. Harrison & & B. Hutton 1984
The Industrial Architecture of Yorkshire. J. Hatcher 1985
Houses of the North York Moors. Royal Commission on Historical Monuments 1987
Looking at Buildings. The East Riding. H. Moffat & D.Neave 1995

History of Education
Primary Education in East Yorkshire. J. Lawson 1959
The Endowed Grammar Schools of East Yorkshire. J. Lawson 1962
Yorkshire Schools and Schooldays. R. W. Unwin & W. B. Stephens Ed 1976
The History of Lady Lumley's School & Foundation J.T. Smith
Charity Schools and the Defence of Anglicanism. James Talbot Rector of Spofforth 1700-708 R. W Unwin 1984

History of Transport

Illustrations of the Scenery on the line of the Whitby and Pickering Railway 1836
A tour of the Whitby & Pickering Railway in 1836. H. Belcher.
A history of the Whitby and Pickering Railway. G.W.K.Potter 1906
The old Coaching Days in Yorkshire. T. Bradley 1889
The beginnings of the East Yorkshire railways. K Macmahon 1953
Navigable Rivers of Yorkshire. B. F Duckham 1964
Roads and Turnpike trusts in Eastern Yorkshire. K. A Macmahon 1964
Transport in Yorkshire. C. Speakman. 1969
Whitby and Pickering Railway. D. Joy 1969
George Hudson of York. A. J Peacock and D Joy 1971
North-East England. K. Hoole (Regional history of the Railways of Great Britain)

Railways in Yorkshire 3. The North Riding. K. Hoole 1977
Stone Causeways of, the North York Moors B. Breakell. 1982
Old Roads & Pannierways in N.E. Yorkshire. R.H.Hayes 1988
Railways in East Yorkshire. M. Bairstow 1990
Lost Railways of East Yorkshire. P.G. Mason 1990
North Yorkshire Railway Stations. N. Ellis 1995
The Malton and Driffield Junction Railway. W. Burton 1997
Navigation on the Yorkshire Derwent. P. Jones 2000

Histories of Villages, Towns and Famous Places
How it Was. (Amotherby) B. Goforth. c 1994
The Ampleforth Country. 1947
The History of Ampleforth Abbey. C. Almond. 1903
Ampleforth College, a Sketchbook. J. Pike 1921
Ampleforth Remembered, World War II, 1939-1945
Ampleforth & its Origins. J.McCain & C.Cary-Elwes.Ed 1952
The Mediaeval Free Chapel of Appleton le Moors (RH13) M. Allison
An early mediaeval community near Appleton le Moors. M. Allison
1980 (SADAS 23)
An ecclesiastical history of the parish of All Saints, Appleton le Street
with St Helen Amotherby. B. Keeton
Appleton le Street. All Saints church. (RH 2000-01) P. Rahtz, L. Watts
& K. Saunders
Ayton Castle. F C Rimington & J G Rutter 1967
Memoirs of a Ryedale Lad. (Beadlam) C Wormington
Birdsall Estate Remembered. Colin Hayfield. 1998
The Report of the Ampleforth College Bransdale Expedition.
Ampleforth College 1958
A History of Burythorpe. F.Francis & J. Smithson
Byland Abbey. C.R. Peers 1945
The Illustrated Handbook to Castle Howard. 1857
Castle Howard. V. Murray 1994
The Building of Castle Howard. C.S. Smith 1990
The Artist and the Autocrat. (Castle Howard) V. Surtees 1988
A History of Cottam. K. Clegg c 2001
Coxwoldshire. D. Wilkinson 1997. Ed
Cropton's Story. Cropton History Group. 1995
Dalby, Valley of Change. J. Rushton 1976
Forty Years in a Moorland Parish, (Danby) J. C. Atkinson 1891
Some Reminiscences and Folklore of Danby. J. Ford 1937

A catalogue of the paintings and statues at Duncombe Park. 1810
Dowthwaite Dale and the Shepherd Family. B. Frank 1977
Vallis Eboracencis (EAsingwold). T. Gill. 1852
A History of Easingwold and the forest of Galtres. G. C Cowling 1965
A History of Ebberston. C. Evans. 1994. Ed
Tithe and glebe in the parishes of Thornton in Pickering Lythe and Ellerburn. (SADAS No 27.) P. Craven. 1986
The Story of Foulbridge. W. Nutt. 1991
Foulbridge and its Preceptory. (SADAS No 26) F. Rimington 1988
A History of Foxholes. K. Clegg 1999
Reflections of Foxholes. E. Spencer & J. Stubbs 2000
Royal Air Force Fylingdales: a History B.C. F. Wilson 1983
The Legards of Anlaby & Ganton. J. D. Legard 1926
The Story of Gillamoor and Fadmoor. R H Hayes 1969.
The great chamber at Gilling castle. H. Murray 1996
Goathland in history and folklore. F. W. Dowson 1947
Goathland. A. Hollings 1971
Harome (RH. 1988-9) R. H. Hayes & M. R. Allison
Helmsley. I. Cooper. 1890
A History of Helmsley. J. McDonnell 1963. Ed
Helmsley & Kirkby through the ages. K. Snowden 1991
Helmsley Castle. Yorkshire. Sir Charles Peers 1966
Hood Castle. (RH. no 5) A. H Whitaker. 1970
Hovingham Hall: York: Sir Marcus Worsley. 1984
The Butler Remembers (Hovingham) R. Marshall. 2000
Keldholme Priory, the early years. (RH No 1) J. H. Rushton
Kingthorpe (SADAS) R. H. Hayes 1973
Excavations at Kirby Misperton (SADAS) R.H. Hayes 1977
Ryedale Recollections (Kirkby Moorside) A.C. H. Cussons
A Brief account of Kirkdale church. C.L. R Taylor 1876
Short account of St Gregory's Minster at Kirkdale F.W. Powell 1907
Archaeology at Kirkdale. L. Watts, J. Grenville & P. Ratz 1996-7
Kirkdale Archaeology 1998-9. P Ratz and L. Watts 1998-9
St Gregory's Minster, Kirkdale. A.W. Penn 1961
Kirkham Priory. Sir C. Peers. 1935
The Tindalls of Scarborough, descendants of Ralph Tyndale of N. Grimston. C. Tindall
The monastic church of Lestingham. J. C. Wall 1894
History of the ancient parish of Lastingham. F. H. Weston 1914
Lastingham. J Winters 2000

Leavening through the ages. D. Howarth
Leavening. R.Hutchinson 1990
Do you remember. Some more memories of Leavening R. Hutchinson 1993
A topographical history of Leavening. R.Addison 1831
Village Voices (Levisham) B. Halse
Levisham, a case study in local history. B. Halse. 2002
Lockton Remembered. R. Strong. 2000
History of Malton and Norton. N. A. Hudleston 1962
Around Malton. J. T Stone 1996
Malton & Norton through the Ages. K. Snowden 1990
Malton in the early 19th Century. D. J. Salmon Ed
Malton memories and IAnson triumphs. J. Fairfax-Blakeborough. 1925
Malton and Norton. A personal view. H. O. Griffiths 1986
In Well Beware (Newbrough Priory) G. R. Smith 1978
Normanby J. Wood. c 1982
Baker's Norton Chronicle and Chronology. 1870-1940
Nunnington a short account by A. C. A.C. 1882
A short history and description of Nunnington parish church. H. N. Pobjoy. 1959
Do You Remember? Pickering Fifty Years Ago. D Cowlin 2000
Pickering Castle.North Yorkshire. M. W. Thompson 1985
Evolution of an English Town: Pickering G. Home & J. Rushton 1999
They Kept Faith (Pickering, Malton) J. Rushton.
Pickering through the Ages. K. Snowden 1992
Pickering Castle. L.Butler. 1997
The Way We Were (Pickering) R. W Scales
Rememberings. (Pickering) R. W Scales 1991
A Boyhood. Pickering. K. Snowden 1997
Pickering. G. Clitheroe 1999. Ed
Rievaulx Abbey. Sir Charles Peers. 1932
Rievaulx Abbey. P. Fergusson & S. Harrison 1999
Historical notes of Rillington and Scampston. W. T. Stratford. 1910
Rillington. N. A. Hudleston 1954
The Rowntrees of Riseborough. C. B. Rowntree. 1940
A History of Rosedale. R. H. Hayes 1971
The Rosedale Ironstone industry and railway. R. H. Hayes & J. G. Rutter
Salton: a shrunken village (In R.H. 1998-9) J. McDonnell
Documents at Scampston. C. V. Collier 1915

The Glass Holes of Spaunton Moor (RH 12) R H Hayes & J Hemmingway 1984

The Sherburn Methodist Circuit. centenary. 1869-1969. 1969

Some account of Sheriff Hutton Castle. G. Todd 1824

Sinnington through the ages. K. McManners. 1954

Slingsby Castle. A. St Claire Brooke. 1904

The Snainton Story. J. Rushton

Some account of the parish and village of Slingsby. W. Walker 1845

The Parish of Slingsby, its history & wildlife. M.Mackinder & M. Thompson. Ed. 2000

The White Vellum Book (Scarborough) I. H. Jeayes. Ed 1914

The History & Antiquities of Scarborough T. Hinderwell. 3rd edition 1832

Scarborough 966-1966. Ed M. Edwards 1966

History of Scarborough. J Binns 2000

The History of Scarborough. A. Rowntree Ed. 1931

Sherburn. A.Collier 2000

Castellum Huttonicum. G.W. Todd 1824

A short Historical guide to Sheriff Hutton Park. C. Gilbert 1965

The parish church of St. Helen and the Holy Cross, Sheriff Hutton.K.E. Nelson 1962

Sheriff Hutton WI Treasure Survey 1975. 1979

Sheriff Hutton and its lords. J.Senior. 2000

The Manor of Spaunton (In R. H. 1992-3) T. Strickland 1992

Sykes of Sledmere. J Fairfax Blakeborough 1929

Sledmere House. Sir Richard Sykes 1980

The Visitor's Book (Sledmere) C.S. Sykes 1978

Finds from Westfield Manor, Snainton (SADAS 19) P.G. Farmer 1976

A history of Staxton with Willerby & Binnington. K. Clegg. 1997

Stories of Staxton. K. Clegg 1998

Terrington - A history of the parish. M. E. Dymond

Thixendale Remembered. C. Hayfield 1988

Thorpe Bassettt. A. Bard

Thornton le Dale. R. W. Jeffery 1931

Thornton le Dale. M. Boyes 1977

The Priestmans of Thornton Dale. S. H. Priestman 1986

Thornton Dale Through the Ages. K. Snowden 2000

Life and Times of Wass and Byland. M. Matson. 2000 Ed

Welburn Hall. (YAJ vol. 4) T. Parker

Wharram Remembered. C. ,Hayfield 1996

Wharram: a study of settlement on the Yorkshire Wolds. P.A. Stamper. 2000

An Archaeological Survey of the Parish of Wharram Percy. C. Hayfield. 1987

Wharram Percy. Deserted Mediaeval Village. M. Beresford & J. Hurst 1990

Whitby Prints. T. H. English 1931

Wilton in the 18th century (SADAS 26) P. Craven 1988

A Life on the Wolds. I. Megginson 2000

The History of Whitby. G. Young. 1817.

Mediaeval York. A Raine 1955

The History of York. P Nuttgens 2001

INDEX

Bulmer, Bertram de, 56

Burdale, 343, 370, 423

Burniston, 108

Burstwick, 17, 124

Burtoft, 12

Burton Agnes, 199, 235, 238, 273

Burton Riggs, 12, 16

Burton, 6, 10, 12, 22

Burythorpe, 10, 192, 280, 287

Buttercrambe, 17, 75, 93, 104, 132, 163, 197, 199, 214, 216, 217, 222, 235, 252, 256, 273, 279,
301, 302, 372

Butterwick, 50, 107, 186, 192, 221, 224, 304, 348

Byland Abbey, 66, 67, 71, 82, 91, 95, 96, 97, 113, 126, 146, 172, 180

Byland, 55, 109, 120, 147, 180, 209, 232, 262, 282, 316, 450

Calais, 159

Calcaria (Tadcaster), 8

California, 345

Cambrough, 12

Canada, 289, 320, 388

Canterbury, 19

Carl, thegn, 36

Carlisle, 39

Carlton, 287, 290

carucates, 25

Castle Howard, 234, 258, 265, 267, 279, 291, 292, 295, 301, 312, 315, 316, 319, 336, 343, 346, 352, 356, 385, 404, 409, 419, 427, 450, 461, 463

Castleton, 75, 227, 255, 261, 331, 355, 394, 434

Cateractonium (Catterick), 8

Catterick, 8, 15

Caulklass, 32

Cawood, 262

Cawthorn, 5, 6, 10, 11, 12, 48, 64, 254, 315, 321,

Cawton, 20, 60, 84, 206, 375

Cayton, 275, 281

Cedd, 16, 19

Central Science Laboratory, 453, 463

Chamberlain, Herbert the, 46

Chauncy, Walter de, 43

Chernobyll, 446

Church Fenton, 424
Claxton, 287
Cleveland, 15
Cloughton, 87, 99
Cnut, King, 36
Coatham, 66, 96, 97
Cockan, 224
Cold harbours, 12
Cold Kirkby, 10, 86, 208, 280, 302, 304
Cold War, 432
Coldbrough, 12
Comines, Robert de, 35
Coneysthorpe, 16, 96, 235, 259, 319, 361, 385, 421, 430, 447
Constantine I, Emperor, 7, 12, 14
Corbridge, 256
Cornbrough, 10, 12, 116, 152, 140, 169, 287
Costa, 5
Cottam, 15, 304
Cottingham Castle, 75
Council of the North, 153, 175, 189, 204
Cowlam, 9, 348
Cowton, 211
Coxwold, 19, 29, 39, 58, 104, 126, 132, 145, 180, 199, 213, 277, 279, 309, 427
Coxwoldshire, 22
Crambe, 9, 30, 165, 247, 294, 319
Crayke, 9, 10, 11, 19, 20, 29, 64, 79, 102, 316, 331 403
Croom, 304
Cropton, 46, 49, 69, 76, 79, 93, 100, 104, 106, 125, 126, 128, 131, 140, 160, 186, 187, 210, 227, 232, 234, 252, 257, 261, 262, 270, 272, 274, 279, 303, 304, 315, 320, 326, 327, 330, 336, 370, 385, 430, 452, 459
Cudbrightgate, 20
Culloden Moor, Battle of, 274
Cumberland, 39
Cuthbert, 19, 21

Dalby, 3, 12, 59, 78, 149, 153, 199, 258, 259, 296, 394, 417, 435, 444, 450
Dale, 149, 153
Daletown, 68, 195
Danby, 25, 46, 48, 75, 78, 89, 101, 103, 135, 140, 152, 156, 209, 227, 229, 255, 261, 262, 271, 274, 299, 312, 355
Danum (Doncaster), 8

Hugh, son of Baldric, 37
Hull, 132, 169, 241, 247, 262, 284, 308, 315, 317, 345, 398, 425
Hunmanby, 5, 53, 56, 109, 280, 281
Huntington, 94, 164, 399, 446
Husthwaite, 49, 211, 272
Hutton Bardolf, 65
Hutton Bushell, 12, 16, 272, 292, 302
Hutton Bushell, 49
Hutton Coleswain, 49
Hutton le Hole, 52, 59, 73, 164, 182, 185, 189, 224, 231, 261, 262, 273, 282, 298, 315, 332, 340, 345, 355, 416, 420, 434, 444
Hutton Low Cross, 64
Hutton on Derwent, 130, 212, 236
Huttons Ambo, 10, 94, 137, 141, 253, 304, 352, 353, 409

Ilfrid's Cave, 19
Ingleby Arncliffe, 237
Ingleby, 205
Ingleby, 87, 205
Inkerman, Battle of, 352
Iona, 18, 19
Isurium Brigantium, 8

Jarrow, 41
Jones, John Paul, 289
Julian Park Castle, 75, 79, 125

Keld Head, 368, 424, 437
Keldholme Priory, 65, 70, 75, 87, 99, 121, 165, 167, 174, 201
Keldholme, 3, 69, 100, 263, 297, 313, 322, 331, 434
Kennythorpe, 253, 304
Kepwick, 342
Kettlethorpe, 59, 90, 91
Kexby, 17, 150, 163, 252,
Kilburn, 132, 437
Kildale, 46, 86, 125, 149
Kilham, 50, 238, 296
Kilton Castle, 81, 170
Kilvington, 219
King's Council in the North, 153, 157, 175, 189, 204
Kingthorpe, 15, 16, 47, 50, 90, 113, 158, 259, 301, 310, 312, 364

491

Kirby in Cleveland, 169

Kirby Mills, 189

Kirby Underdale, 186

Kirby Wiske, 200

Kirkby Grindalythe, 48, 53, 192, 274, 304, 450, 42

Kirkby Knowle, 194, 235

Kirkby Mills, 297, 352, 376, 402

Kirkby Misperton, 30, 51, 59, 65, 68, 87, 91, 112, 195, 208, 211, 237, 261, 271, 273, 301, 309, 319, 337, 345, 346, 347, 369, 411, 417, 447, 449, 451

Kirkby Moorside, 3, 4, 5, 12, 16, 20, 45, 48, 53, 55, 68, 69, 73, 76, 79, 88, 90, 98, 102, 103, 106, 119, 120, 121, 128, 133, 135, 144, 145, 149, 156, 165, 167, 176, 177, 178, 181, 183, 184, 186, 193, 194, 205, 208, 210, 211, 213, 215, 218, 220, 221, 222, 223, 224, 225, 236, 239, 240, 241, 243, 251, 252, 262, 265, 271, 273, 274, 285, 287, 288, 290, 293, 295, 297, 300, 302, 304, 309, 324, 329, 331, 332, 336, 339, 343, 348, 354, 355, 356, 357, 360, 361, 363, 365, 366, 367, 368, 370, 372, 373, 374, 376, 380, 381, 383, 392, 393, 394, 396, 397, 398, 400, 401, 402, 403, 404, 405, 406, 414, 416, 417, 418, 421, 423, 424, 427, 428, 431, 432, 434, 436, 437, 445, 447, 450, 451, 452, 457, 459, 461, 462

Kirkby Over Carr, 267

Kirkby, 32, 120, 147, 230, 242

Kirkdale, 17, 19, 20, 31, 33, 53, 195, 215, 223, 225, 336

Kirkham Priory, 48, 53, 55, 65, 67, 68, 79, 82, 85, 95, 102, 109, 116, 120, 121, 139, 160, 165, 171, 173, 298, 450

Kirkham, 93, 122, 142, 163, 219, 252, 309, 312

Kirkham, Richard Prior of, 139

Knapton, 3, 9, 90, 109, 126, 131, 165, 302, 345, 451

Knaresborough, 17, 44, 46, 76, 410

Knights Hospitaller, 52, 64, 109

Knights Templar, 46, 64, 75, 79, 86, 93, 100, 109

Lancaster, 112

Langbaurgh, 22

Langtoft, 10, 20, 49, 122, 165, 181, 222, 361

Langton, 9, 10, 180, 223, 235, 238, 242, 253, 279, 280, 281, 302, 304, 354, 388, 428

Laskill in Bilsdale, 71, 114

Lastingham, 19, 20, 29, 30, 33, 41, 52, 80, 81, 84, 100, 119, 131, 144, 145, 158, 169, 189, 195, 213, 222, 225, 270, 274, 282, 286, 287, 290, 298, 304, 321, 332, 334, 343, 378

Laysthorpe, 307

Lealholm, 224, 331

Lease Rigg, 7, 10

Leavening, 139, 224, 252, 304, 316, 324, 328, 331, 332, 338, 339, 340, 414, 422, 459

Overton, 167
Ovin, 19
oxgangs, 25

parishes, 25
Parisi, 4, 9, 14, 17
Paulinus cross, 18
Paulinus, 17, 18
Paynel, Ralph, 37
Pearl Harbour, 427
Percy, William de, 37, 41, 42, 52
Petuariensium (Brough), 7, 8
Philadelphia, 286, 291
Pickering Castle, 72, 76, 103, 113, 148, 149, 151, 176, 463
Pickering Lythe, 22, 23
Pickering, 9, 10, 12, 20, 30, 39, 43, 44, 50, 51, 60, 61, 62, 64, 65, 72, 75, 76, 78,
82, 85, 86, 88, 89 94, 96, 97, 98, 99, 100, 101, 102, 103, 107, 108, 109, 112,
113, 114, 115, 118, 119,120, 124, 125, 126, 131, 132, 133, 135, 138, 141, 144,
145, 151, 152, 156, 158, 159, 162, 163, 165, 175 188, 187, 189, 196, 197, 199,
201, 210, 213, 214, 216, 218, 220, 221, 223, 224, 230, 231, 234, 237, 239, 240,
241, 242, 244, 251, 252, 255, 256, 257, 260, 261, 262, 263, 266, 270, 272, 273,
275, 280, 281 299, 298, 294, 292, 291, 290, 287, 286, 284 301, 304, 305, 306,
308, 309, 312, 313, 315, 317, 319, 320, 321, 324, 325, 326, 329, 330, 331, 332,
334, 335, 336, 337, 338, 339, 341, 342, 343, 348, 350, 351, 352, 354, 355, 356,
357, 359, 360, 361, 362, 363, 364, 365, 366, 368, 369, 370, 373, 374, 376 377,
379, 380, 382, 383, 386, 387, 388, 392, 394, 396, 397, 400, 401, 402, 403, 405,
406, 409, 410, 411, 412, 414, 416, 417, 419, 420, 421, 422, 423, 424, 427, 428,
429, 431, 432, 434, 435, 436, 437, 438, 439, 441, 442, 444, 445
Pilfit, 180
Pilmoor, 432
Pockley, 64, 84, 85, 258, 290, 339, 424
Pocklington, 50, 151, 157, 277
Pontefract, 77, 151, 157, 241
Potter Brompton, 10, 66, 99, 304
Prestby, 18, 41, 42

Quebec, Battle of, 289

Ragnall, King, 21
Raisdale, 90
Raskelf, 103
Ravensthorp, 160
Ravenswyke, 12

Salton, 20, 33, 49, 50, 93, 96, 120, 138, 139, 185, 192, 267, 301, 317, 349, 375, 422, 437

Saltwick, 233

Sancton, 15, 181

Sand Hutton, 132, 273, 301, 302, 304, 361, 444, 453

Sandsend, 51, 97, 188, 189

Scackleton, 259, 260

Scagglethorpe, 253, 304, 418

Scalby, 72, 78, 126, 131, 314

Scampston, 52, 120, 122, 126, 346, 362, 372, 416

Scarborough Castle, 5, 72, 101, 135

Scarborough, 11, 12, 14, 56, 57, 61, 64, 65, 71, 75, 76, 79, 86, 94, 95, 96, 97, 99, 100, 101, 103, 104, 109, 112, 113, 116, 124, 131, 132, 133, 140, 141, 144, 145, 146, 147, 152, 153, 163, 164, 168, 169, 181, 187, 188, 197, 199, 200, 212, 214, 216, 217, 221, 222, 224, 225, 232, 233, 238, 239, 240, 241, 247, 251, 252, 253, 254, 256, 258, 259, 260, 263, 267, 268, 269, 274, 275, 277, 289, 293, 295, 296, 301, 301, 307, 308, 310, 313, 316, 317, 319, 320, 326, 330, 332, 333, 336, 338, 342, 343, 345, 356, 376, 385, 388, 389, 404, 405, 406, 413, 419, 422, 423, 430, 432, 435, 441, 452, 456,

Scorbrough, 12

Scrayingham, 20, 39, 94, 166, 292, 304, 325, 386

Scurris, William de, 46

Seamer, 5, 11, 37, 39, 49, 73, 79, 93, 135, 136, 145, 156, 168, 169, 170, 176, 215, 235, 254, 262, 280, 309, 343, 345, 366, 405, 455, 457

Sedburgh, 415

Selby Abbey, 52

Sempringham, St Gilbert of, 69

Serlo de Percy, 41

Settrington, 10, 12, 25, 36, 39, 43, 73, 93, 94, 97 109, 136, 150, 153, 158, 164, 168, 169, 175, 178, 184, 187, 201, 230, 286, 287, 302, 304, 333, 339, 348,

Severus, Emperor, 7

Sexhow, 32

Sheffield, 188, 192, 239, 241

Sherburn in Elmet, 451

Sherburn, 11, 14, 30, 53, 66, 84, 97, 98, 100, 120, 125, 131, 149, 188, 255, 259, 272, 303, 304, 331, 332, 358, 366, 373, 419, 451, 462

Sheriff Hutton, 14, 46, 76, 83, 90, 100, 102, 104, 106, 115, 135, 136, 140, 145, 149, 150, 151, 152, 153, 156, 157, 159, 166, 169, 170, 178, 181,189, 204, 209, 221, 230, 235, 240, 262, 273, 287, 292, 302, 304, 305, 316, 326, 331, 332, 352, 370, 372, 384, 404, 416, 444,

Shipton, 149

Sigtrygr, King, 21

Sinnington, 30, 59, 65, 69, 79, 95, 97, 109, 125, 126, 140, 148, 156, 162, 168, 189, 192, 211, 237, 271, 275, 277, 287, 291, 301, 304, 313, 315, 346, 353, 360, 367, 379, 385, 402, 406, 411, 415, 417, 419, 420, 421, 422, 439, 462

St Hilda's Church, Ellerburn, 19
St John of Beverley, 20
St John the Baptist, 31
St John's Well, 20
St Leonards Hospital, 67, 72
St Mary Magdalane Hospital, 174
St Mary, 20
St Mary's Abbey, York, 41, 47, 52, 55, 59, 65, 66, 78, 79, 87, 88, 90, 95, 96, 100, 120, 167, 189
St Nicholas, Hospital of, 101
St Olaf, 34
St Olav's, Earlsbrough, 32, 41
St Peter, 20
St Wilfrid's Spring, 20
Stainmore, 21
Stainton Dale, 64, 94, 182
Stainton, 12, 64
Staithes, 164
Stamford Bridge, 6, 11, 35, 66, 97, 216, 247, 309, 324, 452
Stamford, 7, 8, 132, 163, 216, 406
Stanghou, 100
Stape, 400, 422
Staple Howe, 3
Staxton, 84, 99, 253, 424
Stearsby, 108, 188
Stephen of York, 41
Stillington, 11, 18, 49, 100, 122, 213, 262, 294, 302, 304, 406
Stilton, 68
Stittenham, 9, 12, 48, 140, 150, 151, 160, 235, 287, 289
Stockton, 342
Stokesley, 20, 45, 48, 61, 73, 97, 252, 262, 274, 354, 372 97,
stone crosses, 30
Stonebrough, 12
Stonegrave, 19, 29, 31, 77, 185, 195, 213, 222, 287, 302, 304, 409
Stoupe, 233
Strensall, 50, 79, 235, 304, 352, 353, 406
Streoneshalch, 18
Studley Royal, 266, 389
Stuteville family, 45, 69, 73, 88, 103
Stuteville, Robert de, 43, 69, 72
Stuteville, Roger de, 48

Tosni, Berenger de, 37
Tostig, 33, 34, 35
Towthorpe, 15, 131
Towton, 151
Towton, Battle of, 111, 151
Troutsdale, 26, 79
Turbar, 22

Ugglebarnby, 158, 221
Ughtred, 37
Uhtred, Earl, 33, 34
Ulf, son of Dolfin, 34
Ulfr son of Thorald, 33
Ulf's Horn, 33
United States, 38, 286
Upsall, 12, 64, 115, 119, 159, 194, 219
Urban, Pope, 41
Urra, 25, 89

Vescy, Eustace de, 76
Vescy, Ivo de, 43, 45, 52
villeins, 26

Wade's Causeway, 6, 9, 12, 76, 85,
Wakefield, 183, 239, 241, 273,
Wakefield, Battle of, 151
Walcher, Bishop, 36
Wales, Lord President of the Council in, 205
Waltheof, 34, 36, 37
Waltun, 16
Warthill, 50
Washington, 291
Waterloo, Battle of, 312
Wath, 49, 73, 77, 107, 174, 257, 435
Watton Priory, 60, 69, 90, 127, 164
Weaverthorpe, 46, 50, 53, 90, 100, 131, 270, 300, 304, 306, 373, 451
Weighton, 343
Welburn, 20, 51, 55, 109, 160, 173, 176, 190, 195, 205, 206, 223, 235, 238, 253,
259, 292, 302, 319, 337, 343, 357, 373, 406, 429, 443, 447
Welham, 11, 218, 235, 302, 419, 444
West Ayton, 135

Wulfstan, Archbishop, 32

Wyedale, 352

Wykeham, 11, 12, 14, 15, 69, 72, 84, 109, 167, 192, 235, 252, 259, 296, 316, 319

Wyville, Richard de, 49

Wyville, Robert de, 49

Yarm, 45, 61, 64, 96, 113, 164, 212, 232

Yarmouth, 292

Yearsley, 1, 58, 94, 116, 170, 193, 261, 299

Yedingham Priory, 69, 93, 96, 109, 116, 125, 127, 165

Yedingham, 2, 17, 90, 126, 136, 163, 214, 216, 252, 282, 294, 295, 313, 314, 351, 434, 366, 447

Yedmandale, 116

York castle, 43

York Hospital, 66

York Minster, 41, 123

York, 6, 7, 9, 11, 12, 14, 18, 20, 21, 22, 31, 32, 34, 35, 36, 37, 41, 52, 64, 65, 71, 78, 79, 96, 98,
99, 101, 112, 113, 118, 119, 120, 132, 145, 147, 153, 156, 163, 164, 166, 168, 169, 174, 175,
178, 180, 181, 183, 188, 189, 193, 197, 198, 199, 204, 206, 211, 212, 213, 216, 217, 221, 231,
233, 234, 237, 238, 239, 240, 241, 247, 251, 253, 254, 256, 267, 268, 269, 271, 280, 286, 289,
290, 293, 295, 301, 308, 309, 317, 372, 380, 385, 388, 398, 402, 406, 417, 419, 420, 423, 435,
442, 446, 452, 456, 457

York, Archbishop of, 36

York, St William of, 75

Yorkshire Earldom, 36